ELECTRICITY

AND

MAGNETISM

Ralph P. Winch

Barclay Jermain
Professor of Natural
Philosophy

Williams College

ELECTRICITY

AND

MAGNETISM

Second Edition

PRENTICE-HALL, INC., Englewood Cliffs, N. J.

Library of Congress Catalogue Card No. 63-7408

Printed in the United States of America

24857-C

TO

Mary Elizabeth Johnson Winch

PREFACE TO SECOND EDITION

This text should apply to the average year course in Electricity and Magnetism at the sophomore or junior level in college. In general, the student should possess a minimum background of a one-year elementary college physics course and an elementary course in differential and integral calculus.

Fundamental concepts of vector analysis are introduced at the appropriate places in the text and are used as tools where they clarify the treatment. These concepts include scalar product, gradient, divergence, curl and vector product, but the text material is complete enough so that the student need not have studied vector analysis elsewhere.

This text employs the rationalized MKS system of units throughout, a procedure consistent with modern practice in engineering and physics. The basic definitions of the electrostatic and electromagnetic systems of units appear at the appropriate places in the text. In the Appendix, Sections A-1 and A-2, the other commonly used units of these systems are defined. Appendix A-3 contains a table of conversion factors.

Most students who continue in science and engineering, nowadays, enter college with a certain amount of familiarity and physical intuition about circuits, but with no physical intuition about field theory. Consequently, this text departs from conventional practice by introducing d-c and a-c circuit analysis ahead of field theory and thus exploits the students' background. Since the author adopted this order in his course, he has learned of many others who have independently made the same change for the same reasons and with equal pedagogical success. Further, with a laboratory in connection with the course, it is much easier to make meaningful progress at an early stage of the laboratory work. Although material all through the book is needed for the complete understanding of Chapter XX on Instruments, students can profitably read parts of it as needed for laboratory work at any stage.

The order of topics adopted here is possible if one exploits fully the electricity and magnetism which students have learned in elementary physics. However, the book is written so that it may be taught in the conventional order if the instructor desires or if the arrangement of courses in the department makes the conventional order advisable. In this case, the order of the chapters would be I, IX through XII, II through VIII, XIII through XIX. If this order is followed, Sec. 4-1 should be assigned just prior to Chapter XII. It is expected that topics in Chapter XX will be assigned as needed for laboratory work, or to amplify principles in earlier chapters.

Many problems are directly assigned at appropriate places in the discussion in order that the student may develop and elucidate important bits of the theory on his own initiative. It is the author's practice to assign such problems every year. There are enough of the other problems, however, so that a given problem need not be assigned oftener than every two or three years. Answers are given with the problems, to many more than half including ones where numerical results are expected and those where the formula to be derived for a given physical situation is stated. The problems are not arranged in order of increasing difficulty because a physicist or an engineer, practicing his profession, does not have his problems so ordered or labeled.

The largest single change from the first edition occurs in Chapter XIX where the fundamental facts about fields and charges developed earlier are collected together and Maxwell's equations in differential form are derived from them by vector analysis. These equations are then used to discuss the transmission of electromagnetic energy through space and to explain some elementary properties of light waves. Finally the first-order relativistic * transformations of electric and magnetic fields to moving systems of reference are derived and used to explain the basic connections between electric and magnetic phenomena.

Much of the duplication in a-c circuit analysis, which was introduced in the first edition for pedagogical reasons, has been eliminated in the second as unnecessary because students are now better prepared in mathematics. For the same reason the subject of electric oscillations has been moved from Chapter XIX to its proper place in Chapter VI.

Although this text has a special application for students who intend to continue in advanced physics, chemistry, or engineering, the treatment of the subject matter has been designed with special emphasis on simplicity and clarity of presentation of basic fundamentals. It is anticipated that a student will follow the presentation here by at least a one-semester course in electromagnetic theory if he plans to enter graduate physics or certain advanced fields of engineering.

The author is deeply indebted to the Coulomb's Law Committee of the American Association of Physics Teachers for their report.† The recommendations of the Committee have been followed in the preparation

---

* The approach developed here was first presented by David A. Park, as an invited paper, to the New England Section of the American Association of Physics Teachers in the spring of 1961.

† "The Teaching of Electricity and Magnetism at the College Level," *Am. J. of Phys.*, **18** pp. 1–25 and 69–88 (1950).

of this text. Numerous references to this report appear, especially in the latter part of the book.

The author wishes to express his gratitude to Professor David A. Park, who wrote Chapter XIX, for his critical reading of all of the manuscript for the first edition and parts of the second edition, and for his many helpful suggestions and discussions. Professors Carleton Murdock and Theodore Soller submitted reviews of the manuscript of the first edition and Professor Joseph G. Hoffman did a critical reading of the manuscript of the second edition. All three offered many helpful comments for which the author is deeply grateful. The author is also indebted to Dr. Wentworth Williams, Jr., who checked the problem solutions for the first edition and read that manuscript with care.

RALPH P. WINCH

Williamstown, Massachusetts

CONTENTS

VIII SOME ALTERNATING CURRENT NETWORKS 166

IX THE ELECTROSTATIC FIELD 188

XIII   MAGNETIC FORCE ON MOVING CHARGES   323

XIV   MAGNETIC FIELD IN FREE SPACE DUE TO CURRENTS   367

XV   MORE ABOUT INDUCED EMF'S   396

A WORD TO THE STUDENT
ABOUT USE OF THIS TEXT

This book is carefully cross-referenced in the text material for your convenience in finding related subject matter when you are studying a particular topic. The cross-referencing is done in terms of figure numbers, section numbers, and equation numbers. An equation with a particular number is readily located because the equation numbers are numerous, are located at the right-hand margins of the pages, and run consecutively through the book. The first number of the triple equation number indicates the chapter in which the equation appears, and the second number is the Sec. number in that chapter, and the third is the equation number in the Sec. Similarly, the triple figure number tells at once the chapter and section where the figure is located.

The Sec. numbers have been printed on each page adjacent to the page number. Thus, you can let the pages glide by and locate a Sec. number as readily as you can a page number. The Sec. numbers are also double, the first number indicating the chapter and the second the section within that chapter.

In Appendix A-3, pages 576-580, a Table of Conversion Factors, appears, with an explanation for its use. You will be saved many hours of tedious hunting and computation if you will become familiar with this table at once and use it whenever a number, expressed in one system of units, is to be converted to the equivalent number in some other system.

Appendix A-4, pages 580-582, contains a list of the Principal Symbols used in this text, arranged alphabetically according to the physical quantities which the symbols represent. In this list is given *the mks unit for each quantity,* and herein lies its greatest usefulness. Often you cannot recall quickly the unit for a particular physical quantity, and you will find it in this list more quickly than you can by a search through the text. Also, in this list is given the reference to the place in the text where the definition of the quantity will be found.

Appendix A-5, pages 582-583, gives a tabulation of the values of some Fundamental Physical Constants which will be useful to you in solving problems. Appendix A-6, page 583, gives the Greek alphabet, and here you can find the names of the Greek letters used in the text.

INTRODUCTION TO

THE MKS SYSTEM

OF ELECTRICAL UNITS

I-I ELECTRICAL STRUCTURE OF MATTER

During your study of elementary physics, you learned that matter is basically electrical in structure. Matter is composed of atoms, and the building blocks that go to make up the individual atoms possess electric charges.

We believe that each atom contains a small central core called a *nucleus*, wherein all the positive charge and most of the mass resides. Experiments indicate that nuclear diameters fall in the range about 10^{-14} meter. Each nucleus contains a certain number of neutrons (basic building blocks of zero charge) and protons (basic building blocks of positive charge). The number of protons in the nucleus determines the total positive charge that the nucleus possesses, and this number is called the *atomic number*. The atomic number specifies uniquely the chemical nature of the atom and thus the chemical element to which the atom belongs. A "normal" atom possesses just as many electrons in shells about the nucleus as there are protons in the nucleus. Since the charge on an electron is the same in magnitude but opposite in sign to that on the proton, a normal atom is electrically neutral. Experiment indicates that there is no electric charge smaller than that on an electron or proton.

Historically, the negative sign was assigned to the charge on a rubber or amber rod which had been rubbed with fur or wool. The charge on the electron is the same kind as that on the rubber or amber rod; in fact, we now believe that the process of rubbing a rubber or amber rod with fur transfers electrons from the fur to the rod and thus leaves the rod with a surplus of electrons. From this arose the usage whereby an electron is said to have a negative charge. The proton has an opposite kind of charge, so its charge is said to be positive.

We do not know what an atom looks like; in fact, it is doubtful that it means anything to talk about the appearance of an atom. However, pictures do help most of us in our thinking and there is no harm in a partially meaningful picture if it is not taken too seriously. Thus we picture an atom as having a spherical nucleus surrounded by shells of electrons, with the electrons in constant motion about the nucleus. Since in an electrical course we are interested in good electric conductors, let us take silver and copper atoms as examples to show the kind of picture that is useful in our thinking.

As found in nature, copper has two isotopes, one of mass number 63 and one of mass number 65. Since there are 29 protons in each copper nucleus, the atomic number of copper is 29. The mass number of an atom is the sum of the numbers of protons and neutrons in its nucleus; thus an atom of one copper isotope has 34 neutrons in its nucleus, and an atom of the other copper isotope has 36 neutrons in its nucleus. The word *nucleon* is used as a collective term for neutrons and protons in the nucleus. Hence the mass number of an atom equals the number of nucleons in the nucleus.

The atoms of both kinds of isotopes of copper have, when normal, 29 electrons in shells about the nucleus. Thus we may picture a normal atom

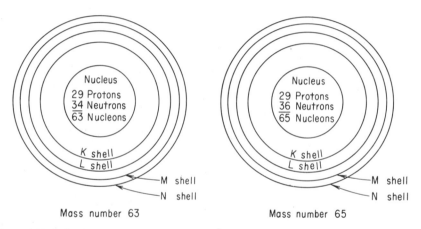

Mass number 63   Mass number 65

Figure 1–1–1. Copper isotopes: there are 2 electrons in the K shell, 8 in the L shell, 18 in the M shell, and 1 in the N shell. The diameter of the shells is of the order of 10^{-10} meter, and the diameter of the nucleus is of the order of 10^{-14} meter; hence, the figure is not to scale since the shells should be about 10,000 times as large in diameter as the nucleus. As found in nature, the atoms of these two isotopes of copper are always mixed in the proportion of 70.1 per cent mass number 63 and 29.9 per cent mass number 65.

of each of the isotopes of copper as shown in Fig. 1–1–1. This figure is not, of course, to scale, since the shells should be about 10,000 times as large in diameter as the nucleus.

A similar picture of the atoms of the two isotopes of silver is shown in Fig. 1–1–2.

It is believed that this type of picture is characteristic of all the atoms of the various chemical elements starting with hydrogen, whose atomic number is 1. At the upper end of the chemical periodic chart of the naturally occurring elements is uranium, whose atomic number is 92, and beyond this are several elements of higher atomic number which are man-made. The most famous of the latter is atomic number 94, plutonium, which is produced in quantity at Hanford, Washington, for use in producing atomic energy.

1–2 CONDUCTORS AND INSULATORS

Since electrical phenomena play such an important part in all atomic and molecular behavior, we might treat most of biology, chemistry, and physics in a course in electricity. However, we shall confine our attention to that very tiny portion of physics which has to do with the effects which result when positive and negative charges are separated, so that a flow of charges may be observed in conductors or a polarization of charge may be observed in insulators. Time will permit a discussion of only a small part of the theory and experimentation which lics in this limited classification.

In Figs. 1–1–1 and 1–1–2 we drew pictures of atoms of the two best electric conductors. Of all the atomic features listed there, only the single, most loosely bound electron in each atom is of primary interest to us in this limited discussion. When a good conductor such as silver is in the solid state, the

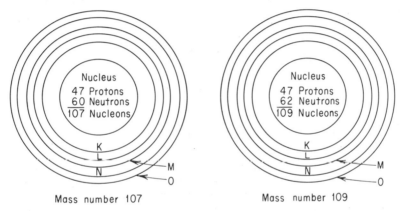

Mass number 107   Mass number 109

Figure 1–1–2. Silver isotopes: there are 2 electrons in the K shell, 8 in the L shell, 18 in the M shell, 18 in the N shell, and 1 in the O shell. As found in nature, the atoms of these two isotopes of silver are always mixed in the proportion of 51.9 per cent mass number 107 and 48.1 per cent mass number 109.

outermost electron (for silver, the one in the O shell) is tied to its parent atom by so very small a force that it is often called a *free electron*. These free electrons wander from atom to atom in a random fashion, due to the thermal agitation of the atoms. When an electric field is applied to such a conductor, the free electrons drift in the opposite direction to the field, in addition to their random thermal motion. Thus there is a flow of electric charge, and we have an electric current flowing in the conductor. *A material is an electric conductor if it has free electrons which can drift in an electric field.* In general, metals are the good electric conductors.

In a perfect insulator (or dielectric) all electrons are tightly bound to the parent atoms and molecules, and there are no free electrons to drift in an electric field. No material is a perfect insulator, because there are always a few electrons that have been freed from their parent atoms by thermal collisions. However, the good insulators such as sulfur, quartz, amber, rubber, etc., have very few free electrons, and we shall assume for most purposes that there is no flow of electric current in such insulators unless the electric field becomes so large that dielectric breakdown (see Sec. 11–10) occurs.

When a dielectric is situated in an electric field, there is a shift of the nucleus in the direction of the field and of the electrons in the opposite direction to that of the field. The electrons are still bound to the parent nuclei and thus cannot drift away as in a conductor, so no current flows in the sense that we considered in a conductor. However, the dielectric atoms have been warped by the field and are said to be *polarized*. We shall see in Chapter XI that the polarization of the atoms of a dielectric is very important in various studies, particularly in capacitors.

Our discussion of conductors and insulators here, while sufficient for the purposes of this book, is much too simple and abbreviated for many purposes and ignores the whole subject of semiconductors. Thus the reader is referred to more advanced treatments* when he encounters problems that require a more detailed understanding.

1–3 GENERAL DISCUSSION OF ELECTRICAL UNITS

Any system of units for measurement purposes is based on one or more arbitrary definitions, with the remainder of the units of the system being derived from these arbitrary definitions. The arbitrary definitions of electrical units are not, of course, completely arbitrary, because they are based on established fundamental physical laws. The arbitrariness comes in the choice of the size of the unit for one or more of the quantities appearing in the physical law. Since these choices are perfectly free ones, as far as logic is concerned, anyone can start his own system of units. Unfortunately, altogether too many people have exercised this privilege, and many of them have found followers because of the special merits of the systems that result. Fortunately, many of these systems have died from neglect but, from the viewpoint of the student, too many have persisted. Thus you must become familiar with many systems of units, as you know from elementary physics. Physical concepts and laws, however, are independent of the system of units used and need be learned only once, regardless of the system of units.

In this text we shall use the mks system of units almost exclusively. We shall, however, introduce the electrostatic system (esu) and electromagnetic system (emu) at appropriate places in the text, since these systems are commonly used and very important. In the Appendices, A–1 and A–2, the fundamental definitions of these two systems of units are given, and with each definition there is a reference to the place in the text where the basic physical concepts and laws are discussed. In Appendix A–3, a table of conversion factors is given, and by its use you can convert a numerical value given in one of the systems to the equivalent numerical value in either of the other two systems. After experience with these three important systems of units, you

* For a useful elementary treatment, see Jacob Millman *Vacuum-tube and Semiconductor Electronics* (New York: McGraw-Hill Book Company, Inc., 1958), pp. 60–89. For greater detail, see Charles Kittel, *Introduction to Solid State Physics*, 2d ed. (New York: John Wiley & Sons, 1956) and William Shockley, *Electrons and Holes in Semiconductors* (New York: D. Van Nostrand, 1950).

will be able to master any other system of electrical units that you may encounter in the literature.

1–4 THE METER-KILOGRAM-SECOND (MKS) RATIONALIZED SYSTEM OF ELECTRICAL UNITS*

You will recall from elementary physics that the mks system is based on the *meter* as the fundamental unit of length, the *kilogram* as the fundamental unit of mass, and the *second* as the fundamental unit of time, From this starting point, and using Newton's second law of motion, the newton is defined as the unit of force in this system as follows. The *newton* is a force of such magnitude that it will give a one-kilogram mass an acceleration of one meter per second per second. Thus 1 newton = 1 kg meter/sec².

The *joule* is the work unit in this system and is defined as the work done by a force of one newton acting through a distance of one meter. Thus 1 joule = 1 newton meter.

The *watt* is the power unit in this system and is defined as one joule per second, or 1 watt = 1 joule/sec.

1. ELECTRIC CURRENT, *I*. Whenever an electric current flows, there is always a magnetic field associated with it. A magnetic field produced by one current will exert a magnetic force on another current. Similarly the magnetic field of the second current will exert a magnetic force on the first current. Thus we say that two currents exert magnetic forces on each other. The mks system of *electrical* units is based on the definition of the ampere as a unit of electric current, and this definition is stated in terms of the magnetic force between two current-carrying conductors (see Sec. 14–4 for the basic law) as follows. *The ampere is defined as that unvarying current which, if present with the same magnitude in each of two parallel straight wires of infinite length and one meter apart in empty space, will cause each wire to experience a magnetic force of precisely* 2 × 10⁻⁷ *newton for each meter of length of wire.* It seems somewhat peculiar, perhaps, to select 2 × 10⁻⁷ newton of force in this definition, but this selection is made in order to have the ampere defined here agree in magnitude with the ampere already in use when the mks system was originated. The ampere then in use was defined as one-tenth abampere (see Sec. 14–5). This system should be designated mksa, since we use the definition of the ampere as the basis for introducing electrical units into the system. For simplicity, however, we shall continue to designate it as mks.

2. QUANTITY OF ELECTRICITY, *Q*. There is an electric current when electric charges are in directed motion, and the electric current in a conductor is the time rate at which electric charge is passing a cross section of the conductor. If we let *i* equal the instantaneous electric current, we may write this definition of the physical concept of electric current as

$$i = dq/dt \qquad (1-4-1)$$

* See the report of the Committee on Electric and Magnetic Units of the American Association of Physics Teachers in the *Am. Physics Teacher*, **5–6**, 1937–1938, pp. 144–51 and "Symbols and Units, International Union of Pure and Applied Physics—Sun Commission," *Physics Today*, **9**, November, 1956, pp. 23–27. For the most part this discussion follows the recommendations given there.

where dq is the infinitesimal charge that passes the cross section in the infinitesimal time dt, and thus dq/dt means the time rate at which electric charge is passing the cross section where the instantaneous current is i. From (1–4–1) it follows that

$$\int_0^Q dq = \int_0^t i\, dt, \quad \text{or} \quad Q = \int_0^t i\, dt \tag{1–4–2}$$

where Q is the quantity of electricity that passes the cross section in the time t. If i is independent of t, as it is in steady direct current, (1–4–2) becomes

$$Q = It \tag{1–4–3}$$

where I indicates a current of constant magnitude.

Using (1–4–3), we can define the coulomb as a unit of quantity of electricity (or charge) as follows. *The coulomb is that quantity of electricity which, in one second, passes through a cross section of a conductor in which there is a constant current of one ampere,* or 1 coulomb = 1 ampere second.

Since the charge on an electron is the smallest quantity of electricity that one can have, i.e., the charge on an electron has not been subdivided, its charge is often referred to as the natural unit of quantity of electricity. Measurement of the charge on an electron, as in Millikan's oil-drop experiment,* shows that the electronic charge is 1.6019×10^{-19} coulomb. The reciprocal of this tells us that the number of electrons per coulomb is

$$\frac{1}{1.6019 \times 10^{-19}\ \text{coulomb/electron}} = 6.2426 \times 10^{18}\ \text{electrons/coulomb.}$$

Thus a body has a negative charge of 1 coulomb if it has 6.2426×10^{18} more electrons on it than are required to make it neutral. Similarly, if a body has a positive charge of 1 coulomb, it has 6.2426×10^{18} electrons fewer than the number required to make it neutral. It turns out that a coulomb of static charge on a body is a very large charge, and rarely does one encounter a situation where a body has a static charge of 1 coulomb. However, a coulomb is a small quantity of electricity when considered in connection with commercial electric circuits.

Since, from the definition of the coulomb just given, 1 ampere = 1 coulomb/sec, if a current of 1 ampere is flowing it means that the electrons are passing a cross section of the wire at the net rate of 6.2426×10^{18} electrons/sec.

3. ELECTRIC FIELD INTENSITY (OR STRENGTH), E. An electric field exists in a region where an electric charge q' experiences a force of electrical origin. By definition *the electric field intensity at a point is the quotient obtained when the force acting on a charge of electricity placed at that point is divided by the magnitude of the charge at the point.* It is assumed, of course, that the charge q' placed at the point is small enough so that it does not alter the field being measured. From this definition

$$E = F/q' \tag{1–4–4}$$

* Consult your elementary physics text.

The direction of E is the direction of the force on a positive charge. Writing units in (1–4–4), we have, unit of E = newton/coulomb.

Field intensity E is a vector-point function, since at every point in the electric field it is completely specified only if both its magnitude and direction at the point are given. (In Chapter IX we shall discuss electric field intensity of an electrostatic field in detail, and in Chapter XV we shall consider electric field intensity due to changing magnetic flux.)

We shall show later [in Sec. 10–8 immediately following (10–8–12)] that E at a point is equal to the negative space rate of change of electric potential at the point, if the space rate of change of potential is taken in the direction in which the potential is changing most rapidly. Thus the unit of E can be expressed by the equivalent unit of volt/meter. (This will be clear after the volt is defined in Sec. 5.)

4. DIRECTION OF ELECTRIC CURRENT. A gas is normally a good insulator. It becomes a conductor only when some of its atoms or molecules are ionized by the removal of one or more electrons per molecule (or, in rarer cases, by accumulation of an extra electron per molecule). If an electric field is applied to an ionized gas, the positive ions experience a force that makes them move in the direction of the applied electric field. Conversely, the negative ions (mostly the liberated electrons in a gas) experience a force due to the electric field which causes them to move in a direction opposite to that of the applied electric field. This motion of charges, positive charges in one direction and negative charges in the opposite direction, is an electric current in the gas.

We need to select one direction that we shall call the *direction of the current*, and we appear to have two possibilities from which to select.

If the gas is hydrogen, the positive ions are individual protons and the negative ions are individual electrons. If the negative electrode in the gas has a hole in it and if the gas is at low pressure, we will have a stream of protons passing through the hole and into the region beyond. Now, if we catch these protons in a metal box, the charge on the box becomes more and more positive because the protons have positive charges. Therefore, letting q represent the instantaneous charge on the box, dq/dt is positive. But $i = dq/dt$, so *the direction of the electric current is the direction of motion of positive charge.*

If, in the same low-pressure hydrogen discharge tube, we have a hole in the anode, there will be a stream of electrons passing through the hole and into the region beyond. This stream of electrons is also an electric current. However, if we catch the electrons in a second metal box, the charge on the box becomes progressively smaller (more and more negative) and dq/dt is negative. It is convenient therefore to stick to our above-stated definition and to say that this current in the direction of electron flow is negative, i.e., that the positive current flows away from the box when the electrons flow toward the box. Then we make the general statement that the *direction of the electric current shall always be in the direction that a positive charge would move* without reference to what sign of charge is *actually* moving.

Notice that this choice follows as a logical algebraic consequence of the earlier *arbitrary* choice which says that electrons have negative charges and protons have positive charges. If one were going to make the opposite choice for the direction of electric current, one should first reverse the choice as to the signs of the charges on the electron and the proton.

In the main body of the ionized hydrogen in our gas-discharge tube, we have two currents, one due to the motion of protons in the direction of the electric field E and the other due to the motion of the electrons in the opposite direction to E. These two currents are in the same direction and the total current is the arithmetic sum of the two.

When we define current as $i = dq/dt$, we do not have, from the definition, a means of identifying which sign of charge is actually in motion or the velocity with which it moves. The motion of positive charge in one direction has the same effect on the change in the quantity of unneutralized charge at any place as does the motion of negative charge in the opposite direction. Also a motion of positive charge in one direction produces exactly the same magnetic field as an equal motion of negative charge in the opposite direction. There are certain phenomena* which depend on the combined effect of electric and magnetic fields, for example the Hall Effect (see Sec. 13–1), that are not symmetrical, and permit one to determine, when other methods fail, whether a current flowing in a solid is due to positive charge moving in one direction or negative charge moving in the opposite direction or, as often happens, due to both. However, this does not alter the above situation with regard to direction of electric current.

Much the same situation exists in a liquid electrolyte as in a gas, for the electrolyte molecules dissociate into positive and negative ions. When an electric field is applied to the electrolyte, the positive ions move in the direction of the field and the negative ions move in the opposite direction. Again, the direction of the electric current is the direction of the applied electric field, just as in the gas.

Historically, the direction of electric current was adopted before the discovery of the electron and prior to the present theories about electrical structure of matter. We now believe that electrical conduction in metals is due to motion of electrons, but this is no reason for changing the direction of electric current. In fact, as pointed out above, if we were to change, we would first have to reverse the arbitrary choice of signs for the charges on the electron and proton (or, less acceptably, say that $i = -dq/dt$).

5. ELECTRIC POTENTIAL DIFFERENCE, V, AND ELECTROMOTIVE FORCE, $\mathscr{E}$

I. *Potential Difference, V.* In mechanics we usually compute work as the product of the force acting times the distance through which it acts.

In electrical problems the electric field intensity E is the force per unit charge, but E is not a convenient quantity to use for work calculations in electric circuits. In a part of an electric circuit where no emf exists, the work W

---

* See, for example, Jacob Millman, *Vacuum-tube and Semiconductor Electronics* (New York: McGraw-Hill Book Company, Inc., 1958), pp. 86–87, and William Shockley, *Electrons and Holes in Semiconductors* (New York: D. Van Nostrand, 1950).

done in moving a unit charge from one point to another is referred to as the potential difference V between the two points. Thus

$$V = \frac{\text{work, due to electrostatic forces, involved in the transfer of charge}}{\text{charge transferred}}$$

or
$$V = W/Q \qquad\qquad (1\text{-}4\text{-}5)$$

Equation 1–4–5 defines potential difference. It is important to remember that *potential difference is work per unit charge.*

When a wire circuit is connected across the terminals of a battery, an electric field is set up in the wires and this electric field causes the free electrons to drift through the wires of the circuit, giving the electric current. It may be difficult or even impossible to measure the electric field intensity at each point in the circuit, and thus it is not convenient to compute work done by an electric current in terms of electric field intensity. You will recall from elementary physics that there are convenient ways of measuring potential difference between points in an electric circuit, e.g., by use of a voltmeter. Thus, in electric circuits, potential difference is a more useful concept for work calculations than is electric field intensity. You must remember that it is the electric field in the conductors which causes the electric current, even though electric field intensity does not enter directly into your work calculations.

The unit of electric potential difference in the mks system of units is the volt, which is defined as follows. *Two points are at a potential difference of one volt if one joule of work is involved in the transfer of one coulomb of charge from one point to the other.* Thus 1 volt = 1 joule/coulomb.

In Chapter X we shall have much more to say about potential difference in an electrostatic field.

II. *Electromotive Force, emf, $\mathscr{E}$.* A *source of emf* is a device in which electrical energy conversions take place reversibly. In order to be more precise, let us consider the two types of situations involving electrical energy conversions:

(A) The first situation is one where the current flows in the same sense as the emf; thus the source is converting some *other form of energy* (e.g., chemical or mechanical) into electrical energy inside itself. The source then furnishes this energy to the electric circuit of which it is a part. In this case we define *the magnitude of the emf of the source* as *the amount of energy converted, inside the source, from some other form of energy into electrical energy when a unit charge flows around the circuit containing the source.* A battery driving an electric circuit would be an example of this case, because, inside the battery, chemical potential energy is being converted into electrical energy. A generator driving an electric circuit would be a second example, because, inside the generator, mechanical energy is being converted into electrical energy.

(B) The second situation is the one where current flows in a sense opposite to that of the emf; thus the source is converting *electrical energy* into some other form of energy inside itself (e.g., into chemical or mechanical energy), but exclusive of electrical energy converted irreversibly into heat. In this case the source is receiving energy from the electric circuit and we define *the magnitude of the emf of the source* as *the amount of electrical energy converted into some other form,* exclusive of electrical energy converted irreversibly into heat, *when a unit charge flows around the circuit containing the source.* A storage battery being charged is an example of this case, because the current flows through it backward from the way it would furnish current and, inside the battery, electrical energy is being converted into chemical potential energy. An electric motor offers a second example, because, inside the motor, the current flows opposite to the motor's emf and electrical energy is being converted into mechanical energy of rotation of the armature.

By the general definition of the emf of a source, emf is work per unit charge and thus has the same unit, the volt, as does potential difference. It is unfortunate that the word *force* appears in "electromotive force" because the concept is one of work, not of force. We shall use emf and thus avoid using the word *force.* Let us now tell what we mean by the emf of a source in volts for both (A) and (B).

(A) *The emf, in volts, of a source which is furnishing energy* is the amount of some other form of energy in joules, which is converted into electrical energy inside the source when one coulomb of charge flows around the circuit; hence emf is *the work in joules that the source can do in sending one coulomb of charge completely around the circuit.*

(B) The emf in volts of a source which is receiving energy is the electrical energy in joules converted in the source into some form of energy other than irreversible heat when one coulomb of charge flows through the source against its emf.

If an automobile storage battery has a chemical situation inside it such that its emf is 6 v, its emf is 6 v, whether it is furnishing or receiving energy. Thus (A) and (B) are just different ways of looking at this 6 v emf,* depending on the way in which the battery is being used.

6. RESISTANCE, *R.* It is an experimental fact that, for steady direct current, the current that flows through a conductor is directly proportional to the electric potential difference across the terminals of the conductor, provided that the dimensions and temperature of the conductor are held constant. This is known as *Ohm's law* and applies to a class of conductors known as "ohmic conductors," which includes the metals. Ohm's law means that the ratio V/I is constant, and this ratio is defined as the resistance R of the conductor. Thus we may write

$$R = V/I \qquad\qquad (1\text{–}4\text{–}6)$$

The value of R depends on the kind of material used for the conductor, as well as its dimensions and temperature.

When an electric current flows through a resistor, electrical energy is changed into heat energy and into heat energy only. In fact, we might think of resistance as the property of a conductor that changes electrical energy into heat energy. When we take this more general view of resistance, we may extend Ohm's law to d-c circuits where the current is not constant and to a-c circuits.

A simple picture will illustrate a mechanism by which electrical energy

---

* See Sec. 20–1 for the potentiometer method of measuring emf.

might be converted into heat energy when a current flows through a conductor. The electric field in the conductor causes the free electrons to drift in the opposite direction to that of the field, in addition to their thermal motion. In the space between atoms, the field accelerates a free electron, but at the end of this free space the electron collides with an atom and gives up a part or all of its energy increment to the atom, after which the electron is again accelerated by the electric field in the next free space. The atoms struck by electrons in this process have greater energy of agitation about their mean positions, and this energy of agitation is thermal energy. Thus the electrical work that the electric field imparts to the electron has been converted into thermal energy of agitation of the atoms. This is repeated over and over as the free electrons drift through the conductor and thus electrical energy is converted into heat energy.

If we were to try to compute the amount of electrical energy converted into heat energy in terms of this picture, we would discover, first, that the picture is much too simple (being only an illustration of a hypothetical mechanism) and, second, that the calculation is a complicated one. If, however, we lump all this together as resistance defined by Ohm's law, the calculation becomes simple. From (1–4–6), $V = IR$, where V is the potential difference across the conductor and thus is electrical work that a unit charge can do in flowing through the conductor whose resistance is R. Hence IR is the amount of electrical energy converted into heat energy when a unit charge flows through the conductor.

The ohm is the unit of electric resistance in the mks system and is defined from (1–4–6) as follows. *A conductor has a resistance of one ohm if one ampere of current flows through the conductor when the potential difference across it is one volt.* Thus 1 ohm = 1 volt/ampere.

7. WORK, W

I. *General.* The fundamental concepts of work and energy are the same in all branches of physics, so in this section we are not introducing a new physical concept or even a new unit. All we are doing here is to expand on results that follow from the definition of potential in order to get equations for computing work in terms of electrical quantities.

Since potential difference is defined as work per unit charge, we can compute the work W from the equation

$$W = QV \qquad (1-4-7)$$

where Q is the quantity of electricity that goes between the points where the potential difference is V. The symbol W means the electrical energy converted into some other form or forms of energy as a result of the transfer of charge. Since $Q = It$,

$$W = IVt \qquad (1-4-8)$$

If I and V are functions of time, we must use the appropriate mathematical methods to compute W, but the physical concept remains the same.

In the mks system, the joule is the unit of work, so as a result of the previous definitions of the ampere and the volt, W in (1–4–8) is in joules if I

is in amperes, V in volts, and t in seconds. This result can be seen by direct substitution of units into (1–4–8) as follows:

$$\text{unit of } W = \text{amp} \times \text{volt} \times \text{sec} = \frac{\text{coulomb}}{\text{sec}} \times \frac{\text{joule}}{\text{coulomb}} \times \text{sec} = \text{joule}$$

II. *Terminal potential difference of a source, TPD_S.* The terminal potential difference (TPD_S) of *a source which is furnishing energy* is the work that the source can do in sending a unit charge around the circuit from its positive terminal to its negative terminal. In Sec. 5, heading II (A), we defined the emf of a source that is furnishing energy as the work that the source can do in sending a unit charge completely around the circuit. This differs from the TPD_S by the work per unit charge done inside of the source, or

$$TPD_S = \text{emf} - \text{work per unit charge inside the source}$$

Let $R_S = $ the resistance inside of the source. By Ohm's law the work per unit charge converted into heat inside the source is IR_S, so

$$TPD_S = \text{emf} - IR_S \qquad\qquad (1\text{–}4\text{–}9)$$

for a source which is furnishing energy.

The TPD_S of *a source which is receiving energy* is the work per unit charge that the circuit is doing on the source. In Sec. 5, heading II (B), we defined the emf of a source which is receiving energy as the electrical energy converted in the source into some form of energy other than irreversible heat when unit charge flows through the source against its emf. The term IR_S is the electrical energy per unit charge converted into heat inside the source. Hence

$$TPD_S = \text{emf} + IR_S \qquad\qquad (1\text{–}4\text{–}10)$$

for a source which is receiving energy.

8. POWER, P. Power is the time rate of doing work. Hence, if work is being done at a constant rate, power P is work divided by time. This is the same concept and definition of power used elsewhere in physics, so again we are not introducing a new physical concept or even new units in this section. As in the case of the section on work, we are merely developing equations that will permit us to calculate power in terms of the electrical quantities which have already been defined.

From the above fundamental definition of power, and from (1–4–8)

$$P = W/t = IV \qquad\qquad (1\text{–}4\text{–}11)$$

Again, if I and V are functions of time, we must use the appropriate mathematical methods, but the physical concepts remain the same.

In (1–4–11), P is the time rate at which electrical energy is being converted into all other forms of energy in the part of the circuit where V is the potential difference and I is the current flowing through this potential difference. Let V_R be the part of V that is associated with the current flowing through the resistance of a conductor. Then $V_R = IR$.

$$P_h = IV_R = I^2R \qquad\qquad (1\text{–}4\text{–}12)$$

where P_h is the rate at which electrical energy is being converted into heat energy, and into heat energy only. Thus P_h may be all of P in (1–4–11) if there is only resistance in the part of the circuit where the potential difference is V and the current is I. If, however, there are sources, i.e., devices for turning electrical energy into forms of energy other than irreversible heat (such as motors, batteries, etc.), then $P_h = I^2R$ gives the rate at which electrical energy is being converted into heat energy and ignores the rate at which electrical energy is being converted into any other form of energy except heat. In any event, (1–4–11) gives the total rate at which electrical energy is being converted into all other forms of energy. Multiplying both sides of (1–4–9) by current I changes it from a potential equation into a power equation, i.e.,

$$I \times TPD_S = I \times \text{emf} - I^2R_S \qquad (1\text{–}4\text{–}13)$$

We can interpret each of these terms as follows: $I \times \text{emf}$ = total rate at which the source is developing electrical energy = total rate at which the source is doing work on *all* the circuit (including itself) to which it is connected. I^2R_S = rate at which electrical energy is being converted into heat energy inside the source, so it is the rate at which the source is furnishing energy to itself. $I \times TPD_S$ = rate at which the source is furnishing energy to the part of the circuit outside the source. Again, multiplying both sides of (1–4–10) by current I changes it from a potential equation into a power equation, i.e.,

$$I \times TPD_S = I \times \text{emf} + I^2R_S \qquad (1\text{–}4\text{–}14)$$

We can interpret each of these terms as follows: $I \times TPD_S$ = total rate at which electrical energy is being converted into all other forms of energy inside the source. I^2R_S = rate at which electrical energy is being converted into heat inside the source. $I \times \text{emf}$ = rate at which electrical energy is being converted into some form of energy other than heat inside the source.

In the mks system, power* has the unit of joules/second wherever it is encountered, and (1–4–11) will give these units as a result of the definitions previously given for the ampere and the volt. As pointed out earlier, 1 joule/sec is called 1 watt, so electrical power in the mks system is measured in watts, just as is mechanical or any other form of power when one uses this system

PROBLEMS

In each problem where a circuit is involved, draw a good circuit diagram and put on it all known constants before attempting the solution.

1–1 Consult the Table of Conversion Factors given in Appendix A–3, and note carefully the instructions given there for its use. Make the following conversions: (a) 6.50 lb force to newtons. [*Ans:* 28.9 newtons.] (b) 5650 dynes to newtons. (c) 2.25 newtons to dynes. [*Ans:* 2.25 × 10⁵ dynes.] (d) 500 ft-lb to joules. [*Ans:* 680 joules.] (e) 20 joules to ergs. (f) 5 × 10⁵ ergs/sec to watt. [*Ans:* 0.05 w.] (g) 2000 w to horsepower. [*Ans:* 2.68 hp.] (h) 50 kg to pounds (mass). (i) 4.2 slugs to kilograms. (j) 25 lb (mass) to kilograms. (k) 1500 in.² to meter². (l) 1 meter² to feet².

* See Sec. 20–9 for the wattmeter as an instrument which measures power.

1–2 The current flowing in a certain circuit is given as a function of time by the equation $i = I_0 e^{-at}$ where $I_0 = 10.0$ amp and $a = 0.0100$ sec^{-1}. (a) What quantity of electricity passes a cross section of a wire in the circuit between the instant $t = 1.00$ sec and the instant $t = 500$ sec? [*Ans:* 983 coulombs.] (b) If the same charge passes a point during the same time interval in a steady direct current circuit, what would an ammeter in this circuit read? [*Ans:* 1.97 amp.] (c) In either case how many electrons pass the point in the circuit during this time? [*Ans:* 6.12×10^{21} electrons.]

1–3 The current as a function of time in a particular circuit is found to be expressed by the equation $i = I_0(1 - e^{-at})$ where $I_0 = 15.0$ amp and $a = 0.0520$ sec^{-1}. What quantity of electricity passes a cross section of a wire in series in the circuit during the time interval from $t = 0$ to $t = 100$ sec?

1–4 A large metal sphere is being charged negatively from an electrostatic generator. There is a large resistor in series between the sphere and generator. The equation which gives the instantaneous charge q on the sphere as a function of time t since the start of the charging process, is $q = Q(1 - e^{-at})$ where $Q = 2.52 \times 10^{-7}$ coulomb and $a = 1.53 \times 10^{-2}$ sec^{-1}. (a) What is the equation for the current i flowing in the wire which connects the generator and resistor to the metal sphere? (b) What is the value of this current at $t = 100$ sec? (c) At $t = 100$ sec, what is the rate at which electrons are accumulating on the metal sphere? [*Ans:* 5.2×10^9 electrons/sec.]

1–5 Hydrogen has atomic number 1, which, as explained in Sec. 1–1, means that there is 1 proton in the nucleus of each hydrogen atom. For ordinary hydrogen the mass of the nucleus is 1.67×10^{-27} kg. A heavy hydrogen (deuterium) atom has a neutron as well as a proton in the nucleus of each atom, and the mass of a deuterium nucleus is, to three significant figures, twice the mass of the ordinary hydrogen nucleus.

Imagine that a mixture of ordinary and heavy hydrogen gas is ionized in an evacuated tube. This statement means that the extranuclear electrons are stripped off the atoms. After the ionization the nuclei are subjected to an electric field and are accelerated through a potential difference of 100 v by this electric field. (a) How much work does the electric field do on each kind of ion? In what form of energy does this work appear, assuming that the ions make no collisions of any kind during the acceleration? [*Ans:* 160×10^{-19} joule.] (b) What is the velocity of each kind of ion after acceleration through the 100 v potential difference? [*Ans:* 13.9×10^4 m/sec and 9.82×10^4 m/sec.]

1–6 Helium has atomic number 2 and ordinary helium has the mass number 4; hence there are two protons and two neutrons in the nucleus of ordinary helium. The mass of the helium 4 nucleus is, to three significant figures, 6.64×10^{-27} kg. Solve Problem 1–5 with the change that this time the gas is ordinary helium and the ionization process removes both extranuclear electrons from each atom.

All the following problems refer to steady direct currents and voltages and are to be so considered even though the fact may not be mentioned in every problem. These are problems like the ones you solved in elementary physics.

1-7 An electric lamp draws 0.980 amp when connected to a 120 v line. (a) What is the resistance of the lamp? (b) What is the rate at which electrical energy is being converted into heat energy? (c) How much electrical energy is converted into heat energy in the lamp if it is turned on for an hour? (d) Does this heat energy remain in the filament of the lamp? If it did remain, what would happen to the lamp filament? If it does not remain, what becomes of it?

1-8 (a) An electric lamp with a tungsten filament is rated at 150 watts and for operation on a 120 v line. What is the resistance of the lamp filament at its normal operating temperature? (b) When this same lamp is connected to a battery whose emf is 6.26 v and essentially zero internal resistance, a current of 0.313 amp flows through its filament. What is the resistance of the lamp filament under these conditions? Why is it not the same as in (a)?

1-9 A certain reservoir for a hydroelectric generating plant has 42×10^8 ft^3 of water in it. The effective height of the water above the water turbines at the plant is 1000 ft. The turbines are operating at their output rating of 50,000 hp and they operate at an efficiency of 75%. How long will the water in the reservoir last if no water is added? [*Ans:* about 83 days.]

1-10 A 15.0 ohm and a 25.0 ohm rheostat are in series, and the combination is connected to a potential difference of 150 v. How much current flows in the 15.0 ohm rheostat?

1-11 A coil of wire with a resistance of 9.58 ohm is connected in series with a rheostat and a battery whose emf is 13.2 v and whose internal resistance is 0.525 ohm. The rheostat is adjusted to such a value that a current of 0.833 amp flows through it. What is the resistance of the rheostat at this setting?

1-12 A series circuit is made up of a generator with an emf of 200 v and an internal resistance of 3.00 ohms, a 40.0 ohm resistor, and an unknown resistor. The potential difference across the unknown resistor is found by measurement to be 90.0 v. What are the terminal potential difference of the generator and the resistance of the unknown resistor? [*Ans:* 192.3 v, 35.2 ohms.]

1-13 A battery, whose emf is 4.00 v and whose internal resistance is 3.00 ohms, is connected in series with a variable rheostat. *Plot* the terminal potential difference of the battery as ordinate against the resistance R of the rheostat as abscissa, as R varies from zero to infinity.

   (When a problem directs you to *plot* a curve, it means to use a piece of good graph paper, select the largest *convenient* scale so that the graph fills the page as nearly as possible, compute enough points so that the curve can be drawn fairly accurately, plot the points so that they are visible after the curve is drawn, and draw a smooth curve through the plotted points. You cannot, of course, have one of your variables go to infinity on your graph paper. In such a case you select a sufficiently large value of that variable so that all of the important part of the curve is shown, and then you plot the curve to this point. In the present problem it is sufficient to use values of R up to 40 or 50 ohms.)

1–14 The battery in a certain car has an emf of 12.43 v and an internal resistance of 0.0251 ohm. On a cold morning, for a short time, the starter motor draws 150 amp from the battery. (a) What is the terminal potential difference of the battery? (b) What is the rate at which chemical potential energy is being converted into electrical energy in the battery? [*Ans:* 1865 watts.] (c) What is the rate at which electrical energy is being supplied by the battery to the circuit outside the battery? (d) What is the rate at which electrical energy is being changed into heat inside the battery? [*Ans:* 565 watts.]

1–15 The generator on a car is connected to the car battery with leads whose total resistance is 0.0100 ohm. The battery is being charged with a 25.0 amp current. The emf of the battery is 6.20 v, and its internal resistance is 0.0200 ohm. (a) What are the terminal potential difference of the battery and that of the generator? (b) What is the emf of the generator if its internal resistance is 0.00500 ohm? (c) What is the rate at which electrical energy is being converted into chemical potential energy? [*Ans:* 155 watts.] (d) What is the rate at which mechanical energy is being converted into electrical energy in the generator? [*Ans:* 177 watts.]

1–16 The current in a series circuit is 10.0 amp. When a resistance of 3.00 ohms is added in series in the circuit, the current becomes 3.50 amp. What was the original resistance of the circuit, and what is the emf of the source used?

1–17 Battery A, whose emf $\mathscr{E}_A$ is unknown and whose internal resistance is 453 ohms, is connected to a certain resistor R_x through an ammeter, and the ammeter reads 2.65×10^{-3} amp. When battery B is connected in series with battery A, with the positive terminal of A connected to the negative terminal of B and the combination connected to R_x through the ammeter, the ammeter reads 5.53×10^{-3} amp. The emf of battery B is 43.3 v and its internal resistance is 822 ohms. Find $\mathscr{E}_A$ and R_x. [*Ans:* 35.5 v, 12,900 ohms.]

1–18 A storage battery of 6.00 v emf and 0.0300 ohm internal resistance, a dry cell of 1.52 v emf and 0.180 ohm internal resistance, and a 3.00 ohm rheostat are all connected in series with the negative terminal of the storage battery connected to the negative terminal of the dry cell. (a) What current flows in the circuit? (b) What is the terminal potential difference of the storage battery? (c) What is the terminal potential difference of the dry cell?

chapter

II

STEADY

DIRECT CURRENT

CIRCUIT PROBLEMS

2–1 KIRCHHOFF'S LAWS

Gustav Robert Kirchhoff (1824–1887) at the age of 23 first stated two simple laws that permit us to solve very complicated circuits.

1. KIRCHHOFF'S FIRST LAW—CONTINUITY OF FLOW. *At every instant the sum of the currents flowing away from a point in a circuit is equal to the sum of the currents flowing toward the point.*

This law states simply that electrons do not pile up at a point in a circuit and that they do not flow away from a point in a circuit rapidly enough so that there is a deficiency of electrons at the point. At any point in a circuit, as many electrons arrive per second as leave in the same time.

If we let I_{in} represent a current flowing toward a point in a network, and I_{out} represent a current flowing away from the same point, we may write

$$\sum I_{out} = \sum I_{in} \qquad (2\text{-}1\text{-}1)$$

where (2–1–1) expresses the same law as does the italicized statement above.

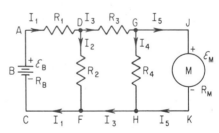

Figure 2–1–1. Example to show the meaning of Kirchhoff's second law.

2. KIRCHHOFF'S SECOND LAW. (a) First Statement: *At every instant the difference of electric potential between any two points in a circuit is the same, regardless of the path in the circuit along which it is measured.*

This statement is simply an expression of the law of conservation of energy applied to an electric circuit, as we can see from the following example. In the circuit of Fig. 2–1–1, B is a battery whose emf is $\mathscr{E}_B$ and whose internal resistance is R_B. The symbol used in the diagram beside B is the usual one for a battery. Symbols R_1, R_2, R_3, and R_4 represent resistors. Symbol M represents a motor whose emf is $\mathscr{E}_M$ and whose internal resistance is R_M. We shall use the symbol of the circle with an M enclosed to represent a motor.

17

The motor is a source that is receiving energy, because in it electrical energy is being converted into mechanical energy. Thus in the motor the current must be flowing against an emf, because electrical energy can be converted to other forms of energy, exclusive of irreversible heat energy, only when a current flows against an emf. The direction of the motor's emf is indicated on the diagram by the $+$ and $-$ signs so placed that I_5 is shown to be flowing through the motor against the direction that $\mathscr{E}_M$ would tend to send a current.* The symbols I_1, I_2, I_3, I_4, and I_5 represent the currents in the places where the symbols appear, and the arrowheads represent the directions of flow of these currents.

Now return to Kirchhoff's second law. Consider two points, say D and F. Kirchhoff's second law says that the potential difference V_{DF} between D and F is the same whether we follow the path $DGHF$, the path $DGJKHF$, the path DR_2F, or the path $DABCF$. By the definition of potential difference, V_{DF} is the work that a unit charge could do in going from D to F.

Let us prove that Kirchhoff's second law follows from the law of conservation of energy by using what the mathematician calls a *reductio ad absurdum* (reducing to an absurdity) argument. Imagine that there is a path (say the path $DGJKHF$) from D to F, along which the potential difference from D to F is greater than it is by the direct path DR_2F. If such a condition existed, a unit charge would do more work for us in going from D to F by the path $DGJKHF$ than we would have to do on it to carry it from F back to D. If this were so, we would build a machine that carried plus charges from F to D along the low work path, and then let them flow from D to F by the high work path. By such a method we would secure more work from the machine than the work put into the machine. In other words, the machine would create energy for us. Since this is impossible, by the law of conservation of energy, it follows that V_{DF} is the same whether we follow the path $DGJKHF$ or the path DR_2F. Since this argument can be used for any pair of paths, it follows that the potential difference between D and F is the same, regardless of the path followed from D to F, and we have Kirchhoff's second law.

Now let us apply this law to the closed loop $DFCBAD$. By the path DR_2F

$$V_{DF} = I_2 R_2 \qquad (2\text{–}1\text{–}2)$$

In the path $DABCF$, we have a source B which is furnishing energy, so its terminal potential difference V_{AC} is given by [see (1–4–9)] as $V_{AC} = \mathscr{E}_B -$

---

* It is sufficient for our purpose at the moment to know, from the above, that the motor must have an emf and to know its direction. It may help your thinking, however, to remind you from elementary physics how the motor develops its back emf. You will recall that the armature of the motor is wound with wire and is situated in the magnetic field of the field coils. The current, from an external source and flowing through the armature wires, experiences a magnetic force due to the magnetic field of the field coils, and thus a torque on the armature results and causes it to rotate. As the armature rotates, the wires of the armature cut the magnetic flux lines of the field coils and induce an emf in the armature. By Lenz's law, this induced emf is in such a direction as to oppose whatever produces it and, since the current sent through the armature from the external source is the primary cause, the induced emf is in such a direction as to oppose this current. Hence the current flows through the armature against the induced emf.

$I_1 R_B$. In the path from A to D, there is a drop in potential given by $V_{AD} = I_1 R_1$ so D is at a lower potential than A by the amount $I_1 R_1$. Hence, by the path $DABCF$, the potential difference between D and F is given by

$$V_{DF} = \mathscr{E}_B - I_1 R_B - I_1 R_1 \qquad (2\text{–}1\text{–}3)$$

Equate the values of V_{DF} in (2–1–2) and (2–1–3) and obtain $\mathscr{E}_B - I_1 R_B - I_1 R_1 = I_2 R_2$. Rearrange, and we have

$$\mathscr{E}_B = I_2 R_2 + I_1 R_B + I_1 R_1 \qquad (2\text{–}1\text{–}4)$$

We can state (2–1–4) in words by saying that, in the closed loop $ADFCBA$, the algebraic sum of the emf's in the loop equals the algebraic sum of the IR drops in potential in the loop.

Again apply Kirchhoff's second law to the loop $DGJMKHFCAD$. In the path $DGJKHF$, we have a motor M which is receiving energy, so its terminal potential difference V_{JK} is given by [see (1–4–10)] as $V_{JK} = \mathscr{E}_M + I_5 R_M$. From G to D there is a rise in potential given by $V_{GD} = I_3 R_3$. Hence the potential difference between D and F by the path $DGJMKHF$ is given by

$$V_{DF} = \mathscr{E}_M + I_5 R_M + I_3 R_3 \qquad (2\text{–}1\text{–}5)$$

Using Kirchhoff's second law, equate the values of V_{DF} in (2–1–3) and (2–1–5) and rearrange terms to obtain

$$\mathscr{E}_B - \mathscr{E}_M = I_1 R_B + I_1 R_1 + I_3 R_3 + I_5 R_M \qquad (2\text{–}1\text{–}6)$$

Again we can state (2–1–6) in words by saying that in loop $DGJKHFCAD$, the algebraic sum of the emf's equals the algebraic sum of the IR drops in the loop.

We can continue this argument for any closed loop in the circuit and always come out with the same statement in words, i.e., the algebraic sum of the emf's in the loop equals the algebraic sum of the IR drops in the loop. We can then continue for any d-c network, however complicated, and always get the same statement for each loop, This result permits us to state Kirchhoff's second law in another form, which is equivalent to the first statement, but is often more convenient in solving networks.

(b) Second Statement of Kirchhoff's Second Law: *At every instant the algebraic sum of the emf's in any closed loop equals the algebraic sum of the IR drops in potential in that loop.*

Written as an equation this law says that, for any loop

$$\sum \mathscr{E} = \sum IR \qquad (2\text{–}1\text{–}7)$$

(For the rules of signs to be used on emf's and IR drops in potential in this sum, see Sec. 2–3, heading 7, of the outline for solving problems.)

We can see that, for a simple series circuit, this result reduces to Ohm's law for the circuit. The following example, where a generator is used to charge a battery, illustrates the argument.

In Fig. 2–1–2, G is the generator whose emf is $\mathscr{E}_G$ and whose internal

resistance is R_G. We shall use a circle with a G enclosed to represent a generator. Symbol B represents a storage battery whose emf is $\mathscr{E}_B$ and whose
internal resistance is R_B. The battery
is being charged, because the current
is flowing through it against its emf.
Symbol R represents a rheostat used
to control the magnitude of the charging current I. By Kirchhoff's first law
the current is everywhere the same in
a series circuit, so we need only one
symbol, I, to represent the current at
every point in the circuit.

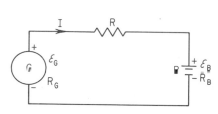

Figure 2–1–2. Generator G charging
battery B.

Apply the second statement of
Kirchhoff's second law, as given in
(2–1–7), to this simple series circuit and we have

$$\mathscr{E}_G - \mathscr{E}_B = IR_G + IR + IR_B$$

or
$$I = \frac{\mathscr{E}_G - \mathscr{E}_B}{R_G + R + R_B} = \frac{\text{algebraic sum of the emf's}}{\text{total series resistance}} \qquad (2\text{–}1\text{–}8)$$

Equation (2–1–8) is probably the form in which you used Ohm's law in
elementary physics when solving problems concerning simple series circuits.
This discussion shows that Ohm's law, in the form given in (2–1–8), is just a
special case of Kirchhoff's second law.

2–2 SHUNTS FOR AMMETERS AND MULTIPLIERS FOR VOLTMETERS

The methods used to change the ranges of d-c ammeters and voltmeters, or
the methods used to change a d-c galvanometer into an ammeter or a voltmeter,
offer good first illustrations of the use of Kirchhoff's laws. The theory and
construction of these d-c meters is discussed in Secs. 13–4 and 13–5, and the
corresponding discussion for some a-c meters appears in Secs. 20–5, 20–6,
and 20–7.

1. SHUNT FOR AN AMMETER. Suppose, we have a galvanometer whose coil
has a resistance R_G, and a current I_G must flow through the coil in order to
make the pointer move from the zero point on the left end of the scale over
to the last mark on the right end of the scale. We wish to make this galvanometer into an ammeter that will measure a current I_L in the line for full-scale
deflection of the pointer. In general, I_L is very large compared with I_G. We
must put a low resistance, known as a *shunt*, in parallel with the galvanometer.
This shunt must have such a resistance that, when I_L flows up to the parallel
combination, it will divide in such a way that I_G flows through the galvanometer, and the remainder (which by Kirchhoff's first law is $I_L - I_G$) flows
through the shunt, as shown in Fig. 2–2–1.

By Kirchhoff's second law, V_{AB} in Fig. 2–2–1 is the same by the path
through the galvanometer as it is by the path through the shunt. Hence

$$I_G R_G = (I_L - I_G)R_S \quad \text{or} \quad R_S = I_G R_G/(I_L - I_G)$$

To put in numerical values, suppose that G is a microammeter that requires 2.00 μa (or 2.00×10^{-6} amp) for full-scale deflection, and the microammeter has a resistance of 400 ohms. We wish to make this instrument into an ammeter that reads 10.0 amp line current for full-scale deflection. We must find the resistance of the shunt.

$$R_S = I_G R_G / (I_L - I_G) = 2.00 \times 10^{-6} \times 4.00 \times 10^2 / (10.0 - 0.00000200)$$

We note, by inspection of the microammeter, that when we have completed the ammeter we shall be able to read current to three significant figures at full scale. Within the accuracy of three significant figures, it does not matter whether or not we subtract 0.000002 from 10 in the denominator of the above fraction. So we may write

$$R_S = 8.00 \times 10^{-4} / 10.0 = 8.00 \times 10^{-5} \text{ ohm}$$

Thus, in Fig. 2–2–1, the resistance in the shunt from A to B must be 8.00×10^{-5} ohm.

As a second numerical example, suppose that we have an ammeter which reads 2.00 amp for full-scale deflection of its pointer. We find, by measurement, that the resistance between the ammeter terminals is 5.00×10^{-3} ohm. We wish to change the range of the ammeter so that it will read 20.0 amp line current for full-scale deflection of its pointer. The ammeter already has a shunt contained in its case, but we do not wish to disturb this arrangement, and our

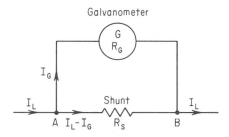

Figure 2–2–1. Shunting a galvanometer to make it into an ammeter.

measurement of 5.00×10^{-3} ohm between its terminals gave the equivalent resistance of the galvanometer and shunt in parallel. Thus we may solve the problem just as we did before. We simply consider that the 2 amp ammeter is a galvanometer which has 5.00×10^{-3} ohm resistance and requires 2.00 amp current for full-scale deflection. We may now solve for the resistance of the external shunt which we must add.

$$R_S = I_G R_G / (I_L - I_G) = 2.00 \times 5.00 \times 10^{-3} / (20.0 - 2.00) = 5.56 \times 10^{-4} \text{ ohm}$$

Hence a shunt of 5.56×10^{-4} ohm must be added to this 2 amp ammeter in order to make it into a 20 amp ammeter.

2. MULTIPLIER FOR A VOLTMETER. Let us make the same galvanometer, with which we started in No. 1 above, into a voltmeter that reads full-scale deflection when connected between two points where the potential difference is V. The resistance of the galvanometer is still R_G, and a current I_G must flow through its coil in order to cause the pointer to move to the right end of the scale. The problem requires that we put a resistor in series with the galvanometer, and the resistance must be of such magnitude that a current I_G flows through the two in series when a potential V is applied across the series

combination. The required circuit is shown in Fig. 2–2–2, where R is the resistor to be added in series with G. Resistor R is referred to as a multiplier, in this case, because it multiplies the voltage range of the instrument. From Fig. 2–2–2

$$V = I_G R + I_G R_G, \quad \text{or} \quad R = (V - I_G R_G)/I_G$$

As an example, consider that G is a microammeter that requires 2.00 μa for full-scale deflection, and has a resistance of 400 ohms. We wish to make a voltmeter that reads 100 v full scale so, in Fig. 2–2–2, $V = 100$ v. From the above we have

$$R = (V - I_G R_G)/I_G = (100 - 8.00 \times 10^{-4})/2.00 \times 10^{-6}$$

This microammeter will give only three significant figures at full-scale deflection, so we can neglect the 8×10^{-4} with respect to the 100 in the numerator of the fraction. Thus

$$R = 100/2.00 \times 10^{-6} = 50.0 \times 10^{6} \text{ ohms}$$

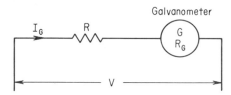

Figure 2–2–2. Multiplier in series with a galvanometer to make it into a voltmeter.

Hence we must add a resistance of 50.0 megohms in series with the galvanometer in order to have a 100 v voltmeter.

As a second numerical example, suppose that we have a 10 v voltmeter whose resistance is 10,000 ohms, and we wish to make it into a 500 v voltmeter. The fact that it is a 10 v voltmeter tells us that, when 10.0 v potential difference is applied across its terminals, a current I_G will flow through it of such magnitude that the pointer will move over to the right end of the scale. We can solve for I_G at once.

$$I_G = V/R_G = 10.0/1.00 \times 10^{4} = 10.0 \times 10^{-4} \text{ amp}$$

There is a multiplier inside the case of the instrument, but we do not wish to disturb it, so we calculate the resistance of the external multiplier that must be added in series.

$$R = (V - I_G R_G)/I_G = (500 - 10.0)/10.0 \times 10^{-4} = 490,000 \text{ ohms}$$

Hence an external multiplier of 490,000 ohms must be added in series with the existing 10 v voltmeter in order to make a 500 v voltmeter of it.

2–3 METHODS FOR THE SOLUTION OF STEADY DIRECT-CURRENT NETWORK PROBLEMS

You now have the theory necessary for the solution of complicated d-c networks. However, you are in the position of the boy who has memorized all of the rule book for basketball. The boy is not yet a basketball player. Only hours of practice under every condition that can arise in a game will make him into a good player. Similarly, you can become a player in the game of networks only by practice in the solution of a wide variety of problems, and the problems at the end of the chapter afford this opportunity. These start with problems from elementary physics and progress into more complicated networks. Just as the coach can teach the boy techniques by example, so here we can solve sample networks in order to bring out the tricks of the game.

We cannot write down a procedure for solving networks that will always be the best, but you will be well advised if you follow the steps listed below.

1. *Draw a good circuit diagram.* Such a diagram is not necessarily a thing of beauty, but it will show every circuit element in its proper relationship to all other parts of the circuit.

2. *Write on the diagram every known constant.* You are much better than most if you can keep a long list of constants in mind while you solve the problem. If, however, these constants all appear on the diagram adjacent to the circuit elements to which they apply, they are obvious at a glance when desired.

3. *Indicate with arrows the directions for those currents where the directions are known.* The problem may tell you explicitly the direction of a current, or it may imply the direction of current by the phraseology. For example, if you are told that a battery is being charged, you know that the current is flowing through the battery in the direction opposite to that of the emf of the battery. If you are to find out whether a battery is being charged or not, you will have to determine the direction of the current through it.

Similarly, in the case of a motor, the current through the motor must be in the opposite direction to that of the emf of the motor. If the current through the motor were in the same direction as its emf, the motor would be furnishing electrical energy to the circuit. Then it would be a generator, and the law of conservation of energy tells you that some outside source such as a diesel engine, a steam engine, or a water turbine would have to supply mechanical energy to be converted into electrical energy by the generator. Thus, if you know that a certain circuit element is operating as a motor, not as a generator, you immediately know that a current is flowing through it against its emf. There may be occasions when you have to decide whether a certain circuit element is a motor or a generator, and this you can decide after you have found the direction of flow of the current through the circuit element.

4. *Letter your circuit diagram so that you can refer to each part by means of the letters.*

5. *For currents or emf's whose directions are unknown, assume a direction for each, and mark the assumed direction on the diagram.* Indicate the assumed direction of each unknown current by means of an arrow. Assumed directions of unknown emf's can be marked on the diagram either by properly placed plus and minus signs or by means of arrows. Once you have started the solution of a problem, do not change any of the assumed directions unless you start afresh on the solution. In such a case, discard all prior work on the problem. There is no need to change the assumed directions, however, since the solution of the problem will give the correct magnitude of the unknown currents or emf's, regardless of your originally assumed directions. If a current or emf comes out with a negative number for its magnitude, the actual

direction is opposed to the assumed direction. In such cases you know at once the actual directions, but do not at this stage change the arrows or plus and minus signs on your original diagram. Simply note that the current or emf is opposite to the assumed direction.

6. *Assign letters to unknown currents, emf's, and resistances.* Keep the number of unknowns as small as possible. In order to keep the number of unknowns small, apply Kirchhoff's first law as you assign letters to the unknown currents. Never assign a new letter to an unknown current if, by the use of Kirchhoff's first law, you can possibly express that current in terms of letters already assigned to other currents.

7. *Making use of Kirchhoff's second law and closed loops in the network, set up as many independent simultaneous equations as there are unknowns.* Never set up any more simultaneous equations than there are unknowns. Extra equations are very likely to lead you into confusion and difficulty. Occasionally, in the solution, you will come out with the result that $0 = 0$ or with some other identity. Such equations are true but not helpful. This result means that you have, by chance, selected two loops which are redundant, so that the equations are not independent. In such a case start the solution over again, omit one or more loops previously used, and select others to replace them.

In the application of Kirchhoff's second law to a loop, first decide whether you intend to go around the loop clockwise or counterclockwise. Once you have decided this, do not change your mind when you are part way around the loop. It does not matter which choice you make, but you must make one choice or the other and then stick to it.

When you write Kirchhoff's second law for a loop, write the algebraic sum of the emf's on the left side of the equation and the algebraic sum of the *IR* drops in potential on the other side of the equation. The following rules for signs will determine for you whether an emf or a *IR* drop is to be given a plus or a minus sign in the algebraic sum.

Sign rule for emf's:

If your chosen direction of progression around the loop is the same as the direction of an emf, that emf is to be given a plus sign. If your chosen direction is opposite to that of an emf, that emf is to be given a minus sign. This rule has nothing to do with the actual or assumed directions of currents, it has only to do with the directions of the emf's.

Sign rule for currents:

Wherever your chosen direction of progression around the loop is in the same direction as a current, that current is to be given a plus sign. In those places where your chosen direction is opposite to the current, that current is to be given a minus sign. The sign on the *IR* drop is the same as that of the current.

8. *Solve the equations simultaneously and thus evaluate the unknowns.*

9. *Check the resulting answers.* Select a loop not used in the solution of the problem and apply Kirchhoff's second law, using the numerical values for currents and voltages obtained in the solution. If, for this loop, the algebraic

sum of the emf's comes out equal to the algebraic sum of the IR drops, your answers are probably correct. If you wish to be sure, repeat this test for all loops in the network.

2–4 EXAMPLES OF SOLUTIONS OF STEADY DIRECT-CURRENT NETWORK PROBLEMS

EXAMPLE A. The circuit in Fig. 2–4–1 shows a shunt-wound d-c motor M, connected to a generator G and battery B. Here F represents the resistance of the shunt field windings of the motor. The emf of the motor at its present speed of rotation is 20.0 v. All the known constants are written on the diagram. Assume that each is known to three significant figures and a slide rule is to be used. Our problem is to calculate the currents I_1 through I_8 shown on the diagram.

At first glance, there would seem to be eight unknowns, so our first job is to assume a direction of flow for each current, and then apply Kirchhoff's first law and reduce the number of unknowns to the minimum number.

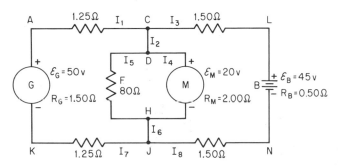

Figure 2–4–1. Example of a d-c network.

Kirchhoff's first law shows us that the current is everywhere the same in the series part of a circuit, so we can at once equate $I_1 = I_7$ and $I_3 = I_8$. A little more thought will show that $I_2 = I_6$. Let us redraw the circuit, put on it the assumed directions of flow of currents, and apply Kirchhoff's first law at each junction point of two or more wires. We may assume any direction of flow that we like for the currents whose directions are not specified. Since we know that G is operating as a generator, so that the current I_1 is flowing away from its positive terminal and toward its negative terminal, we should designate it this way, as shown in Fig. 2–4–2. Also we know that M is operating as a motor, so I_4 must be flowing against its emf, and we should designate it this way, as shown in Fig. 2–4–2.

First, we assign the directions shown in Fig. 2–4–2 for I_1, I_2, and I_3. Then apply Kirchhoff's first law at the point C, and we see that $I_3 = I_1 - I_2$. Hence we omit I_3 entirely and write $I_1 - I_2$ in its place in order to save confusion. (We could just as well have retained I_3 and written I_2 as equal to $I_1 - I_3$. The final result would have been the same.) Application of Kirchhoff's first law at the point D shows that $I_5 = I_4 - I_2$ for the assumed direction of I_5 shown in Fig. 2–4–2. Hence we omit I_5 entirely and write $I_4 - I_2$ in its place. Application of Kirchhoff's first law at other junction points, such as H and J, simply verifies the current relationships that we have already obtained.

A look at Fig. 2–4–2 shows that we now have only three unknown currents, I_1, I_2, and I_4. Therefore we need apply Kirchhoff's second law to only three closed loops in order to secure three independent equations in these three unknowns.

We may select any loops that we like. Let us select loop $ACLNJKA$ and decide to go around this loop clockwise. We designate this choice of loop and direction of progression around the loop by writing:

Loop ACLNJKA ↻

Now write the equation for this loop, putting the algebraic sum of the emf's

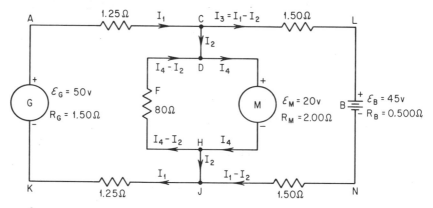

Figure 2–4–2. The same as Fig. 2–4–1, but with current directions designated.

on the left, and the algebraic sum of the IR drops on the right. Start at K, and go systematically around the loop for the IR drops.

$$50 - 45 = 1.5I_1 + 1.25I_1 + 1.5(I_1 - I_2)$$
$$+ 0.5(I_1 - I_2) + 1.5(I_1 - I_2) + 1.25I_1$$

which reduces to

$$I_1 = (5 + 3.5I_2)/7.5 = 0.667 + 0.467I_2 \qquad (1)$$

Loop ACDMHJKA ↻ $50 - 20 = 4I_1 + 2I_4$

or $30 = 4I_1 + 2I_4 \qquad (2)$

Loop MDFHM ↺ $20 = -2I_4 - 80(I_4 - I_2)$

or $20 = -82I_4 + 80I_2 \qquad (3)$

Equations (1), (2), and (3) are the three simultaneous equations in the three unknowns I_1, I_2, and I_4. These equations may be solved simultaneously by any appropriate method that appeals to you in order to obtain $I_1 = 4.07$ amp,

$I_2 = 7.28$ amp, and $I_4 = 6.86$ amp. From these results we get for $I_3 = I_1 - I_2 = -3.21$ amp. Thus I_3 has the magnitude of 3.21 amp, but as indicated by the minus sign, it is flowing in the opposite direction to that shown for it by the arrow in Fig. 2–4–2. $I_4 - I_2 = 6.86 - 7.28 = -0.42$ amp, which means that the current $I_4 - I_2$ is 0.42 amp, but is flowing in the opposite direction to that shown for it by the arrow in Fig. 2–4–2.

The preceding equations give the answers required for the currents. All that remains is to check these currents in various loops to see whether or not they will satisfy Kirchhoff's second law in any (and every) loop. Mistakes are sometimes such that the answers will, by chance, satisfy within slide-rule accuracy the first loop selected for a check, and may even satisfy the second loop selected and still be wrong. Hence, it is well to check with three loops and, if you want to be sure, you should check every possible loop.

We wish now to find answers to the following questions.

(a) What would a very high resistance voltmeter read if it were connected with its positive terminal hooked to A and its negative terminal hooked to K? The voltmeter is specified to be a very high resistance one, so that it will draw a very small current, i.e., a current that is negligibly small compared with I_1. This question then asks us to find the terminal potential difference of the generator G.

When you are to calculate the potential difference between two points, first decide the path along which you wish to make the calculation. By Kirchhoff's second law, the potential difference is the same regardless of the path selected, so you may select the path that seems to you to be the most direct or, for some other reason, the easiest for calculation.

Next determine, from the circuit, whether or not the path contains a source. If it does not contain a source, the potential difference is given by IR. If it does contain a source, determine from the current arrows on the diagram whether it is a source that is furnishing electrical energy to the circuit or a source that is receiving electrical energy from the circuit. (Review the concepts here by reference to Sec. 1–4, heading 5, II.) Equation (1–4–9) tells us how to compute the terminal potential difference of a source which is furnishing electrical energy to the circuit, and (1–4–10) tells us how to compute the terminal potential difference of a source which is receiving electrical energy from the circuit.

We recognize G as a source, and we see from the direction of I_1 that G is furnishing electrical energy to the circuit, i.e., an engine of some sort is driving the generator, and the mechanical energy supplied by the engine is being converted into electrical energy by G. Select the path from A directly through G to K. Hence by (1–4–9) we have

$$TPD_G = V_{AK} = \mathscr{E}_G - I_1 R_G \quad \text{or} \quad V_{AK} = 50.0 - 4.07 \times 1.50 = 43.9 \text{ v}$$

(b) What would a very high resistance voltmeter read if it were connected across the points L and N?

We select the path from L directly through B to N. The battery is a source in this path, and from the direction of the arrow for the current $I_1 - I_2$, we treat it as a source which is receiving electrical energy from the circuit, because the current arrow is opposite to the direction of $\mathscr{E}_B$. Hence, from (1–4–10) we have $TPD_B = V_{LN} = \mathscr{E}_B + (I_1 - I_2)R_B = 45 + (-3.21)$ (0.5) = 43.4 v. We see that the equation automatically takes care of the fact that $I_1 - I_2$ is actually flowing in the opposite direction to that of the arrow drawn for it on the diagram, and thus B is actually furnishing electrical energy to the circuit. When we substitute the negative value obtained for $I_1 - I_2$, the equation for TPD automatically becomes $\mathscr{E} - IR$, which is proper for a source which is furnishing energy to the circuit.

(c) What would a very high resistance voltmeter read if it were connected across the motor M?

We select the path directly through the motor. We recognize the motor as a source which is receiving electrical energy from the circuit, i.e., it is converting electrical energy into mechanical energy. Hence, by (1–4–10), we have $TPD_M = \mathscr{E}_M + I_4R_M = 20 + 6.86 \times 2 = 33.7$ v.

(d) What is the rate at which electrical energy is being developed by the generator G?

This question asks for the rate at which the generator is converting mechanical energy into electrical energy. In the discussion following (1–4–13), we showed that, for a source that is furnishing electrical energy to a circuit, the rate at which the source is developing electrical energy is given by the emf of the source times the current flowing through the source. Hence $P_G = I_1\mathscr{E}_G = 4.07 \times 50 = 204$ w.

(e) What is the power output of the generator G to the remainder of the circuit ?

By (1–4–13) this power output is given by $I \times TPD_S$, so we have $I_1V_{AK} = 4.07 \times 43.9 = 179$ w.

(f) What is the rate at which electrical energy is being converted into heat energy in the generator G?

We may compute this from $P_{hG} = P_G - I_1V_{AK} = 204 - 179 = 25$ w or from $P_{hG} = I_1^2R_G = (4.07)^2 \times 1.50 = 24.9$ w. The two answers, which should be the same, agree within slide-rule accuracy.

(g) What is the rate at which electrical energy is being converted into mechanical energy in the motor?

In the discussion following (1–4–14), we have shown that, for a source which is receiving electrical energy from the circuit, the rate at which electrical energy is being converted into some form of energy other than heat is given by the product of the current flowing through the source times the emf of the source. In the case of a motor, electrical energy is converted into mechanical energy. Hence $P_{\text{mechanical}} = I_4\mathscr{E}_M = 6.86 \times 20 = 137$ w.

(h) What is the rate at which electrical energy is being converted into heat energy in the armature of the motor (i.e., what is the power loss as heat in the armature of the motor)? $P_{hM} = I_4^2R_M = (6.86)^2 \times 2.00 = 94.4$ w.

(i) What is the total power input to the armature circuit of the motor?

We may compute this power as the sum $P_{\text{total}} = P_{\text{mechanical}} + P_{hM} = 137 + 94.4 = 231$ w, or from $P_{\text{total}} = I_4 \times TPD_M = 6.86 \times 33.7 = 231$ w.

(j) What is the power input to the field windings F of the motor?

Since F is a pure resistance on steady direct current, $P_{hF} = (I_4 - I_2)^2R_F = 0.42^2 \times 80 = 14.1$ w.

EXAMPLE B. The main d-c generator G, of a certain single-line street railway system, has a maintained terminal potential difference of 500 v between its bus bars. This statement means that generator G has a voltage regulator so designed that the terminal potential difference of the generator is kept constant at 500 v, regardless of the current flowing through the generator. When a generator has such a maintained terminal potential difference it may be treated, in circuit calculations, as a source of constant emf equal to the maintained TPD and with zero internal resistance. Actually the regulator increases the emf of the generator, as the armature current increases, in such a way that the increase in emf just equals the IR drop inside the generator, and the TPD remains constant. As the current through the generator decreases, this process operates in reverse, again keeping the TPD constant. The bus bars are simply heavy copper bars that serve as terminals for the generator, and to which the trolley wire and rails of the railway line are electrically connected. For example, the trolley wire might be connected to the positive terminal and the rails to the negative terminal.

In this installation there is a booster generator B, connected so that its negative terminal is hooked to the positive terminal of the main generator (and thus to the trolley wire), and the positive terminal is hooked to the far end of the trolley wire by means of a feeder wire. The purpose of this booster generator and feeder wire is to keep the potential difference, across a car near the far end of the line, higher than it would be without the booster. The emf of the booster generator is 100 v, and its internal resistance is 0.0100 ohm. The feeder wire has a total resistance of 1.24 ohms. The far end of the line is 10.0 miles along the track from the generating station.

The trolley wire has a resistance of 0.300 ohm per mile, and the welded rails have a resistance of 0.0400 ohm per mile. Assume that all circuit constants are known to three significant figures.

There is a single car on the track, and it requires a constant current of 60 amp. Find the distance from the generating station to the car at the place where the potential difference across the car is a minimum, and determine the value of this minimum potential difference.

Figure 2–4–3 is the circuit diagram drawn from the description given in the problem, and with the circuit constants marked on the diagram. It also includes the assumed directions of flow of the currents, and Kirchhoff's first law has been applied to reduce the number of unknown currents to a minimum. Symbol V represents the potential difference across the car when the car is x miles from the generating station, where x may be any value up to 10 miles.

We want an equation giving V as a function of x, so that we may differentiate it and find the value of x at which V is a minimum. We need to consider two loops in order to eliminate I_1 and thus have an equation giving V as a function of x.

Loop CJKA $\circlearrowleft$ $500 = 0.3I_1x + V + 2.4x$

$$I_1 = \frac{500 - V - 2.4x}{0.3x} \tag{1}$$

Loop DFEHJCD $\circlearrowleft$　$100 = 1.25(60 - I_1) + 0.3(10 - x)(60 - I_1) - 0.3I_1x$

Solve for I_1.

$$I_1 = 36.5 - 4.23x \qquad (2)$$

Equate the values of I_1 in (1) and (2) and solve for V:

$$V = 1.27x^2 - 13.4x + 500 \qquad (3)$$

Equation (3) gives the potential difference across the car for any value of x from $x = 0$ to $x = 10$ miles. There is one feature of this equation that we can observe to be correct at a glance. At $x = 0$ the car will be directly across the

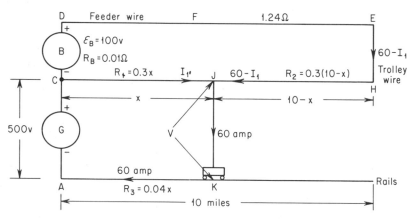

Figure 2–4–3. Booster generator B and feeder F for a trolley line. R_1 is the resistance of the trolley wire from C to J, and R_2 is its resistance from J to H. R_3 is the resistance of the rails from K to A.

main generator G, where the maintained potential difference is 500 v; so at least the constant term in (3) is correct. This one term being correct does not assure us that the other terms are free from errors in arithmetic. These terms we can check only by using some other loop such as *DFEHJKACD*. However, had the constant term been any number other than 500, we would have known that we had made a mistake.

To find the value of x, where the car experiences a minimum potential, set the first derivative of V with respect to x equal to zero and solve for x.

$$dV/dx = 2.54x - 13.4, \qquad x = 13.4/2.54 = 5.28 \text{ miles} \qquad (4)$$

Equation (4) gives the position of the car where there will be a minimum potential difference across the car. The usual tests of calculus show that this result is a minimum for V, not a maximum.

To find the potential difference across the car at the position of minimum,* put (4) into (3).

$$V_{\min} = 1.27(5.28)^2 - 13.4(5.28) + 500 = 465 \text{ v}$$

---

* As mentioned earlier, the purpose of the booster and feeder is to keep the potential difference across the car at the far end of the line higher than it would be without the booster and feeder. As a side light, it is interesting to test its effectiveness in achieving

EFFICIENCY OF TRANSMISSION. The efficiency of transmission of a distribution circuit is defined as

$$\text{efficiency} = \frac{\text{useful power output of the circuit}}{\text{total power input to the circuit}} \qquad (2\text{–}4\text{–}1)$$

It is somewhat a matter for individual decision as to the items to be included as useful power in a circuit. In the circuit under consideration in Fig. 2–4–3, the total electrical power converted to mechanical power and heat power in the car at $x = 5.28$ miles is given by $P_{car} = 60$ amp $\times$ 465 v = 27,900 w = 27.9 kw. If the weather is cool and the heat developed helps to make the car comfortable, then P_{car} is all useful. If, however, the weather is warm, the heat developed is not useful.

Let us assume that all of P_{car} is useful and compute the efficiency of transmission of this circuit. Substitution of $x = 5.28$ miles and $V = 465$ v into (1) gives

$$I_1 = (500 - 465 - 2.4 \times 5.28)/0.3 \times 5.28 = 14.1 \text{ amp}$$

and then $\qquad\qquad 60 - I_1 = 60 - 14.1 = 45.9 \text{ amp}$

Power developed by G is $500 \times 60 = 30,000$ w = 30 kw. Power developed by B is $100 \times 45.9 = 4,590$ w = 4.59 kw.

$$\text{efficiency} = 27.9 \text{ kw}/34.6 \text{ kw} = 0.778$$
$$\% \text{ efficiency} = 100 \times 0.778 = 77.8\%$$

EXAMPLE C. WHEATSTONE BRIDGE. A very simple but important d-c network is the Wheatstone bridge, which is used to measure the resistance of an unknown resistor by comparison with known resistors. Figure 2–4–4 shows the schematic circuit diagram. Here R_1, R_3, and R_4 are known variable standard resistors. The fact that each is variable is shown by the diagonal arrow drawn through the symbol for the resistor. Resistance R_x is the unknown resistance that is to be determined. Symbol G represents a d-c galvanometer, B is a battery, and S_1 and S_2 are switches.

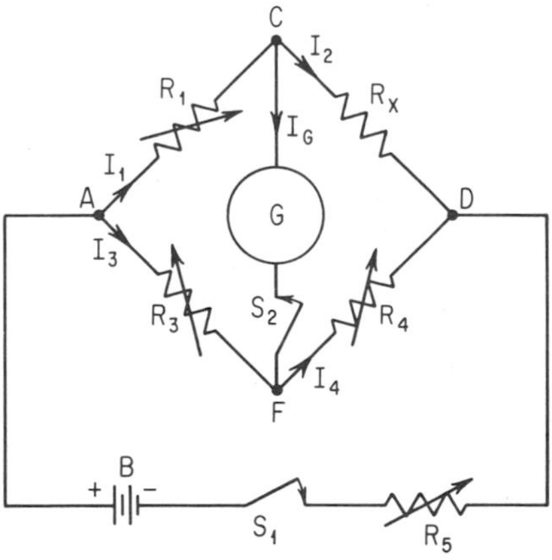

The bridge is "balanced" by adjusting R_1, R_3, and R_4 to such values that the galvanometer shows no deflection when S_1 and S_2 are closed.

Figure 2–4–4. Wheatstone bridge.

When the bridge is far from balance, the current through the galvanometer

this purpose. From (3), the potential difference across the car at the far end of the line will be 493 v. If the booster and feeder were disconnected, there is a simple series circuit, and you can solve at once, finding that the potential difference across the car would be 296 v. This result is much smaller than the potential difference across the car, even at the position of minimum potential difference in Fig. 2–4–3.

may be high enough to harm the galvanometer. To protect the galvanometer, the variable resistance R_5 is set at a high value before the switches are closed for the first time. As balance of the bridge is approached, R_5 is decreased and is finally set at zero resistance in the final test for balance.

At balance $I_G = 0$, so $I_1 = I_2$ and $I_3 = I_4$. Also, since $I_G = 0$, then C and F must be at the same potential, so $I_1 R_1 = I_3 R_3$ and $I_2 R_x = I_4 R_4$. Divide, and solve the resultant equation to obtain $R_1/R_x = R_3/R_4$. This equation expresses the balance condition for the bridge and from it

$$R_x = R_1 R_4 / R_3 \qquad (2\text{–}4\text{–}2)$$

Thus, with R_1, R_3, and R_4 known, R_x may be computed. We do not need to know either R_4 or R_3 separately but only the ratio of their values. Various standard forms of Wheatstone bridges are constructed as self-contained units for rapid measurement of resistance, but all employ the circuit in Fig. 2–4–4. In most of them a dial can be set to fix the ratio R_4/R_3, and the dial gives the value of the ratio at each setting without giving R_3 or R_4 separately. The available ratios usually vary by factors of 10, from 0.001 to 1000. The choice of the ratio to be used in a particular case is dictated by the magnitude of R_x.

Resistors R_1, R_3, and R_4 are wound with wire in such a way that they are noninductive. If the unknown resistance R_x is inductive, and S_2 is closed before S_1, there will be a deflection of G of short duration even when the bridge is balanced. To avoid confusion from this effect, S_1 is closed first, and a few seconds later the galvanometer switch S_2 is closed.

2–5 REGULATION

Regulation is defined by the equation

$$\text{regulation} = \frac{\text{rise in terminal potential difference from full load to no load}}{\text{full load terminal potential difference}}$$

or, in symbols, $$\text{regulation} = \frac{V_{\text{no load}} - V_{\text{full load}}}{V_{\text{full load}}} \qquad (2\text{–}5\text{–}1)$$

If we are talking about a transmission line, the voltages involved are those between the line wires at the load end of the line. Most electrical machines and appliances used in the home or in industry are constructed for operation at a specified potential difference across their terminals, and this voltage is usually given on the name plate. Machines or appliances operate best at the specified voltage, although most of them will behave fairly well over some range on either side. The ideal situation for such a load is one in which the voltage of the line remains constant, at the specified value, across the terminals of the load. However, because of the resistance of the line wires between the source and the load, there will be some drop in potential along the line, and this drop in potential will increase as the load current increases. Thus the potential difference across the wires of the line will change as the load current changes. Regulation is used to measure how good a line is in this respect. From the definition the regulation would be zero for a perfect line, and the larger the number for regulation the worse the line.

The term *regulation* is also applied to sources which are furnishing electrical energy to a circuit. In this case the voltages in the definition refer to the terminal potential difference of the source.

PROBLEMS

The following problems refer to steady direct currents and voltages, even though the fact is not mentioned in every problem.

2–1) A car battery, with an emf of 6.10 v and internal resistance of 0.0300 ohm, is furnishing energy to light two identical headlamps in parallel. The total resistance of the series lead wires, from the battery to the parallel combination of headlamps, is 0.0200 ohm. An ammeter in series with the battery reads 10.0 amp. Find the resistance of each headlamp and the terminal potential difference of the battery.

2–2 An automobile storage battery, with an emf of 12.30 v and an internal resistance of 0.0105 ohm, is furnishing 105.0 amp to the starter motor whose equivalent internal resistance is 0.00155 ohm. The total resistance of the cable from the battery to the motor and the return path through the frame of the car is 0.00100 ohm. The contacts of the solenoid starter switch have a resistance of 0.00025 ohm. What is the emf of the starter motor at its speed of operation under these conditions? [*Ans:* 10.9 v.]

2–3 A laboratory bank of 40 lead storage batteries in series, each with an emf of 2.01 v and an internal resistance of 0.0038 ohm, is being charged from a generator whose emf is 102 v and whose internal resistance is 0.0503 ohm. Each lead wire from the battery to the generator has a resistance of 0.0635 ohm and the control rheostat in series has a resistance of 1.22 ohms. What is the rate at which electrical energy is being converted into chemical potential energy?

2–4 The bus bars at a generating station are maintained at 120 v potential difference by the generator and its regulator. Two line wires connect a load to the bus bars, and the resistance of these wires may be considered constant as the load current changes. (a) If the potential difference across the load is 115 v when the load current is 50.0 amp, what is the resistance of the line wires? (b) If the load current is now changed to 75.0 amp, what is the potential difference across the load? (c) What is the load current when the potential difference across the load is 110 v?

2–5 A generator, with a maintained terminal potential difference of 220 v, is connected to a factory 2.00 miles down the road. The wire used for the line has a resistance of 0.0150 ohm per mile of wire. What is the potential difference across the line at the factory when the load current is 60.0 amp?

2–6 In an experiment on a generator with a maintained terminal potential difference of 121.01 v, the generator is located in the basement and the experiment is conducted on a load located on the fourth floor. When the load-current ammeter reads 50.5 amp, the voltmeter across the terminals of the load reads 119.85 v. What is the rate at which electrical energy is being converted into heat energy in the line?

2–7 In Problem 2–3, while the storage battery is still connected to the generator as described, a d-c motor is connected across the terminals of the battery, and a voltmeter across the motor terminals reads 75.0 v. The leads from the motor to the battery have a total resistance of 0.175 ohm. Assuming that all resistances and emf's remain at the values stated in Problem 2–3, what is the current through the battery and which way is it flowing?

2–8 A 1000 ohm voltmeter reads 10.0 v for full-scale deflection of its pointer. How can it be made to read 150 v for full-scale deflection of its pointer?

2–9 A 120 v voltmeter is labeled on its face as having a 1000-ohm-per-volt "sensitivity." What current through its coil will cause the pointer to deflect to the full-scale position? How can it be made into a 500 v voltmeter? [*Ans:* Add 380,000 ohms in series.]

2–10 A galvanometer with a resistance of 25.0 ohms requires 2.00 ma current for full-scale deflection of its pointer. (a) Tell quantitatively how to make this galvanometer into a voltmeter that reads 10.0 v for full-scale deflection. (b) Tell quantitatively how to make this galvanometer into an ammeter that reads 5.0 amp for full-scale deflection.

2–11 A galvanometer, to be used in a test set, requires 0.505×10^{-6} amp for full-scale deflection of its pointer and has a resistance of 115 ohms. (a) Draw the circuit diagram showing how to make this galvanometer into an ammeter which reads 10.0 milliamp for full-scale deflection and label all circuit elements with their numerical values. (b) Draw the circuit diagram showing how to make this galvanometer into a voltmeter which reads 50.0 v for full-scale deflection and label all circuit elements with their numerical values.

2–12 An ammeter gives its full-scale reading of 5.00 amp when there is a potential difference of 0.0250 v across its terminals. How can it be changed to read 25.0 amp for full-scale deflection?

2–13 A 50 mv galvanometer is one which requires a potential difference of 50.0 mv across its terminals in order that the current through its coil shall be of the correct magnitude to deflect the pointer to the right end of the scale. A certain 50 mv galvanometer has a resistance of 100 ohms. Calculate the resistance of the shunt that should be used in order to convert the galvanometer into a 100 amp ammeter.

2–14 The 50 mv galvanometer of Problem 2–13 is to be converted into a 100 v voltmeter. Compute the resistance of the multiplier required.

2–15 The emf of a certain B battery is 45.0 v as measured with a potentiometer. When a 50.0 v voltmeter, whose resistance is 100 ohms, is connected across the terminals of the battery, the voltmeter reads 42.9 v. What is the internal resistance of the battery? [*Ans:* 4.9 ohms.]

2–16 A d-c generating station supplies power to three loads, A, B, and C, connected in parallel with each other across its transmission line. The transmission line wires are No. 000 American Wire Gauge stranded copper, which has a resistance of 0.0652 ohm per thousand feet of wire. Load A is 1000 ft from the generator, load B is 500 ft beyond load A, and load C is 1500 ft beyond B. Load A takes 50.0 amp, load B takes 30.0 amp, and load C takes 20.0 amp. The voltage across the line at the generator is maintained at 500 v. (a) What is the potential difference across each load? [*Ans:* $V_A = 487$ v, $V_B = 484$ v, $V_C = 480$ v. (b) The current through load B is increased to 100 amp and that through C to 60.0 amp, while the current through A remains constant at 50.0 amp. What is now the potential difference across each load? (c) If the current drawn by each load is to be that specified in part (a) above, and the potential across load C must not be less than 485 v, what is the highest resistance per thousand feet of line wire that may be used? [*Ans:* 0.0484 ohm per thousand feet.] What size (American Wire Gauge or B. and S.) standard annealed copper wire should be used for the line wire? (Consult the wire tables for standard annealed copper wire as given in the *Handbook of Physics and Chemistry* or any other suitable handbook. Assume that the wire is at 0°C.)

2–17 In Problem 2–16, part (a), load C is a motor whose internal resistance is 0.835 ohm. What is the rate at which electrical energy is being converted into mechanical energy in this motor?

2–18 A street railway line is supplied by a d-c generator whose terminal potential difference is maintained at 500 v. The trolley wire has a resistance of 0.0100 ohm per mile and the rails have a resistance of 0.00100 ohm per mile. At a particular instant there are 4 cars on the line: car No. 1 is 1.00 mile from the generator and is drawing 75.0 amp; car No. 2 is 2.00 miles beyond car No. 1 and is drawing 50.0 amp; car No. 3 is 0.500 mile beyond car No. 2 and is drawing 80.0 amp; and car No. 4 is 1.00 mile beyond car No. 3 and is drawing 50.0 amp. What is the potential difference across each car? [*Ans:* $V_1 = 497$ v, $V_2 = 493$ v, $V_4 = 492$ v.]

2–19 A 3.00 ohm, a 6.00 ohm, and a 4.00 ohm resistor are connected in parallel, and the combination is connected in series with a 5.00 ohm resistor in a circuit. The current in the 4.00 ohm resistor is 5.00 amp. Find the current in each of the other resistors.

2–20 A 27.5 ohm resistor is in parallel with a resistor of unknown resistance R_z and the parallel combination is in series with a 48.6 ohm resistor. When a potential difference of 122.0 v is applied across the series-parallel combination, a current of 2.15 amp flows in the series resistor. What is the value of R_z and what current flows through this resistor? [*Ans:* 11.5 ohms, 1.52 amp.]

2–21 A battery whose emf is $\mathscr{E}$ and whose internal resistance is R_B is connected to a load whose resistance is R_L. Assume that R_L includes the resistance of the lead wires from the battery to the load. (a) Show that the power delivered by the battery to the load is given by $P_L = \mathscr{E}^2 R_L/(R_B + R_L)^2$. (b) Assuming that $\mathscr{E}$ and R_B are constant and that R_L is variable, prove that maximum power transfer from the battery to the load occurs at the setting of R_L that makes $R_L = R_B$. (c) Assuming that all power transferred to the load is useful, show that at maximum power transfer the efficiency of transmission is 50%.

2–22 A generator whose emf is 100 v and whose internal resistance is 0.500 ohm is connected to a motor with a 1.70 ohm resistor in series in the line. The internal resistance of the motor is 1.20 ohms and its emf is 75.0 v as it operates in this circuit. What are the *TPD* of the generator and that of the motor? [*Ans:* 96.3 v and 83.8 v.]

2–23 A generator whose emf is 60.0 v and whose internal resistance is 1.00 ohm is used to charge a battery whose emf is 30.0 v and whose internal resistance is 0.600 ohm. A control rheostat of 3.40 ohm is in series in the line. (a) Find the *TPD* of the generator. [*Ans:* 54.0 v.] (b) Find the *TPD* of the battery. Calculate this in two different ways. [*Ans:* 33.6 v.]

2–24 In Fig. 2–P–1 assume that numerical constants are known to three significant figures. (a) Find the currents I, I_1, and I_2. (b) What would a voltmeter

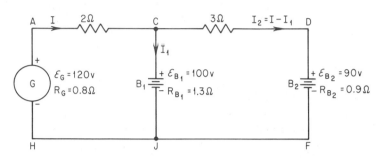

Figure 2–P–1. A generator charging two storage batteries.

read if hooked from C to J? From D to F? [*Ans:* (a) $I_1 = 2.56$ amp, $I_2 = 3.41$ amp, $I = 5.97$ amp; (b) $V_{CJ} = 103$ v, $V_{DF} = 93.1$ v.]

2–25 In a charging circuit like the one in Fig. 2–P–1, the numerical constants have the following values: $\mathscr{E}_G = 22.1$ v, $R_G = 0.431$ ohm, $\mathscr{E}_{B_1} = 12.2$ v, $R_{B_1} = 0.851$ ohm, $\mathscr{E}_{B_2} = 6.61$ v, $R_{B_2} = 0.0915$ ohm, resistor between A and C has 0.854 ohm and the one between C and D has 0.453 ohm. What are the values of I_1 and I_2?

2–26 An electric light bulb is marked 100 w 115 v. What resistance must be connected in series with the bulb in order that it may operate at its normal rating on a 230 v line?

2–27 What is the resistance of a 10.0 kw heater designed for operation on a 115 v line? How much more power is used by two such heaters connected in parallel on a 115 v line than is used if they are connected in series on the same line? Assume that the resistance of each heater remains constant.

2–28 A battery whose internal resistance is 0.500 ohm is connected to an external resistance of 3.10 ohms. The battery is converting chemical potential energy into electrical energy at the rate of 27.8 joules/sec. What are the emf and *TPD* of the battery?

2–29 A motor which has an internal resistance of 0.961 ohm is converting electrical energy into mechanical energy at the rate of 746 joules/sec when it is connected to a 220 v line. What is the emf of the motor when it is operating under conditions which do not permit the power loss as heat in the motor to exceed 20 watts? (*Note:* You do not know the power loss as heat in the motor, you simply know that it is less than 20 watts.) [*Ans:* 216 v.]

2–30 A generator is connected to a load by a transmission line whose total resistance (including both wires) is 0.150 ohm. The potential difference across the line at the generator is 225 v and that at the load is 210 v. What is the power loss on the line?

2-31 In Fig. 2-P-2, assuming that all circuit constants are known to three significant figures: (a) Find the values of the currents I_1, I_2, and I_B. [*Ans:* $I_1 = 12.8$ amp, $I_2 = 18.6$ amp, $I_B = -5.80$ amp.] (b) What would a volt-

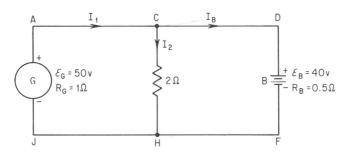

Figure 2-P-2.

meter read if connected to the points *A* and *J*? To the points *D* and *F*? (c) What power is being used by the 2 ohm resistor? (d) What is the total power developed by the generator? (e) What is the rate at which electrical energy is being converted into heat energy in the battery?

2-32 In Fig. 2-P-3, assuming that all circuit constants are known to three significant figures: (a) Find the magnitudes and directions of the currents I_1, I_2, I_3, I_4, and I_5. [*Ans:* for magnitudes, $I_1 = 26.2$ amp, $I_2 = 5.51$ amp, $I_3 = 0.918$ amp, $I_4 = 20.7$ amp, $I_5 = 4.59$ amp.] (b) What is the total

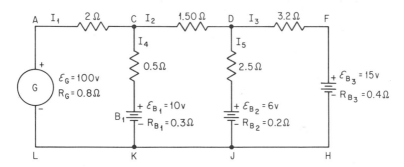

Figure 2-P-3.

power developed by the generator? (c) What is the rate at which electrical energy is being converted into chemical potential energy in the battery B_1? (d) What is the *TPD* of B_2? (e) What is the *TPD* of the generator? (f) What is the efficiency of the circuit? The purpose of the circuit is to charge the three storage batteries.

2-33 In Fig. 2-P-4: (a) Find the values of all the currents in the above circuit. (b) What is the terminal potential difference of the battery whose emf is $\mathscr{E}_1$? (c) What is the rate at which mechanical energy is being converted into electrical energy in the generator *G*?

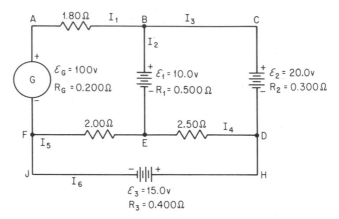

Figure 2–P–4.

2–34 In Fig. 2–P–5, assuming that all circuit constants are known to three significant figures: (a) Find the magnitudes and directions of the currents I_1, I_2, I_3, I_4, I_5, and I_6. [*Ans:* for magnitudes, $I_1 = 9.29$ amp, $I_2 = 5.24$ amp, $I_3 = 4.05$ amp, $I_4 = 1.10$ amp, $I_5 = 5.15$ amp, $I_6 = 4.14$ amp.] (b) What are the *TPD*'s of G, B_1, and B_2? (c) What is the rate at which electrical

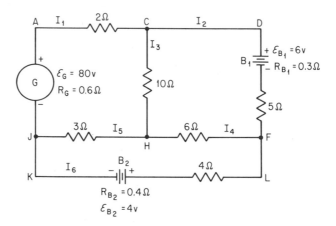

Figure 2–P–5.

energy is being converted into chemical potential energy in the battery B_1? (d) What is the rate at which electrical energy is being converted into heat in the 10 ohm resistor?

2–35 In Fig. 2–P–6, G_1 has a maintained *TPD* of 250 v, G_2 has a maintained *TPD* of 240 v, and the rest of the constants, marked on the diagram, are known to three significant figures. (a) Find the values of I_1, I_2, and I_3. (b) What is the potential difference across each load? [*Ans:* $V_1 = 240$ v, $V_2 = 236$ v.] (c) What is the efficiency of this distribution circuit?

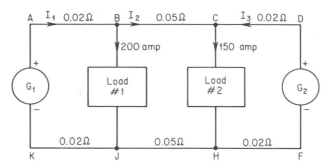

Figure 2–P–6.

2–36 In Fig. 2–P–7: (a) Find the values of all the currents in the circuit shown. G is a generator, M is a motor, and $\mathscr{E}_2$ and $\mathscr{E}_3$ are emf's of batteries. (b) What is the terminal potential difference of the battery whose emf is $\mathscr{E}_3$? (c) What

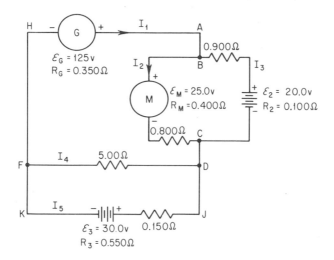

Figure 2–P–7.

energy transformation is taking place in M? What is the rate at which this energy transformation is taking place?

2–37 Figure 2–P–8 shows a schematic circuit diagram of a loop distribution circuit in which a generator G is furnishing energy to two loads. The generator has a maintained TPD of 220 v, and the circuit constants marked on the diagram are known to three significant figures. (a) Find the values of the currents I_1, I_2, and I_3. (Prove that $I_5 = I_1$, $I_4 = I_2$, and that $I_6 = I_3$.) [*Ans:* I_1 = 105 amp, I_2 = 5.00 amp, I_3 = 45.0 amp.] (b) Find the potential difference across each load. (c) What is the efficiency of the distribution circuit?

2–38 Figure 2–P–9 represents a distribution circuit with one generator furnishing energy for three loads. The maintained TPD of the generator is 225 v

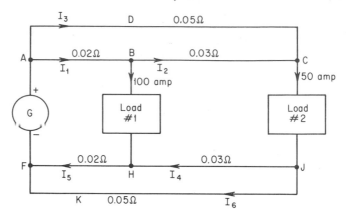

Figure 2–P–8.

and the other constants marked on the diagram are known to three significant figures. Find the potential difference across each load. [*Ans:* $V_1 = 220$ v.]

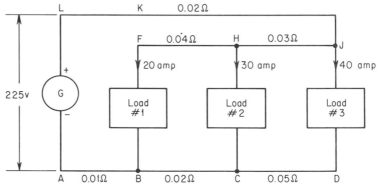

Figure 2–P–9.

2–39 The circuit in Fig. 2–P–10 shows two generators, G_1 and G_2, furnishing energy to two motors, M_1 and M_2. The emf's of the motors under the conditions of the problem are given by $\mathscr{E}_{M_1}$ and $\mathscr{E}_{M_2}$. The emf's of the

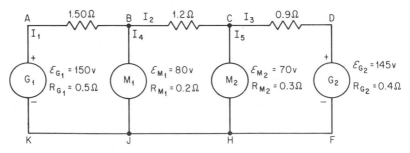

Figure 2–P–10.

generators are given by $\mathscr{E}_{G_1}$ and $\mathscr{E}_{G_2}$. Assume that all constants marked on the diagram are known to three significant figures. (a) Find the magnitudes and directions of the currents I_1, I_2, I_3, I_4, and I_5. [*Ans:* for magnitudes, $I_1 = 31.7$ amp, $I_2 = 1.48$ amp, $I_3 = 46.6$ amp, $I_4 = 30.4$ amp, $I_5 = 48.1$ amp.] (b) What are the *TPD*'s of G_1 and M_1? (c) What is the rate at which electrical energy is being converted into mechanical energy in M_2?

2–40 A street railway line is 10.0 miles long and is fed by two generators, one at each end of the line. Both generators have their positive terminals connected to the trolley wire and their negative terminals connected to the rails. The generator at the west end of the line has a maintained potential difference of 600 v, and the one at the east end of the line has a maintained potential difference of 650 v. The trolley wire (with its feeder) has a resistance of 0.200 ohm per mile. The welded rails have a resistance of 0.0400 ohm per mile. How far from the west end of the line will a car drawing 100 amp have a minimum potential difference across it, and what will be the magnitude of this minimum potential difference? [*Ans:* 3.96 miles, 562 v.]

Plot a curve of potential difference across the car as ordinate against distance from the west end of the line as abscissa, assuming that the car draws a constant current of 100 amp.

2–41 Figure 2–P–11 represents a street railway line where the feeder wire is connected to the trolley wire at the two ends of the system only. The line is 10.0 miles long and is supplied by the single generator G, which has a maintained *TPD* of 500 v. The resistance of the trolley wire is 0.400 ohm per mile and that of the feeder is 2.00 ohm for the full 10.0 mile length. The welded rails have a resistance of 0.0400 ohm per mile. At what value of x will the car have a minimum potential across it, and what is the value of this minimum potential?

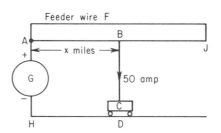

Figure 2–P–11.

2–42 In a certain factory, d-c motors are to be used because of the ease of regulating their speeds. A motor generator set is to supply the direct voltage for the motors. The d-c generator is to be situated in the central heating plant 1000 ft from the location of the motors. The transmission line from generator to motors is made of No. 0000 American Wire Gauge stranded copper wire having a resistance of 0.0517 ohm per thousand feet. In either installation referred to below, the *power output from the generator* is to be 50.0 kw for 16.0 hr a day, 300 days each year. It is estimated that the cost of electrical energy at the generator terminals will be 1.50 cents per kw-hr. How much money will be saved in a year on transmission-line losses if the generator is chosen for operation at 550 v maintained terminal potential difference instead of 115 v?

2–43 Figure 2–P–12 shows two generators, G_1 and G_2, supplying power to a 3-wire circuit. The maintained *TPD* of each generator is 220 v. The four lamp loads are connected between the outer wires and the central wire, while the motor M is connected between the two outer wires. The magnitude and

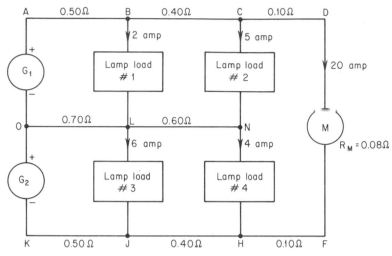

Figure 2–P–12.

direction of the current through each lamp load and the motor are as shown on the diagram. Assume that all constants marked on the diagram are known to three significant figures. (a) What are the *TPD* and emf of the motor? [*Ans: TPD_M* = 388 v.] (b) What is the potential difference across each lamp load? [*Ans: V_1* = 209 v, *V_2* = 198 v, *V_3* = 203 v, *V_4* = 194 v.]

2–44 A street railway line has a generator, whose maintained *TPD* is 550 v, at one end of the 5.00 mile line; and a storage battery at the other end. The storage battery has an emf of 500 v and an internal resistance of 0.450 ohm. The positive terminal of the generator and the positive terminal of the battery are both connected to the trolley wire and their negative terminals are both connected to the rails. The trolley wire and its feeder combined have a resistance of 0.0800 ohm per mile, and the welded rails have a resistance of 0.0400 ohm per mile. A single car is on the line and it is at the mid-point. (a) As the car is starting, an ammeter at the battery end shows a battery discharge current of 100 amp. What power is the car using? (b) A very short time later the car is running at constant speed, and the ammeter shows that the battery is being charged at the rate of 10.0 amp. What power is the car using? (Very little error will be made in assuming that the car is still at mid-point of the line.)

INTRODUCTION TO

MAGNETIC FLUX

AND INDUCED EMF'S

3–1 MAGNETIC FIELD

When we speak of a moving charge (or any other moving entity), we mean moving with respect to us as observers in our laboratory frame of reference. The description of the charge's motion, or of any force acting on it, will most conveniently be made in this laboratory frame. When we speak of anything as being fixed, or at rest, or stationary, we mean at rest with respect to us. We shall use the terms *moving* and *fixed* in this sense throughout the book, even though we do not always repeat this basis for their use.

By definition *a magnetic field exists in a region where a moving electric charge experiences a force over and above any electrostatic or gravitational forces.* If the moving electric charge experiences any electrostatic forces in the region under consideration, it is because there is an electric field present in the region as well as the magnetic field about which we are talking.

You will recall from elementary physics that magnet poles also experience forces when placed in a magnetic field. We shall reserve our detailed discussion of magnet poles for Chapter XVII, but this reminder will help to relate the concept of a magnetic field to your experience with magnets and compass needles.

You will also recall from elementary physics that a magnetic field always exists in the region around any magnet, such as a bar or horseshoe magnet, and that there is always a magnetic field in the region around an electric current. In fact we believe that the revolving and spinning electrons of the atoms of a magnetic material are responsible for the magnetic field of a magnet. Revolving and spinning electrons constitute electric charges in motion and thus constitute an electric current. Hence it is sufficient to say that there is always a magnetic field in the region around an electric current. We shall discuss these ideas in some detail in Chapters XVI and XVII.

In Chapter XIV, we shall study some of the quantitative details of the magnetic fields produced by currents, but in our present discussion we are interested in the properties of a magnetic field without reference to the physical events that set up and maintain the magnetic field. Perhaps these physical events are hidden from us, but at present we wish to determine whether or not there is a magnetic field in a particular region that is open to our observation. By the definition given above, we can settle this question by allowing an electric charge to move through the region. If this moving charge experiences a force over and above electrostatic and gravitational forces when it moves through this region, there is a magnetic field in the region. We can distinguish between an electrostatic force (which would be due to the presence of an electric field in the same region) and a magnetic force, because the charge will experience the electrostatic force even when it is at rest, but it will experience the additional magnetic force only when it is in motion.

We may have to send the moving charge along more than one path through the region in order to determine whether or not a magnetic field is present. This is due to the fact that, even with a magnetic field present in the region, we can find experimentally two directions, at 180° with respect to each other, along which the moving charge experiences no force due to the magnetic field. One of these two directions (we shall select the one in Sec. 3–2) is referred to as the *direction of the magnetic field*, and the other is, of course, opposite to the direction of the magnetic field. Thus we must modify our previous definition by saying that a magnetic field exists in a region where a moving electric charge experiences a force, over and above any electrostatic or gravitational forces, provided that the charge does not move along a line parallel to the direction of the magnetic field.

3–2 MAGNETIC FLUX DENSITY, B

Let us continue our experiment in a region where we have discovered that a magnetic field exists. We continue the experiment by sending a positive charge q through the region, with a velocity v. In Fig. 3–2–1, the direction of v is at an angle ϕ with respect to the straight line AD along which the charge can move and experience no magnetic force. Remember that in Sec. 3–1 we defined the direction of the field as being along this line AD where the moving charge experiences no magnetic force, and we have determined this line AD experimentally. Since we have not yet selected the sense along AD in Fig. 3–2–1 which we shall call that of the field (i.e., the arrow for the field direction might point from A toward D or from D toward A), the angle between v and the direction of the field might be either ϕ or $\pi - \phi$. For the moment we arbitrarily select ϕ as the angle which we shall measure in this experiment, realizing that perhaps our data ought to be in terms of $\pi - \phi$.

Now we carry out a systematic experiment in which we determine the functional relationships between the magnetic force F acting on the moving charge and q, v, and ϕ. As a result of this experiment we find that F is proportional to the product $qv \sin \phi$. This is a fortunate result, since $\sin \phi = \sin (\pi - \phi)$, so the functional relationship is the same whether we express the data in terms of ϕ or in terms of $\pi - \phi$.

We can write this proportionality as an equation if we insert a constant of proportionality. Let B be this constant of proportionality, and we may write the equation

$$F = Bqv \sin \phi \qquad (3-2-1)$$

Solve for B.

$$B = F/qv \sin \phi \qquad (3\text{--}2\text{--}2)$$

Here B is called the *magnetic flux density* of the magnetic field in which the experiment was conducted, and (3–2–2) is the defining equation for B. The term B is also called the *magnetic induction* of the field and we shall use the two names interchangeably.

A study of the data obtained in this experiment shows that the direction of F is perpendicular to the plane determined by the direction of the magnetic field and the direction of v, i.e., perpendicular to the plane of the paper in Fig. 3–2–1.

Now we are ready to specify the arbitrary choice, historically made, as to which sense along AD in Fig. 3–2–1 shall be called the direction of the magnetic field. This arbitrary convention is called *Fleming's left-hand rule* and is stated as follows: As shown in Fig. 3–2–2, extend the thumb, first finger, and

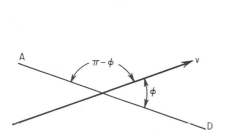

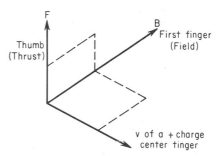

Figure 3–2–1. AD is the line along which the moving charge experiences no magnetic force; v indicates the direction of the velocity of the positive charge in the present experiment.

Figure 3–2–2. Fleming's left-hand rule for the direction of B. The direction of motion of a positive charge is the sense of the current, so the center finger points in the sense of the current.

center finger of the *left hand* so that they are mutually perpendicular. Imagine the charge to be moving perpendicular to line AD in Fig. 3–2–1, so $\phi = \pi/2$. As shown in Fig. 3–2–2, point the thumb along the direction of F. Point the center finger along the direction of v. The first finger will point along the arbitrarily chosen direction of B.

Incidentally, if an ordinary compass were placed in the magnetic field at this point, its north-seeking end would point along the direction that has been chosen for the direction of B. Thus we have another easy way to remember the direction of a magnetic field.

If v is not perpendicular to B, we have the situation shown in Fig. 3–2–3 and referred to in (3–2–1).

In the experiment discussed in connection with Fig. 3–2–1, suppose that the force on the moving positive charge were found to be directed down into the paper. Application of Fleming's left-hand rule to the figure shows that the magnetic field is directed from A toward D.

In many cases we know the direction of the magnetic field in a particular physical situation and the direction of motion of the charge. In this case, Fleming's left-hand rule tells the direction of the magnetic force on the moving charge. An electric motor is an example, where we can tell the direction of the magnetic force on the armature wires when we know the sense of the current flowing through these wires and the direction of the magnetic field set up at the armature by the field coils. Hence, Fleming's left-hand rule is often called the *motor rule*.

Using Fig. 3–2–3 and (3–2–2) we can now state the definition of *B* in words as follows. *The magnitude of B at a point is the quotient obtained when the magnetic force on a moving charge at the point is divided by the magnitude of the charge and by the component of the velocity along a line perpendicular to B.*

Magnetic flux density *B* is a vector-point function, because it has a value at every point in a magnetic field and that value is a vector quantity, i.e., both its magnitude and its direction must be given. The vector quantity *B* completely describes the nature of what we mean by a magnetic field.

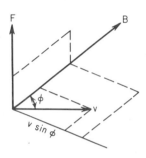

It is frequently convenient to represent a magnetic field graphically by drawing "lines of magnetic flux." These lines of magnetic flux are purely imaginary, but they are a great aid to quantitative thinking about a magnetic field. In order to use the graphical representation quantitatively, we must have a quantitative convention to tell us how many lines of magnetic flux we shall draw to represent a specific field and in what direction we shall draw them. The following is the convention that has been adopted. *The lines of magnetic flux shall be parallel to B at each point, and the number of magnetic flux lines drawn through an imaginary unit area perpendicular to B shall be numerically equal to B.*

Figure 3–2–3. A positive charge is moving with a velocity *v* at an angle ϕ with respect to a magnetic field of flux density *B*. If a negative charge were moving in the direction indicated by *v*, *F* would be reversed. *F* and *v* are always perpendicular to each other.

By this convention, *B* is the number of magnetic flux lines per unit area. From this arises the name *magnetic flux density*, which we have been using for *B*. Also, from this convention, the unit of *B* is given the composite name of weber/meter² in the mks system. (Magnetic flux itself is discussed in Sec. 3–3.)

From the defining equation (3–2–2), the unit of *B* in the mks system is:

$$\text{unit of } B = \text{newton/[coulomb (meter/sec)]}$$

Just above, we have arbitrarily given *B* the unit of weber/meter²; hence 1 wb/m² = 1 newton/(coulomb m/sec). This relationship between units can be written in several different forms. A useful alternative is 1 wb/m² = 1 newton/(amp m), and in modern usage, 1 wb/m² is called a *tesla*. One wb/m² is a fairly large magnetic flux density. The magnetic fields that are encountered in the cores of commercial machines, such as motors, generators, and transformers, have magnetic flux densities of the order of 1 wb/m². The largest magnetic flux density that has been produced in the laboratory is of the order of 150 wb/m² in transient fields, but fields of 10 wb/m² can be maintained continuously in some laboratories for experimentation. However, the usual fields encountered in the laboratory are more likely to be in the neighborhood of 10^{-2} wb/m². The earth's magnetic field is of the order of 10^{-5} wb/m². The milliweber per square meter (mw/m²) is frequently used to express the flux density for these weaker fields. Whenever a value of magnetic flux density* is to be substituted into an equation and the mks system of units is being used, the flux density must be expressed in wb/m², not a multiple or submultiple of this unit.

3–3 MAGNETIC FLUX, Φ

The total number of magnetic flux lines through a surface is called the *magnetic flux*, and the symbol Φ is used to represent it.

It follows, from our definition of B as magnetic flux lines per unit area, that if an area A is perpendicular to the flux lines and B is uniform over A, then

$$\Phi = BA \qquad (3\text{–}3\text{–}1)$$

If B is not uniform over A and if A is not perpendicular to B, we must use the appropriate mathematical methods to compute Φ, but the physical concept remains the same. In such a case, let α be the angle between B and the normal to an element of surface area dA, where dA is small enough so that B may be considered uniform over dA. Then the element of magnetic flux through the element of area is $d\Phi = B \cos \alpha \, dA$

and
$$\Phi = \int B \cos \alpha \, dA \qquad (3\text{–}3\text{–}2)$$

where Φ is the total flux through the area over which the integration is performed.

Magnetic flux Φ has the weber as its unit in the mks system, as can be seen by substitution of units into (3–3–1). In Sec. 3–2 we had 1 wb/m² = 1 newton/(amp m), so we obtain 1 wb = 1 newton m/amp = 1 joule/amp. Also, using the facts that 1 amp = 1 coulomb/sec and 1 joule/coulomb = 1 volt, we can obtain the relationship 1 wb = 1 volt sec.

3–4 MOTIONAL INDUCED EMF†

We have seen in Sec. 3–1 that whenever a charge q moves in a magnetic field it experiences a force F given by (3–2–1). The direction of this force is given by Fleming's left-hand rule if the moving charge is positive; and the direction of the force is opposite to that of Fleming's left-hand rule if the moving charge is negative. If the charge is free to respond to the influence of F, it will move in the direction of F.

An electric conductor, e.g., a copper wire, has free electrons in it. Hence, if the wire moves across a magnetic field, the electrons will move along the

---

* See Secs. 20–3 and 20–4 for some methods of measuring B.

† See Chapter XV for further discussion of induced emf.

length of the wire under the influence of F, provided that F or a component of F is along the length of the wire. To visualize such a situation more clearly, let us study Fig. 3–4–1. Here we imagine a uniform magnetic field directed perpendicular to the page and out of the page. To represent such a field we use dots that we are to think of as tips of arrows pointed out of the page toward us and thus, in Fig. 3–4–1, each dot represents a magnetic flux line directed out of the page.

Let AD, in Fig. 3–4–1, be the piece of copper wire that is placed as shown in the magnetic field. This copper wire is moving with a velocity v as indicated by the vector that represents v and, as drawn, v is perpendicular to the magnetic flux lines. By Fleming's left-hand rule, positive charges in the wire experience magnetic forces directed toward D, and negative charges in the wire experience magnetic forces directed toward A. The free electrons in the wire may move under the influence of the magnetic force; thus electrons accumulate at A, leaving a deficiency of electrons at D. Hence we mark end D with a plus sign and end A with a minus sign. Since the value of the angle ϕ in this drawing is $90°$, (3–2–1) gives the force on a charge q as

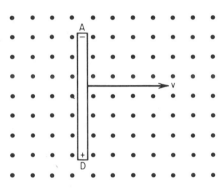

$$F = Bqv \qquad (3\text{--}4\text{--}1)$$

or

$$F/q = Bv \qquad (3\text{--}4\text{--}2)$$

This situation is the same as if an electric field had been set up in the conductor directed from A toward D, with a magnitude

Figure 3–4–1. A wire moving with velocity v perpendicular to magnetic flux lines.

$$E = Bv \qquad (3\text{--}4\text{--}3)$$

Thus the motion of the conductor across the magnetic field has set up an electric field in the conductor, the intensity of the electric field in this case being given by (3–4–3).

Now let us provide another conducting path from A to D and arrange it so that this second path is either at rest or is completely outside the magnetic field. We make the arrangement in this fashion so that there will be no magnetic force on the free electrons of the second path. Electrons will then flow around this second path from A to D, or current will flow from D to A. Mechanical work must be done by an external agency to keep the wire AD moving, because the external agency must furnish the work done by the electric current in the circuit. Wire AD is, then, a source of emf because mechanical energy of AD is being converted into electrical energy in AD. This situation is usually described by saying that an emf is induced in AD due to the motion of AD across the magnetic field. The above gives us an explanation of the way in which the emf is induced.

The emf is induced in AD whether or not the second path is provided, i.e., whether or not provision is made so that a current can flow around a completed circuit. If the second path is not provided, electrons will accumulate at A until the electric field, set up by negative charge at A and plus charge at D, is equal and opposite at each point in the wire to the electric field set up by the magnetic force. From then on, the charge separation will remain static as long as the wire moves with constant velocity perpendicular to the uniform magnetic field. (In Sec. 15–1, we shall have more to say about motional induced emf's.)

3–5 FARADAY'S LAWS OF INDUCED EMF'S

Michael Faraday* on November 24, 1831, read his paper "On the Induction of Electric Currents" before the Royal Society of London. There is reason to believe that Joseph Henry in America anticipated Faraday in many of the discoveries of laws concerning induced emf's; certainly he discovered them independently. Since Faraday first published the laws, however, he is given credit for their discovery by common consent. In 1833 Emil Lenz most clearly stated the law for determining the sense of the induced emf in the wire or circuit where it is induced.

The essential facts about the induced emf's can, for our present purpose, be stated as follows.

1. *Whenever* a conductor moves across magnetic flux lines or magnetic flux lines move across a conductor, or *the magnetic flux through a circuit changes, an emf is induced.* We have pictured the physical reason for the induced emf when a conductor moves across magnetic flux lines, and in Chapter XV we shall relate the picture to the general case where the magnetic flux through a circuit changes.

2. *The induced emf lasts only during the change.*

3. *The induced emf is proportional to the rate of change of the number of magnetic flux lines.*

Let e = instantaneous induced emf, where e is in volts in the mks system; Φ = number of magnetic flux lines through a circuit, where Φ is in webers in the mks system. Then, by this experimental law, e is proportional to $d\Phi/dt$ and, in the mks system, the constant of proportionality is unity for a single turn of wire, so $e = d\Phi/dt$. We can see that the units are satisfactory because, in Sec. 3–3, we had 1 weber = 1 volt sec.

4. *Lenz's law: The sense of the induced emf is such as to oppose the change that produces it.*

Since it is $d\Phi/dt$ that causes the induced emf, e will be in such a sense as to oppose $d\Phi/dt$; hence a minus sign is usually introduced to express this fact. Thus Faraday's law for a single turn of wire is usually written,

$$e = -d\Phi/dt \qquad (3\text{–}5\text{–}1)$$

We must remember that e opposes the change in magnetic flux, not necessarily the flux itself.

3–6 SINUSOIDAL EMF

Let us compute the emf induced in a plane coil rotating with constant angular velocity in a uniform magnetic field, as shown in Fig. 3–6–1. The magnetic

* Henry Crew, *The Rise of Modern Physics* (Baltimore, Md.: The Williams and Wilkins Company, 1928), pp. 258, 261.

flux lines are shown in Fig. 3–6–1 (a) as horizontal straight lines directed toward the right. They are parallel and equally spaced, because the magnetic field is assumed to be uniform, i.e., to have the same magnitude and direction at all points. Take the X-axis to be parallel with the flux lines. The line AD represents the cross section of the coil that is rotating with constant angular velocity ω about the origin of coordinates at O with its axis of rotation along the Z-axis. At the instant shown, the plane of the coil is at an angle θ with respect to the YZ plane of the coordinate system.

Figure 3–6–1 (b) shows the face of the coil with the wire $JACFDH$ wound around its edge. Here S_1 and S_2 are slip rings that rotate with the coil. Wire DH is fastened electrically to slip ring S_1. Wire AJ is fastened electrically to S_2 but is insulated from S_1; K and L are brushes that make electrical contact

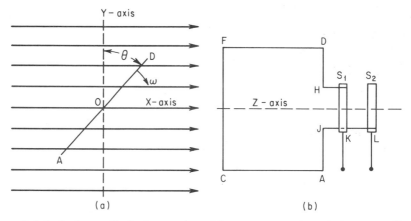

Figure 3–6–1. A plane coil of wire rotating with constant angular velocity in a uniform magnetic field. The Z-axis is the axis of rotation. (a) Cross section of the coil in the magnetic field. (b) View of the face of the coil.

with the slip rings as they rotate, and to which an external circuit may be connected.

Let B = magnetic flux density (wb/m²) of the magnetic field in which the coil is rotating; Φ = total number of magnetic flux lines (wb) through the face of the coil at any instant; e = instantaneous emf (volts) induced in the coil; ω = constant angular velocity (radians/sec) of the coil; A = area of the face of the coil. The coil may have any shape as long as the coil is plane and A represents the area of its face. The coil is drawn rectangular merely for convenience.

At any instant t, $\Phi = B \times$ (projection of the area of the face of the coil on the YZ-plane), or $\Phi = BA \cos \theta$. But $\theta = \omega t$, where $t = 0$ at the instant when the plane of the coil was in the YZ-plane, so $\Phi = BA \cos \omega t$. But $e = -d\Phi/dt$ by Faraday's law in (3–5–1), so

$$e = BA\omega \sin \omega t \qquad (3\text{–}6\text{–}1)$$

The coefficient of the sine function is the amplitude of the function, and this amplitude is the maximum value of the induced emf, i.e., the emf at those instants when sin $\omega t = \pm 1$. Hence let $\mathscr{E}_m = BA\omega$, where $\mathscr{E}_m$ represents the maximum value of the emf. Thus (3–6–1) becomes

$$e = \mathscr{E}_m \sin \omega t \qquad (3–6–2)$$

Equation (3–6–2) says that the simple generator pictured here produces a sinusoidal alternating emf. This example was selected to illustrate a calculation of an induced emf because shortly we shall be studying the response of circuits that have sinusoidal emfs applied to them. This example illustrates how such an emf may be produced. Such a simple generator would not be practical for commercial circuits, but the alternators used for electrical power distribution are carefully designed to give emf's that, as nearly as possible, satisfy (3–6–2). Alternators are so designed because a sinusoidal emf is the simplest kind of alternating emf for circuit calculations, and when such an emf is applied to the circuit, accurate predictions of circuit behavior can be made very easily.

Using (3–6–2), let us plot in Fig. 3–6–2 the instantaneous emf induced in the coil as a function of time. In Fig. 3–6–1 we started measuring time when the plane of the coil coincided with the YZ-plane, since at this place we considered θ to be zero. We can see that, in this position, the sides DF and AC are moving parallel to the magnetic flux lines, so there is no rate of change of the number of magnetic flux lines through the coil, and thus no emf is induced in the wires of the coil. Therefore, at $t = 0$, e is plotted with zero magnitude in Fig. 3–6–2.

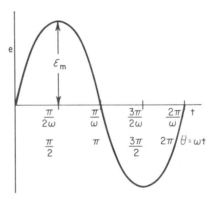

Figure 3–6–2. Sinusoidal emf. Plot of equation (3–6–2).

As the coil moves from the YZ-plane to the position shown in Fig. 3–6–1 (a), the rate of change of the number of flux lines through the coil increases, so the induced emf increases. Application of Fleming's left-hand rule at the point D shows that plus charge in wire DF experiences a magnetic force up out of the paper or toward D (negative charge experiences a force toward F), so D and thus K become positive with respect to F. Application of Fleming's left-hand rule at A shows that plus charge in wire AC experiences a magnetic force down into the paper or toward C (negative charge experiences a force toward A), so A and thus L become negative with respect to C. Sides CF and AD of the coil always move so that no component of their velocity is perpendicular to the magnetic flux lines. Thus they introduce no rate of change of the number of magnetic flux lines through the coil, and thus no emf is induced in these two sides. The net result is that D is positive with respect to A. Hence K becomes the positive brush of the generator and L the negative brush during this part of the motion. If an external circuit were connected to the brushes, current would flow out of the generator from brush

K and back into the generator through brush L. We indicate this polarity of the brushes in the plot of Fig. 3–6–2 by showing the emf as positive in this part of the rotation. This same polarity continues as the coil rotates with D moving downward. The rate of change of the magnetic flux through the coil, and thus the induced emf, become a maximum when AD is along the X-axis. Since AD is along the X-axis when the plane of the coil is in the XZ-plane ($\theta = \pi/2$ radians or 90°), the maximum of the curve in Fig. 3–6–2 comes at $\theta = \pi/2$. From this position the emf decreases until it is again zero when the plane of the coil is in the YZ-plane, with D at the bottom and A at the top (when $\theta = \pi$ radians or 180°), so the curve in Fig. 3–6–2 goes to $e = 0$ at $\theta = \pi$. As D moves up the left side of Fig. 3–6–1 (a) and A moves down the right, application of Fleming's left-hand rule shows A to be positive with respect to D, and thus L positive with respect to K. This condition means that the emf in the coil has reversed, and the fact is shown by the negative value of the emf from $\theta = \pi$ to $\theta = 2\pi$ in Fig. 3–6–2. The emf increases to a maximum at $\theta = 3\pi/2$ (plane of the coil in the XZ-plane) and decreases to zero at $\theta = 2\pi$, and one *cycle* of the emf is completed. As the coil passes $\theta = 2\pi$, the emf again reverses and the cycle is repeated. The emf continues to go through this cycle of changes as long as the coil continues to rotate with constant angular velocity in the uniform magnetic field.

The above describes what we mean by a sinusoidal alternating emf. Here ω is called the *angular frequency* of the emf, and is in radians/second. The frequency of an alternating emf is often expressed by giving the number of cycles per second instead of the angular frequency. For example, a common frequency for power distribution is 60 cycles/sec. The frequency in cycles per second is usually designated by f. Since there are 2π radians in a cycle we have the relationship that

$$\omega = 2\pi f \tag{3–6–3}$$

and (3–6–2) may be written

$$e = \mathscr{E}_m \sin 2\pi f t \tag{3–6–4}$$

3–7 SELF-INDUCTANCE, L

As a second example illustrating induced emf's, let us consider the emf of self-induction. We have pointed out that whenever the magnetic flux through a circuit changes, an emf is always induced. This statement is true, regardless of the reason why the number of magnetic flux lines linking the circuit changes.

Whenever a current flows, it always has a magnetic field associated with it and thus produces magnetic flux that links the circuit in which the current is flowing. When the current changes, there is a change in the magnetic flux linking the circuit and thus an emf is induced in the circuit. By Lenz's law, this emf will be in such a sense as to oppose the change that produced it and thus will oppose the change in the current. Remember that *this emf opposes the change in the current*, not necessarily the current itself. This induced emf is called an *emf of self-induction*, because it is set up in the circuit itself where the current is changing.

If the current in the circuit is increasing, the emf of self-induction will oppose the increase and thus will be in the opposite sense to that of the current. This fact means that we have, in this emf, a source which is receiving energy from the circuit. Hence, in the source, electrical energy is being converted into some other form of energy. The "some other form of energy" in this case is the potential energy of the magnetic field around the current. As long as the current is increasing, the emf opposes the current and electrical energy is being changed into magnetic potential energy of the magnetic field. If the current becomes constant, the emf of self-induction becomes zero, and electrical energy is no longer changed into magnetic potential energy. Thus energy is required from the electrical circuit to establish the magnetic field around the current, but no energy is required to maintain a constant magnetic field.

If the current decreases, the emf of self-induction opposes the decrease of the current and thus is in the same sense as the current. In this case we have an emf which is furnishing energy to the circuit; hence, in the source, some other form of energy is being converted into electrical energy. Again, the "some other form of energy" is the energy of the magnetic field around the current. Thus as the current decreases, the potential energy of the magnetic field is fed back into the circuit and keeps the current flowing in its initial sense.

It is an experimental fact (which we shall relate to more fundamental facts in Chapter XIV) that the number of magnetic flux lines that link the circuit is directly proportional to the current flowing in the circuit, provided there is no ferromagnetic material near the circuit. In Chapter XIV we shall derive the quantitative relationships between the number of magnetic flux lines and the current for various geometrical shapes of electric circuits, but for the present it is sufficient for our purpose to know that the number of magnetic flux lines is directly porportional to the current. If we let Φ = total number of magnetic flux lines linking the circuit and i = instantaneous current flowing in the circuit, we can express the preceding experimental fact as

$$\Phi \quad \text{is proportional to} \quad i \qquad (3\text{–}7\text{–}1)$$

But, by Faraday's law of induced emf's,

$$e_L = -d\Phi/dt \qquad (3\text{–}7\text{–}2)$$

where e_L = the instantaneous emf of self-induction set up in the circuit. From (3–7–1) and (3–7–2) we may write

$$e_L \quad \text{is proportional to} \quad di/dt \qquad (3\text{–}7\text{–}3)$$

A factor of proportionality is introduced in (3–7–3) so an equality may be written, and this factor of proportionality is represented by L and is called the *self-inductance* of the circuit. Thus (3–7–3) becomes

$$e_L = -L\, di/dt \qquad (3\text{–}7\text{–}4)$$

If there is no ferromagnetic material (such as iron, nickel, cobalt, or ferromagnetic alloys) near the circuit, L is found to be a constant for a circuit of fixed geometry (see Sec. 16–7 for an example). Thus, for this case, there is a constant of proportionality relating Φ and i in (3–7–1).

If, however, ferromagnetic material is present near the circuit, L is found to be a complicated function of i because, in (3–7–1), Φ is a complicated function of i. For some time we shall treat L in (3–7–4) as a constant, which means that there is no ferromagnetic material near the circuits considered. Later we shall study ferromagnetic materials and determine some of the relationships between Φ and i in their presence.

Solve (3–7–4) for L.

$$L = -e_L/(di/dt) \tag{3–7–5}$$

Equation (3–7–5) defines L.

If we have a certain circuit, with no ferromagnetic materials about, and wish to change the self-inductance of the circuit, we *cannot* do so by changing di/dt. We find that as di/dt is changed, e_L will change with it in such a way that the ratio of (3–7–5) remains constant. Thus L for a given circuit does not depend on either e_L or di/dt, but upon their ratio, which is constant. We find by experimentation that the L of a circuit depends on the number of turns of wire on the circuit and the geometry of the circuit. If we wish to change the L of the circuit, we must change one of these two. In spite of this, (3–7–5) is the most convenient definition of L, because it is simple and extremely useful. On the other hand a formula that gives the L for a circuit in terms of the number of turns of wire and the geometry is complicated and is different for each different kind of geometry. For this reason (3–7–5) is generally accepted as the defining equation for L.

The henry is the unit of self-inductance in the mks system of units and is defined from (3–7–5) as follows. *A circuit has a self-inductance of one henry if one volt of self-induced emf is set up in the circuit when the current flowing in the circuit is changing at the rate of one ampere per second.*

Substitution of units into (3–7–5) gives 1 henry = 1 volt sec/ampere.

3–8 MAGNETIC FLUX LINKAGES

In stating Faraday's experimental law for induced emf's in (3–5–1), we assumed that the magnetic flux lines were linking a single turn of wire. If, however, the wire is wound into a coil so that there are N turns of wire in series, the emf given by (3–5–1) will be induced in each turn of wire. Then, if these turns of wire are all in the same sense (e.g., all clockwise as viewed from one end of the coil), the emf's in the turns will all be in the same sense. The total emf, for emf's in series and in the same sense, is the arithmetic sum of the separate emf's. In the case where all the Φ flux lines link all N turns of wire of the coil, the N emf's induced will be equal, and the total emf will be N times the emf induced in one turn of wire. So for this case Faraday's law of induced emf's should be written

$$e = -N \, d\Phi/dt \tag{3–8–1}$$

or this may be written as

$$e = -d(N\Phi)/dt \tag{3–8–2}$$

The quantity $N\Phi$ is given the name *magnetic flux linkages*, and in the mks system its unit* is *weber turn*.

Above, we assumed the ideal case, where all the flux lines Φ linked all the N turns. In many cases this will not be true. All the flux lines may link some of the turns, but only a part of the flux lines link the other turns. Let N_1 turns be linked by Φ_1 flux lines, N_2 turns be linked by Φ_2 flux lines, etc. Then the number of magnetic flux linkages is given by

$$N\Phi = N_1\Phi_1 + N_2\Phi_2 + N_3\Phi_3 + \cdots$$

and (3–8–2) still gives the induced emf. However, now N may not be taken out in front of the differentiation symbol, and the emf induced is the negative time rate of change of the magnetic flux linkages. Thus $d(N\Phi)/dt$ can be evaluated only for particular problems where the functional relationships between $(N\Phi)$ and t are known.

3–9 SELF-INDUCTANCE OF AN INDUCTOR EXPRESSED IN TERMS OF MAGNETIC FLUX LINKAGES

A circuit or a part of a circuit that has self-inductance is called an *inductor*. Usually the self-inductance of a circuit whose wires are spread out fairly well in space is small. If, however, a part of the circuit is made up of many turns of wire closely spaced in a coil, that part of the circuit has a large self-inductance. This result is due to the fact that the magnetic flux linkage in that part is large, and thus a given rate of change of the current will produce a large emf of self-induction. Hence one or more coils of wire in a circuit make the chief contributions to the self-inductance of the circuit, and the coils are usually referred to as the inductors in the circuit. All the self-inductance is looked upon as concentrated in the coils for many purposes. The usual symbol for an inductor is ——ℓℓℓ—— because this symbol looks like a coil of wire. We shall take this point of view and usually refer to the self-inductances of coils, considering that all the self-inductance of the circuit is concentrated in the coils. If no inductor is drawn in a circuit, we assume that the circuit has no self-inductance, a condition which can never be completely realized but can be approximated very closely.

If we let $N\Phi$ be the number of magnetic flux linkages of a coil with itself, then by (3–8–2)

$$e_L = -d(N\Phi)/dt \qquad (3\text{–}9\text{–}1)$$

where e_L is again the emf of self-induction in the coil. From (3–7–4) we also have $e_L = -L\,di/dt$. Therefore $L\,di/dt = d(N\Phi)/dt$ from which $L\,di = d(N\Phi)$ or $\int L\,di = \int d(N\Phi)$. If there is no ferromagnetic material about the coil (as we shall assume for some time) L is independent of i, and we may write

---

* The turn is not really a unit in the proper sense, because N is a pure number. However, it is often convenient to include the *turn* as if it were a unit, just to keep track of our meaning when we use N. This situation is analogous to the case where we express an angular velocity in radians/sec. The radian has the units of a length divided by a length and thus is not properly a unit. However, we keep on using it as if it were a unit in order to remind ourselves that we are measuring angles in radians, not in degrees or some other angular measure.

$L \int di = \int d(N\Phi)$　or　$Li = N\Phi + K$ where K is the constant of integration. We may evaluate K from the fact that when $i = 0$, $\Phi = 0$, if there is no ferro-magnetic material near the coil. From this fact it follows that $K = 0$, so $Li = N\Phi$, or

$$L = N\Phi/i \qquad (3\text{–}9\text{–}2)$$

Thus the *self-inductance of an inductor is equal to the number of magnetic flux linkages of the inductor with itself when unit current flows through the inductor*. Substitution of units into (3–9–2) gives 1 henry = 1 weber turn/ampere. Since 1 weber = 1 volt sec and the turn is not a real unit, this is the same unit for the henry that we had in Sec. 3–7.

The henry is a fairly large unit of self-inductance, so the self-inductances of smaller coils are often expressed in millihenrys. There are 1000 millihenrys per henry. Remember that the self-inductance of a coil must always be expressed in henrys when the mks system is used, before substitution for L in an equation.

PROBLEMS

3–1 Refer to Problem 1–5 at the end of Chapter I. After the ordinary and heavy hydrogen ions are accelerated through the electric potential difference of 100 v, as described in Problem 1–5, they travel on into a region where there is a uniform magnetic field. The flux lines of this magnetic field are vertical and directed downward. The ions are traveling along a horizontal line toward the east as they enter the magnetic field. (a) What is the direction of the force on each ion as it enters the magnetic field? (b) You will recall from mechanics that, when a body is moving with constant speed and experiences a constant force which is always perpendicular to its direction of motion, the force causes the body to move in a circle. The radius of the circle is such that the force acting on the body furnishes the required centripetal force. Appropriate measuring apparatus shows that the ions of ordinary hydrogen in this problem describe a circle of 0.500 m radius. What is the flux density of the magnetic field? What is the radius of the circle followed by the heavy hydrogen ions? [*Ans:* 29.1×10^{-4} wb/m², 0.705 m.]

3–2 The doubly-ionized helium ions of Problem 1–6 are to be deflected in a semicircle of radius 0.105 meter *after* they have attained a velocity of 1.13×10^5 m/sec. This deflection is to be accomplished by having them travel perpendicular to a uniform magnetic field of flux density B [read part (b) of Problem 3–1]. What value must B have? Substitute units with numerical quantities and show that the correct units appear on the answer. [*Ans:* 22.3×10^{-3} wb/m².]

3–3 Figure 3–P–1 represents a beam of positive hydrogen ions traveling toward the right. Each ion in the beam has a velocity of 5.00×10^3 m/sec. In the region of the dotted square is a uniform electric field with an electric field intensity $E = 200$ newtons/coulomb directed upward, as shown by the arrows on the electric flux lines drawn. This field obviously exerts a force upward (toward the top of the page) on each positive ion. Perpendicular to the plane of the paper, and in the same region outlined by the dotted square, is a uniform magnetic field so directed that it exerts a force downward (toward the bottom of the page) on each ion. The magnetic flux density is adjusted to such a magnitude that the ion beam travels straight through the region of the dotted square. (a) Is the magnetic field directed up out of the page or down into the page? (b) What is the magnetic flux density of the magnetic field if the ordinary hydrogen ions go straight through? If the heavy hydrogen ions go straight through? [*Ans:* 0.0400 wb/m².]

3–4 In an experimental arrangement like the one pictured in Fig. 3–P–1 and described in Problem 3–3, $E = 150$ newton/coulomb and $B = 0.0765$ wb/m². What velocity must the ions have, in a beam of doubly-ionized helium, in order to go straight through? Substitute units with the numerical quantities and show that the correct units appear on the answer. [*Ans:* 1960 m/sec.]

3–5 In Fig. 3–P–2, AD is a wire that is free to move toward the left; $CFGH$ is a very long wire loop that is fixed in place. As AD moves to the left it remains in electrical contact with the wires CF and HG. All through this region is a uniform magnetic field of flux density 1.55 wb/m² directed up out of the page. The wire AD is moving toward the left with a constant

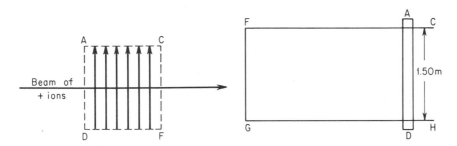

Figure 3–P–1.   **Figure 3–P–2.**

velocity of 2.50 m/sec. (a) What is the sense of the emf induced in wire AD, and what is the sense of the current that flows around the loop? (b) What is the magnitude of the emf induced in wire AD? [*Ans:* 5.81 v.] (c) At the instant when the resistance of the loop $AFGD$ is 0.0100 ohm, what mechanical power must be used to keep wire AD moving at this velocity? (neglect friction). [*Ans:* 3380 w.] (d) You will recall from mechanics that mechanical power is given by Fv. What mechanical force must be exerted on wire AD in the situation of part (c) above to keep the wire moving with the constant velocity v given. [*Ans:* 1350 newtons.]

3–6 Solve Problem 3–5 with the single change that wire AD is moving with a constant velocity of 3.76 m/sec.

3–7 Suppose that wire AD of Fig. 3–P–2 is suspended as a pendulum so that it swings left and right with small amplitude while maintaining electrical contact with the wires CF and HG. Assume that the resistance of the loop $AFGDA$ is very large so electromagnetic damping (due to Lenz's law) is negligible and that damping due to friction is also negligible.

Let x equal the distance from end wire FG to the swinging wire AD. The value of x as a function of time is given by the equation $x = X - X_m \sin \omega t$ where X has the constant value of 10.5 m and X_m has the constant value of 0.452 m. The angular frequency ω has the value 52.1 radian/sec. If the effective length of AD is 1.50 m as shown in Fig. 3–P–2 and B has the value 1.55 wb/m^2, what is the equation giving the emf induced in AD as a function of time and what are the values of the numerical constants in this equation?

3–8 A coil with 200 turns of wire in series is perpendicular to a uniform magnetic field whose magnetic flux density is 0.150 wb/m^2. The area of the face of the coil is 0.0400 m^2. The coil is turned to a position parallel with the field in 0.0100 sec. (a) What is the average rate of change of the flux linking the coil while the coil is turning? (b) What is the average emf induced in each turn of the wire on the coil? (c) What is the average emf induced in the coil? [Ans: 120 v.]

3–9 A straight wire of length 1.50 m is moved with a velocity of 5.00 m/sec perpendicular to a uniform magnetic field whose flux density is 0.00800 wb/m^2. The length of the wire is perpendicular to v and to B. (a) What electric field strength is set up in the wire by the magnetic force on the free electrons in the wire? [Ans: 0.0400 newton/coulomb.] (b) What emf is induced in the wire? [Ans: 0.0600 v.]

3–10 A flat coil with one turn of wire is rotating with a uniform angular velocity of 377 radians/sec in a uniform magnetic field of flux density 0.136 wb/m^2. The area of the face of the coil is 0.250 m^2. What is the instantaneous rate of change of magnetic flux linkage with the coil 0.00100 sec after the plane of the coil was perpendicular to the magnetic flux lines? [Ans: -4.70 wb/sec.]

3–11 In a certain region near an a-c circuit, the magnetic flux density as a function of time is given by the equation $B = B_m \sin 2\pi f t$ where f is 60.0 cycles/sec and $B_m = 0.00590$ wb/m^2. A coil of 500 turns of wire is placed in this region, so that the area of its face is perpendicular to the magnetic flux lines. The area of the face of the coil is 0.0130 m^2, and the flux density is the same, at a given instant, over the face of the coil. What is the equation of the emf induced in the coil as a function of time? [Ans: $e = \mathcal{E}_m \sin(\omega t - \pi/2)$ where $\mathcal{E}_m = 14.4$ v.]

3–12 An autotransformer, connected to a 60 cycle/sec a-c line, is on a laboratory table near a plane coil of 125 turns of wire which is part of an experimental circuit. An emf, extraneous to the intention of the experiment (a 60-cycle pick-up), is induced in the coil due to the "stray" magnetic field of the autotransformer. The magnetic flux density at the coil, due to this stray field, is given by $B = B_m \sin \omega t$ where $B_m = 3.12 \times 10^{-3}$ wb/m^2 and $\omega = 377$ sec^{-1}. The area of the face of the coil is 0.0131 m^2, and B may be considered at every instant to be uniform over this area. The direction of B makes an angle of 12.5° with respect to a line drawn normal to the face of the coil. What is the equation for the emf of the 60-cycle pick-up as a function of time and what are the values of the numerical constants in the equation? [Ans: $e = \mathcal{E}_m \sin(\omega t - \pi/2)$ where $\mathcal{E}_m = 1.88$ v.]

3–13 A certain coil of wire has a self-inductance of 0.0270 henry, and the current flowing through it as a function of time is given by the equation $i = I(1 - e^{-at})$ where $I = 20.0$ amp, and $a = 1.73$ /sec. Here e is the base of natural logarithms. (a) What is the equation for the emf of self-induction in the coil as a function of time? (b) What is the value of the emf of self-induction at $t = 0$, at $t = 3.00$ sec? What does the minus sign on each answer mean? [*Ans:* -0.935 v, -0.00520 v.]

3–14 The emf of self-induction in a certain coil is given, as a function of time, by the equation $e_L = LIbe^{-bt}$ and a condition determined by the circuit is that, at $t = 0$, $i = I$, where L is the constant self-inductance of the coil, i is the instantaneous current flowing in the coil, and the condition above means that I is the value of i at the instant $t = 0$. Here b is a constant, e is the base of natural logarithms, and e_L is the instantaneous emf of self-induction. What is the equation for the current i flowing in the circuit as a function of time? [*Ans:* $i = Ie^{-bt}$.]

3–15 In a certain coil the instantaneous emf of self-induction is given, as a function of the instantaneous current i flowing in the coil, by the equation $e_L = Di$ where D is a constant. L is the constant self-inductance of the coil and one condition imposed by the circuit, of which the coil is a part, is that $i = I$ at $t = 0$, so that I is the initial value of the current flowing in the coil. Derive an equation giving the current i as a function of time. [*Ans:* $i = Ie^{-Dt/L}$.]

3–16 The instantaneous emf of self-induction in a certain coil is given, as a function of current, by the equation $e_L = Di - A$ where i is the instantaneous current flowing in the coil and A and D are constants. One condition imposed by the circuit, of which the coil is a part, is that $i = 0$ at $t = 0$. L is the constant self-inductance of the coil. (a) Derive an equation giving the instantaneous current i flowing in the coil as a function of time. [*Ans:* $i = (A/D)(1 - e^{-Dt/L})$.] (b) Derive an equation giving the instantaneous emf of self-induction as a function of time.

3–17 The sinusoidal alternating current flowing through a coil, of self-inductance 0.0950 henry, is given as a function of time by the equation $i = I_m \sin 2\pi ft$ where I_m is 5.00 amp, and f is 60 cycles/sec. (a) What is the equation that gives the emf of self-induction in this coil as a function of time? (b) What is the value of the emf of self-induction at $t = 0$, at $t = 0.0130$ sec, at $t = 3.00$ sec? [*Ans:* -179 v, -33.2 v, -179 v.]

3–18 A certain coil of constant self-inductance L is connected to an a-c line, and its emf of self-induction as a function of time is given by the equation $e_L = A \sin \omega t$ where A is a constant and ω is the constant angular frequency of the a-c line to which the coil is attached. Derive an equation giving the current i flowing in the coil as a function of time. A condition of the circuit is that at $t = \pi/2\omega$, $i = 0$. [*Ans:* $i = D \sin(\omega t + \pi/2)$ where $D = A/L\omega$.]

3–19 A 1000 turn coil of wire has a self-inductance of 8.19 millihenrys, and a current of 20.0 amp is flowing through it. The coil is closely wound, so that all flux lines link all the turns of wire on the coil. (a) What is the number of magnetic flux linkages of the coil with itself? [*Ans:* 0.164 weber turns.] (b) What is the number of magnetic flux lines through the coil? [*Ans:* 1.64×10^{-4} weber.]

3–20 An air-core primary coil with 500 turns of wire has a self-inductance of 0.0135 henry and the coil is so closely wound that all flux lines link all turns of wire on the coil. A current, given by the equation $i = I_m \sin \omega t$ where $I_m = 11.5$ amp and $\omega = 377$ sec^{-1}, is flowing in the coil. (a) What is the equation which expresses the number Φ of magnetic flux lines linking the coil as a function of time? State the numerical values of the constants in the equation. [*Ans:* $\Phi = \Phi_m \sin \omega t$ where $\Phi_m = 3.11 \times 10^{-4}$ weber and $\omega = 377$ sec^{-1}.] (b) What emf is induced in an adjacent air-core secondary coil of 1500 turns if, at every instant, the magnetic flux linkage with the secondary can be considered as equivalent to 50.5 per cent of the magnetic flux from the primary coil linking all the turns of this secondary coil? Write the equation for this emf as a function of time and give the maximum value of the emf induced in the secondary. [*Ans:* Maximum value of emf 88.8 v.]

SOME OF THE PROPERTIES

OF A CAPACITOR

AS A CIRCUIT ELEMENT

4–1 REVIEW

In elementary physics you studied capacitors (or condensers as they formerly were called), and here we shall review quickly some of the concepts that you learned.

Suppose that you go to the machine shop and select two large sheets of metal of the same size and set them up so that they face each other. You mount them so that no electric conduction path exists between the plates and so that the plates are fairly close together. You now have a capacitor. The sheets of metal are called the *plates* and the insulating material between the plates is called the *dielectric*. A perfect capacitor is one whose dielectric, supports, etc. permit no current to flow from one plate to the other. We shall assume for some time that we are dealing with perfect capacitors, and later (in Sec. 8–3) shall see how to deal with a leaky capacitor. Well-built capacitors with carefully selected dielectrics, such as quartz, mica, and air under proper conditions, behave very nearly as perfect capacitors.

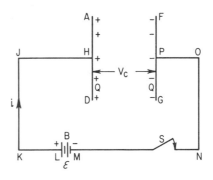

Figure 4–1–1. Capacitor connected to a battery.

After setting up the sheets of metal so that you have a very nearly perfect capacitor, connect the positive terminal of a battery to one plate and the negative terminal of the battery to the other plate as shown in Fig. 4–1–1. In this figure, AD is one of the sheets of metal and FG is the other; B is a battery whose emf is $\mathcal{E}$; $HJKL$ is a wire connecting the positive terminal of the battery to a plate AD; and $MNOP$ is the wire connecting the negative terminal of the battery to plate FG through the switch S.

The negative terminal of the battery is negative, because it has a surplus of electrons, which repel each other. The positive terminal is positive, because it has a deficiency of electrons and thus attracts electrons. The chemical action in the battery has set up this condition. When the switch S is closed, electrons flow up the wire onto plate FG, inducing a positive charge on plate AD. This statement means that electrons leave plate AD under the repulsion of the electrons on FG and the attraction of the plus terminal of the battery. Essentially, electrons are going from plate AD through the battery to plate FG, and a current is flowing in the wire and battery parts of the circuit. This current will continue until the potential difference V_C across the plates of the capacitor is equal (and opposite in the circuit) to the emf of the battery. At this stage the current ceases to flow and the capacitor has a charge Q on each plate.

During the charging process, chemical potential energy has been changed to electrical energy in the current flow, and some of this electrical energy in turn has been changed into the potential energy of the charged capacitor. There is always resistance in the circuit, so some of the energy furnished by the battery has been changed into heat energy.

Now disconnect the battery and discharge the capacitor. The fact that the capacitor had potential energy when it was charged is shown in the discharge process, because the capacitor sends a current through the discharge circuit attached to it, and electrical energy is changed into other forms of energy in the elements of the discharge circuit. If, as a special case, the discharge circuit contains resistance only, the potential energy of the charged capacitor is all changed into heat energy in the resistance.

The charge Q of a capacitor can be measured in the discharge process. After the capacitor has been charged, it can be disconnected from the battery without loss of charge and then discharged through a ballistic galvanometer. The first maximum deflection of the ballistic galvanometer is a measure of the charge which flows through the galvanometer coil, provided that the flow occurs in a time which is short compared to the period of the galvanometer. The charge which flows through the coil of the galvanometer is the charge Q which was on the capacitor prior to discharge. Hence the first maximum deflection of the ballistic galvanometer is a measure of the charge Q. In Sec. 13–6, we shall study the ballistic galvanometer and show that it can measure charge in the manner stated above. For the moment, it is sufficient to know that an easy method of measurement of Q is available.

Next, remove the discharge circuit and reconnect the capacitor in the circuit of Fig. 4–1–1, but this time use a battery of larger emf. The charging process will be repeated, and again will cease when V_C becomes equal to the new, larger emf of the battery. It will be found that the charge Q on the capacitor is larger than it was before.

A repetition of this experiment with a variety of batteries, each with a different emf, shows that the charge Q obtained is directly proportional to the potential difference V_C across the plates or

$$Q \quad \text{is proportional to} \quad V_C \tag{4–1–1}$$

For this purpose it is conventional to let Q be the charge on one plate of the capacitor. There is an equal and opposite charge on the other plate, but it is always the charge Q on one plate that appears in the formulas. This usage is due to the fact that it was a quantity of electricity Q (not $2Q$) which moved through the wires in the charging process. You can understand this statement by visualizing the charging process in Fig. 4–1–1. In this process a number of electrons, sufficient to equal the charge Q, moved from the negative terminal of the battery up onto plate FG, and the same number of electrons left plate AD and went down through the battery back to the negative terminal of the battery. Thus, at any point in the wire part of the circuit, a quantity Q of electricity passed the point during the charging process. Similar reasoning shows that a quantity Q (not $2Q$) of electricity moves from the negative plate FG around the discharge circuit to plate AD in the discharge process. We shall talk in terms of current, rather than in terms of electron motion, so we will think only in terms of positive charge as moving in a direction opposite to that of the actual electron motion in each circuit.

Further study of the data from which we wrote the proportionality in (4–1–1) shows that the ratio of Q/V_C is a constant, so that a constant of proportionality is appropriate to change (4–1–1) from a proportionality to an equality. Thus we may write

$$Q = CV_C \quad \text{or} \quad C = Q/V_C \qquad (4\text{–}1\text{–}2)$$

This constant of proportionality C is given the name *capacitance* of the capacitor, and (4–1–2) is the defining equation for capacitance.

The capacitance of a capacitor does not depend on either Q or V_C, i.e., as V_C is changed, Q will change with it in such a way that the ratio Q/V_C remains constant. This statement is true until V_C becomes so large that dielectric breakdown (see Sec. 11–10) occurs; a current then actually flows from one plate to the other through the dielectric. If dielectric breakdown occurs, the capacitor no longer behaves like a perfect one, and, at the moment, we are not interested in its behavior. Hence we agree to keep V_C below the breakdown potential for the capacitor.

In setting up the capacitor initially, had you selected metal sheets with a different area of faces, or placed them with a different separation, or used a different dielectric between the plates as an insulator, you would have arrived at a different numerical value for C in (4–1–2). Thus the capacitance of a capacitor depends on the kind of dielectric between the plates and the geometry of its construction. A wide variety of geometries of construction is used in fabricating capacitors. We used one of these when we placed the plates parallel to each other. Later (Chapter XII) we shall derive formulas for a few of the common types of capacitors and show how we may compute the capacitance of a capacitor from its geometry and the kind of dielectric used. We shall find that the kind of formula is different for each different kind of geometry, so it is not convenient to define capacitance in terms of such formulas. For any given capacitor (one with constant geometry and kind of dielectric), however, the experimental result in (4–1–2) is true and thus (4–1–2) is by far the most convenient relationship to use in defining capacitance.

The *farad* is the unit of capacitance in the mks system of units, and is defined from (4–1–2) as follows. *A capacitor has a capacitance of one farad if there is a potential difference of one volt between its plates when the charge on one plate is one coulomb.* Thus 1 farad = 1 coulomb/volt. A farad is a very large capacitance, and submultiples of it are commonly used to express the capacitance of capacitors usually encountered. The submultiples most used are the microfarad, which is usually abbreviated μf, and the micro-microfarad, which is abbreviated μμf, where 1 μf = 10^{-6} farad and 1 μμf = 10^{-12} farad. One μμf is often called a *picofarad*. Remember that, when substituting in an equation, the capacitance must be expressed in farads if the mks system is being used.

4–2 RELATIONSHIP OF CURRENT AND CHARGE

In Fig. 4–2–1 we have a capacitor C, connected so that it can be charged from a battery whose emf is $\mathcal{E}$. Here S is a switch that can be closed when we are ready to start the charging process, and R represents the resistance of the circuit, including the internal resistance of the battery and that of the wires. We close the switch, and the charging process starts. Let i = instantaneous current (amperes) flowing in the circuit at any time t; q = instantaneous charge (coulombs) that has accumulated on the capacitor at time t; v_C = instantaneous potential difference (volts) across the capacitor at the time t; and t = time since the switch was closed (seconds).

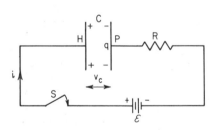

As we pointed out in Sec. 1–4, by definition, the current flowing in a circuit is the rate at which electric charge passes a cross-section of a wire in the circuit. Look at the point H, in Fig. 4–2–1, where the wire is connected to

Figure 4–2–1. Charging a capacitor from a battery of constant emf.

one plate of the capacitor. At this point, the rate at which charge passes a cross-section of the wire equals the rate at which positive charge accumulates on the left plate of the capacitor and thus is the rate at which the charge on the capacitor is changing. Hence we may write

$$i = dq/dt \qquad (4\text{–}2\text{–}1)$$

The same reasoning at P gives the same result. In a series circuit, the current is everywhere the same in the conductor part of the circuit. Hence we have the result that at every instant the current in the conductor part of the circuit equals the rate of change of charge on the capacitor.

Equation (4–1–2) is true not only after the charging process is complete, but it is true at every instant during the charging process. Thus we may write $C = q/v_C$, or

$$q = Cv_C \qquad (4\text{–}2\text{–}2)$$

Let us differentiate (4–2–2) with respect to time so that we will have dq/dt, which equals the current. In this differentiation, let us assume that the capacitance of the capacitor, as well as v_C, may change with time. Differentiation of (4–2–2) yields

$$i = C\, dv_C/dt + v_C\, dC/dt \qquad (4\text{–}2\text{–}3)$$

Equation (4–2–3) gives the general relationship between i, v_C, C, and t when both v_C and C change with time.

As a special case, consider that C is constant, and (4–2–3) becomes

$$i = C \, dv_C/dt \qquad (4\text{–}2\text{–}4)$$

This special case is the most common and the one which will interest us most.

As a second special case, consider that v_C is constant, and (4–2–3) becomes

$$i = v_C \, dC/dt \qquad (4\text{–}2\text{–}5)$$

This second special case is a more unusual one, and we shall not encounter it very often. An example would be a capacitor microphone with constant potential maintained across it. The diaphragm of the microphone is one plate of the capacitor and, as the condensations and rarefactions of the sound waves strike it, the diaphragm vibrates. The vibration of the diaphragm makes the distance between the plates of the capacitor a function of time and thus makes the capacitance a function of time.

4–3 CHARGING A CAPACITOR OF CONSTANT CAPACITANCE FROM A SOURCE OF CONSTANT EMF WITH A RESISTOR OF CONSTANT RESISTANCE IN SERIES IN THE CIRCUIT. TIME CONSTANT OF THE CIRCUIT

Refer to Fig. 4–2–1 and consider R, C, and $\mathscr{E}$ to be constant, i.e., not functions of time or current. Use the symbols defined in Sec. 4–2.

PROBLEM I. Find an equation giving the current flowing in this circuit as a function of time after the switch S was closed.

We call $t = 0$ the instant that the switch was closed and start our measurement of time from this instant. We consider that the self-inductance of this circuit is zero. The self-inductance of a circuit is never strictly zero, but it can be extremely small in such a circuit and we shall consider it zero.

By Kirchhoff's second law, at every instant the emf of the battery equals the sum of the potential drops around the circuit. At any instant when the charge on the capacitor is q, the potential difference across the capacitor is given by (4–2–2) as

$$v_C = q/C \qquad (4\text{–}3\text{–}1)$$

At the same instant, the current equals i, and the potential difference across the resistor is given by

$$v_R = iR \qquad (4\text{–}3\text{–}2)$$

Hence, at every instant, by Kirchhoff's second law,

$$\mathscr{E} = iR + q/C \qquad (4\text{–}3\text{–}3)$$

Equation (4–3–3) gives the relationship between i and q, but our problem requires a relationship between i and t. By (4–2–1), $i = dq/dt$, so we can eliminate q from (4–3–3) by differentiating it with respect to time. Note that we treat R, C, and $\mathscr{E}$ as constants in this differentiation.

$$0 = R \, di/dt + i/C \qquad (4\text{–}3\text{–}4)$$

Equation (4–3–4) is a simple differential equation in which we can separate the variables and obtain

$$di/i = -dt/(RC) \qquad (4\text{--}3\text{--}5)$$

Integrate both sides of (4–3–5) and we have (since R and C are constant)

$$\ln i = -t/(RC) + \ln A \qquad (4\text{--}3\text{--}6)$$

where ln means the natural logarithm, and $\ln A$ is the constant of integration. From (4–3–6) $\ln i/A = -t/(RC)$. Take the antilog of both sides, and

$$i = Ae^{-t/RC} \qquad (4\text{--}3\text{--}7)$$

where e is the base of natural logarithms. We can evaluate A from the boundary condition that at

$$t = 0, \qquad q = 0 \qquad (4\text{--}3\text{--}8)$$

because the switch was closed at $t = 0$ and there had been no time for charge to accumulate on the capacitor. Put (4–3–8) into (4–3–3) and we have, at $t = 0$,

$$\mathscr{E} = iR, \quad \text{or} \quad i = \mathscr{E}/R \quad (4\text{--}3\text{--}9)$$

Put (4–3–9) into (4–3–7) at $t = 0$, and obtain the value of A, as

$$A = \mathscr{E}/R \qquad (4\text{--}3\text{--}10)$$

Here A is a constant, so if it equals $\mathscr{E}/R$ at $t = 0$, it has this value at all instants of time after the switch was closed. Thus (4–3–7) becomes

$$i = (\mathscr{E}/R)e^{-t/RC} \qquad (4\text{--}3\text{--}11)$$

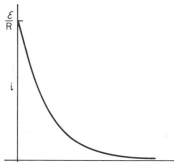

Figure 4–3–1. Charging current as a function of time for the circuit in Fig. 4–2–1.

and tells us the current flowing in the circuit as a function of time after the switch was closed. Thus (4–3–11) is the answer to our problem.

Let us sketch a plot of (4–3–11) in order to visualize more clearly how the current in this circuit changes with time. At the instant when the switch is closed ($t = 0$), the current starts at $\mathscr{E}/R$, which is the Ohm's law value that the current would have if the capacitor were removed from the circuit and points P and H were joined to each other. This initial current, of magnitude $\mathscr{E}/R$, results from the fact that no charge has accumulated on the capacitor, so there is as yet no potential difference across the capacitor. Hence, from (4–3–3), the potential difference across the resistor equals the emf of the source at $t = 0$. As charge accumulates on the capacitor, the potential difference across the capacitor grows, and according to (4–3–11) the current in the circuit decreases exponentially. The plot of (4–3–11) is shown in Fig. 4–3–1, where current is plotted as ordinate and time as abscissa.

From the curve in Fig. 4–3–1 or from (4–3–11), we can see that an infinite time is required to charge the capacitor, because the current curve approaches the value of $i = 0$ asymptotically. This statement would be true for any values of R and C; yet we can see from (4–3–11) that the larger the value of the RC product, the more slowly does the exponential curve fall. Conversely, the smaller the RC product, the faster the exponential curve falls. Thus the rapidity of response of the circuit depends on the RC product.

We wish to compare the rapidity of response of circuits of this sort that may have all sorts of values of R and C. We cannot do so by comparing the times required for the charging current to fall to zero, because all circuits take an infinite time for this to happen. We can, however, compare the times required for the charging current to fall to some predetermined fraction of its initial value. We might select for this fraction $\frac{1}{2}$ or $\frac{1}{5}$ or $\frac{1}{10}$ or any value that we like. Any fraction would serve equally well for comparing the rapidity of response of the circuits. None of these fractions has been selected, but instead the fraction that is conventionally used for this purpose is $1/e$, where again e is the base of natural logarithms.

The time required for the current to fall to $1/e$th *of its initial value is called the time constant of the circuit, and we shall use T to represent the time constant.*

We can evaluate T by the use of (4–3–11). At $t = T$, $i = (1/e)(\mathscr{E}/R)$ from the above definition of T. Put these values of i and t into (4–3–11), and we have $e^{-1} = e^{-T/RC}$ which can be satisfied only if

$$T = RC \qquad (4\text{–}3\text{–}12)$$

Thus (4–3–12) gives the value of the time constant for a capacitor and resistor in series. We can see now why $1/e$ was selected as the fraction, since it gives a very simple value for the time constant.

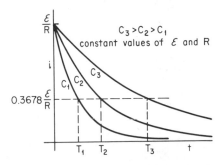

Figure 4–3–2. Effect of capacitance on the time constant of an R, C circuit.

Figure 4–3–1 shows the current as a function of time for the circuit in Fig. 4–2–1. This curve is replotted and marked C_1 in Fig. 4–3–2. Suppose that we discharge the capacitor and start over with the same resistor and battery, but this time use a capacitor of larger capacitance C_2 in this circuit. The curve labeled C_2 in Fig. 4–3–2 shows the current as a function of time in this case. The curve labeled C_3 shows the result of repeating the experiment with a still larger capacitance in the circuit. These three curves show clearly the change in rapidity of response as the capacitance is increased. Since $1/e = 1/2.718 = 0.3678$, we may state that the time constant of an RC circuit is the time required for the charging current to fall to 36.78% of its initial value. In Fig. 4–3–2, let us draw a horizontal dotted line at the value of i on the ordinate scale that corresponds to $0.3678\ \mathscr{E}/R$. The abscissa value for the point where this line crosses the curve marked C_1 is the time constant T_1 for the circuit when capacitor C_1 was used in the circuit. Similar statements apply to the points where this line crosses the C_2 and C_3 curves. The values of T_1, T_2, and T_3 are marked on the time axis of Fig. 4–3–2.

The R in the circuit has an equal effect with C in determining the rapidity of response, because it is the RC product which determines the time constant. However, this much discussion makes it possible for you to visualize the effect that R would have. It should be noted, however, that if R is changed in the circuit of Fig. 4–2–1, the initial charging current is changed because the initial current is given by $\mathscr{E}/R$. Thus, if curves were drawn for the case where C and $\mathscr{E}$ were held constant and R was varied, the curves would start at different points on the ordinate axis (at $t = 0$). Also, 36.78% of the initial current would have different values for the different curves. However, the RC product would still give the time constant.

PROBLEM II. Find an equation giving the charge on the capacitor as a function of time after the switch was closed in Fig. 4–2–1.

This problem we can solve at once, using Kirchhoff's second law for the circuit as written in (4–3–3). In (4–3–3) substitute for i its value as a function of time from (4–3–11) and solve for q:

$$q = C\mathscr{E} - C\mathscr{E}e^{-t/RC} \quad (4\text{–}3\text{–}13)$$

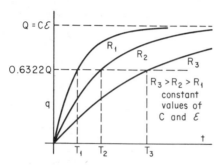

Let Q represent the final charge on the capacitor, and $Q = C\mathscr{E}$, so

$$q = Q - Qe^{-t/RC} = Q(1 - e^{-t/RC}) \quad (4\text{–}3\text{–}14)$$

which is the answer to the problem.

Let us sketch a plot of (4–3–14), plotting q as ordinate and t as abscissa. This plot is shown in Fig. 4–3–3 as the curve labeled R_1. Now, discharge the capacitor and charge it again, using the same battery and capacitor but a larger resistance R_2

Figure 4–3–3. The charge on the capacitor in Fig. 4–2–1 as a function of time. Effect of resistance in an R, C circuit.

in the circuit. The result is shown in Fig. 4–3–3 as the curve marked R_2. A repetition of this experiment, using a still larger resistance, yields the curve marked R_3. These curves show the effect of R on the rapidity of response of the circuit.

The time constant of this circuit is RC as before. Let us substitute the value $t = T = RC$ into (4–3–14) to see what the time constant means in this connection.

$$q = Q(1 - e^{-RC/RC}) = Q(1 - 0.3678) = 0.6322Q. \quad (4\text{–}3\text{–}15)$$

Hence, in this case, *the time constant means the time required for the charge on the capacitor to reach 63.22% of its final value.* The time constants for the three curves in Fig. 4–3–3 are marked on the time axis.

4–4 DISCHARGE OF A CAPACITOR OF CONSTANT CAPACITANCE THROUGH A RESISTOR OF CONSTANT RESISTANCE

PROBLEM I. Find an equation giving the charge q remaining on the capacitor in Fig. 4–4–1 as a function of time after the switch S is closed.

Let $t = 0$ be the instant that the switch is closed. Since there is no emf* in this circuit, if we go around the loop clockwise, Kirchhoff's second law gives

$$0 = -iR + q/C \qquad (4\text{–}4\text{–}1)$$

But $i = -dq/dt$; we must use the minus sign on dq/dt because q is decreasing, so dq/dt is negative. Substitute this value of i in (4–4–1) and obtain a differential equation in q and t with i eliminated. Separate the variables, integrate, and obtain

$$q = Ae^{-t/RC} \qquad (4\text{–}4\text{–}2)$$

Let $Q =$ the initial charge on the capacitor. Evaluate the constant of integration A, using the boundary conditions that at $t = 0$, $q = Q$, and obtain the fact that $A = Q$. Hence (4–4–2) becomes

$$q = Qe^{-t/RC} \qquad (4\text{–}4\text{–}3)$$

The time constant of this series combination of a capacitor and resistor is still RC. Let us substitute $t = T = RC$ into (4–4–3) in order to see what the time constant means in this case. At $t = T = RC$,

$$q = Qe^{-1} = Q/e = 0.3678\ Q \qquad (4\text{–}4\text{–}4)$$

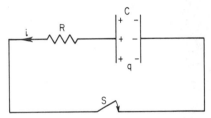

Hence, *in this case, the time constant means the time required for the charge on the capacitor to fall to 36.78% of its initial value.*

Figure 4–4–1. Discharge of a capacitor through a resistor.

PROBLEM II. Find an equation giving the current as a function of time after the switch was closed in Fig. 4–4–1. Here $i = -dq/dt$, hence from (4–4–3)

$$i = Qe^{-t/RC}/RC \qquad (4\text{–}4\text{–}5)$$

If we let $V_C =$ initial potential difference across the capacitor, we may write $V_C = Q/C$, and (4–4–5) becomes

$$i = V_C e^{-t/RC}/R \qquad (4\text{–}4\text{–}6)$$

Thus V_C/R is the initial current that flows at the instant that the switch is closed.

At $t = T = RC$, (4–4–6) gives $i = V_C e^{-1}/R$. Hence, in this case, as in the case when the capacitor was being charged, the time constant means the time required for the current to fall to 36.78% of its initial value.

---

* When considering energy conversion, one must look upon the capacitor as a source of emf in which electrical potential energy of the charged capacitor is changed into electrical energy of the current in the circuit during the discharge, and electrical energy of the current in the circuit is changed into electrical potential energy of the capacitor during the charging process. However, when using Kirchhoff's laws the author prefers to treat the potential difference across the capacitor as a potential drop rather than an emf. This is purely a personal preference, and the result is the same either way. The only difference in practice arises in deciding on which side of the equation for Kirchhoff's second law the q/C term should be placed. But the sign is reversed, if the point of view is changed and q/C is moved to the other side, so the mathematical result is the same.

4-5 ENERGY OF A CHARGED CAPACITOR

PROBLEM. Find an equation giving the electrical potential energy of a capacitor, of capacitance C, when it is charged to a potential difference V_C.

We can solve this problem by computing the work done on the capacitor during the charging process. Since it is a perfect capacitor, it will have this work as electrical potential energy after it is charged.

For this purpose refer to Fig. 4–2–1, where a capacitor is being charged from a source of constant emf; refer also to the results of Sec. 4–3. In (4–3–3) we had Kirchhoff's second law expressed for this circuit and in (4–3–14) we had the charge on the capacitor as a function of time. Substitute the value of q from (4–3–14) into (4–3–3) and obtain an instantaneous potential equation for the circuit in Fig. 4–2–1. We can change it into an instantaneous power equation by multiplying both sides by the instantaneous current i, and obtain

$$\mathscr{E}i = i^2R + iQ(1 - e^{-t/RC})/C \qquad (4\text{--}5\text{--}1)$$

We recognize $\mathscr{E}i$ as the instantaneous power input to the circuit from the battery, i^2R as the instantaneous rate at which electrical energy is being converted into heat in the resistor. Hence $(i\,Q/C)\,(1 - e^{-t/RC})$ must be the instantaneous power input to the capacitor. Let W_C represent energy stored in the capacitor at the time t, so dW_C/dt equals the last term in (4–5–1). From (4–3–11) we have the value of i as a function of time, so

$$dW_C/dt = \mathscr{E}e^{-t/RC}\,Q(1 - e^{-t/RC})/RC \qquad (4\text{--}5\text{--}2)$$

From (4–5–2)

$$W_C = \frac{\mathscr{E}Q}{RC}\left[-RC\int_0^\infty e^{-t/RC}\left(-\frac{dt}{RC}\right) + \frac{RC}{2}\int_0^\infty e^{-2t/RC}\left(-\frac{2dt}{RC}\right)\right]$$

The limits are determined by the fact that the time required to charge the capacitor extends from 0 to ∞. Performing the integration, we have $W_C = \mathscr{E}Q/2$, but $\mathscr{E} = V_C$, the final potential difference across the capacitor, so

$$W_C = \tfrac{1}{2}V_C Q \qquad (4\text{--}5\text{--}3)$$

We may write (4–5–3) in alternate equivalent forms by substituting into it the fact that $Q = CV_C$.

$$W_C = \tfrac{1}{2}CV_C^2 \quad \text{or} \quad W_C = Q^2/(2C) \qquad (4\text{--}5\text{--}4)$$

We have derived the equation for the energy of a charged capacitor by charging it from a source of constant emf. But once the capacitor is charged to a potential difference V_C, and thus has a charge Q, the equation for its energy is the same regardless of the method by which it acquired the charge (see Problem 4–13). Thus the equivalent equations (4–5–3) and (4–5–4) are general equations for the energy of a charged capacitor.

4-6 A CAPACITOR OF CONSTANT CAPACITANCE CONNECTED TO A LINE THAT HAS A MAINTAINED SINUSOIDAL ALTERNATING POTENTIAL DIFFERENCE BETWEEN THE WIRES OF THE LINE

The line referred to here could be obtained by connecting two wires to a plug and then inserting the plug into a duplex outlet in the laboratory. This would be the case provided that the outlet is supplied from a source of sinusoidal emf, of the kind discussed in Sec. 3–6, whose output voltage may be represented by (3–6–2) and shown graphically in Fig. 3–6–2. As explained in Sec. 3–6, the potential difference across commercial a-c lines, under favorable conditions, is very closely approximated by (3–6–2), and we shall assume that (3–6–2) is a true representation of the voltage as a function of time.

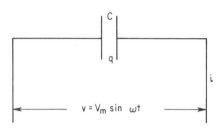

Here we shall use V_m for the maximum potential difference across the line, and v for the instantaneous potential difference. Thus we shall represent the line voltage by the equation

$$v = V_m \sin \omega t \qquad (4\text{–}6\text{–}1)$$

Figure 4–6–1. Capacitor of constant capacitance connected to a sinusoidal a-c line. We consider that the resistance in this circuit is negligible.

We consider this line to have a maintained potential in the sense that V_m remains constant, independent of the load on the line. This situation means that the regulation of the line is zero (see Sec. 2–5), and zero regulation is an ideal that power companies make a valiant effort to achieve; and they are, for the most part, very successful. If this condition is not met fairly well at the consumer's outlets, the consumer soon complains and the power company makes changes to improve the situation. By considering that the line has a maintained potential difference, we may consider it as an emf with zero impedance when applying Kirchhoff's second law. The case of the d-c generator, with a maintained terminal potential difference, is similar.

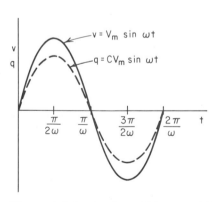

The circuit that we are to study is shown in Fig. 4–6–1, which represents a capacitor of constant capacitance connected to a sinusoidal a-c line.

PROBLEM I. Find an equation giving the charge q on the capacitor as a function of time for the circuit in Fig. 4–6–1.

Figure 4–6–2. A sinusoidal potential difference v across a capacitor produces a sinusoial charge q on the capacitor. q and v are in phase.

Using Kirchhoff's second law, we may write for the circuit in Fig. 4–6–1,

$$V_m \sin \omega t = q/C$$

from which $\quad q = CV_m \sin \omega t \quad (4\text{–}6\text{–}2)$

which is the answer to the problem.

Equation (4–6–2) shows that the charge on the capacitor rises to a maximum $Q_m = CV_m$, falls to zero, reverses, rises to the same maximum in the reverse direction, falls to zero, etc., all in phase with the applied sinusoidal voltage. Figure 4–6–2 shows this relationship graphically. In Fig. 4–6–2, time has a common abscissa scale for both curves but, since q and v are different physical quantities, different scales are used as ordinate for q and v. In fact it is meaningless to talk about plotting them to the same ordinate scale, because they are different physical quantities. Thus the maximum value for q might lie above the maximum value for v, instead of below, depending on the scale adopted for the plot of q.

PROBLEM II. Find an equation giving the current i flowing in the circuit of Fig. 4–6–1 as a function of time.

Since $i = dq/dt$, all we need do to solve this problem is to differentiate (4–6–2) with respect to time.

$$i = CV_m\omega \cos \omega t \tag{4-6-3}$$

Since a cosine curve leads a sine curve by $\pi/2$ radians [i.e., $\cos \omega t = \sin (\omega t + \pi/2)$], we may write (4–6–3) as $i = CV_m\omega \sin (\omega t + \pi/2)$. An equivalent form is

$$i = \frac{V_m}{(1/C\omega)} \sin (\omega t + \pi/2) \tag{4-6-4}$$

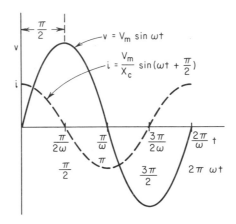

Figure 4–6–3. Phase relationship between current i and voltage v for a pure capacitance on a sinusoidal a-c line. i leads v by $\pi/2\omega$ seconds or $\pi/2$ radians.

Equation (4–6–4) is written in this form because $1/C\omega$ is given the name *capacitive reactance* and is represented by the symbol X_C. Hence, by definition,

$$X_C = 1/C\omega = 1/2\pi f C \tag{4-6-5}$$

[See (3–6–3) for the relationship between ω and the frequency f in cycles/sec.] The unit of X_C is the ohm, the same unit as the one used for resistance, as can be seen by substitution of units into (4–6–5), that is, unit of $X_C = 1/($farad $sec^{-1}) = sec/($coul$/$volt$) = $ volt sec/amp sec $= $ volt/amp $= $ ohm. Using this abbreviation, we may write (4–6–4) as

$$i = (V_m/X_C) \sin (\omega t + \pi/2) \tag{4-6-6}$$

Comparing (4–6–1) and (4–6–6), we see that the current into and out of the plates of the capacitor *leads* the potential difference across the capacitor by $\pi/2$ radians, or 90°. We can see this because v is a simple sine curve. The $\pi/2$ phase constant in the current equation shows a $\pi/2$ phase difference with a simple sine curve, and the plus sign shows this phase difference to be a lead. Hence we conclude that the *current leads the voltage by $\pi/2$ radians for a perfect capacitor.* Figure 4–6–3 shows this phase relationship graphically by the plots of v and i as functions of time. In (4–6–6) the amplitude value of the sine function is the maximum value of the current, so

$$I_m = V_m/X_C \qquad (4\text{–}6\text{–}7)$$

We say, from the above, that the current *leads* the voltage, because we

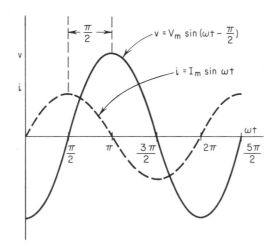

Figure 4–6–4. Phase relationship between v and i for a pure capacitance on a sinusoidal a-c line. v lags i by $\pi/2$ radians.

elected to write the voltage as a simple sine function and used it for reference in stating phase. We could as well have written the voltage equation as

$$v = V_m \sin(\omega t - \pi/2) \qquad (4\text{–}6\text{–}8)$$

so that the voltage curve lags a simple sine curve by $\pi/2$ radians. Since the current leads the voltage by $\pi/2$ radians, the current equation would be

$$i = I_m \sin \omega t \qquad (4\text{–}6\text{–}9)$$

and it then becomes the convenient equation to use as a reference for stating phase relationships. Figure 4–6–4 is a plot of (4–6–8) and (4–6–9), and in this case we say that, for a pure capacitance, the voltage *lags* the current by $\pi/2$ radians. You can see that Fig. 4–6–4 is the same as Fig. 4–6–3, except that in Fig. 4–6–4 the ordinate axis has been shifted $\pi/2$ radians to the left from its position in Fig. 4–6–3. Of course, if the current leads the voltage by 90°, the voltage lags the current by 90°. We may express the phase relationship either way that suits our need at the moment.

PROBLEM III. Find an equation giving the instantaneous power input to the capacitor in Fig. 4–6–1 as a function of time.

Let p represent the instantaneous power input to the capacitor, and $p = vi$. Use (4–6–1) for v as a function of time and (4–6–3) for i as a function of time, and the instantaneous power equation becomes $p = (V_m \sin \omega t)$ $(CV_m\omega \cos \omega t)$. Using the trigonometric relation that $\sin A \cos A = \frac{1}{2}\sin 2A$, we have

$$p = \tfrac{1}{2}CV_m^2\, \omega \sin 2\omega t \quad (4\text{–}6\text{–}10)$$

This is the answer to our problem, and we see that the power is also sinusoidal but of twice the frequency of the current or voltage. Figure 4–6–5 is a replot of the curves in Fig. 4–6–3 with the power curve added.

Since p is power input to the capacitor, negative values of p mean power output from the capacitor. Thus, in the positive part of the power cycle, energy is being stored in the capacitor, but, in the negative part of the power cycle, energy is being fed from the capacitor back into the line. Since the negative part of the power curve is of the same size as the positive part, the capacitor feeds as much energy back into the line on discharge as it receives from the line during the charging process. In Problem 4–20 you are asked to prove mathematically that this latter statement is true.

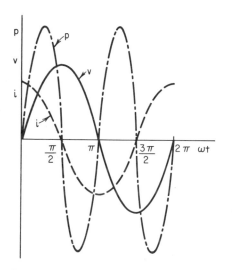

Figure 4–6–5. Instantaneous values of current i, voltage v, and power p for a pure capacitance on a sinusoidal a-c line.

4–7 SINUSOIDAL ALTERNATING POTENTIAL DIFFERENCE APPLIED TO CONSTANT R AND CONSTANT C IN SERIES

Again we assume that the line to which we connect our circuit has the characteristics discussed in Sec. 4–6. This time, however, we have a switch in series with R and C and wish to close the switch at any time that we like and thus start the current flowing. We start the timing at the instant that we close the switch, so this instant is to be $t = 0$. The potential difference across the wires of the line is present and changing sinusoidally with time, whether we have the switch closed or not. The fact that we wish to close the switch at any time that we may select means that we may close the switch at any point in the voltage cycle. If we were to write the voltage equation for the line as $v = V_m$ $\sin \omega t$, and then call $t = 0$ the instant that we close the switch, we would have to close the switch at an instant when $v = 0$ and dv/dt is positive (point A or B

in Fig. 4–7–1) in order to have this equation be the appropriate one at subsequent times.

In Fig. 4–7–1 let the sinusoidal curve represent the line voltage; on the left
is the line voltage prior to the closing of the switch, and on the right the line
voltage subsequent to the closing of the switch. At the point on the voltage

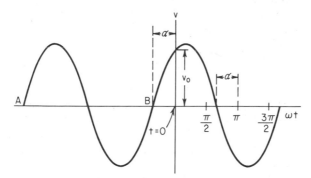

Figure 4–7–1. Sinusoidal line voltage. Switch was closed at $t = 0$ and, subsequent to
this time, the line voltage is represented by the equation $v = V_m \sin(\omega t + \alpha)$.

curve where the switch was closed, we draw the ordinate axis, then we write
the appropriate equation for the curve subsequent to this time, taking the
origin as $t = 0$. In Fig. 4–7–1 the curve to the right of the ordinate axis leads
a simple sine curve by the angle α radians, so the appropriate equation is

$$v = V_m \sin(\omega t + \alpha) \tag{4–7–1}$$

Angle α may have any value from 0 to 2π, but its value is uniquely fixed by
the point in the voltage cycle at which
the switch was closed; subsequently it is
constant at this value. If the instantaneous value v_0 of the voltage is known
at the instant the switch is closed, the
value of α can be computed at once from
(4–7–1) by substituting $t = 0$ into the
equation.

Thus, in this discussion, we must use
(4–7–1) to represent the line voltage,
since we wish to be free to close the
switch at any point in the line voltage
cycle.

Figure 4–7–2 represents the circuit

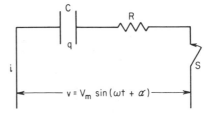

Figure 4–7–2. Sinusoidal alternating
voltage applied to constant R and constant C in series. Instant that the switch
is closed is called $t = 0$.

that we are to consider, C represents the constant capacitance, R the constant resistance, and S the switch.

PROBLEM. Find an equation giving the instantaneous current flowing in
the circuit of Fig. 4–7–2 as a function of time after the switch was closed.

Kirchhoff's second law applied to this circuit gives

$$V_m \sin(\omega t + \alpha) = iR + q/C \tag{4–7–2}$$

Our problem calls for current as a function of time, and (4–7–2) contains q as well as i and t. Thus, to eliminate q, we take the derivative with respect to time and substitute i for dq/dt, obtaining

$$V_m \omega \cos(\omega t + \alpha) = R\, di/dt + i/C$$

Rearrange this equation in the standard form. This statement means that we are to put all terms containing the dependent variable i and its derivatives on the left side of the equation, so that the term on the right side contains the independent variable only.

$$di/dt + i/RC = [V_m \omega \cos(\omega t + \alpha)]/R \qquad (4\text{–}7\text{–}3)$$

Equation (4–7–3) is a linear differential equation of the first order with constant coefficients. The mathematicians have a general method for solving equations of this type,* but in this text we assume that you have not as yet reached this stage in differential equations. Those who have reached this stage are urged to apply the methods learned in the mathematics courses and check the results obtained here.

We shall employ a method that mathematicians reserve for more complicated differential equations, namely, one assumes a solution and then determines whether or not the assumed solution is a correct one. This method is one that you can carry out with ease even though you have never solved a differential equation.

In order to understand the method, let us first consider what we mean by a solution of this equation. A solution of (4–7–3) would be of the form i equals some function of t, that is, $i = f(t)$. The requirement imposed on it is that, when the first derivative of $f(t)$ with respect to t is substituted for di/dt in the first term, and $f(t)$ is substituted for i in the second term, the left side of the equation will reduce to an identity with the right side. In other words, substitution of the solution into the left side of (4–7–3) will reduce the left side to $[V_m \omega \cos(\omega t + \alpha)]/R$ which is just what we have on the right side of (4–7–3).†

* For example, see L. M. Kells, *Analytical Geometry and Calculus* (Englewood Cliffs, N.J.: Prentice-Hall, Inc., 1950), Par. 224, pp. 535–36, and Problem 16, p. 539.

† This is what we mean by a solution of any equation, i.e., the solution will reduce the left side of the equation to an identity with the right side. Consider, for example, the quartic equation $x^4 + 3x^3 - 2x = 36$. Let us say that you wish a solution of this equation, and imagine that the equation will not factor. As you buy your evening newspaper, you show this problem to the newsboy. He takes one glance and says "Everyone knows that $x = 2$ is a solution of that equation." You may doubt the "Everyone knows" part of his statement, but you can immediately determine the validity of the remainder of his remark by substituting $x = 2$ into the equation. You obtain $16 + 24 - 4 = 36$, or $36 = 36$, and $x = 2$ is indeed a solution, because it reduces the left side of the equation to an identity with the right side. You may have all sorts of qualms about the methods or lack of methods that the newsboy used in arriving at this solution, but you are absolutely sure that $x = 2$ is a solution.

You show the equation to the bootblack and, with a little more hesitation, he comes out with an equally positive answer that a solution is $x = -3.61$. Again, you immediately test and obtain $169.9 - 141.2 + 7.2 = 36$, or $35.9 = 36$. The bootblack didn't do quite as well, but you are content with three significant figures and, to this accuracy, $x = -3.61$ is a solution.

The point is, you have at your disposal an immediate test and can decide at once whether or not a proposed solution is indeed a solution.

Next we need a theorem from differential equations. This theorem says that if $f(t)$ is a solution of (4–7–3) and if $f_1(t)$ is a solution of the equation obtained from (4–7–3) by setting the right side equal to zero, then the complete solution is

$$i = f_1(t) + f(t) \qquad (4\text{–}7\text{–}4)$$

Here $f_1(t)$ is called the *complementary function* and $f(t)$ is called the *particular integral*. We can see that (4–7–4) is valid, because $f_1(t)$ substituted into (4–7–3) reduces the left side to zero, and $f(t)$ substituted into (4–7–3) reduces the left side to an identity with the right side. Hence $f_1(t) + f(t)$ substituted into (4–7–3) will reduce the left side to an identity with the right side.*

Let us solve for the complementary function first. For this purpose we must solve

$$di/dt + i/RC = 0 \qquad (4\text{–}7\text{–}5)$$

which is the same as (4–3–4) that we solved in Sec. 4–3, by separating the variables and integrating. The answer is given in (4–3–7) and is

$$i = Ae^{-t/RC} \qquad (4\text{–}7\text{–}6)$$

where A is the constant of integration. We cannot evaluate A, however, until we have the complete solution. The right side of (4–7–6) is the complementary function for (4–7–3) and thus is $f_1(t)$ in our discussion above.

Next, we must secure the particular integral of (4–7–3), i.e., we must secure a solution of (4–7–3) as it stands. As mentioned above, we shall secure the particular integral by assuming a solution and then show that it is a solution. The physics of the circuit will guide us in the selection of a solution. Let us assume that:

1. *The current that flows in this circuit is sinusoidal and of the same frequency as the voltage.* We certainly expect an alternating current, and our solution with a capacitor alone in Sec. 4–6 showed that a sinusoidal current resulted from a sinusoidal voltage and that the current and voltage are of the same frequency. We do not anticipate that the introduction of a series resistance will alter this situation but, of course, this is an assumption which we shall test.

2. *The current i is out of phase with v by an unknown constant phase angle ϕ.* In the case of a capacitor alone, i leads v by $\pi/2$ radians. We still expect i to lead v in the present case, but we do not tie ourselves down to a definite numerical value for the amount of lead. If our assumptions are correct, we shall attempt to make the test tell us the value of ϕ.

3. *The maximum value of the current is an unknown constant that we shall call I_m.* In the case of the capacitor alone, the maximum value of the current is constant, so we assume that it will be in the present case. Again, we shall attempt to make the test of the solution tell us the value of I_m.

An equation that incorporates all three of these assumptions is

$$i = I_m \sin \left[(\omega t + \alpha) + \phi \right] \qquad (4\text{–}7\text{–}7)$$

---

* See any text on differential equations, e.g., M. Morris and O. E. Brown, *Differential Equations*, 3d ed. (Englewood Cliffs, N.J.: Prentice-Hall, Inc., 1952), p. 80.

so the right side of (4–7–7) we assume to be the particular integral $f(t)$. Substitute (4–7–7) into (4–7–3) and we obtain

$$I_m\omega \cos [(\omega t + \alpha) + \phi] + \{I_m \sin [(\omega t + \alpha) + \phi]\}/RC$$
$$= [V_m\omega \cos (\omega t + \alpha)]/R \quad (4–7–8)$$

In (4–7–8), expand $\cos [(\omega t + \alpha) + \phi]$ as the cosine of the sum of the two angles $(\omega t + \alpha)$ and ϕ, and expand $\sin [(\omega t + \alpha) + \phi]$ as the sine of the sum of the same two angles. Also, multiply through by $R/V_m\omega$, and rearrange to obtain

$$\cos (\omega t + \alpha) \left[\frac{I_m R}{V_m} \cos \phi + \frac{I_m}{V_m C\omega} \sin \phi - 1\right] +$$
$$\sin (\omega t + \alpha) \left[\frac{-I_m R}{V_m} \sin \phi + \frac{I_m}{V_m C\omega} \cos \phi\right] = 0 \quad (4–7–9)$$

If (4–7–9) is true it must be true at every instant of time. We can see that the left side of (4–7–9) can be zero at every instant only if each term in a square bracket is equal to zero. One way to see this is to consider an instant of time when $\sin (\omega t + \alpha)$ is zero, and at this time the second term drops out, so (4–7–9) becomes

$$\cos (\omega t + \alpha) \left[\frac{I_m R}{V_m} \cos \phi + \frac{I_m}{V_m C\omega} \sin \phi - 1\right] = 0$$

But $\cos (\omega t + \alpha)$ cannot be zero at the same instant that $\sin (\omega t + \alpha)$ is equal to zero; hence the term in the square bracket must be equal to zero. Now, return to (4–7–9) and use this fact that the coefficient of $\cos (\omega t + \alpha)$ is equal to zero. Then (4–7–9) becomes

$$\sin (\omega t + \alpha) \left[\frac{-I_m R}{V_m} \sin \phi + \frac{I_m}{V_m C\omega} \cos \phi\right] = 0$$

which must be true at every instant of time. But $\sin (\omega t + \alpha)$ is not equal to zero in general, so the square bracket coefficient of $\sin (\omega t + \alpha)$ must be equal to zero. Hence we have the conclusion, stated above, that each term in a square bracket in (4–7–9) must be zero if (4–7–9) is a valid equation. Now we use this conclusion to solve for the unknown constants I_m and ϕ.

First, in (4–7–9) equate the coefficient of $\sin (\omega t + \alpha)$ to zero and obtain

$$\tan \phi = 1/RC\omega, \quad \text{or} \quad \phi = \tan^{-1} 1/RC\omega \quad (4–7–10)$$

From this value of $\tan \phi$, $\sin \phi$ and $\cos \phi$ are given by

$$\sin \phi = 1/\sqrt{1 + R^2C^2\omega^2} \quad \text{and} \quad \cos \phi = RC\omega/\sqrt{1 + R^2C^2\omega^2}$$

Now, in (4–7–9), equate the coefficient of $\cos (\omega t + \alpha)$ to zero, substitute the above values of $\sin \phi$ and $\cos \phi$, and solve for I_m.

$$I_m = V_m/\sqrt{R^2 + 1/C^2\omega^2} \quad (4–7–11)$$

By our method of solution these values of I_m and ϕ are guaranteed to be the values of I_m and ϕ that will make the left side of (4–7–8) reduce to an identity with the right side (see Problem 4–23); hence these are the values of

I_m and ϕ that make (4–7–7) a solution of (4–7–3). Substitute these values of I_m and ϕ into (4–7–7) and we have

$$i = V_m \{\sin [(\omega t + \alpha) + \tan^{-1} 1/RC\omega]\}/\sqrt{R^2 + 1/C^2\omega^2} \quad (4\text{–}7\text{–}12)$$

The right side of (4–7–12) is, then, the particular integral of (4–7–3). From (4–7–4), the complete solution of the differential equation is the sum of the right sides of (4–7–6) and (4–7–12), or the complete solution is (see Problem 4–24)

$$i = Ae^{-t/RC} + \frac{V_m}{\sqrt{R^2 + 1/C^2\omega^2}} \sin \left[(\omega t + \alpha) + \tan^{-1} \frac{1}{RC\omega}\right] \quad (4\text{–}7\text{–}13)$$

We now have the problem solved, except for the evaluation of the constant of integration A that appears in the exponential term. We can evaluate this constant from the boundary condition that at $t = 0$, $q = 0$; so, by Kirchhoff's second law as expressed in (4–7–2), $i = (V_m/R) \sin \alpha$ at $t = 0$. Put these boundary conditions into (4–7–13) and obtain

$$A = \frac{V_m}{R} \sin \alpha - \frac{V_m}{\sqrt{R^2 + 1/C^2\omega^2}} \sin \left(\alpha + \tan^{-1} \frac{1}{RC\omega}\right) \quad (4\text{–}7\text{–}14)$$

By about half a page of algebra and trigonometry, which you are urged to carry out in Problem 4–25, it can be shown that the value of A can be transformed into the value used for it in (4–7–15) below.

$$i = \left[\frac{-V_m}{RC\omega\sqrt{R^2 + 1/C^2\omega^2}} \cos \left(\alpha + \tan^{-1} \frac{1}{RC\omega}\right)\right] e^{-t/RC}$$

$$+ \frac{V_m}{\sqrt{R^2 + 1/C^2\omega^2}} \sin \left[(\omega t + \alpha) + \tan^{-1} \frac{1}{RC\omega}\right] \quad (4\text{–}7\text{–}15)$$

Equation (4–7–15) is the complete solution of the differential equation (4–7–3) and, therefore, is the current flowing in the circuit of Fig. 4–7–2 as a function of time after the switch was closed. This is a formidable looking equation, but it can be broken down into simple parts for analysis. Let us substitute into (4–7–15) I_m and ϕ for their values as given in (4–7–11) and (4–7–10), and (4–7–15) becomes

$$i = \left[\frac{-I_m}{RC\omega} \cos (\alpha + \phi)\right] e^{-t/RC} + I_m \sin \left[(\omega t + \alpha) + \phi\right] \quad (4\text{–}7\text{–}16)$$

The coefficient of the exponential in the first term on the right is a constant, and the exponential itself is going to decrease rapidly with time, soon becoming negligibly small. Hence the first term on the right is called the *transient term* and is of importance in the solution only for a short time after the switch was closed.

The second term on the right gives a sinusoidal variation of the current with time and continues to be of importance as long as the switch is closed. This term is called the *steady state*. In a short time after the switch is closed, the transient has died out and the steady state alone remains. Hence, after this short time the current in the circuit is given by

$$i = I_m \sin [(\omega t + \alpha) + \phi] \qquad (4\text{-}7\text{-}17)$$

In Problem 4–26 you are asked to consider a circuit with constant values of V_m, R, C, and ω, and to find the greatest and least values that the transient can have.

4-8 STEADY STATE CURRENT FOR R AND C IN SERIES ON A SINUSOIDAL A-C LINE

We assume the switch in Fig. 4–7–2 has been closed for some time, so the transient has died out and we are concerned only with the steady state solution given in (4–7–17). A comparison of the voltage equation in (4–7–1) and the current in (4–7–17) shows that the current leads the applied voltage by the angle ϕ radians when $\phi = \tan^{-1} 1/RC\omega$.

The angle α contributes nothing to our information after the transient has died out, since at this stage it is only a phase constant that appears in the same fashion in both the current and voltage equations. Hence let us drop α from both equations and write

$$v = V_m \sin \omega t \qquad (4\text{-}8\text{-}1)$$

$$i = I_m \sin (\omega t + \phi) = \frac{V_m}{\sqrt{R^2 + X_C^2}} \sin \left(\omega t + \tan^{-1} \frac{X_C}{R}\right) \qquad (4\text{-}8\text{-}2)$$

Omission of α means only a shift of the ordinate axis in Fig. 4–7–1 to the right by several complete cycles of the voltage plus $2\pi - \alpha$, during which time the transient was dying out. In (4–8–1) and (4–8–2), i still leads v by ϕ, and the maximum value of the current is unchanged by this shift. Figure 4–8–1 is a plot of these equations, showing the phase relationship between the current and the line voltage.

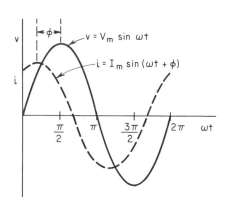

Figure 4–8–1. Phase relationship between current i and voltage v for R and C in series on a sinusoidal a-c line. i leads v by $\phi = \tan^{-1} 1/(RC\omega)$.

The quantity $\sqrt{R^2 + X_C^2}$ is called the *impedance* for this circuit and is represented by the letter z,

$$z = \sqrt{R^2 + X_C^2} \qquad (4\text{-}8\text{-}3)$$

The unit of z is the ohm, since both R and X_C are expressed in ohms.

You can see from (4–8–2) that, if R in this circuit is decreased to zero, the solution obtained here reduces to (4–6–6), and (4–6–6) is the solution that we obtained for a capacitor alone on a sinusoidal a-c line.

Also, an argument similar to the one used in connection with (4–6–8) and

(4–6–9) could be made here. As a result, for this circuit containing R and C in series, we could write

$$i = (V_m/\sqrt{R^2 + X_C^2}) \sin \omega t \qquad (4\text{–}8\text{–}4)$$

and $$v = V_m \sin (\omega t - \tan^{-1} X_C/R) \qquad (4\text{–}8\text{–}5)$$

In words, if i leads v by $\tan^{-1} X_C/R$, then v lags i by the same angle. The current i can be written as a simple sine curve if the phase angle is incorporated in the applied voltage equation.

4–9 POWER INPUT TO R AND C IN SERIES ON A SINUSOIDAL A-C LINE

PROBLEM I. Find an equation giving the instantaneous power input to a circuit with constant R and C in series on a sinusoidal a-c line, after the transient has died out.

Let p represent the instantaneous power input to the circuit, and we have $p = vi$. Use (4–8–1) and (4–8–2) for v and i respectively, and p is given by

$$p = (V_m \sin \omega t)[I_m \sin (\omega t + \phi)] \qquad (4\text{–}9\text{–}1)$$

Expand the $\sin (\omega t + \phi)$ as the sine of the sum of two angles; make use of the fact that $\sin^2 \omega t = \frac{1}{2}(1 - \cos 2\omega t)$ and $\sin \omega t \cos \omega t = \frac{1}{2} \sin 2\omega t$ and then (4–9–1) reduces to

$$p = V_m I_m (\cos \phi)/2 - V_m I_m [\cos (2 \omega t + \phi)]/2 \qquad (4\text{–}9\text{–}2)$$

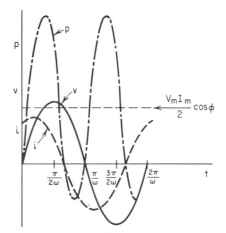

Figure 4–9–1. Instantaneous values of current i, voltage v, and power p for R and C in series on a sinusoidal a-c line. At instants when either v or i is zero, p must be zero.

We see from (4–9–2) that the instantaneous power equation is also sinusoidal, but it has twice the frequency of the current or voltage, as was the case with the capacitor alone. In the present case, however, there is an initial positive constant term $\frac{1}{2}V_m I_m \cos \phi$. The presence of the constant term means that the sinusoidal variation with time given by the second term is symmetrical about a line parallel with the t-axis but displaced in the positive ordinate direction by an amount $\frac{1}{2}V_m I_m \cos \phi$. Let us make a plot of v, i, and p with respect to time in Fig. 4–9–1.

PROBLEM II. Find the energy input W to the circuit during one cycle of the power curve.

Since all cycles of the power curve are alike, as can be seen from Fig. 4–9–1, select the cycle from $t = 0$ to $t = \pi/\omega$. In Problem 4–30 you are asked to show that

$$W = V_m I_m \pi (\cos \phi)/2\omega \qquad (4\text{–}9\text{–}3)$$

which is the answer to our problem.

PROBLEM III. Find the time average power input to this circuit.

Time average power is defined as the *total work done during a time interval divided by the time elapsed during the time interval*. If the instantaneous power is constant, the time average power is the same as the instantaneous power. If, however, the instantaneous power is varying periodically with time, as it is in our present problem, the time average power is computed by dividing the total work done in a selected number of cycles by the time elapsed during these cycles. Since all power cycles are alike in the circuit we are considering, the time average power can be computed for one cycle of the power curve, and it will be constant as long as the circuit constants remain unchanged. Let P = time average power, and by definition

$$P = \frac{\text{energy input to circuit in one cycle of the power curve}}{\text{time for one cycle of the power curve}}$$

Using (4–9–3), P for our present problem becomes

$$P = \frac{V_m}{\sqrt{2}} \frac{I_m}{\sqrt{2}} \cos \phi \qquad (4\text{–}9\text{–}4)$$

4–10 SINUSOIDAL ALTERNATING VOLTAGE APPLIED TO A PURE RESISTANCE

PROBLEM I. Find an equation giving the current flowing in the circuit of Fig. 4–10–1 as a function of time.

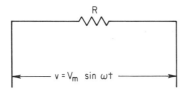

Figure 4–10–1. Sinusoidal a-c voltage applied to a pure resistance.

By Kirchhoff's second law applied to the circuit in Fig. 4–10–1, $V_m \sin \omega t = iR$, from which

$$i = (V_m/R) \sin \omega t = I_m \sin \omega t \quad (4\text{–}10\text{–}1)$$

Equation (4–10–1) is the answer to this problem and it shows, for a pure resistance, that the current and voltage are in phase.

PROBLEM II. Find an equation giving the instantaneous power input p to the circuit as a function of time. We know that $p = iv$, but for the circuit in Fig. 4–10–1, $v = iR$, so

$$p = i^2 R = I_m^2 R \sin^2 \omega t \qquad (4\text{–}10\text{–}2)$$

Equation (4–10–2) expresses the instantaneous rate at which electrical energy is being converted into heat energy in the resistance. But $\sin^2 \omega t = \frac{1}{2}(1 - \cos 2\omega t)$, so

$$p = I_m^2 R/2 - I_m^2 R (\cos 2\omega t)/2 \qquad (4\text{–}10\text{–}3)$$

Thus, again the power is sinusoidal and of twice the frequency of the current or voltage. In Fig. 4–10–2, let us plot the instantaneous values of current, voltage, and power as functions of time on the same axes. As before in (4–9–2), the cosine part of the power equation is symmetrical about a line parallel to the t-axis, but now this line is displaced upward by an amount equal to the amplitude of the cosine part of the power equation. Thus the power is not negative in any part of the cycle, as you can see in Fig. 4–10–2. This result expresses the fact that electrical energy is converted into heat energy in the resistance, but none of this heat energy is converted back into electrical energy.

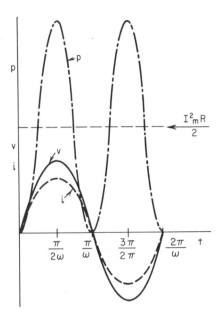

PROBLEM III. Find the total energy input W to the resistance during one cycle of the power curve.

By evaluating the integral of $p\, dt$ for one cycle of the power curve, you can show that

$$W = I_m^2 R\pi/2\omega \quad (4\text{–}10\text{–}4)$$

Equation (4–10–4) expresses the electrical energy changed into heat energy during one cycle of the power curve.

PROBLEM IV. Find the time average power input to the resistance.

$$P = W/(\pi/\omega) = I_m^2 R /2 \quad (4\text{–}10\text{–}5)$$

Figure 4–10–2. Instantaneous values of current i, voltage v, and power p for pure resistance on a sinusoidal a-c line.

Equation (4–10–5) expresses the time average rate at which electrical energy is being converted into heat energy in the resistance.

4–11 ROOT MEAN SQUARE, OR EFFECTIVE, VALUES OF CURRENT AND VOLTAGE IN SINUSOIDAL A-C CIRCUITS

We wish to consider now an average value for a sinusoidal alternating current or an alternating voltage. If we take a straight arithmetical average, it is obvious that the average will be zero, because the current and voltage have symmetrical negative and positive values. Ordinary d-c meters read the arithmetical average and thus will read zero when connected in a sinusoidal a-c circuit. Further, they read zero regardless of the maximum value that the current or voltage may have. Obviously, such an average is useless for a-c calculations. We need to base the average on an effect of the current, which is independent of the direction of the current.

For this purpose, the heating effect is selected because the instantaneous rate of producing heat depends on the square of the instantaneous current, which is always positive. On this basis *the root mean square or effective a-c ampere is defined as the current which, flowing through a given pure resistance, will produce heat at the same average rate as the d-c ampere flowing through the same resistance.*

With a direct current, the rate at which heat is produced is given by the square of the current times the resistance. It follows from the preceding definition that an alternating root mean square or effective current I_{eff} flowing through a resistance R must produce heat at the time average rate given by $I_{\text{eff}}^2 R$. Now we must find out how this kind of an average alternating current is related to I_m.

The time average rate of producing heat during one cycle of the power curve =

$$\frac{\text{total heat produced}}{\text{time to produce it}} - \frac{\int_0^{\pi/\omega} p \, dt}{\pi/\omega} \tag{4-11-1}$$

But (4-11-1) is just the calculation which we carried out in Problems III and IV of Sec. 4-10 when we computed the time average power P, and the answer is given in (4-10-5) as $P = I_m^2 R/2$. But, from the above definition of I_{eff},

$$P = I_{\text{eff}}^2 R \qquad \text{for a pure resistance} \tag{4-11-2}$$

so, $I_{\text{eff}}^2 R = I_m^2 R/2, \quad \text{or} \quad I_{\text{eff}} = I_m/\sqrt{2} = 0.707 I_m$ \hfill (4-11-3)

Hence *the root mean square or effective current in a sinusoidal a-c circuit is the maximum current divided by the square root of two.*

In Problem 4-31 you are asked to prove that we can make the same sort of calculation with the voltage starting with (4-10-2) and obtain

$$V_{\text{eff}} = V_m/\sqrt{2} \tag{4-11-4}$$

Hence *the root mean square or effective voltage in a sinusoidal a-c circuit is the maximum voltage divided by the square root of two.* The term "root mean square" is usually abbreviated rms and is applied here, because this method of averaging takes the square root of the time average of the squares of the instantaneous values.

*From now on we shall represent the root mean square or effective current with the symbol I, and the root mean square or effective value of the voltage with the symbol V when dealing with alternating current.**

4-12 MORE ABOUT THE POWER EQUATION FOR R AND C IN SERIES ON A SINUSOIDAL A-C LINE

Refer back to (4-9-4), where we had the power equation for a circuit with R and C in series on a sinusoidal a-c line. Replace $V_m/\sqrt{2}$ with its equivalent V, and $I_m/\sqrt{2}$ with its equivalent I, and the power equation becomes

$$P = VI \cos \phi \tag{4-12-1}$$

An ordinary a-c voltmeter* reads the root mean square or effective voltage V, unless there is a notation on the scale to the contrary. Similarly, an ordinary a-c ammeter* reads the root mean square or effective current I, unless there is a notation on the scale to the contrary. Thus, the power equation in (4-12-1) is expressed in terms of ammeter and voltmeter readings.

The term $\cos \phi$ *is referred to as the power factor,* and we see from (4-12-1) that on alternating current the product of the ammeter reading and voltmeter

* See Secs. 20-5, 20-6, and 20-7 for descriptions of some instruments for measuring I and V, and Sec. 20-10 for the description of a wattmeter.

reading must be multiplied by the power factor for the circuit in order to compute power. On steady direct current, the current and voltage are always in phase, so ϕ is always zero, and the power factor is always unity. We see that this is not the case on alternating current, except for a pure resistance.

For the case of a sinusoidal alternating voltage applied to R and C in series, from (4–7–10)

$$\cos \phi = R/\sqrt{R^2 + 1/C^2\omega^2} = R/\sqrt{R^2 + X_C^2} = R/z \qquad (4\text{–}12\text{–}2)$$

Now refer back to the power equation in (4–9–4), and use the fact that $V_m = I_m z$. Put this value of V_m and also the value of $\cos \phi$ from (4–12–2) into (4–9–4), and obtain $P = I_m^2 R/2$

or $$P = I^2 R \qquad (4\text{–}12\text{–}3)$$

Since $I^2 R$ is the time average rate at which electrical energy is being changed into heat energy in the resistance in the circuit, (4–12–3) says that the total time average power input to the circuit is all going into heat in the resistance, none into the capacitor. This we know to be true because in Sec. 4–6 we showed that, on discharge, the capacitor feeds as much energy back into the circuit as it received from the circuit while being charged. Thus the time average power for a capacitor is zero. This statement assumes a perfect capacitor as we have assumed all along. We shall show later (see Sec. 8–3) that an imperfect capacitor can be looked upon as a perfect capacitor with a resistance in series.

PROBLEMS

4–1 In a d-c circuit the potential difference across a capacitor is increasing at the constant rate of 2.50 v/sec. The capacitance of the capacitor is 1.10 μf. (a) What is the charging current? (b) What is the charge on the capacitor 5.20 sec after the charging current starts to flow?

4–2 A capacitor of 9.35 μf capacitance is being charged at the constant rate of 5.75×10^{-6} coulomb/sec. (a) What is the potential difference across the capacitor 7.33 sec after the time when the charge on the capacitor started at zero? [*Ans:* 4.51 v.] (b) Draw and label a circuit diagram to show an arrangement which could be used to charge this capacitor at the specified constant rate (within experimental error if the charging current can be read to three significant figures) for about 10 sec.

4–3 A 5.00 μf capacitor has been connected to a battery, whose emf is 500 v, for a long time. How many electrons were forced onto the negative plate of the capacitor during the charging process?

4–4 A series circuit is made up of a battery, a switch, a resistor, and a capacitor. The battery has an emf of 500 v and negligible internal resistance. The resistor has 50.0 ohms resistance, and the capacitor has a capacitance of 15.0 μf. (a) What is the instantaneous current 0.00100 sec after the switch is closed? (b) What is the time constant of this circuit? (c) What is the current 0.000750 sec after the switch is closed? (d) What is the charge on the capacitor 0.00100 sec after the switch is closed? (e) What is the rate of change of the current at the instant the switch is closed? What is the current at this instant?

(f) What is the rate of change of the current 0.00150 sec after the switch is closed? Is the current increasing or decreasing?

4–5 A series circuit is made up of a battery, a switch, a resistor, and a capacitor. The battery has an emf of 1000 v and a negligible internal resistance. The resistor has 1.00 megohm resistance and the capacitor has 5.00 μf capacitance. (a) What is the potential difference across the capacitor 5.00 sec after the switch is closed? (b) What is the time required for the current to fall to one-half of the initial current? [*Ans:* 3.47 sec.] (c) What is the potential difference across the capacitor plates when the current is one-half of the initial current? [*Ans:* 500 v.] (d) What is the value of the time constant for this circuit? (e) *Plot* a curve with charging current in milliamperes as ordinate and with time in seconds, since switch was closed, as abscissa. Label the time constant on the graph. Read again the instructions for plotting a curve, which appear in Problem 1–13. In this problem it is sufficient to plot times from 0 to 20 sec.

4–6 Equation (4–3–11) gives the charging current for an *RC* circuit when the capacitor is charged from a source of constant emf $\mathscr{E}$. Using the fact that $i = dq/dt$, derive (4–3–13) directly by integration.

4–7 A battery of $\mathscr{E} = 1.50$ v emf is connected in series with a resistor $R = 20{,}000$ ohm, a capacitor of capacitance C, and a switch. A vacuum-tube voltmeter, whose input resistance can be considered to be infinite for the purposes of this problem, is connected across the capacitor and set on the 1.5 v scale. The switch is closed at $t = 0$. (a) Derive an equation giving the voltmeter reading as a function of time after the switch is closed. The electrical changes are slow enough so that the voltmeter can follow them. (b) What must be the value of C if the voltmeter is to reach a reading 1.24 v in 15.7 sec? [*Ans:* 450 μf.]

4–8 One method of measuring the resistance R of a high resistor makes use of equation (4–4–3). With Q and C known, q is measured as a function of t and then R is computed. The measurement of q is accomplished with a ballistic galvanometer as suggested in Sec. 4–1 and described in detail in Sec. 13–6. In a certain laboratory experiment with $C = 1.00$ μf, the following data are obtained:

t sec	q coulomb	t sec	q coulomb
0.0	0.410×10^{-6}	60.0	0.233×10^{-6}
15.0	0.366×10^{-6}	75.0	0.202×10^{-6}
30.0	0.310×10^{-6}	90.0	0.175×10^{-6}
45.0	0.269×10^{-6}	105.0	0.152×10^{-6}

(a) Arrive at a formula, and a method of using it, which will permit you to use all of the above data, and a straight line, to determine a *single* (average) value of R. (It is not a suitable answer to compute seven values of R and then average them.) (b) Find the average value of R required by the above data. [*Ans:* 106 megohm.]

4–9 Draw and label a circuit diagram which would permit you to carry out the experiment of Problem 4–8.

4–10 A neon glow tube (i.e., a gas discharge tube) will not "strike" and thus start glowing, if the potential difference across it is less than V_s, its striking potential. Hence its equivalent series resistance is infinite when the voltage across it is below V_s. Using the fact that the rapidity of response of a circuit that has resistance R and capacitance C in series and that is connected to a d-c source of emf $\mathscr{E}$ can be fixed by proper adjustment of the RC product, a glow tube of this sort can be made to delay its striking for a predictable time interval after the switch in the circuit is closed. (a) Draw the diagram of a circuit which will start the potential across the glow tube at zero and will permit the striking of the tube to be delayed a known length of time t_s after the switch is closed. Derive a formula for the potential difference v across the tube as a function of t, in your circuit, for times $t \leqq t_s$. (b) If $\mathscr{E} = 100$ v, $C = 2.25$ µf, and $V_s = 75.0$ v, what value must R have in your circuit so the tube will strike 11.5 sec after the switch is closed? [*Ans:* 3.68 megohm.]

4–11 The glow tube of Problem 4–10 has a negligible resistance compared to R while the gas discharge is occurring (i.e., while it is glowing). Also the gas discharge in the tube will cease when the potential difference across it drops below its extinction voltage V_a where V_a is less than V_s but appreciably greater than zero. Sketch a graph showing the potential v across the glow tube in the circuit you drew for Problem 4–10. Start your graph at $t = 0$, when the switch was closed, and assume that the switch is left closed.

4–12 A series circuit is made up of a capacitor of constant capacitance C, a resistor of constant resistance R, a battery whose constant emf is $\mathscr{E}$, and a switch. The switch is closed at the time $t = 0$. (a) From the equation $p = i\mathscr{E}$ for the instantaneous power input from the battery to the circuit, compute the total energy input from the battery to the circuit during the total time that the current flows. Use $p = i\mathscr{E}$ directly; do not use (4–5–1). [*Ans:* $W = C\mathscr{E}^2$.] (b) Write the equation for the instantaneous rate at which electrical energy is being converted into heat energy in the resistor. Using this equation, compute the total electrical energy converted into heat energy during the total time that the current flows. [*Ans:* Heat $= \frac{1}{2} C\mathscr{E}^2$.]

Of the total energy supplied by the battery what fraction is stored as potential energy in the capacitor? How does this fraction depend on the R of the circuit?

4–13 Immediately following (4–5–4) in the text we state that the energy of a given charged capacitor of constant capacitance C is the same when it has a potential difference V_C, and thus a charge Q, regardless of the method used to charge it. Test this by imagining that you start with the capacitor completely uncharged; and charge it by carrying small positive charges, of magnitude dq, one after the other from one plate directly across between the plates, and deposit them on the other plate. From this compute the total work done in charging the capacitor to the point where its charge is Q. Compare your result with (4–5–4).

4–14 Plot a curve showing y as a function of x for the equation $y = 6 \sin (2\pi x/3 + \pi/6)$. Plot x (not the argument of the sine) as abscissa and y as ordinate. Assign values to the argument, $(2\pi x/3 + \pi/6)$, of the sine at $\pi/12$ (or $15°$) intervals from zero to 2π and in each case solve for x as the quantity to be plotted as abscissa.

Instructions for Problems 4–15, 4–16, *and* 4–17: Using the suggestions given in the previous problem, plot the following functions. Plot the three curves on the same sheet of graph paper, putting 4–15 at the top, 4–16 in the middle, and 4–17 at the bottom of the sheet. Plot all to the same time scale as abscissa.

Express the time in decimal fractions of a second on the abscissa axis. For example, a suitable scale might be 0.00100 sec for each centimeter space on the graph paper. Take your points not more than 22.5° ($\pi/8$ radian) apart, and preferably not more than 15° ($\pi/12$ radian) apart. Tables of values must be worked out neatly for each plot.

4–15 $v = 160 \sin \omega t$ for the instantaneous voltage across an ordinary a-c power line as a function of time. The frequency of the line is 60 cycles/sec and ω, which is in radians per second, is given by $\omega = 2\pi \times 60$. Plot v as ordinate, and t as abscissa.

4–16 Let $i = 20 \sin [\omega t - (\pi/3)]$ for the instantaneous current flowing in the circuit as a function of time. Plot i as ordinate against t as abscissa.

4–17 Let $p = [(160 \times 20)/2] \cos \pi/3 - [(160 \times 20)/2] \cos (2\omega t - \pi/3)$ for the instantaneous power used in the above circuit as a function of time. Plot p as ordinate against t as abscissa.

4–18 In the circuit referred to in Problems 4–15, 4–16, and 4–17, does the current lead or lag the voltage and by how much? Is this circuit a capacitive one? Give the reason for your answer.

4–19 (a) Using the power equation (4–6–10) for a pure capacitance connected to a sinusoidal a-c line, find the equation for the energy stored in the capacitor at the instant when the potential difference across the capacitor is a maximum. [*Ans:* $W_C = \frac{1}{2}CV_m^2$.] (b) How does the energy stored in the capacitor at this instant compare with the energy that would be stored in the same capacitor by a battery whose emf is equal to V_m?

4–20 Near Fig. 4–6–5 it is stated, from the symmetry of the power curve, that the capacitor feeds as much energy back into the line on discharge as it receives from the line during the charging process. Prove by a mathematical argument that this statement is true.

4–21 Two branches in parallel are connected to a sinusoidal a-c line. The instantaneous current as a function of time in branch number 1 is given by the equation $i_1 = 50 \sin \omega t$ and the instantaneous current as a function of time in branch number 2 is given by the equation $i_2 = 30 \sin \omega t$ where the amplitude values are in amperes.

According to Kirchhoff's first law, the instantaneous current i in the line is given by $i = i_1 + i_2$. In this problem we are to find i as a function of time by a graphical method. To do this: (a) Plot curves for i_1 and i_2 on the same axes. This time plot ωt (instead of t) along the abscissa axis. Make a complete table of values as before, spacing the points not more than 15° apart. Continue the plot for one full cycle of each equation. (b) Add instantaneous ordinates of the two graphs obtained in (a), and plot these values against ωt on the same axes used in (a). This gives the plot of i as a function of time. (c) Write the equation for i as a function of time, i.e., the equation of the curve that you obtained in (b).

4–22 The load of branch 2 in Problem 4–21 is changed to one having inductance and resistance in series, so that the equation of i_2 as a function of time becomes $i_2 = 30 \sin (\omega t - 30°)$. The equation for i_1 remains as in Problem 4–21. Repeat Problem 4–21 for this case.

4-23 Substitute the value of I_m given in (4–7–11) and the value of ϕ given in (4–7–10) into (4–7–8), and show that the left side of the equation can then be reduced to an identity with the right side. In doing this you prove only that we did not make a mistake in algebra or trigonometry when we derived (4–7–11) and (4–7–10), but it is none the less worth the trouble in order to prove that the statement immediately following (4–7–11) is correct.

4-24 Prove that (4–7–13) is the solution of the differential equation in (4–7–3) by direct substitution of (4–7–13) into (4–7–3). After the substitution has been made, show that the left side of (4–7–3) reduces to an identity with the right side. When you have accomplished the above, you have demonstrated that, in this case at least, (4–7–4) is true.

4-25 Prove that the value of A given in (4–7–14) can be transformed into the value used for A in (4–7–15).

4-26 Consider the transient term of (4–7–16). Show (a) that the greatest negative value the transient term can have is $(-I_m/RC\omega)e^{-t/RC}$, (b) that the greatest positive value is $(I_m/RC\omega)e^{-t/RC}$, and (c) that the smallest value is zero. State the conditions under which (a) gives a proper description. Make similar statements for (b) and for (c).

4-27 A resistance of 5.00 ohms and a capacitor whose capacitive reactance is 50.0 ohms on 60 cycles/sec alternating current are hooked in series and connected to a sinusoidal 60 cycles/sec a-c line through a switch. The maximum value of the voltage V_m for this line is 170 v. The switch is closed at such a point in the voltage cycle of the line that the transient has its largest positive value. (a) What is the value of α in degrees and in radians in (4–7–1)? Write the equation giving the instantaneous potential difference across the line as a function of time after the switch was closed. Include the appropriate numerical values in this equation. [*Ans:* $\alpha = 95° \, 42' = 1.67$ radians, $v = 170 \sin (377t + 1.67)$.] (b) What is the value of the current that flows in the circuit at the instant that the switch is closed? [*Ans:* $i = 33.9$ amp.] (c) What is the value of the transient part of the current 0.00100 sec after the switch is closed? [*Ans:* 0.774 amp.]

4-28 A resistor with 15.1 ohm resistance is in series with a capacitor of 49.2 μf capacitance and the series combination is connected through a switch to a 60 cycle/sec sinusoidal a-c line whose maximum voltage is 310 v. The switch is closed at such a point in the voltage cycle that the transient term in the current equation has its largest negative value. What is the value of α? What current is flowing in this circuit 5.12×10^{-4} sec after the switch is closed and what is the charge on the capacitor at this instant?

4-29 A capacitor of capacitance 3.16×10^{-5} farad is in series with a resistance of 72.0 ohms, and the combination has been connected to a sinusoidal a-c line for a long time. The maximum value of the line voltage is 88.5 v, and the frequency of the line is 100 cycles/sec. The equation for the instantaneous current flowing in this circuit as a function of time is $i = I_m \sin \omega t$ where $I_m = 1.00$ amp. (a) Draw the circuit diagram. Write the equation for the instantaneous potential difference across the capacitor v_C, as a function of time, and the equation for the instantaneous potential difference across the resistance v_R, as a function of time. Be sure that you have the correct phase angles in the equations for v_C and v_R with reference to the current equation given above. (b) On the same axes, plot curves for v_C and v_R as functions of time. Carry each curve through one complete cycle. By the application of Kirchhoff's second law and the method of adding instantaneous ordinates, plot the curve for the instantaneous applied line voltage as a function of time. Check the statement that the maximum applied line voltage is 88.5 v. Write the equation for the instantaneous applied line voltage as a function of time.

4-30 Solve the problem stated as Problem II in Sec. 4–9 and arrive at equation (4–9–3).

4-31 Starting with (4–10–1), (4–10–2), and the fact that in this case $i = v/R$ so $p = v^2/R$, prove that $V_{eff} = V_m/\sqrt{2}$ as given in (4–11–4).

4-32 As the time constant T of an RC circuit is defined, it is a length of time; thus T must have the units of time. Show, with units equations, that $T = RC$ does give the unit of T in seconds when R is in ohms and C in farads.

4-33 A resistor of 20.2 ohm resistance and a capacitor of 18.8 ohm reactance at 60 cycle/sec have been connected in series to an a-c line for a long time. A very high resistance voltmeter across the line reads 120 v and the frequency of the line is 60 cycles/sec. What would a very high resistance voltmeter read if connected across R? if connected across C? [*Ans:* $V_R = 87.9$ v, $V_C = 81.9$ v.]

4-34 A capacitor of 16.2 ohm reactance at 60 cycles/sec is connected in series with a resistor of 11.3 ohm resistance and the series combination has been connected to a sinusoidal 60 cycle/sec a-c line for a long time. The rms value of the line voltage is 220 v. What is the power factor of this circuit and what is the time average power input from the line to the circuit? [*Ans:* 0.572, 1390 watts.]

4-35 Prove that the time average of a sinusoidal alternating current for the positive half cycle is equal to $2I_m/\pi$.

4-36 A half-wave rectifier transmits the positive half cycle of each voltage alternation while eliminating the negative half cycle. The ordinary D'Arsonval type of d-c meter reads the time average of the current that flows through its coils, whereas an electrodynamometer type of meter (which may be used for either direct or alternating current) reads the rms value of the current that flows through its coil. A D'Arsonval ammeter and an electrodynamometer ammeter (calibrated to read I_{eff} in a sinusoidal a-c circuit) are connected in series in the circuit using the half-wave rectified sinusoidal a-c voltage from the above rectifier. Prove that the numerical reading of the electrodynamometer is $\pi/2$ times as big as that of the D'Arsonval in this particular case.

4-37 The electrodynamometer ammeter and the D'Arsonval ammeter of Problem 4–36 are connected in series in a circuit where the current is given by the equation $i = D + A \sin \omega t$ where $D = 2.50$ amp, $A = 10.0$ amp, and $\omega = 377/\sec$. What is the reading of each meter? Remember that, since the electrodynamometer reads the rms value of the current, its reading must be computed by taking the square root of the time average of the squares of the instantaneous currents. [*Ans:* D'Arsonval 2.50 amp, electrodynamometer 7.50 amp.]

4-38 Find the rms value of an alternating current of which each half cycle is a semicircle and whose maximum value is I_m. [*Ans:* $I = 0.816I_m$.]

4-39 Find the rms value of a saw-tooth direct current which rises linearly from zero to 5.00 amp in 1.00 sec, drops to zero in a negligible time, and then repeats this cycle of operations over and over. Use the same definition for the rms ampere as the one given in Sec. 4–11 for the rms a-c ampere. [*Ans:* 2.89 amp.]

4-40 A neon tube, which will not light until the voltage across it reaches 170 v, is connected across a capacitor of 0.0160 μf. This parallel combination is connected in series with a resistor of 300×10^3 ohms, a battery of 200 v emf and negligible internal resistance, and a switch. The switch is closed at $t = 0$. The neon tube can be considered to have infinite resistance before it lights. (a) At what value of t will the neon tube light? [*Ans:* 91.2×10^{-4} sec.] (b) Assume that while the neon tube is lighted its resistance is essentially zero, and when the voltage across it drops to 140 v it will extinguish and its equivalent resistance immediately becomes infinite again. How long after the neon tube lights the first time before it lights the second time? [*Ans:* 33.6×10^{-4} sec.] (c) What will be the frequency of the flashes of the neon tube? Make a sketch of the voltage across the capacitor as a function of time after the switch is closed. [*Ans:* 298 flashes/sec.]

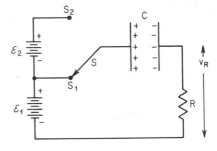

Figure 4–P–1.

4-41 (a) Prior to this problem, the switch S in Fig. 4–P–1 has been in contact with S_1 for a long time, the capacitor C is charged to a potential difference $\mathscr{E}_1$, and the current has become zero. At the instant $t = 0$, S is moved to make contact with S_2. Set up the differential equation and derive an equation giving the potential v_R across R as a function of time after the switch is moved to position S_2; then sketch a plot of v_R as a function of t. (b) After S has been in contact with S_2 for a time $t = RC$, switch S is suddenly moved back to position S_1. Derive an equation giving v_R as a function of time after S is moved back to position S_1. Incorporate this in your plot sketched in part (a).

SOME PROPERTIES OF

AN INDUCTOR AS A

CIRCUIT ELEMENT

5–I RISE OF CURRENT IN AN INDUCTIVE CIRCUIT WITH CONSTANT EMF APPLIED. TIME CONSTANT. ENERGY OF THE MAGNETIC FIELD

Figure 5–1–1 shows the circuit that we are to consider. Here B is a source of constant emf $\mathscr{E}$; R represents the total resistance in the circuit; L represents the total self-inductance in the circuit, most of which is in a coil of wire that

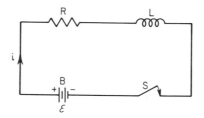

Figure 5–1–1. Constant emf $\mathscr{E}$ applied to a circuit having constant R and L in series.

is connected in series in the circuit. The value of L is constant, which means that there is no ferromagnetic material nearby; S represents a switch that we can close when we are ready, and we shall start the timing at the instant when the switch is closed. Hence the instant that the switch is closed is $t = 0$.

PROBLEM I. Find an equation giving the current flowing in the circuit of Fig. 5–1–1 as a function of time after the switch is closed.

We have seen in (3–7–4) that the emf of self-induction e_L is given by

$e_L = -L\, di/dt$. Since the current in the circuit of Fig. 5–1–1 is increasing after the switch is closed, this emf of self-induction opposes the rise of the current and thus is oppositely directed in the circuit to $\mathscr{E}$. The net emf in the circuit at any instant is $\mathscr{E} - L\, di/dt$, so Kirchhoff's second law gives the equation

$$\mathscr{E} - L\, di/dt = iR \qquad (5\text{–}1\text{–}1)$$

This is a simple differential equation in which the variables may be separated, yielding, after integration

$$\ln\,(i - \mathscr{E}/R) = -Rt/L + \ln K \qquad (5\text{–}1\text{–}2)$$

where ln represents the natural logarithm and $\ln K$ is the constant of integration. Rearrange the equation, take the antilog of both sides, and obtain

$$i - \mathscr{E}/R = Ke^{-Rt/L} \qquad (5\text{–}1\text{–}3)$$

We may evaluate K from the boundary condition that at

$$t = 0, \qquad i = 0 \qquad (5\text{–}1\text{–}4)$$

We know that $i = 0$ at $t = 0$ from the following reasoning. Before the switch was closed, $i = 0$. If at the instant that the switch is closed the current immediately has some value greater than zero, there is an infinite rate of change of the current at that instant. But an infinite rate of change of current would produce an infinite emf of self-induction in the inductor, which would send an infinite current backward through the battery, charging the battery in the process. Such behavior would mean that electrical energy is changed into chemical potential energy in the battery, and there is no source of energy in the circuit to furnish the electrical energy for this purpose. At the outset, the only source of energy in the circuit is the battery; hence the law of conservation of energy tells us that the above behavior is impossible. Thus, in any inductive circuit the current must start at zero when the switch is closed and must have a finite rate of change.

Put (5–1–4) into (5–1–3) in order to evaluate the constant K, and (5–1–3) becomes

$$i = \mathscr{E}(1 - e^{-Rt/L})/R \qquad (5\text{–}1\text{–}5)$$

Let I represent the final value that the current will reach after infinite time. From (5–1–5) we see that $I = \mathscr{E}/R$, so (5–1–5) becomes

$$i = I(1 - e^{-Rt/L}) \qquad (5\text{–}1\text{–}6)$$

Equation (5–1–6) states the current flowing in the circuit of Fig. 5–1–1 as a function of time and thus is the answer to the problem that we set out to solve.

Figure 5–1–2 is a plot of (5–1–6), showing graphically how the current in the circuit changes with time, and the curve is labeled L_1. The value of I is indicated by a dotted line parallel to the t-axis, and i approaches I asymptotically.

An infinite time is required for the current in the circuit to reach its final value I, and this would be true for any value of R and L. Yet from (5–1–6) we can see that the rapidity of response of the circuit depends on the values of R and L. This situation is analogous to the one for the capacitive circuit discussed in Sec. 4–3 and, as there, we define a time constant that is useful in comparing the rapidity of response of circuits like the one shown in Fig. 5–1–1.

For this circuit, *we define the time constant as the time required for the current to reach* $(1 - 1/e)$ *of its final value and call the time constant T.*

We may evaluate T from (5–1–6) by substituting

$$i = (1 - 1/e)I \quad \text{at} \quad t = T$$

Then (5–1–6) becomes $(1 - e^{-1})I = I(1 - e^{-RT/L})$, which can be satisfied only if $T = L/R$. Hence the value of the time constant is L/R and is the time required for the current to reach 63.22% of its final value. In Fig. 5–1–2,

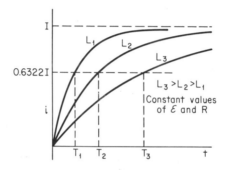

Figure 5–1–2. Current as a function of time for a series circuit with constant R and L and with a constant emf applied. Effect of L on the time constant of the circuit.

a dotted line is drawn parallel to the t-axis at the value $i = 0.6322I$. The abscissa of the point where this dotted line crosses the L_1 curve is the time constant for this circuit and is labeled T_1.

Suppose now that we open the switch, remove the inductor L_1, and replace it with an inductor with a larger self-inductance L_2. The curve marked L_2 in Fig. 5–1–2 shows the slower growth of the current, and T_2 shows the larger time constant. A repetition of this experiment, using an inductor of still larger self-inductance L_3, is represented by the curve labeled L_3 with the still larger time constant T_3. In Fig. 5–1–2, we have assumed that the emf of the applied battery and the total resistance of the circuit remained the same for all three curves. Resistance R is equally important in determining the time constant of the circuit but, while the time constant varies directly with L, it varies inversely with R.

In the circuit of Fig. 5–1–1, we have drawn the diagram as if R and L were separate circuit elements. Actually the inductor is a coil of wire, so it will have the resistance of the wire as a part of itself. The R shown includes this resistance of the wires of the coil. In fact it is often the case that the R of the circuit is primarily the resistance of the wires of the inductor. However, the result is the same for R and L are in series as if they were separate circuit elements. Figure 5–1–1 is the equivalent circuit for the actual situation.

PROBLEM II. Find an equation giving the energy in the magnetic field about a self-inductor.

We may compute the energy stored in the magnetic field about a self-inductor by computing the work that the battery does in building up this magnetic field about the inductor. While the current in the circuit is rising the inductor is a source that is receiving energy from the electric circuit. This we know to be the case because the current in the circuit is flowing through the inductor against the emf of self-induction. We know that, whenever a current flows through a source against the emf of the source, electrical energy is changed to some form of energy other than heat. In this case the "some other form of energy" is the energy of the magnetic field that the current is building up around the inductor. Let p = instantaneous power input to the magnetic field, and

$$p = e_L i \qquad\qquad (5\text{–}1\text{–}7)$$

Let W = energy stored in the magnetic field during the rise of the current from 0 to i, and we have

$$W = \int p \, dt = \int e_L i \, dt = \int L \, (di/dt) \, i \, dt$$

Since there is no ferromagnetic material near the coil, L is independent of and may be placed in front of the integral. Then

$$W = L \int i \, di = Li^2/2 + K \qquad\qquad (5\text{–}1\text{–}8)$$

where K is a constant of integration. We can evaluate K from the known condition that, when $i = 0$, $W = 0$ since there is no magnetic field about the inductor when no current flows. From this we determine that the value of K is zero. Hence

$$W = Li^2/2 \qquad\qquad (5\text{–}1\text{–}9)$$

Equation (5–1–9) states the energy stored in the magnetic field of the inductor when a current i is flowing through the wires of the inductor. It is to be noted that in deriving (5–1–9) we did not have to insert the relationship giving current as a function of time. Thus W is the energy stored in the magnetic field when the current is i, regardless of the way in which the current changed in the process of arriving at the value i. As pointed out above, all this assumes no ferromagnetic material near the coil.

When the current flowing in the circuit of Fig. 5–1–1 reaches its final value I, the energy stored in the magnetic field is

$$W = LI^2/2 \qquad\qquad (5\text{–}1\text{–}10)$$

5–2 FALL OF CURRENT IN AN INDUCTIVE CIRCUIT

In Problem 5–7 (refer to the circuit diagram there) you are asked to derive the equation

$$i = Ie^{-Rt/L} \tag{5–2–1}$$

for the fall of current in a circuit, with R and L in series, when the energy in the magnetic field is fed back into the circuit. As the current decreases, the magnetic flux linking the coil decreases and an emf of self-induction is set up in such a sense as to oppose the decrease of the current. This statement means that the emf of self-induction is in the same sense as that of the current and keeps the current flowing until all the energy of the magnetic field has been fed back into the circuit.

5–3 SINUSOIDAL ALTERNATING POTENTIAL DIFFERENCE APPLIED TO CONSTANT R AND CONSTANT L IN SERIES

Refer to Sec. 4–7 where the same problem was solved for R and C in series. The same method of solution will be used here but with a minimum of discussion, so you will do well to review Sec. 4–7.

Problem: Find an equation giving the current in the circuit of Fig. 5–3–1 as a function of time after the switch was closed. We wish to close the switch S at any point in the applied voltage cycle and start timing at that instant. Hence we use

$$v = V_m \sin(\omega t + \alpha) \tag{5–3–1}$$

as the equation for the applied voltage. Application of Kirchhoff's second law to this circuit yields the equation

$$V_m \sin(\omega t + \alpha) - L\, di/dt = iR \tag{5–3–2}$$

Rearrange (5–3–2) in the standard form,

$$di/dt + (R/L)i = V_m [\sin(\omega t + \alpha)]/L \tag{5–3–3}$$

Equate the left side to zero to obtain the complementary function. Separate the variables and integrate, obtaining

$$i = Ke^{-Rt/L} \tag{5–3–4}$$

The right side of (5–3–4) is the complementary function, where K is a constant of integration; K cannot be evaluated until we have the complete solution of (5–3–3).

To obtain the particular integral we must solve (5–3–3) as it stands. As in Sec. 4–7, we shall assume a solution and then test it. From the physics of the circuit in Fig. 5–3–1 and our previous experience with a-c circuits we assume that:

1. The current is sinusoidal and of the same frequency as the voltage.

2. The current is out of phase with the voltage by the phase angle ϕ, where ϕ is an unknown constant.

3. The maximum or amplitude value of the current is an unknown constant I_m.

The equation that incorporates all these assumptions is

$$i = I_m \sin [(\omega t + \alpha) - \phi] \tag{5-3-5}$$

Substitute (5–3–5) into (5–3–3), in order to determine whether it can be a solution of (5–3–3). After this substitution, carry out the same procedure

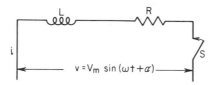

Figure 5–3–1. Sinusoidal alternating voltage of constant maximum value applied to constant R and constant L in series. Switch S is closed at $t = 0$.

used following (4–7–7), since the logic of the situation is the same. The equation you will obtain here, corresponding to (4–7–9) in Sec. 4–7, is

$$\cos (\omega t + \alpha) \left[\frac{I_m L\omega}{V_m} \cos \phi - \frac{I_m R}{V_m} \sin \phi \right]$$

$$+ \sin (\omega t + \alpha) \left[\frac{I_m L\omega}{V_m} \sin \phi + \frac{I_m R}{V_m} \cos \phi - 1 \right] = 0 \tag{5-3-6}$$

If (5–3–6) is true, it must be true at every instant of time. We can see that the left side of (5–3–6) can be zero at every instant only if the terms in the square brackets are each equal to zero. The argument is the same as that following (4–7–9). Hence we may equate the square bracket terms to zero separately and solve the two resulting equations simultaneously to obtain

$$\tan \phi = L\omega/R, \quad \text{or} \quad \phi = \tan^{-1} L\omega/R \tag{5-3-7}$$

and

$$I_m = V_m/\sqrt{R^2 + L^2\omega^2} \tag{5-3-8}$$

By our method of solution, these values of ϕ and I_m are guaranteed to be the values of ϕ and I_m which will make the left side of (5–3–6) reduce to an identity with the right side; hence these are the values of ϕ and I_m which make (5–3–5) a solution of (5–3–3). Substitute these values of ϕ and I_m into (5–3–5).

$$i = V_m \{\sin [(\omega t + \alpha) - \tan^{-1} L\omega/R]\}/\sqrt{R^2 + L^2\omega^2} \tag{5-3-9}$$

The right side of (5–3–9) is the particular integral of (5–3–3). From (4–7–4), the complete solution of (5–3–3) is the sum of the right sides of (5–3–4) and (5–3–9), so the complete solution (see Problem 5–11) is

$$i = Ke^{-Rt/L} + \frac{V_m}{\sqrt{R^2 + L^2\omega^2}} \sin\left[(\omega t + \alpha) - \tan^{-1}\frac{L\omega}{R}\right] \quad (5\text{–}3\text{–}10)$$

We must next evaluate the constant of integration K, which we can do from the boundary condition that

$$\text{at} \quad t = 0, \quad i = 0 \quad\quad\quad (5\text{–}3\text{–}11)$$

Put (5–3–11) into (5–3–10), solve for K, and we have

$$K = -V_m \{\sin[\alpha - \tan^{-1} L\omega/R]\}/\sqrt{R^2 + L^2\omega^2} \quad\quad (5\text{–}3\text{–}12)$$

Substititue this value of K into (5–3–10).

$$i = -V_m \{\sin(\alpha - \tan^{-1} L\omega/R)\}e^{-Rt/L}/\sqrt{R^2 + L^2\omega^2}$$
$$+ V_m \{\sin[(\omega t + \alpha) - \tan^{-1} L\omega/R]\}/\sqrt{R^2 + L^2\omega^2} \quad (5\text{–}3\text{–}13)$$

Equation (5–3–13) is the answer to the problem that we set out to solve and thus states the current that flows in the circuit of Fig. 5–3–1 as a function of time after the switch was closed.

We recognize the first term on the right as the *transient term*, since it will decrease rapidly as time increases, soon becoming negligibly small. The second term on the right we recognize as the *steady state*, since it is of importance as long as the switch in the circuit remains closed.

In Problem 5–12 you are to consider a circuit with fixed values of V_m, R, L, and ω and to find the greatest and the least values that the transient can have.

The duration of the transient term is too short to be of importance, if the switch in the circuit is to be closed an appreciable length of time (see, for example, Problem 5–13).

5–4 STEADY STATE CURRENT FOR R AND L IN SERIES ON A SINUSOIDAL A-C LINE

When the switch in Fig. 5–3–1 has been closed for some time and thus the transient term of (5–3–13) has become negligibly small, the steady state term alone is of importance. Hence the current in the circuit as a function of time is given by

$$i = V_m \{\sin[(\omega t + \alpha) - \tan^{-1} L\omega/R]\}/\sqrt{R^2 + L^2\omega^2} \quad (5\text{–}4\text{–}1)$$

The expression $L\omega$ is given the name *inductive reactance* and is represented by the symbol X_L. Hence by definition

$$X_L = L\omega = 2\pi f L \quad\quad\quad (5\text{–}4\text{–}2)$$

where f is the frequency of the voltage in cycles/sec. The unit of X_L is the ohm, the same unit as for resistance, as can be seen by substitution of units into (5–4–2) (solve Problem 5–16). Put X_L into (5–4–1), and we have

$$i = V_m \{\sin[(\omega t + \alpha) - \tan^{-1} X_L/R]\}/\sqrt{R^2 + X_L^2} \quad (5\text{–}4\text{–}3)$$

We see by comparison of the voltage in (5–3–1) and the current in (5–4–3) that, for R and L in series, the *current lags the voltage by* $\tan^{-1} X_L/R$.

After the transient has died out, the angle α contributes nothing to our information, for at this stage it is only a phase constant that appears in the same fashion in both the current and voltage equations. By a shift of the ordinate axis, as discussed in Sec. 4–8, we may drop α from both equations when we are interested in the steady state solution only. Thus we may write

$$v = V_m \sin \omega t \qquad (5\text{–}4\text{–}4)$$

$$i = V_m \left[\sin \left(\omega t - \tan^{-1} X_L/R\right)\right] / \sqrt{R^2 + X_L^2} \qquad (5\text{–}4\text{–}5)$$

The quantity $\sqrt{R^2 + X_L^2}$ is called the *impedance* for this circuit and is represented by z, or, by definition,

$$z = \sqrt{R^2 + X_L^2} \qquad (5\text{–}4\text{–}6)$$

The unit of z is the ohm since both R and X_L are expressed in ohms. Equation (5–3–8) gives the relationship between I_m, V_m, and z, so we may write

$$I_m = V_m/z \qquad (5\text{–}4\text{–}7)$$

Let us put this value of I_m into (5–4–5) and also replace $\tan^{-1} (X_L/R)$ by ϕ, and (5–4–5) becomes

$$i = I_m \sin (\omega t - \phi) \qquad (5\text{–}4\text{–}8)$$

Figure 5–4–1 is a plot of (5–4–4) and (5–4–8), showing the phase relationship between the current and the line voltage.

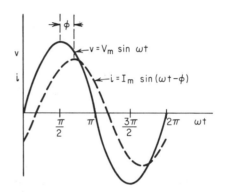

Figure 5–4–1. Phase relationship between current i and voltage v for R and L in series on a sinusoidal a-c line. i lags v by $\phi = \tan^{-1}(X_L/R)$.

An argument similar to the one used in connection with (4–6–8) and (4–6–9) may be used here, and as a result we may write for this circuit

$$i = I_m \sin \omega t \qquad (5\text{–}4\text{–}9)$$

$$v = V_m \sin (\omega t + \tan^{-1} X_L/R) \qquad (5\text{–}4\text{–}10)$$

Stating the result in words, if i lags v by the angle ϕ, then v leads i by the same angle ϕ. The graph of i is a simple sine curve if the phase angle is incorporated in the voltage equation.

It can be seen from (5–4–5) that, if the resistance R in the circuit is reduced to zero, the equation becomes

$$i = V_m \left[\sin (\omega t - \pi/2)\right] / X_L \qquad (5\text{–}4\text{–}11)$$

On comparison with (5–4–4), Eq. (5–4–11) says that, *for a pure inductance, the current through the inductance lags the potential difference across the inductance by* 90°. A similar argument using (5–4–9) and (5–4–10) shows that, *for a pure inductance, the potential difference across the inductance leads the current through the inductance by 90°.*

In (5–4–11), the amplitude value of the sine function is the maximum current I_m, or

$$I_m = V_m/X_L \quad \text{or} \quad V_m = I_m X_L \tag{5-4-12}$$

Divide both sides of (5–4–12) by $\sqrt{2}$, and we have $V_m/\sqrt{2} = X_L(I_m/\sqrt{2})$. But from (4–11–4), $V_m/\sqrt{2} = V$; and from (4–11–3), $I_m/\sqrt{2} = I$; hence,

$$V = IX_L \tag{5-4-13}$$

Equation (5–4–13) says that *the rms potential difference across a pure inductance is equal to the rms value of the current flowing through the inductance times the inductive reactance.*

5–5 POWER INPUT TO R AND L IN SERIES ON A SINUSOIDAL A-C LINE

In Problem 5–15 you are asked to prove that the instantaneous power input from the line to the circuit in Fig. 5–3–1, after the steady state has been established, is given by the equation

$$p = V_m I_m (\cos \phi)/2 - V_m I_m [\cos (2\omega t - \phi)]/2 \tag{5-5-1}$$

Equation (5–5–1) shows that the instantaneous power input is also sinusoidal but of twice the frequency of the current or voltage. Since p represents power input to the circuit, negative values of p represent power output from the circuit back to the line. This power output from the circuit to the line is possible because the energy stored in the magnetic field about the inductor during the rise of the current is fed back into the circuit during the fall of the current. This was discussed briefly in Sec. 5–2 and brought up for your consideration in Problem 5–8.

Also, in Problem 5–15, you are asked to prove that the time average power input to this circuit is given by

$$P = (V_m/\sqrt{2})(I_m/\sqrt{2}) \cos \phi \tag{5-5-2}$$

We recognize $V_m/\sqrt{2}$ as the root mean square (or effective) value of the line voltage as read by an a-c voltmeter across the line and we have agreed to represent this by V. Also we recognize $I_m/\sqrt{2}$ as the root mean square (or effective) value of the current flowing in the circuit as read by an a-c ammeter in series in the circuit and have agreed to represent this by I. Hence (5–5–2) becomes

$$P = VI \cos \phi \tag{5-5-3}$$

Again, as in Sec. 4–12, $\cos \phi$ is referred to as the *power factor*. In this circuit with R and L in series, from (5–3–7),

$$\cos \phi = R/\sqrt{R^2 + L^2\omega^2} = R/z \tag{5-5-4}$$

From (5–4–7) we have the relation that $V_m = I_m z$. Put this relation and (5–5–4) into (5–5–3).

$$P = (I_m z I_m/2)(R/z) = I_m^2 R/2 = I^2 R \tag{5-5-5}$$

So we see, as in Sec. 4–12, that the time average power input to this circuit is equal to the time average rate at which electrical energy is being converted into heat energy in the resistance. Thus there is no time average power input to the inductance. We know this statement to be true because, as the current decreases, the inductance feeds back into the circuit all the energy that was stored in its magnetic field while the current was increasing.

If the circuit contains some device, such as a motor, that converts electrical energy into a form other than heat, and this converted energy is not fed back into the circuit, then (5–5–5) is not the total time average power input to the circuit. However, (5–5–3) still gives the total time average power input to the circuit. It is fairly common practice to consider such a device as a motor in terms of an equivalent circuit that consists of a resistance and re-actance in series. The requirement is that the equivalent circuit shall draw the same current as the actual device when hooked to the same voltage and that the phase angle between current and voltage shall be the same in the equivalent circuit as in the actual circuit. However, it is important to re-member that (5–5–3) is a general equation for time average power,* whereas (5–5–5) refers to a special case.

PROBLEMS

5–1 The time constant for a resistor and inductor in series is given by $T = L/R$. Since T is a length of time it must have the unit of time. Show that T is in seconds if L is in henrys and R is in ohms in this equation for T.

5–2 A coil with a resistance of 50.0 ohms and a self-inductance of 1.50 henry is connected to a d-c generator whose maintained terminal potential difference is 150 v, and the switch in the circuit is closed at $t = 0$. (a) What is the initial rate of change of the current? [*Ans:* 100 amp/sec.] (b) What are the current and the rate of change of the current at $t = 0.10$ sec? [*Ans:* 2.89 amp, 3.58 amp/sec.] (c) What is the time constant for the inductor? [*Ans:* 0.0300 sec.] (d) What are the current and rate of change of the current at the instant of the time constant? [*Ans:* 1.90 amp, 36.8 amp/sec.]

5–3 A coil on the laboratory shelf is marked 25.0 ohms, 352 millihenrys, and its inductance is the proper one for a particular experiment. It is to be used in a circuit where the voltage across it is to be suddenly applied and then held constant at 58.3 v and where the experiment requires that the current through it must rise from zero to 1.38 amp in a time less than 2.52×10^{-3} sec, but more than 2.50×10^{-3} sec, after the switch is closed. Is the coil satisfactory for this experiment? If it is not, what can be done to make it satisfactory? Give a numerical answer.

5–4 Consider the circuit given in Fig. 5–1–1. Change (5–1–1) into an instan-taneous power equation. (a) Derive a formula for total energy input from the battery to the circuit during the time interval 0 to L/R. Show that your formula gives the unit of energy. [*Ans:* $W_{\text{total}} = 0.368\mathscr{E}^2L/R^2$.] (b) Derive a formula for electrical energy converted into heat during the same time interval. [*Ans:* $W_{\text{heat}} = 0.169\mathscr{E}^2L/R^2$.] (c) Show that the energy converted into heat in this time interval, plus the energy stored in the magnetic field

* See Sec. 20–10 for the description of a wattmeter.

during the same time interval, as given by (5–1–9), equals the energy input from the battery.

5–5 A coil has a resistance of 20.0 ohms and a self-inductance of 550 milli-henrys. A current of 20.0 amp is flowing. The switch in the circuit is suddenly opened. (a) What energy is received by the circuit from the magnetic field about the coil? [*Ans:* 110 joules.] (b) What chain of events occurs to make it possible for the circuit to receive this energy from the magnetic field? (c) Why does sparking occur at a switch in an inductive circuit when the switch is opened?

5–6 A coil of resistance R_1 and self-inductance L_1 is connected in parallel with a second coil of resistance R_2 and self-inductance L_2. The parallel combination is connected through a switch to a battery whose emf is $\mathscr{E}$. Assuming that all other resistances in the circuit are negligible compared to R_1 and R_2, and starting with Kirchhoff's second law, derive an equation for the current flowing in the wires to the battery as a function of time after the switch is closed.

5–7 In the circuit of Fig. 5–P–1 the battery, whose emf is $\mathscr{E}$, is sending a current I through the resistance R and inductance L in series. The switch S_1 has been closed for a long time and the current I has reached the Ohm's law value of $I = \mathscr{E}/R$. At a certain instant, which we shall call $t = 0$, the switch S_2 is suddenly closed and the switch S_1 is opened immediately afterward. Derive an equation [see (5–2–1)] giving the instantaneous current flowing in the circuit $ABCDA$ as a function of time after the switch S_2 was closed. Sketch a curve showing i as a function of t. What is the meaning of the time constant of the circuit in this case?

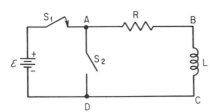

Figure 5–P–1. Fall of current in an inductive circuit.

5–8 In Problem 5–7, let $p_h = i^2R$ be the instantaneous rate at which electrical energy is being converted into heat energy in the resistance as the current in the loop $ABCDA$ decreases according to the equation which you derived in Problem 5–7. Prove that the total energy converted into heat during the decrease of the current is equal to the energy that was stored in the magnetic field before the switching operation described in Problem 5–7.

5–9 In Fig. 5–P–1 assume that a lamp bulb of resistance R_B is connected in place of the switch S_2. Switch S_1 has been closed for a long time and the current through the lamp bulb is $I_B = \mathscr{E}/R_B$ and that through the inductor is $I = \mathscr{E}/R$. Switch S_1 is opened at $t = 0$. Assuming that the lamp filament is a pure resistance, derive the current equation $i = Ie^{-at}$, where $a = (R + R_B)/L$, for the current in the loop $ABCDA$. Show why and under what conditions it is possible for the lamp bulb to flash much brighter momentarily just as S_1 is opened than it was when S_1 was closed.

5–10 In Problem 5–9, $R_B = 100$ ohms, $R = 5.00$ ohms, $L = 2.56$ henrys, and $\mathscr{E} = 12.2$ v. For how long a time, after S_1 is opened, is the current through the lamp greater than or equal to its value with S_1 closed?

5–11 Prove that (5–3–10) is a solution of the differential equation (5–3–3) by direct substitution of (5–3–10) into (5–3–3). Do this by showing that, after this substitution, the left side of (5–3–3) reduces to an identity with the right side. (*Do not* follow the procedure given in the text.) Do you need to know the value of K in order to carry out this proof? Why?

5–12 Consider the transient term of (5–3–13). Show that (a) the greatest negative value the transient term can have is $-I_m e^{-Rt/L}$, (b) the greatest positive value is $I_m e^{-Rt/L}$, and (c) the smallest value is zero. State the conditions under which (a) gives a proper description. Make similar statements for (b) and for (c).

5–13 A circuit like the one in Fig. 5–3–1 has a resistance of 5.00 ohms in series with a self-inductance of 250 millihenrys. It is connected to a 60 cycles/sec sinusoidal a-c line across which a voltmeter reads 120 v. The switch is closed at such a point in the voltage cycle that the transient has its largest negative value. (a) What is the value of α? Write the equation giving the instantaneous potential difference across the line as a function of time after the switch was closed. [*Ans:* 3.09 radians, $v = 170 \sin{(377\,t + 3.09)}$.] (b) What is the value of the current flowing in the circuit when $t = 0.00835$ sec (i.e., $\omega t = \pi$ radians)? [*Ans:* -3.32 amp.] (c) What contribution does the transient alone make to the current $\frac{1}{6}$ sec (10 cycles) after the switch was closed? [*Ans:* 0.0638 amp.]

5–14 Make a careful plot of the curve of (5–3–13). Take the maximum voltage $V_m = 100$ v and a frequency of 60 cycles/sec. The inductance L of the circuit is 0.0100 henry and the resistance of the circuit is 2.00 ohms. The switch was closed, at the instant $t = 0$, when the instantaneous applied voltage was -46.8 v, thus making $\alpha = -28°$. (Check this last statement.) To plot this curve: First evaluate the transient term for various values of t from $t = 0$ to $t = 0.025$ sec and plot it carefully to scale, using time as abscissa and current as ordinate. Second, evaluate the second (or steady state) term for various values of t from $t = 0$ to $t = 0.05$ sec and plot it on the same axes as before. Third, using the method of adding ordinates, plot the final curve for current as a function of time on the same axes. Fourth, evaluate the instantaneous voltage for various values of t from $t = 0$ to $t = 0.05$ sec and plot on the same graph paper, using the same time scale and adopting a suitable voltage scale as ordinate. Plot each curve in a different color and label each curve clearly.

5–15 A sinusoidal voltage given by (5–4–4) has been applied for some time to a circuit having R and L in series. The steady state current flowing in this circuit is given by (5–4–8). Review Sec. 4–9. (a) Prove that the instantaneous power equation is given by (5–5–1), where ϕ has the value given in (5–3–7). Sketch the current, voltage, and power curves. (b) Prove that the time average power is given by (5–5–2).

5–16 Using the defining equation for X_L, show that the unit of X_L is the ohm.

5–17 An inductance of 0.0663 henry and a resistance of 25.0 ohms are connected in series to a 60 cycles/sec sinusoidal power line. The instantaneous current flowing in the circuit as a function of time is given by

$$i = I_m \sin \omega t \qquad (1)$$

where $I_m = 2.00$ amp. (a) Draw the circuit diagram. Write the equation for the instantaneous potential difference v_L across the inductance as a function of time, and the equation for the instantaneous potential difference v_R across the resistance as a function of time. Be sure that you have the correct phase angles in the equations for v_L and v_R when the current is given by (1) above. (b) On the same axes, plot curves for v_L and v_R as functions of ωt. (Note that you use ωt, not t, for the abscissa.) Construct complete tables of values before plotting. Carry each curve through one complete cycle.

By the application of Kirchhoff's second law and the method of adding instantaneous ordinates, plot the curve for the instantaneous applied voltage as a function of time. Write the equation for this curve.

5–18 A coil with negligible resistance has a self-inductance of 23.6 mh. This coil is in series with a resistor of 5.60 ohms, and the series combination has been connected to a 60 cycle/sec sinusoidal a-c line for a long time. A very high resistance voltmeter connected across the line reads 123 v. What would this voltmeter read if connected across the coil? across the resistor? [*Ans:* $V_R = 65.4$ v, $V_L = 104$ v.]

5–19 A coil with an inductive reactance of 5.53 ohms at 25 cycles/sec and a resistance of 2.87 ohms is connected in series with a resistor of 7.92 ohms and the series combination has been connected to 25 cycle/sec sinusoidal a-c line for a long time. The rms value of the line voltage is 207 v. What is the power factor of this circuit and what is the time average power input from the line to the circuit?

5–20 The voltage across an inductance and resistance in series is given by $v = V_m \sin \omega t$ and the current flowing in this series circuit is given by $i = I_m \sin (\omega t + \phi)$, where $V_m = 136.2$ v, $I_m = 9.33$ amp, and $\phi = -30.5°$. What is the time average power input from the line to the circuit? [*Ans:* 547 watts.]

5–21 A coil with a resistance of 20.0 ohms and an inductance of 200 millihenrys is connected through a switch to an a-c line whose maximum potential difference is 170 v and whose frequency is 60 cycles/sec. Write the equation giving the current i as a function of time if the line switch is closed at (a) the instant in the cycle when the line voltage is a maximum, (b) the instant in the cycle when the line voltage is zero and has a positive slope. [*Ans:* $i = Ae^{-Bt} + D \sin (\omega t + \beta)$ where $B = 100$ sec^{-1}, $\omega = 377$ sec^{-1}, and $D = 2.19$ amp. In part (a) $A = -0.560$ amp and $\beta = 14° \, 51'$, while in part (b) $A = 2.12$ amp and $\beta = -75° \, 9'$.]

TRANSIENT AND STEADY-STATE

SOLUTIONS FOR

SOME *RLC* CIRCUITS

6-I SUMMARY OF THE ALGEBRA
OF COMPLEX NUMBERS

1. GEOMETRIC REPRESENTATION OF REAL AND IMAGINARY NUMBERS. In the algebra of complex numbers all real numbers are represented by lengths along the horizontal axis, the length being measured from an arbitrarily selected origin. Positive real numbers are represented to the right of the origin and negative real numbers to the left of the origin. This horizontal axis is referred to as the *axis of reals.*

Multiplication of a positive real number a_1 by -1 yields $-a_1$. This is equivalent to rotating the line that previously represented a_1 along the plus axis of reals, by 180°, so that the line now lies along the negative axis of reals. Double multiplication by -1 rotates the line through 360° and thus leaves it in its original position. By this reasoning we may think of -1 as an operator. When -1 operates on a quantity it rotates that quantity through 180°.

By the usual definition of the square root of a number, the $\sqrt{64}$ means the number that multiplied by itself yields 64. Thus, $\sqrt{64}$ is the real number 8. By the same definition of square root, the $\sqrt{-1}$ means the number that multiplied by itself yields -1. Obviously, $\sqrt{-1}$ cannot be a real number since the square of any real number is positive. Hence, $\sqrt{-1}$ is called an *imaginary number.* Let us represent $\sqrt{-1}$ by j, so that j is the number that multiplied by itself yields -1. Hence, by definition,

$$j = \sqrt{-1}, \quad \text{so} \quad j^2 = -1 \qquad (6\text{--}1\text{--}1)$$

The number $\sqrt{-64}$, for example, may be written as $8\sqrt{-1}$ or $8j$. Thus in general the square root of any negative number may be written

$$\pm \sqrt{-q} = \pm j\sqrt{q} \qquad (6\text{--}1\text{--}2)$$

where $\sqrt{q}$ is a real number.

Since multiplication of a quantity by -1 rotates that quantity through 180°, double multiplication of the quantity by j rotates that quantity through 180°. *Let us postulate that single multiplication of a quantity by j*

rotates that quantity through 90°. Thus let us represent all imaginary numbers by lines drawn along an axis at right angles to the axis of reals. This axis is called the *axis of imaginaries*. Positive imaginary numbers are represented by lines drawn upward from the origin, and negative imaginary numbers by lines drawn downward from the origin as shown in Fig. 6–1–1.

In Fig. 6–1–1 the positive real number a_1 is represented by the line from the origin out to the point labeled a_1. The fact that a_1 is a positive real number is shown by its position on the positive axis of reals. The magnitude of a_1 is shown by the length of the line from the origin to the point labeled a_1 in terms of a previously adopted scale. Similarly the negative real number $-a_2$ is represented by the line along the negative axis of reals from the origin to the point labeled a_2.

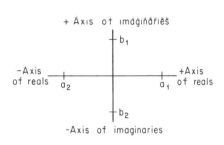

Figure 6–1–1. Complex plane. Geometric representation of real and imaginary numbers.

The positive imaginary number jb_1 is represented by the line from the origin to the point labeled b_1 in Fig. 6–1–1. The fact that jb_1 is a positive imaginary number is shown by the position of b_1 on the positive axis of imaginaries. The magnitude of jb_1 is shown by the length of the line, from the origin to the point labeled b_1, in terms of the scale. Similarly the negative imaginary number $-jb_2$ is represented by the line along the negative axis of imaginaries from the origin to the point labeled b_2. The plane determined by the axis of reals and the axis of imaginaries is called the *complex plane*.

We may think of j as an operator. When j operates on a quantity it rotates that quantity through 90°.

2. COMPLEX NUMBERS. *By definition, a number is called a complex number if it is made up of a sum of a real part and an imaginary part.* Thus

$$A_1 = a_1 + jb_1 \qquad (6\text{–}1\text{–}3)$$

is a complex number. If $b_1 = 0$, then A_1 is a real number. Hence real numbers may be considered to be complex numbers for which $b_1 = 0$.

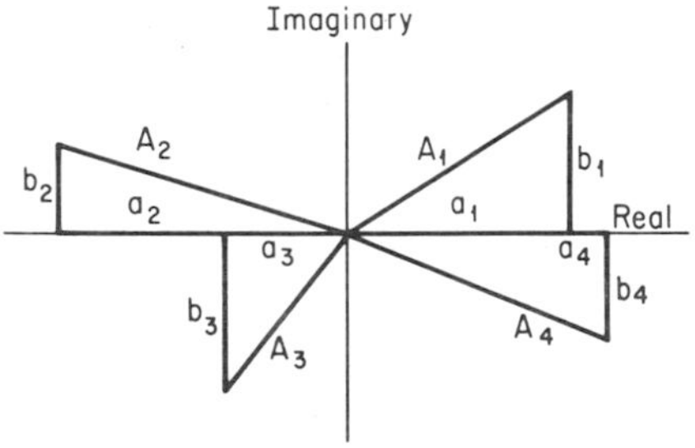

Figure 6–1–2. Geometric representation of the complex numbers $A_1 = a_1 + jb_1$, $A_2 = -a_2 + jb_2$, $A_3 = -a_3 - jb_3$, and $A_4 = a_4 - jb_4$.

If $a_1 = 0$ and $b_1 \neq 0$, then A_1 is a pure imaginary.

The complex number in (6–1–3) is represented in the complex plane as a line drawn from the origin to the point whose abscissa is a_1 and whose ordinate is b_1 as is shown in Fig. 6–1–2. Three other complex numbers are also represented in Fig. 6–1–2.

Two complex numbers are defined to be equal if, and only if, their real parts are equal to each other, and their imaginary parts are equal to each other. Thus, if

$$a_1 + jb_1 = a_2 + jb_2 \qquad (6-1-4)$$

then

$$a_1 = a_2 \quad \text{and} \quad b_1 = b_2 \qquad (6-1-5)$$

One of the rules of the algebra of complex numbers is that all the rules of ordinary algebra shall apply. This is in addition to the special rules indicated above.

3. ADDITION OF COMPLEX NUMBERS. We wish the sum of $A_1 = a_1 + jb_1$ and $A_2 = a_2 + jb_2$. Since the laws of ordinary algebra apply we may write

$$A = A_1 + A_2 = a_1 + jb_1 + a_2 + jb_2$$
$$= (a_1 + a_2) + j(b_1 + b_2) \qquad (6-1-6)$$

The sum is a complex number whose real part is the algebraic sum of the real parts of the separate numbers and whose imaginary part is the algebraic sum of the imaginary parts of the separate numbers. As shown in Fig. 6–1–3, this suggests the geometric addition of two vectors. Consequently for many purposes it is convenient to look upon complex numbers as vector quantities and the complex number algebra as one form of vector algebra.*

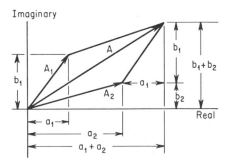

The magnitude of a complex number is defined as the length of the line which represents the complex number in the complex plane. The magnitude is frequently designated by $|A|$ which is read, the absolute magnitude (or just magnitude) of the complex number A.

Figure 6–1–3. Addition of complex numbers is equivalent to geometric addition of vectors.

From this definition of the magnitude of a complex number and the Pythagorean theorem, we may write for the magnitudes of the complex numbers shown in Fig. 6–1–2:

$$|A_1| = \sqrt{a_1^2 + b_1^2}, \qquad |A_2| = \sqrt{a_2^2 + b_2^2}$$
$$|A_3| = \sqrt{a_3^2 + b_3^2}, \qquad |A_4| = \sqrt{a_4^2 + b_4^2}$$

We see that this definition of the magnitude of a complex number also agrees with the concept of a complex number as a vector quantity since the magnitude of a vector is equal to the square root of the sum of the squares of its components along two mutually perpendicular axes.

* For a discussion of the relationship between the vector algebra of complex numbers and the vector algebra of vector analysis, see D. E. Richmond, "Complex Numbers and Vector Algebra." *Am. Math. Monthly,* **58,** 622 (1951).

4. TRIGONOMETRIC EXPRESSION FOR A COMPLEX NUMBER. The direction of the line (*OP* in Fig. 6–1–4) that represents a complex number, is usually specified by the angle θ between the line and the positive axis of reals. This angle is positive when measured in the counterclockwise direction. The length of the line and this direction angle give the polar coordinates of the tip of the line. Thus in Fig. 6–1–4 the polar coordinates of *P* are $|A_1|$ and θ.

From Fig. 6–1–4 we see that

$$|A_1| = \sqrt{a_1^2 + b_1^2}; \qquad a_1 = |A_1| \cos \theta; \qquad b_1 = |A_1| \sin \theta \quad (6\text{–}1\text{–}7)$$

so
$$A_1 = a_1 + jb_1 = |A_1| \cos \theta + j|A_1| \sin \theta$$
$$= |A_1| (\cos \theta + j \sin \theta) \qquad (6\text{–}1\text{–}8)$$

Thus $|A_1| (\cos \theta + j \sin \theta)$ represents the same complex number (or vector) as does $a_1 + jb_1$, where (6–1–7) gives the relationships between $|A_1|$, θ, a_1, and b_1.

5. EXPONENTIAL EXPRESSION FOR A COMPLEX NUMBER. Consider the complex number *y* of magnitude *r* and at an angle *x* with respect to the plus axis of reals.

$$y = r(\cos x + j \sin x) \quad (6\text{–}1\text{–}9)$$

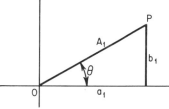

Take the derivative of *y* with respect to *x*.

$$dy/dx = r(-\sin x + j \cos x)$$
$$= r(j^2 \sin x + j \cos x)$$
$$= jr(j \sin x + \cos x)$$
$$(6\text{–}1\text{–}10)$$

Figure 6–1–4. The complex number $A_1 = a_1 + jb_1$ may be expressed in terms of the polar coordinates of the tip of the vector by the expression $A_1 = |A_1|(\cos \theta + j \sin \theta)$.

or $dy/dx = jy$. Separate the variables and integrate obtaining the result $\ln y = jx + c$, or

$$y = e^{jx+c} = e^{jx}e^c \qquad (6\text{–}1\text{–}11)$$

From (6–1–9), when $x = 0$, $y = r$. Put this into (6–1–11), and $r = e^c$. Hence

$$y = re^{jx} \qquad (6\text{–}1\text{–}12)$$

Thus re^{jx} represents the same complex number (or vector quantity) as does $r(\cos x + j \sin x)$. In Problem 6–4 you are asked to prove this same equivalence by the use of series expansions for e^{jx}, $\cos x$, and $\sin x$.

From (6–1–8) and (6–1–12) and Fig. 6–1–4 we see that if we have a complex number $A_1 = a_1 + jb_1$ we may express this same complex number in either the trigonometric form or the exponential form by the following relationships.

$$A_1 = a_1 + jb_1 = |A_1| (\cos \theta_1 + j \sin \theta_1) = |A_1|e^{j\theta_1} \qquad (6\text{–}1\text{–}13)$$

where $|A_1| = \sqrt{a_1^2 + b_1^2}$ is the magnitude of the complex number, and θ_1 is the angle between the plus axis of reals and the line that represents the complex number. The value of θ_1 is given by [see (6–1–7)]

$$a_1 = |A_1| \cos \theta_1 \quad \text{and} \quad b_1 = |A_1| \sin \theta_1 \qquad (6\text{–}1\text{–}14)$$

Hence we may express a complex number in any one of the three equivalent forms given in (6–1–13). The choice of the form to be used is dictated by convenience in a particular problem.

6. EXPONENTIAL REPRESENTATION OF A VECTOR THAT IS ROTATING WITH UNIFORM ANGULAR VELOCITY. In the expression for a complex number

$$A_1 = |A_1|e^{j\theta} \tag{6–1–15}$$

the angle may be changing uniformly with time, so that

$$\theta = \omega t \tag{6–1–16}$$

Then
$$A_1 = |A_1|e^{j\omega t} \tag{6–1–17}$$

If $|A_1|$ is independent of time, (6–1–17) represents a vector of constant length that is rotating with the constant angular velocity ω.

7. MULTIPLICATION OF COMPLEX NUMBERS. Since the rules of ordinary algebra apply in the algebra of complex numbers, we proceed to multiply two complex numbers in the ordinary fashion. Consider the two complex numbers $A_1 = a_1 + jb_1$ and $A_2 = a_2 + jb_2$. Form the product A_1A_2 by usual methods of algebra.

$$A_1A_2 = (a_1 + jb_1)(a_2 + jb_2) = a_1a_2 + jb_1a_2 + ja_1b_2 + j^2b_1b_2$$

But $j^2 = -1$, so
$$A_1A_2 = (a_1a_2 - b_1b_2) + j(b_1a_2 + a_1b_2) \tag{6–1–18}$$

Hence the product of two complex numbers is itself a complex number whose component along the axis of reals is $a_1a_2 - b_1b_2$ and whose component along the axis of imaginaries is $b_1a_2 + a_1b_2$.

The magnitude of A_1A_2 is given, by the usual method, as the square root of the sum of the squares of its real and imaginary components. Hence the square of the magnitude is

$$|A_1A_2|^2 = (a_1a_2 - b_1b_2)^2 + (b_1a_2 + a_1b_2)^2 = (a_1^2 + b_1^2)(a_2^2 + b_2^2),$$

or
$$|A_1A_2|^2 = |A_1|^2|A_2|^2$$

from which
$$|A_1A_2| = |A_1||A_2| \tag{6–1–19}$$

Thus we have the result that *the magnitude of the product of two complex numbers is the product of their magnitudes.*

Now let us look into the relationship between the angles that the separate complex numbers make with the axis of reals, and the angle that their product makes with the axis of reals. To do this let us express the complex numbers in the exponential form.

$$A_1 = a_1 + jb_1 = |A_1|\,e^{j\theta_1} \quad \text{and} \quad A_2 = a_2 + jb_2 = |A_2|\,e^{j\theta_2} \tag{6–1–20}$$

where A_1 and A_2 are shown in Fig. 6–1–5. By the usual laws of algebra

$$A_1A_2 = |A_1|\,|A_2|\,e^{j\theta_1}e^{j\theta_2} = |A_1|\,|A_2|e^{j(\theta_1 + \theta_2)} \tag{6–1–21}$$

Equation (6–1–21) shows, by the coefficient of the exponential term, that the product of the two complex numbers A_1A_2 is a complex number whose magnitude is the product of the magnitudes of the separate numbers. This duplicates the result that we had in (6–1–19). The exponent in (6–1–21) shows that the angle that the product complex number makes with the plus axis of reals is the sum of the angles that the separate complex numbers make with the plus axis of reals. Thus in Fig. 6–1–5, $\theta = \theta_1 + \theta_2$.

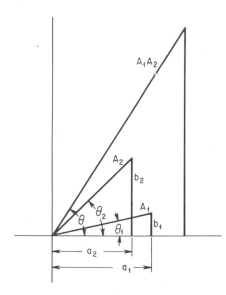

RULE: *When two complex numbers A_1 and A_2 are multiplied, the product complex number has a magnitude equal to the product of the separate magnitudes $(|A_1A_2| = |A_1|\,|A_2|)$ and the angle of the product complex number is the sum of the separate angles $(\theta = \theta_1 + \theta_2)$. If $\theta_1 + \theta_2$ is equal to or greater than $360°$, then $360°$ is to be subtracted.*

8. DIVISION OF COMPLEX NUMBERS. Consider the two complex numbers

Figure 6–1–5. Multiplication of A_1 and A_2 yields A_1A_2.

$$A_1 = |A_1|e^{j\theta_1}$$

and $$A_2 = |A_2|e^{j\theta_2} \qquad (6\text{–}1\text{–}22)$$

By the ordinary rules of algebra, the quotient is given by

$$\frac{A_1}{A_2} = \frac{|A_1|}{|A_2|}\, e^{j(\theta_1 - \theta_2)} \qquad (6\text{–}1\text{–}23)$$

RULE: *The quotient of two complex numbers is itself a complex number whose magnitude is the quotient of the separate magnitudes*

$$\left(\left|\frac{A_1}{A_2}\right| = \frac{|A_1|}{|A_2|} \right)$$

and whose angle with the plus axis of reals is the difference of the separate angles $(\theta = \theta_1 - \theta_2)$.

Let us also obtain the quotient with the complex numbers expressed in the algebraic form.

$$A_1/A_2 = (a_1 + jb_1)/(a_2 + jb_2) \qquad (6\text{–}1\text{–}24)$$

The expression in (6–1–24) is in a form such that the reals and imaginaries cannot be separated as it stands, i.e., we see that it is a complex number but we cannot pick out at a glance its component along the axis of reals and its component along the axis of imaginaries. This arises from the fact that j appears in the denominator. The process of removing the j from the denominator is called *rationalizing*.

In order to rationalize the expression on the right in (6–1–24), multiply its numerator and denominator by the *conjugate* of the denominator. The conjugate of the complex number $a_2 + jb_2$ is, by definition, $a_2 - jb_2$.

Now rationalize the right side of (6–1–24)

$$\frac{A_1}{A_2} = \frac{a_1 + jb_1}{a_2 + jb_2} \cdot \frac{a_2 - jb_2}{a_2 - jb_2}$$

$$= \frac{a_1a_2 + ja_2b_1 - ja_1b_2 - j^2b_1b_2}{a_2^2 - j^2b_2^2}$$

but $j^2 = -1$, so

$$A_1/A_2 = (a_1a_2 + b_1b_2)/(a_2^2 + b_2^2) + j(a_2b_1 - a_1b_2)/(a_2^2 + b_2^2) \quad (6\text{--}1\text{--}25)$$

From (6–1–25) we can immediately pick out the real and imaginary parts of the complex number A_1/A_2, so (6–1–25) is said to be in a rationalized form. See Problem 6–6, where you are asked to prove that (6–1–23) and (6–1–25) represent the same complex number.

9. EXPONENTIAL EXPRESSION FOR A VECTOR OF UNIT LENGTH. Using (6–1–13), we may express $e^{j\alpha}$ in the trigonometric form as $e^{j\alpha} = \cos \alpha + j \sin \alpha$, where α is any angle with the positive axis of reals as shown in Fig. 6–1–6. The fact that $e^{j\alpha}$ has a magnitude of unity can be seen from the fact that its coefficient is unity or from $|e^{j\alpha}| = \sqrt{\cos^2 \alpha + \sin^2 \alpha} = 1$. Thus if $\alpha = 0$, or $\pi/2$, or π, or $3\pi/2$ we have

$$e^{j0} = 1; \qquad e^{j\pi/2} = j;$$
$$e^{j\pi} = -1; \qquad e^{j3\pi/2} = -j \quad (6\text{--}1\text{--}26)$$

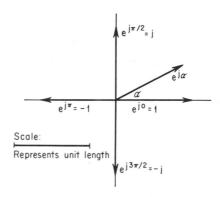

Figure 6–1–6. Unit vector $e^{j\alpha}$ at any angle α with respect to the positive axis of reals and special cases where $\alpha = 0$, $\alpha = \pi/2$, $\alpha = \pi$, and $\alpha = 3\pi/2$.

Equation (6–1–26) is a special case of the general proposition that multiplication of a quantity by $e^{j\alpha}$ rotates that quantity counterclockwise by the angle α. We can see this very simply from the following. Let $A = |A|e^{j\theta}$ be any vector quantity. Multiply it by $e^{j\alpha}$, so that we have

$$Ae^{j\alpha} = |A|e^{j\theta}e^{j\alpha} = |A|e^{j(\theta + \alpha)}$$

This may be represented by a vector of the same length as the initial vector but at the angle $\theta + \alpha$ with respect to the positive axis of reals. Hence the initial vector has been rotated through the angle α by the process of multiplying it by $e^{j\alpha}$.

6–2 TRANSIENTS* IN A SERIES CIRCUIT CONTAINING CONSTANT *R*, *L*, AND *C*.

Figure 6–2–1 shows the circuit that we wish to consider. The switch *S* has been connected to contact *a* for a long time so the capacitor *C* is charged to a

---

* Secs. 6–2 and 6–3 are adaptations of the treatment given by David Park in the early part of Chapter XIX of the first edition.

potential difference equal to the emf $\mathcal{E}$ of the battery. At an instant which we shall call $t = 0$, switch S is moved from contact a to contact b as shown in Fig. 6–2–2, and the capacitor starts to discharge.

PROBLEM: Find an equation giving the current flowing in the circuit in Fig. 6–2–2 as a function of time after the switch is moved to contact b.

Kirchhoff's second law applied to the circuit in Fig. 6–2–2 gives the equation

$$-L\, dI/dt = IR - q/c \tag{6–2–1}$$

Differentiate with respect to t and substitute i for $-dq/dt$ in order to remove the variable q. Note that we have recognized dq/dt as negative because the capacitor is discharging, not charging. Next, rearrange the resulting equation into the standard form and obtain

$$L\, d^2i/dt^2 + R\, di/dt + i/C = 0 \tag{6–2–2}$$

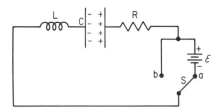

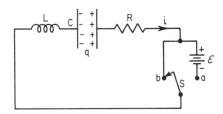

Figure 6–2–1. An *LCR* circuit for the study of transients. The switch S is in position to charge the capacitor. At $t = 0$, the switch is turned to contact b and the capacitor begin to discharge.

Figure 6–2–2. Discharge of the capacitor after the switch was moved from contact a to contact b, at the instant called $t = 0$.

which is the equation we must solve in order to secure the answer to the problem.

Let us assume that the solution of (6–2–2) is of the form

$$i = Ae^{\lambda t} \tag{6–2–3}$$

where A and λ are unknown constants. To test the assumed solution, substitute (6–2–3) into (6–2–2) and obtain

$$A(\lambda^2 L + \lambda R + 1/C)e^{\lambda t} = 0 \tag{6–2–4}$$

Since neither A nor $e^{\lambda t}$ vanishes, the expression in parentheses must. Hence, equate the expression in parentheses to zero and solve it for λ, obtaining

$$\lambda = (-R/2L) \pm \sqrt{(R/2L)^2 - 1/LC}$$

This gives two possible values of λ; let us call them λ_1 and λ_2. Also, let $\delta = \sqrt{(R/2L)^2 - 1/LC}$, and the two possible values of λ for which (6–2–3) satisfies (6–2–2) are

$$\lambda_1 = (-R/2L) + \sqrt{(R/2L)^2 - 1/LC} = (-R/2L) + \delta \tag{6–2–5}$$

and $$\lambda_2 = (-R/2L) - \sqrt{(R/2L)^2 - 1/LC} = (-R/2L) - \delta \tag{6–2–6}$$

But suppose we write, instead of (6-2-3),

$$i = A_1 e^{\lambda_1 t} + A_2 e^{\lambda_2 t} \qquad (6\text{-}2\text{-}7)$$

where A_1 and A_2 are arbitrary constants. Since either (6-2-5) or (6-2-6) will satisfy (6-2-2), their sum will also satisfy (6-2-2), and this is what (6-2-7) says. Further, it has two arbitrary constants, so it is the general solution,* and we can determine the constants from the boundary conditions. Solve Problem 6-7 at this point.

This method breaks down, however, in the special case in which

$$(R/2L)^2 = 1/LC, \quad \text{or} \quad R^2 = 4L/C \qquad (6\text{-}2\text{-}8)$$

because in this case λ_1 and λ_2 become equal and we have produced only one distinct solution, with one arbitrary constant. But we can find another solution by means of a limiting process: namely, we consider the difference of the two solutions given by (6-2-5) and (6-2-6) (this is itself a solution) as δ approaches zero. Of course, this quantity vanishes unless we multiply it by something that keeps it finite. For this purpose $1/\delta$ will do. The solution is

$$i = B(e^{(-R/2L + \delta)t} - e^{(-R/2L - \delta)t})/\delta = Be^{-Rt/2L}(e^{\delta t} - e^{-\delta t})/\delta \qquad (6\text{-}2\text{-}9)$$

where B is an arbitrary constant. It satisfies (6-2-2) in any case, and continues to do so as $\delta \to 0$. In this limit we can expand the exponentials and write

$$i = \lim_{\delta \to 0} Be^{-Rt/2L} \frac{1 + \delta t + \dfrac{\delta^2 t^2}{2!} + \dfrac{\delta^3 t^3}{3!} + \cdots \left(1 - \delta t + \dfrac{\delta^2 t^2}{2!} - \dfrac{\delta^3 t^3}{3!} + \cdots\right)}{\delta}$$

$$= \lim_{\delta \to 0} Be^{-Rt/2L}(2t + \tfrac{1}{3}\delta^2 t^3 + \cdots) = 2Bte^{-Rt/2L} \qquad (6\text{-}2\text{-}10)$$

which is accordingly a second solution of (6-2-2), valid when $\delta = 0$. Our general solution in this case is therefore of the form

$$i = (A_1 + A_2 t)e^{-Rt/2L} \qquad \text{(when } \delta = 0) \qquad (6\text{-}2\text{-}11)$$

where $A_2 = 2B$, and once again, we have two arbitrary constants. Equation (6-2-11) says that, since $i = A_1 e^{-Rt/2L}$ as well as $i = A_2 t e^{-Rt/2L}$ is a solution of

---

* The fact that there are n arbitrary constants in the general solution of a differential equation of the nth order can be explained (but not rigorously proved) in the following way. Consider some function f of a variable, say x, and of n constants. Take the first derivative df/dx of this function with respect to x; then d^2f/dx^2, and so on up to $d^n f/dx^n$. This gives n expressions in x and the n constants, from which the constants can be eliminated by suitable manipulations, leaving a relation between f and the n derivatives. This is the differential equation satisfied by f, and we see that the n constants which f contains are in no way specified by the differential equation and are therefore, as far as the equation is concerned, said to be arbitrary. Hence a general solution of the second-order differential equation (6-2-2) must involve two arbitrary constants. These are shown in (6-2-7), and will be determined in any particular case by the use of some additional information regarding the solution, generally in the form of an initial condition.

(6–2–2), their sum must also be a solution* of (6–2–2). Solve Problem 6–8 at this point.

To summarize our discussion so far, (6–2–2) is the differential equation we were obliged to solve in order to find an equation giving the current flowing in the circuit of Fig. 6–2–2 as a function of time after the switch was closed. Equation (6–2–7) gives the solution if $\delta \neq 0$, and (6–2–11) gives it if $\delta = 0$. Now let us look into the physical behavior of the current as predicted by these equations

We see that there are three different kinds of physical behavior of the current depending on the value of δ relative to zero. These three are: CASE 1 where $\delta > 0$; CASE 2 where $\delta = 0$; and CASE 3 where δ is imaginary. Let us treat each of these cases separately.

CASE 1, NORMAL DAMPING:

$$(R/2L)^2 - 1/LC > 0 \qquad (6\text{–}2\text{–}12)$$

Here δ is real, and we can write the solution in (6–2–7) as

$$i = e^{-Rt/2L}(A_1 e^{\delta t} + A_2 e^{-\delta t}) \qquad (6\text{–}2\text{–}13)$$

At the instant the switch is closed, the current is zero, though it at once starts to increase. Thus we have the initial condition

$$i = 0 \quad \text{at} \quad t = 0 \qquad (6\text{–}2\text{–}14)$$

Putting this into (6–2–13), we see that $A_2 = -A_1$, so that (6–2–13) may be written

$$i = Ae^{-Rt/2L}(e^{\delta t} - e^{-\delta t}) \qquad (6\text{–}2\text{–}15)$$

where one of the arbitrary constants has been eliminated and the remaining one has been designated as A.

We must now find the value of A. This can be done by first finding the boundary condition on di/dt at $t = 0$, the instant the switch was closed. At $t = 0$, $i = 0$; so the voltage drop across R is zero and (6–2–1) tells us that the emf induced in L is equal to the potential difference across the capacitor. At $t = 0$, no charge has had time to flow from the capacitor plates; so the potential difference across it is $\mathscr{E}$, the same as it was prior to the closing of the switch. Hence (6–2–1) becomes

$$L\, di/dt = \mathscr{E} \quad \text{at} \quad t = 0 \qquad (6\text{–}2\text{–}16)$$

and this establishes the boundary condition on di/dt. Differentiate (6–2–15) with respect to time and rearrange to obtain

$$di/dt = A[-R(e^{\delta t} - e^{-\delta t})/2L + \delta(e^{\delta t} + e^{-\delta t})]e^{-Rt/2L}$$

Put $t = 0$ into this value of di/dt and obtain $di/dt = 2A\delta$ at $t = 0$. From this result and the one in (6–2–16), we have

$$L(di/dt)_{t=0} = 2AL\delta = \mathscr{E} \quad \text{and} \quad A = \mathscr{E}/2\delta L \qquad (6\text{–}2\text{–}17)$$

* This solution is given here so that our treatment of (6–2–2) shall be complete. Note, however, that it is not in general necessary to go through this argument to find the solution of (6–2–2) corresponding to the special case $\delta = 0$, as the discussion just prior to (6–2–20) will show.

so that (6–2–15) is

$$i = \mathscr{E}e^{-Rt/2L}(e^{\delta t} - e^{-\delta t})/2L\delta \qquad (6\text{–}2\text{–}18)$$

From the definition of δ, it follows that $\delta < R/2L$, so that both terms of (6–2–18) decay in time, though at different rates.

Numerical example. In the circuit of Fig. 6–2–2, let us choose $R = 1500$ ohms, $L = 3.50$ henrys, $C = 20.0$ µf, $\mathscr{E} = 90.0$ v. We find that $R/2L = 214$ sec^{-1} and $\delta = 178$ sec^{-1}. Hence (6–2–18) becomes $i = D(e^{-Ft} - e^{-Gt})$, where $D = 0.0722$ amp, $F = 36.4$ sec^{-1}, and $G = 392$ sec^{-1}. It is clear that the second term of this decreases much faster than the first; after 6 milliseconds it is less than 10% of the first and may essentially be neglected. The function is plotted as the upper curve in Fig. 6–2–3.

CASE 2, CRITICAL DAMPING:

$$(R/2L)^2 = 1/LC \qquad (6\text{–}2\text{–}19)$$

We can obtain the solution in this case from (6–2–11) with the aid of the information in (6–2–14) and (6–2–16). Solve Problem 6–9 to verify this statement. However, it is unnecessary to appeal to (6–2–11), because (6–2–18) is regular in the limit as $\delta \to 0$, being actually an expression identical in form with (6–2–9). Taking the limit as we did before in order to get (6–2–10), we obtain

$$i = \mathscr{E}te^{-Rt/2L}/L \qquad (6\text{–}2\text{–}20)$$

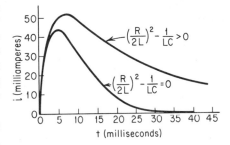

Figure 6–2–3. Behavior of the circuit of Fig. 6-2-2 when $R = 1500$ ohms, $L = 3.50$ henrys, $\mathscr{E} = 90.0$ volts. The upper curve shows normal damping, when $C = 20.0$ µf. The lower curve shows the behavior of the same circuit with C decreased to 6.23 µf, which produces critical damping. Note that R/L is the same in both cases.

The lower curve in Fig. 6–2–3 shows the behavior of a critically damped circuit. The constant R/L is the same as that of the previous example, but C has been reduced to the value of 6.23 µf, satisfying (6–2–19). The formula for i in this case is $i = Dte^{-Ft}$, where $D = 25.7$ amp and $F = 214$ sec^{-1}.

From Fig. 6–2–3 it can be seen that, in the circuit of Fig. 6–2–2, if $R/2L$ is kept constant and C is decreased through various values that satisfy the conditions of CASE 1 to a value which satisfies CASE 2, the current dies away faster and faster until at the condition of CASE 2 it dies away the most rapidly. This is the reason why CASE 2 is called the critically damped case.

CASE 3, OSCILLATORY:

$$(R/2L)^2 < 1/LC \qquad (6\text{–}2\text{–}21)$$

This is physically the most interesting case, for now the circuit will oscillate when the switch is thrown. In (6–2–5) and (6–2–6), δ is imaginary; let us write it as j times a real number,

$$\delta = j\eta, \qquad \eta = \sqrt{(1/LC) - (R/2L)^2} \qquad (6\text{–}2\text{–}22)$$

But reviewing the steps leading to (6–2–18), we see that nothing has been assumed about the real or imaginary character of δ; (6–2–18) must still be correct, even though somewhat surprising in form in that it contains the imaginary quantity j. Nevertheless, let us write it down, using (6–2–22).

$$i = \mathscr{E}e^{-Rt/2L}(e^{j\eta t} - e^{-j\eta t})/2Lj\eta \qquad (6\text{–}2\text{–}23)$$

This can be simplified by the use of an identity which we can prove from (6–1–13), namely, that

$$e^{j\alpha} - e^{-j\alpha} = \cos\alpha + j\sin\alpha - [\cos(-\alpha) + j\sin(-\alpha)] = 2j\sin\alpha$$

so that (6–2–23) is

$$i = \mathscr{E}e^{-Rt/2L}(\sin\eta t)/\eta L \qquad (6\text{–}2\text{–}24)$$

from which the explicit dependence upon j has now disappeared.

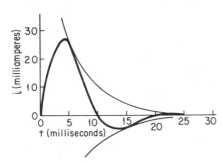

Let us call η the *natural angular frequency* of the circuit since it appears as the frequency factor in the sine term of (6–2–24). From the value of η as given in (6–2–22), we have for the *natural frequency in cycles per second*,

$$f = \frac{1}{2\pi}\sqrt{\frac{1}{LC} - \left(\frac{R}{2L}\right)^2}$$

Figure 6–2–4. Damped oscillations in the circuit of Fig. 6–2–2 when $R = 1500\,\text{ohms}$, $L = 3.50$ henrys, $\mathscr{E} = 90.0$ volts, and $C = 2.00\,\mu\text{f}$. The heavy curve shows i, and the light one shows the damping factor, in this case equal to e^{-214t} with t in seconds.

Figure 6–2–4 shows how the current in an actual series circuit behaves according to this formula. We have chosen the same values of R, L, and $\mathscr{E}$ as in Fig. 6–2–3 but have reduced C to 2.00 µf. With these values of R, L, and C, the value of η is 311 sec^{-1} and (6–2–24) is

$$i = De^{-Ft}\sin\eta t$$

where $D = 0.0826$ amp and $F = 214$ sec^{-1}. An interesting special case of (6–2–24) is that in which R is so small as to be negligible in (6–2–22). We find that

$$i = \mathscr{E}\sqrt{C/L}\,\sin\omega_0 t, \qquad \omega_0 = 1/\sqrt{LC} \qquad (6\text{–}2\text{–}25)$$

so that the current continues to oscillate back and forth around the circuit until the resistance, which can be made small but not eliminated, damps it out. The frequency of this oscillation is

$$f_0 = \omega_0/2\pi = 1/2\pi\sqrt{LC}\ \text{cycles/sec}$$

which is the natural frequency under conditions where R may be neglected. From (6–2–25) we can derive

$$\omega_0 L = 1/\omega_0 C \qquad (6\text{–}2\text{–}26)$$

which shows that, if R is small, oscillations occur at the frequency which makes the inductive and capacitive reactances equal in magnitude.

6–3 SINUSOIDAL ALTERNATING POTENTIAL DIFFERENCE APPLIED TO CONSTANT R, L, AND C IN SERIES

Having discussed the transients in the circuit of Fig. 6–2–2, we can now go on to the more general question of how such a circuit responds to being driven by a sinusoidal voltage of constant amplitude and frequency, starting from an arbitrary initial state. Let us suppose for definiteness that L, C, and R satisfy the inequality of (6–2–21), so that the circuit is of the oscillatory type. Figure 6–3–1 shows the circuit that we are to consider.

PROBLEM: Find an equation giving the current flowing in the circuit of Fig. 6–3–1 as a function of time after the switch is closed.

Just to vary our treatment a little from that used earlier, we shall select $t = t_0$ (instead of $t = 0$) as the time when S is closed; thus we shall not put the phase constant α in the voltage equation. Hence, we write the applied voltage equation as

$$v = V_m \sin \omega t \qquad (6\text{–}3\text{–}1)$$

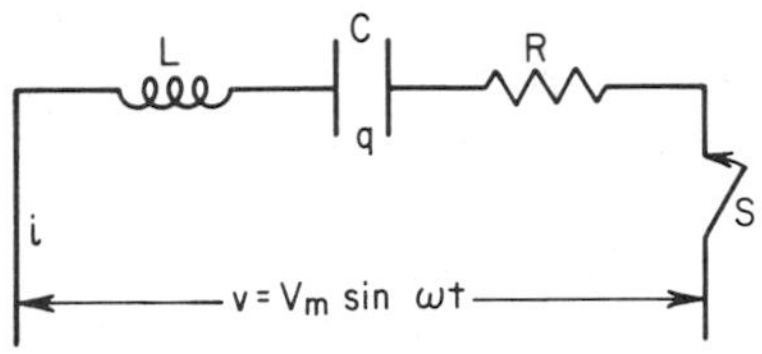

Figure 6–3–1. Sinusoidal alternating voltage of constant maximum value applied to constant R, constant L, and constant C in series.

and the applied voltage at the instant the switch is closed is given by $v = V_m \sin \omega t_0$.

Using (6–1–13) we can write $V_m e^{j\omega t} = V_m \cos \omega t + jV_m \sin \omega t$, so the right side of (6–3–1) is the imaginary part of $V_m e^{j\omega t}$. Hence, let us write the applied line voltage as

$$v = V_m e^{j\omega t} \qquad (6\text{–}3\text{–}2)$$

when we set up Kirchhoff's second law for the circuit in Fig. 6–3–1. Then, in the final answer, we can pick the imaginary part as the expression for i as a function of t when the applied line voltage is given by (6–3–1). (The real part of the answer will give i as a function of t if the applied line voltage were to be expressed as $v = V_m \cos \omega t$).

Now let us write Kirchhoff's second law for the circuit in Fig. 6–3–1. Using (6–3–2), this equation is

$$V_m e^{j\omega t} - L\, di/dt = iR + q/C \qquad (6\text{–}3\text{–}3)$$

Differentiating with respect to t gives

$$L\, d^2i/dt^2 + R\, di/dt + i/C = j\omega V_m e^{j\omega t} \qquad (6\text{–}3\text{–}4)$$

and (6–3–4) is the equation we must solve in order to have the answer to the problem we have stated.

We equate the left side of (6–3–4) to zero in order to obtain the complementary function. But the equation which results from this process is simply (6–2–2), which we have already solved in Sec. 6–2, where we obtained

$$i_{tr} = A_1 e^{\lambda_1 t} + A_2 e^{\lambda_2 t} \qquad (6\text{–}2\text{–}7)$$

as the solution. Here i_{tr} stands for the transient current because we know that the complementary function gives the transient. The symbols λ_1 and λ_2 are the same ones defined in (6–2–5) and (6–2–6).

Above we have assumed that the circuit constants of Fig. 6–3–1 satisfy the inequality of (6–2–21) and thus that the circuit is oscillatory. Hence, let us write $\delta = j\eta$, as we did in (6–2–22). Then (6–2–7) becomes

$$i_{tr} = e^{-Rt/2L}(A_1 e^{j\eta t} + A_2 e^{-j\eta t}) \qquad (6\text{–}3\text{–}5)$$

The right side of (6–3–5) is the complementary function where A_1 and A_2 are undetermined constants which must be evaluated, after we have the complete solution, by imposing the boundary conditions dictated by this circuit.

Let i_{st} represent the steady-state solution of (6–3–4) and, from what we know about the probable behavior of the circuit in Fig. 6–3–1, let us assume that i_{st} can be represented as a function of time by the equation

$$i_{st} = I_m e^{j(\omega t + \phi)} \qquad (6\text{–}3\text{–}6)$$

Here I_m is the unknown maximum value of the current, ϕ is the unknown phase angle between the steady-state current and the applied line voltage, and I_m and ϕ are assumed to be constants.

In order to test the validity of this assumption, substitute (6–3–6) into (6–3–4) and determine, by the method we used before, whether or not there are constant values of I_m and ϕ which make (6–3–6) a solution of (6–3–4). Make this substitution, cancel the expression $e^{j\omega t}$ which appears in each term, and rearrange to obtain

$$I_m e^{j\phi}(-L\omega^2 + j\omega R + 1/C) = j\omega V_m$$

Divide by ω and use $X_L = L\omega$ and $X_C = 1/C\omega$.

$$I_m e^{j\phi}(X_C - X_L + jR) = jV_m \qquad (6\text{–}3\text{–}7)$$

Using the fact that $e^{j\phi} = \cos\phi + j\sin\phi$ [see (6–1–13)], let us separate the real and imaginary parts of (6–3–7). Substitute this value of $e^{j\phi}$ into (6–3–7) and rearrange to obtain

$$I_m[(X_C - X_L)\cos\phi - R\sin\phi] + jI_m[(X_C - X_L)\sin\phi + R\cos\phi] = jV_m$$

In any equation, the reals on the two sides must be equal and the imaginaries on the two sides must be equal, so we obtain the two equations

$$I_m[(X_C - X_L)\cos\phi - R\sin\phi] = 0$$
$$I_m[(X_C - X_L)\sin\phi + R\cos\phi] = V_m$$

The first of these gives at once the expression for the phase

$$\tan\phi = -\frac{X_L - X_C}{R} \qquad (6\text{–}3\text{–}8)$$

while the second of them yields

$$I_m = V_m/z \qquad (6\text{–}3\text{–}9)$$

Here, as before, z is the magnitude of the impedance of the circuit, but now

$$z = \sqrt{(X_L - X_C)^2 + R^2} \tag{6-3-10}$$

which is a general expression for the impedance of a series circuit and will reduce to either of the earlier expressions if the circuit in Fig. 6–3–1 is altered to agree with the cases considered previously.

The values of ϕ and I_m in (6–3–8) and (6–3–9) are constants and will make (6–3–6) a solution of (6–3–4). Thus put (6–3–8) and (6–3–9) into (6–3–6) to obtain

$$i_{st} = V_m e^{j[\omega t - \tan^{-1}(X_L - X_C)/R]}/z \tag{6-3-11}$$

The right side of (6–3–11) is the particular integral of (6–3–4), and the imaginary part of it,

$$i_{st} = V_m \left[\sin\left(\omega t - \tan^{-1}\frac{X_L - X_C}{R}\right)\right]\bigg/z \tag{6-3-12}$$

gives the steady-state current of the circuit in Fig. 6–3–1.

Since the complete solution of the differential equation is the sum of the complementary function and the particular integral, we can now use (6–3–5) and (6–3–11) to write the complete solution as

$$i = V_m e^{j(\omega t + \phi)}/z + e^{-Rt/2L}(A_1 e^{j\eta t} + A_2 e^{-j\eta t}) \tag{6-3-13}$$

As before, the two arbitrary constants are to be determined by imposing the boundary conditions. Since this is an inductive circuit, the current must be zero at the instant the switch is closed. We have agreed to call $t = t_0$ the instant the switch is closed; so one initial condition is

$$i = 0 \quad \text{at} \quad t = t_0 \tag{6-3-14}$$

A second initial condition arises from the fact that at $t = t_0$, $q = 0$, because there has been no time for charge to accumulate on C. Thus in (6–3–3), the terms iR and q/C are both zero at $t = t_0$; so (6–3–3) becomes at this instant

$$L(di/dt)_{t=t_0} = V_m e^{j\omega t_0} \tag{6-3-15}$$

Let us put (6–3–14) into (6–3–13)

$$V_m e^{j(\omega t_0 + \phi)}/z + e^{-Rt_0/2L}(A_1 e^{j\eta t_0} + A_2 e^{-j\eta t_0}) = 0 \tag{6-3-16}$$

while (6–3–13) and (6–3–15) give

$$j\omega L V_m e^{j(\omega t_0 + \phi)}/z - Re^{-Rt_0/2L}(A_1 e^{j\eta t_0} + A_2 e^{-j\eta t_0})/2$$
$$+ j\eta L e^{-Rt_0/2L}(A_1 e^{j\eta t_0} - A_2 e^{-j\eta t_0}) = V_m e^{j\omega t_0} \tag{6-3-17}$$

This can be simplified, for by (6–3–16)

$$-e^{-Rt_0/2L}(A_1 e^{j\eta t_0} + A_2 e^{-j\eta t_0}) = V_m e^{j(\omega t_0 + \phi)}/z$$

and putting this into the second term of (6–3–17) gives (after dividing through by $j\eta L$)

$$\frac{V_m}{z}\left(\frac{\omega}{\eta} - j\frac{R}{2\eta L}\right) e^{j(\omega t_0 + \phi)} + e^{-Rt_0/2L}(A_1 e^{j\eta t_0} - A_2 e^{-j\eta t_0}) = -j\frac{V_m}{\eta L} e^{j\omega t_0} \tag{6-3-18}$$

Now add this to (6–3–16)

$$V_m(1 + \omega/\eta - jR/2\eta L)e^{j(\omega t_0 + \phi)}/z + 2A_1 e^{-Rt_0/2L + jnt_0} = -jV_m e^{j\omega t_0}/\eta L \tag{6–3–19}$$

Then subtract the same pair.

$$V_m\left(1 - \frac{\omega}{\eta} + j\frac{R}{2\eta L}\right)e^{j(\omega t_0 + \phi)}\bigg/z + 2A_2 e^{-Rt_0/2L - jnt_0} = jV_m e^{j\omega t_0}/\eta L \tag{6–3–20}$$

Equations (6–3–19) and (6–3–20) can now be solved for our unknown constants A_1 and A_2.

$$A_1 = -\frac{1}{2}\frac{V_m}{z}e^{Rt_0/2L}\left[\left(1 + \frac{\omega}{\eta} - j\frac{R}{2\eta L}\right)e^{j\phi} + j\frac{z}{\eta L}\right]e^{j(\omega - n)t_0} \tag{6–3–21}$$

$$A_2 = -\frac{1}{2}\frac{V_m}{z}e^{Rt_0/2L}\left[\left(1 - \frac{\omega}{\eta} + j\frac{R}{2\eta L}\right)e^{j\phi} - j\frac{z}{\eta L}\right]e^{j(\omega + n)t_0} \tag{6–3–22}$$

and putting these into (6–3–13) gives the full solution,

$$i = \frac{v}{z}\left\{1 - \tfrac{1}{2}e^{-(R/2L)(t-t_0)}\left[(1 + \frac{\omega}{\eta} - j\frac{R}{2\eta L} + j\frac{z}{\eta L}e^{-j\phi})e^{-j(\omega-n)(t-t_0)}\right.\right.$$
$$\left.\left. + \left(1 - \frac{\omega}{\eta} + j\frac{R}{2\eta L} - j\frac{z}{\eta L}e^{-j\phi}\right)e^{-j(\omega+n)(t-t_0)}\right]\right\}e^{j\phi} \tag{6–3–23}$$

where we have written

$$V_m e^{j\omega t} = v \tag{6–3–24}$$

the (complex) voltage applied to the system.

Now that we have found this expression for i, we can simplify it considerably. Let us begin by putting in the value of $e^{-j\phi}$ from (6–3–8) and (6–3–10). Writing $X = X_L - X_C$, we get

$$e^{-j\phi} = (R + jX)/z$$

Now consider the first expression in parentheses in (6–3–23). It becomes $1 + \omega/\eta - X/\eta L + jR/2\eta L$. But $X = \omega L - 1/\omega C$ so that this is $1 + 1/\eta\omega LC + jR/2\eta L$. Similarly, the second expression in parentheses becomes $1 - 1/\eta\omega LC - jR/2\eta L$ so that (6–3–23) is

$$i = \frac{v}{z}\left\{1 - \tfrac{1}{2}e^{-(R/2L)(t-t_0)}\left[\left(1 + \frac{1}{\eta\omega LC} + \frac{jR}{2\eta L}\right)e^{-j(\omega-n)(t-t_0)}\right.\right.$$
$$\left.\left. + \left(1 - \frac{1}{\eta\omega LC} - \frac{jR}{2\eta L}\right)e^{-j(\omega+n)(t-t_0)}\right]\right\}e^{j\phi} \tag{6–3–25}$$

We can distinguish the transient term in this rather formidable expression by the fact that it is multiplied by $e^{-(R/2L)(t-t_0)}$. As t increases, this tends towards zero, and we have left

$$i_{st} = \lim_{t \to \infty} i = ve^{j\phi}/z$$

which is just our previous particular solution (6–3–11) with (6–3–24). When $t - t_0$ is small, the relationships in phase and magnitude between i and v are complicated, but we can comment on some of the general features. In (6–3–25) i falls naturally into three parts. The first is the steady-state value i_{st} to which it will ultimately settle down. Writing as before

$$i = i_{st} + i_{tr} \tag{6–3–26}$$

where i_{tr} denotes the transient current, we see that i_{tr} has two components. One has the frequency $\eta + \omega$, that is, the sum of the natural angular frequency of the circuit and the impressed angular frequency, and the other has the frequency $\eta - \omega$. Let us consider a circuit with a resistance R which is small enough so that the terms in R in the parentheses in (6–3–25) are negligible compared with the others; in this case R will act only so as to produce the

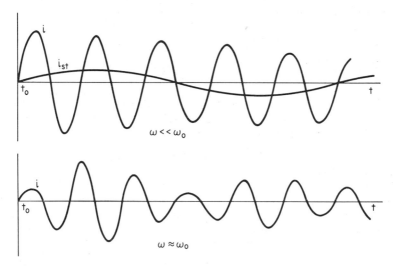

Figure 6–3–2. The relation between the instantaneous current, i, and the asymptotic current, i_{st}, in an *LCR* series circuit of natural angular frequency ω_0 when driven by a voltage of angular frequency ω.

eventual damping-out of the transient. In this case we have $\eta \approx \omega_0 = 2\pi f_0$, as in (6–2–25) and

$$i \approx \frac{v}{z}\left\{1 - \frac{1}{2\omega_0 L}e^{-(R/2L)(t-t_0)}\left[\left(\omega_0 L + \frac{1}{\omega C}\right)e^{-j(\omega - \omega_0)(t-t_0)}\right.\right.$$
$$\left.\left. + \left(\omega_0 L - \frac{1}{\omega C}\right)e^{-j(\omega + \omega_0)(t-t_0)}\right]\right\}e^{j\phi} \tag{6–3–27}$$

This can be further simplified by the use of (6–2–26), which enables us to write $1/\omega\omega_0 LC = \omega_0/\omega$, so that

$$i \approx \frac{v}{z}\left\{1 - \tfrac{1}{2}e^{-(R/2L)(t-t_0)}\left[\left(1 + \frac{\omega_0}{\omega}\right)e^{-j(\omega - \omega_0)(t-t_0)}\right.\right.$$
$$\left.\left. + \left(1 - \frac{\omega_0}{\omega}\right)e^{-j(\omega + \omega_0)(t-t_0)}\right]\right\}e^{j\phi} \tag{6–3–28}$$

If the applied frequency ω lies in the neighborhood of ω_0, this approaches the simple form

$$i \approx \frac{v}{z} \left[1 - e^{-(R/2L)(t-t_0)} e^{-j(\omega-\omega_0)(t-t_0)} \right] e^{j\phi} \qquad (6\text{–}3\text{–}29)$$

The transient current is slowly damped, and it oscillates in time.

The curves in Fig. 6–3–2 show the general features of (6–3–25) in some special cases. It is the magnitude of the imaginary part that we plot. You will note that the current, and consequently the various potential differences across the component parts of the circuit, may at times greatly exceed their asymptotic values. The existence of such surges of voltage when the voltage applied to the line is varied must always be taken into account in the design of electrical equipment.

6–4 STEADY-STATE SOLUTION

Equation (6–3–12)

$$i = V_m \{\sin [\omega t - \tan^{-1} (X_L - X_C)/R]\}/z \qquad (6\text{–}4\text{–}1)$$

gives the steady-state solution for the circuit in Fig. 6–3–1. It is the only part of (6–3–25) that is of interest after the switch has been closed for some time and the transient has damped out.

PROBLEM I. Find an equation giving the instantaneous power input p to the circuit shown in Fig. 6–3–1 after the steady state has been established.

The method of argument here is the same as the one carried out in detail in Sec. 4–9, and the same as the one that you are asked to carry out in Problem 5–15. The only difference in the three cases comes in the values of I_m and ϕ. Since I_m and ϕ are constant in all three cases we may write down the result here by analogy with the other two results. Hence

$$p = V_m I_m (\cos \phi)/2 - V_m I_m [\cos (2\omega t + \phi)]/2 \qquad (6\text{–}4\text{–}2)$$

where the values of I_m and ϕ are given in (6–3–9) and (6–3–8), respectively.

Again the instantaneous power equation is sinusoidal but of twice the frequency of the current or voltage. Also, as before, positive values of p mean power input from the line to the circuit and negative values of p mean power fed from the circuit back to the line. We have visualized earlier how the capacitor feeds energy back to the line on discharge and how the inductor feeds energy back to the line when its magnetic field is decreasing.

PROBLEM II. Find an equation giving the time average power input P to the circuit shown in Fig. 6–3–1 after the steady state has been established.

As in Problem I above, we may write this equation at once by analogy with our earlier proofs.

$$P = (V_m/\sqrt{2})(I_m/\sqrt{2}) \cos \phi = VI \cos \phi \qquad (6\text{–}4\text{–}3)$$

and again $\cos \phi$ is called the *power factor* for the circuit. In this circuit, using the value of ϕ in (6–3–8) we have for the power factor

$$\cos \phi = R/\sqrt{R^2 + (X_L - X_C)^2} = R/z \qquad (6\text{–}4\text{–}4)$$

Solve Problem 6–20 at this stage to supplement the discussion here.

6–5 DISCUSSION OF PHASE DIFFERENCES FOR A SINUSOIDAL A-C SERIES CIRCUIT FOR STEADY STATE CONDITIONS

Kirchhoff's first law applied to successive points in the conductor parts of the series circuit shows that the *current is everywhere the same at a given instant of time in an a-c series circuit and thus is everywhere in the same phase.* This statement shows that the current rises to a maximum at all points at the same time, falls to zero at all points at the same time, reverses everywhere at the same time, rises to a negative maximum at all points at the same time, etc.

Since current is everywhere in the same phase in a series circuit, it is the logical quantity to use for reference when expressing phase differences between current and voltage. Hence it will be convenient to write the current equation without a phase constant and to put all phase constants on the various voltage equations. Let us, then, write the equation for the steady state current in the series circuit in Fig. 6–5–1 as

$$i = I_m \sin \omega t \qquad (6\text{--}5\text{--}1)$$

Since, in (6–5–1) we have removed the phase constant from the current

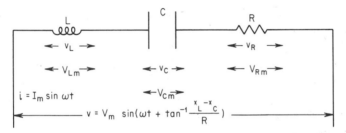

Figure 6–5–1. Steady state conditions for R, L, and C in series on a sinusoidal a-c line.

equation, we must incorporate it in the applied voltage equation and thus write the applied voltage as [review the discussion in connection with equations (4–6–8) and (4–6–9) and with (5–4–9) and (5–4–10)]

$$v = V_m \sin [\omega t + \tan^{-1} (X_L - X_C)/R] \qquad (6\text{--}5\text{--}2)$$

The equation for applied voltage is written in this form in Fig. 6–5–1. Let us adopt the following notation:

v_L = instantaneous potential difference across the inductor L,
v_C = instantaneous potential difference across the capacitor C,
v_R = instantaneous potential difference across the resistor R,
V_{Lm} = maximum potential difference across the inductor L,
V_{Cm} = maximum potential difference across the capacitor C,
V_{Rm} = maximum potential difference across the resistor R.

The following is a summary of the results that we have obtained for phase differences between current and voltage for the individual circuit elements expressed in terms of Fig. 6–5–1 and the above notation.

1. The potential difference across a pure inductance *leads* the current flowing through the inductance by $\pi/2$ (or $90°$). Using the current as expressed

in (6–5–1) as the basis for reference, we may then write $v_L = V_{Lm} \sin (\omega t + \pi/2)$. But by (5–4–12), $V_{Lm} = I_m X_L$, so

$$v_L = I_m X_L \sin (\omega t + \pi/2) \qquad (6\text{--}5\text{--}3)$$

2. The potential difference across a pure capacitance *lags* the current flowing into and out of the plates of the capacitor by $\pi/2$ (or 90°). Again using (6–5–1) as the basis for reference, we may write $v_C = V_{Cm} \sin (\omega t - \pi/2)$. But from (4–8–7), $V_{Cm} = I_m X_C$, so

$$v_C = I_m X_C \sin (\omega t - \pi/2) \qquad (6\text{--}5\text{--}4)$$

3. The potential difference across a pure resistance is in phase with the current flowing through the resistance. Thus with (6–5–1) as the basis for reference for phase, we may write $v_R = V_{Rm} \sin \omega t$. But, from (4–10–1), $V_{Rm} = I_m R$, so

$$v_R = I_m R \sin \omega t \qquad (6\text{--}5\text{--}5)$$

PROBLEMS

6–1 Find the sum of the complex numbers $4 + j3$, $8 - j6$, and $-15 - j4$. Draw to scale, in the complex plane, the construction indicated by this sum. [*Ans:* $-3 - j7$.]

6–2 Find the magnitude of each of the complex numbers given in Problem 6–1 and the magnitude of their sum. [*Ans:* 5, 10, 15.5, 7.63.]

6–3 Express the complex number, $A = 9 + j12$, in the trigonometric form. [*Ans:* $A = 15 (\cos 53° 8' + j \sin 53° 8')$.]

6–4 Write the series expansions for e^z, $\sin x$, and $\cos x$. If you do not recall these series expansions they may be found in mathematical tables, for example see the mathematical tables in the *Handbook of Physics and Chemistry*,* in the index of which these are listed under "Series, Algebraic." From these series expansions write the series for e^{jx} and for $j \sin x$. Substitute into these the values of j raised to various powers such as $j^2 = -1$, $j^3 = -j$, $j^4 = 1$ etc. Use these to show that (a) $re^{jx} = r (\cos x + j \sin x)$. (b) $re^{-jx} = r (\cos x - j \sin x)$.

6–5 Refer to (6–1–18) and (6–1–21). Prove that the right sides of these two equations are the same. This is most conveniently done by starting with the right side of (6–1–21) and expressing it in the trigonometric form. From this it can be transformed into the algebraic form of (6–1–18) by expanding the sine and cosine of the sum of two angles and expressing the sines and cosines in terms of the components and magnitudes of A_1 and A_2. This proof shows that the result is the same whether we multiply complex numbers in the algebraic form or in the exponential form. This result must be true if the algebra is valid and useful.

6–6 Prove that the right side of (6–1–23) is equal to the right side of (6–1–25), thus proving that they represent the same complex number. This proof shows that the rule for division of complex numbers, which is stated immediately following (6–1–23), is valid whether we write the complex numbers in the

* Compiled by Charles D. Hodgman, Cleveland, Chemical Rubber Publishing Co.

exponential form and follow the procedure of (6–1–23) or write them in the algebraic form and rationalize to obtain (6–1–25).

This proof is most readily made by the procedure suggested in Problem 6–5 but, of course, with proper modification to fit this case.

6–7 By direct substitution of (6–2–7) into (6–2–2), show that (6–2–7) will reduce the left side of (6–2–2) to an identity with the right side and thus that (6–2–7) is a solution, regardless of the values of A_1 and A_2, as long as they are constants.

6–8 Refer to (6–2–11) and the statement immediately following this equation. By direct substitution of (6–2–11) into (6–2–2), show that the left side of (6–2–2) is reduced to zero under conditions where $\delta = 0$ (but only if $\delta = 0$) and thus that (6–2–11) is a solution of (6–2–2) under these conditions.

6–9 Verify the statement immediately following (6–2–19); that is, obtain (6–2–20) from (6–2–11) using the boundary conditions given in (6–2–14) and (6–2–16), which boundary conditions must be satisfied regardless of the value of δ.

6–10 Formula (6–2–20) was derived in the text as the limiting form of (6–2–18) as δ was allowed to approach zero. On the other hand, it may also be regarded as the limit of (6–2–24) when the frequency of oscillation becomes zero. Show that this is true.

6–11 Derive for each of the three cases discussed in Sec. 6–2 an equation which gives the charge q remaining on the capacitor in Fig. 6–2–2 as a function of time t after the switch S was moved to the b contact. For each case, make a rough sketch of a curve showing q as a function of t.
Ans:

CASE 1:

$$q = \mathscr{E}Ce^{-Rt/2L}[R(e^{\delta t} - e^{-\delta t})/2L\delta + (e^{\delta t} + e^{-\delta t})]/2$$

CASE 2:

$$q = \mathscr{E}CRte^{-Rt/2L}/2L + \mathscr{E}Ce^{-Rt/2L}$$

CASE 3:

$$q = \mathscr{E}Ce^{-Rt/2L}[R(\sin \eta t)/2L\eta + \cos \eta t]$$

6–12 Consider that the switch S in Fig. 6–2–2 has been on contact b for a long time, so the capacitor is completely discharged. Then, at the instant called $t = 0$, S is moved over to contact a; so one has the situation pictured in Fig. 6–2–1 and the capacitor is charging. Mark on your diagram the direction you select for the positive sense of the current, write Kirchhoff's second law for this circuit, and solve it for the current as a function of time after the switch was closed. Wherever it is appropriate to do so, take results from Sec. 6–2 without bothering to repeat the mathematics given there, if the mathematics would be identical. Work out the answer for each of the three cases discussed in Sec. 6–2 and sketch a rough curve for each case showing the current as a function of time after the switch was moved to contact a.

6–13 Derive an equation which gives the charge q that has accumulated on C in Problem 6–12 as a function of time t after S was moved to contact a, for each of the three cases discussed in Sec. 6–2. For each case make a rough sketch showing q as a function of t. Note that, in a sense, this repeats Problem 6–11 for the situation set forth in Problem 6–12. Do not repeat any

mathematics where it is the same as that in Problem 6–11. In such cases set up the initial equation, point out where the situation is the same in Problem 6–11, and take over from Problem 6–11 the appropriate formula which results from the mathematics.
Ans:

CASE 1:

$$q = \mathscr{E}C - \{\mathscr{E}Ce^{-Rt/2L}[R(e^{\delta t} - e^{-\delta t})/2L\delta + (e^{\delta t} + e^{-\delta t})]\}/2$$

CASE 2:

$$q = \mathscr{E}C - (\mathscr{E}CRte^{-Rt/2L})/2L - \mathscr{E}Ce^{-Rt/2L}$$

CASE 3:

$$q = \mathscr{E}C - \mathscr{E}Ce^{-Rt/2L}[R(\sin \eta t)/2L\eta + \cos \eta t]$$

6–14 In Fig. 6–2–2 at $t = 0$ all the energy is energy of the charged capacitor. Explain, for CASE 3, the energy changes which occur as the current oscillates in the way shown in Fig. 6–2–4.

6–15 In the circuit in Fig. 6–P–1, the switch S is initially open and there is no charge on capacitors C_1 and C_2. At the instant called $t = 0$, S is closed and time is measured from this instant. (a) Write Kirchhoff's second law for loops $\mathscr{E}WUR_1C_1Y\mathscr{E}$ and $\mathscr{E}WUR_2C_2Y\mathscr{E}$, then combine these two equations to obtain

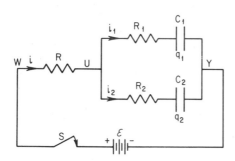

Figure 6–P–1.

$$P\, d^2i_1/dt^2 + S\, di_1/dt + Fi_1 = 0 \quad \text{(A)}$$

where

$$P = [(R + R_1)(R + R_2)/R] - R;$$
$$S = (R + R_2)/RC_1 + (R + R_1)/RC_2$$

and

$$F = 1/RC_1C_2$$

(b) Solve equation (A), which is the same form as (6–2–2), and obtain

$$i_1 = A_1e^{\lambda_1 t} + A_2e^{\lambda_2 t} \tag{B}$$

where A_1 and A_2 are arbitrary constants,

$$\lambda_1 = (-S/2P) + \delta, \qquad \lambda_2 = (-S/2P) - \delta$$

and

$$\delta = \sqrt{(S/2P)^2 - F/P} \tag{C}$$

(c) Prove that δ of equation (C) above cannot be imaginary. This proves that i_1 cannot be oscillatory. From the energy interchanges possible in this circuit, would you expect that i_1 could be oscillatory? Why? (d) Using appropriate boundary conditions for this circuit, evaluate the arbitrary constants A_1 and A_2 under conditions where $\delta > 0$. [*Ans:* Let $B = \mathscr{E}R_2/(RR_2 + RR_1 + R_1R_2)$, and the constants are $A_1 = [C_1\mathscr{E}(S^2 - 4P^2\delta^2) - 2PB(S - 2P\delta)]/8P^2\delta$ and $A_2 = B - A_1$.]

6–16 In the circuit in Fig. 6–P–2, the switch S is initially open and there is no charge on capacitor C_2. At the instant called $t = 0$, S is closed and time is measured from this instant. (a) Write Kirchhoff's second law for loops $\mathscr{E}WXR_1L_1Y\mathscr{E}$ and $\mathscr{E}WXR_2C_2Y\mathscr{E}$ and then combine the two equations to obtain

$$Pd^2i_1/dt^2 + Sdi_1/dt + Fi_1 = G \quad \text{(A)}$$

where

$P = L_1(R + R_2)/R;$

$S = [(R + R_2)(R + R_1)/R]$
$\quad - R + L_1/RC_2;$

$F = (R + R_1)/RC_2;$

and

$$G = \mathscr{E}/RC_2. \qquad \textbf{Figure 6–P–2.}$$

(b) Solve equation (A) by finding both the complementary function and the particular integral and take their sum to obtain

$$i_1 = A_1e^{\lambda_1 t} + A_2e^{\lambda_2 t} + \mathscr{E}/(R + R_1) \qquad \textbf{(B)}$$

where A_1 and A_2 are the arbitrary constants, $\lambda_1 = (-S/2P) + \delta$, $\lambda_2 = (-S/2P) - \delta$, and $\delta = \sqrt{(S/2P)^2 - F/P}$. (c) Assume that $\delta > 0$ and evaluate A_1 and A_2 to get

$$A_2 = [\mathscr{E}\lambda_1/(R + R_1)(\lambda_2 - \lambda_1)] + [\mathscr{E}R_2/L_1(R + R_2)(\lambda_2 - \lambda_1)] \quad \text{and}$$

$$A_1 = -[\mathscr{E}\lambda_1/(R + R_1)(\lambda_2 - \lambda_1)] - [\mathscr{E}R_2/L_1(R + R_2)(\lambda_2 - \lambda_1)] - [\mathscr{E}/(R + R_1)]$$

(d) Show that δ can be imaginary and thus that i_1 can be oscillatory if proper values of the circuit constants are chosen.

6–17 Find the solution to the differential equation (5–3–3) for the circuit in Fig. 5–3–1, by the use of complex numbers. To do this, notice that (5–3–3) is the imaginary part of

$$di/dt + Ri/L = V_m e^{j(\omega t + \alpha)}/L \qquad \text{(A)}$$

Assume that the steady-state solution of (A) is $i = I_m e^{j(\omega t + \alpha + \phi)}$ where I_m and ϕ are unknown constants. Evaluate I_m and ϕ, write the resulting solution, pick its imaginary part as the solution to (5–3–3), and show that it is the same as (5–3–9).

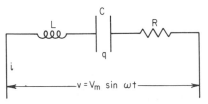

$v = V_m \sin \omega t$

Figure 6–P–3.

6–18 When we assume that (6–3–6) is the solution of (6–3–4), what physical assumptions are we making concerning the behavior of the circuit in Fig. 6–3–1 and what physical bases do we have for these assumptions?

6–19 The circuit in Fig. 6–P–3 shows a pure inductance L, a pure capacitance C, and a pure resistance R in series and connected to a sinusoidal a-c line. Equation (6–4–1) gives the steady-state current as a function of time for this circuit.

Imagine that it is possible to short-circuit any of the circuit elements L, C, and R. By this we mean that it is possible to put a heavy copper bar across the terminals of the circuit element that we wish to eliminate, and with this heavy copper bar in place all current will flow through the bar and no current will flow through the circuit element that is short-circuited. (a) If the capacitor is short-circuited, explain why it is that the capacitance goes to infinity, not to zero. Show that (6–4–1) becomes: (b) (5–4–5) if C is short-circuited. (c) (4–8–2) if L is short-circuited. (d) (4–10–1) if L and C are short-circuited. (e) (5–4–11) if C and R are short-circuited. (f) (4–6–6) if L and R are short-circuited.

6–20 For R, L, and C in series on a sinusoidal a-c line (see Fig. 6–3–1), prove that the time average power input P, given by (6–4–3), is equal to $P = I^2 R$. Explain in detail the meaning of this equivalence. Is this equivalence always valid? (Review Sec. 5–5.)

COMPLEX-NUMBER VECTOR

METHOD FOR SOLVING

A-C CIRCUIT PROBLEMS

7–1 THE SINUSOIDAL THEOREM

Let us consider two sinusoidal functions of the same frequency, which we write as

$$y_1 = A_1 \sin (\omega t + \alpha_1) \qquad (7\text{–}1\text{–}1)$$

$$y_2 = A_2 \sin (\omega t + \alpha_2) \qquad (7\text{–}1\text{–}2)$$

The terms A_1 and A_2 are the amplitudes or maximum values of the two sine functions, and α_1 and α_2 are their phase constants. The amplitudes and phase constants are in general not the same in the two sine functions; hence the difference in their subscripts. The frequency is the same for the two, as shown by the fact that ω is the same. Figure 7–1–1 shows plots of examples of two sine functions of the kind that we are considering. In the curves drawn in Fig. 7–1–1, both values of α happen to be positive because both curves have been drawn as leading a simple sine curve. However, either or both values of α might as well have been negative, for our purpose. It is important, however, that the A's and the α's are constants, not functions of time.

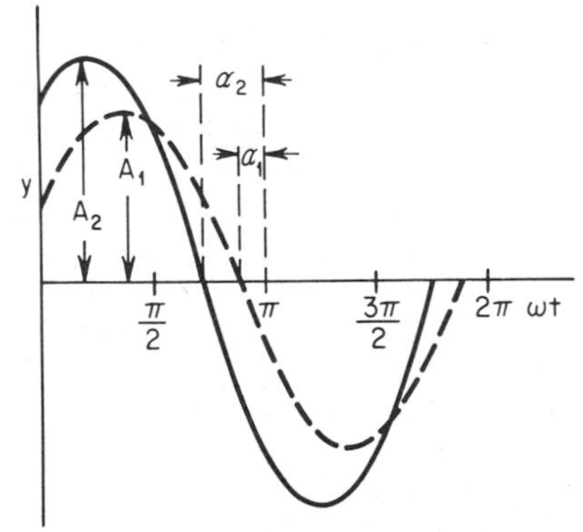

We decide that we wish to combine these two sinusoidal functions by adding their instantaneous values algebraically, and we define y as this instantaneous algebraic sum. Hence

$$y = y_1 + y_2 \qquad (7\text{–}1\text{–}3)$$

Equation (7–1–3) expresses an algebraic sum (rather than an arithmetic sum)

Figure 7–1–1. Two sinusoidal functions of the same frequency but with any amplitude relationship and any phase relationship.

since at any particular moment either or both values, y_1 or y_2, may be negative. From (7–1–1), (7–1–2), and (7–1–3),

$$y = A_1 \sin (\omega t + \alpha_1) + A_2 \sin (\omega t + \alpha_2)$$

Expand the sines of the sums of two angles and collect terms.

$$y = (A_1 \sin \alpha_1 + A_2 \sin \alpha_2) \cos \omega t + (A_1 \cos \alpha_1 + A_2 \cos \alpha_2) \sin \omega t \quad (7–1–4)$$

To simplify (7–1–4), let us make the substitution

$$A \sin \theta = A_1 \sin \alpha_1 + A_2 \sin \alpha_2 \quad (7–1–5)$$

and
$$A \cos \theta = A_1 \cos \alpha_1 + A_2 \cos \alpha_2 \quad (7–1–6)$$

The separate values of A and θ may be obtained from (7–1–5) and (7–1–6) as follows. Divide (7–1–5) by (7–1–6) and obtain

$$\tan \theta = (A_1 \sin \alpha_1 + A_2 \sin \alpha_2)/(A_1 \cos \alpha_1 + A_2 \cos \alpha_2) \quad (7–1–7)$$

Square (7–1–5) and (7–1–6) and add, with the result that

$$A^2 = A_1^2 + A_2^2 + 2A_1 A_2 \cos (\alpha_2 - \alpha_1) \quad (7–1–8)$$

Equations (7–1–7) and (7–1–8) give the values of A and θ for (7–1–5) and (7–1–6), in terms of the known constants A_1, α_1, A_2, and α_2; A and θ are constants, since they are expressed in terms of constants.

Now make the substitution called for just prior to (7–1–5) by putting (7–1–5) and (7–1–6) into (7–1–4).

$$y = A \sin \theta \cos \omega t + A \cos \theta \sin \omega t$$

or
$$y = A \sin (\omega t + \theta) \quad (7–1–9)$$

The conclusion from all this is: *If two sinusoidal functions of the same frequency are combined by adding their instantaneous values algebraically, the result (7–1–9) is a sinusoidal function of the same frequency as the initial functions. The amplitude of the resultant function may be calculated from the amplitudes and phase constants of the initial functions by the use of (7–1–8). The phase constant of the resultant function may be computed from the amplitudes and phase constants of the initial functions by the use of (7–1–7).*

In terms of Fig. 7–1–1, this result means that if we construct the resultant curve by adding instantaneous ordinates of the two curves drawn there, the resultant curve will be a sine curve of the same frequency as the ones drawn, and its amplitude and phase constant may be computed from (7–1–8) and (7–1–7), respectively.

This result may be extended to any number of sinusoidal functions of the same frequency, for our resultant equation (7–1–9) is the same form as the initial equations (7–1–1) and (7–1–2). After combining two sinusoidal functions as we have here, we may combine a third with (7–1–9), and so on.

The author likes to refer to this result as the *sinusoidal theorem*, for want of a better name and an easy way to refer to the results obtained here. This name is by no means commonly used when these results are employed.*

* See, for example, F. A. Jenkins and H. E. White, *Fundamentals of Optics*, 3d ed. (New York: McGraw-Hill Book Co., Inc., 1957), pp. 211–13, where these results are derived for use in the study of optics.

7–2 VECTOR METHOD OF USING THE RESULTS OF THE SINUSOIDAL THEOREM

Equation (7–1–8) gives the amplitude of the sinusoidal function that results when two sinusoidal functions of the same frequency are combined by adding their instantaneous values algebraically. Equation (7–1–8) suggests, by its form, the cosine law of trigonometry by means of which one may compute the length of the third side of a triangle if two sides and their included angle are known. In the cosine law, however, there is a minus before the term that contains the cosine of the included angle. The cosine of an angle equals minus the cosine of the supplement of that angle, so this fact suggests that in (7–1–8) the angle $(\alpha_2 - \alpha_1)$ is the exterior angle of the triangle. In Fig. 7–2–1 the triangle has been drawn according to this suggestion, and the cosine law, applied to the triangle, gives (7–1–8).

When we combine quantities by such a geometric means as the one in Fig. 7–2–1, we are immediately reminded of the method used to add vector quantities. For example, if A_1 and A_2 were two forces acting on a body, and the vectors drawn for A_1 and A_2 in Fig. 7–2–1 represented the magnitudes and directions of these two forces, then A in Fig. 7–2–1 would represent their resultant, and the cosine law in (7–1–8) would be employed to compute the magnitude of the resultant.

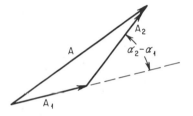

This discussion gives us a suggestion with regard to the two sinusoidal functions that were combined in Sec. 7–1. Perhaps the amplitude of the resultant sinusoidal function, expressed by (7–1–9), is the vector sum of the amplitudes of the two component sinusoidal functions in (7–1–1) and (7–1–2), where $(\alpha_2 - \alpha_1)$ is to be taken as the angle between A_1 and A_2 when they are

Figure 7–2–1. A is the vector sum of A_1 and A_2, where the angle $\alpha_2 - \alpha_1$ is the exterior angle between A_1 and A_2.

added vectorially. If this suggestion be valid, the vector method must satisfy the conditions of the problem proposed in Sec. 7–1 and must give all the results obtained in that paragraph. With this suggestion in mind, let us start a vector method of attack on the problem of Sec. 7–1.

In Fig. 7–2–2 (a), lay out the X and Y-axes. At an angle ωt with respect to the X-axis draw a line that we shall refer to as the ωt line. Since ω is a constant angular velocity, as t progresses this line rotates around the origin with the constant angular velocity ω. We imagine that it is rotating in this fashion in Fig. 7–2–2 (a). At the angle α_1 with respect to the ωt line, draw a vector in Fig. 7–2–2 (a) whose length represents the amplitude A_1 of the number one sinusoidal function given in (7–1–1). This vector is rotating with the constant angular velocity ω but stays ahead of the ωt line by the constant angle α_1. The projection of A_1 on the Y-axis gives (7–1–1).

At the angle α_2 with respect to the ωt line, in Fig. 7–2–2 (a), draw a vector whose length represents the amplitude A_2 of the number two sinusoidal function given in (7–1–2). This vector is rotating with the constant angular velocity ω but stays ahead of the ωt line by the constant angle α_2. The projection of A_2 on the Y-axis gives (7–1–2).

Now, in Fig. 7–2–2 (a), add A_1 and A_2 vectorially by completing the parallelogram $OWPQ$. Draw the resultant OP and label it A. From triangle OPQ, the magnitude of A satisfies the requirements of (7–1–8). Also, A is rotating with the constant angular velocity ω, and its projection y on the Y-axis, from the figure, equals $y_1 + y_2$ at every instant. This result satisfies

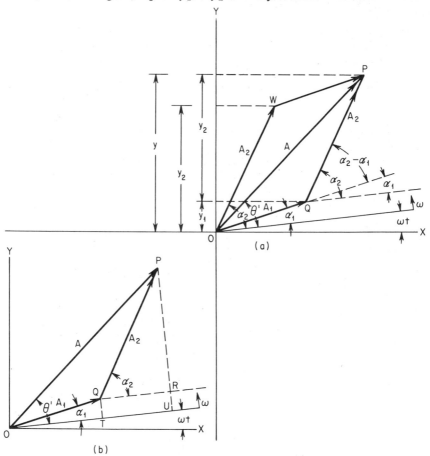

Figure 7–2–2. The rotating vector diagram for the sinusoidal theorem.

the requirement of (7–1–3) that at every instant y shall be the algebraic sum of y_1 and y_2. A makes an angle θ' with the ωt line, so from the figure, the equation for y is

$$y = A \sin (\omega t + \theta') \qquad (7\text{–}2\text{–}1)$$

Thus this vector method with a rotating vector diagram satisfies all the requirements and gives all the results of Sec. 7–1 provided that θ' of (7–2–1) is the same as θ of (7–1–9). Using Fig. 7–2–2 (b) we can prove that $\theta' = \theta$. In

Fig. 7–2–2 (b), the ωt line and triangle OPQ are redrawn. From P and from Q drop perpendiculars to the ωt line. From the right triangle OPU, you can see that

$$\tan \theta' = (PR + RU)/(OT + TU) = (PR + QT)/(OT + QR)$$

Then from the right triangles OQT and QPR, this becomes

$$\tan \theta' = (A_2 \sin \alpha_2 + A_1 \sin \alpha_1)/(A_1 \cos \alpha_1 + A_2 \cos \alpha_2) \qquad (7\text{–}2\text{–}2)$$

Compare (7–1–7) and (7–2–2) and we see that $\theta = \theta'$. Hence the rotating vector diagram of Fig. 7–2–2 (a) satisfies all the requirements and gives all the results of Sec. 7–1.

This result can be extended to any number of sinusoidal functions of the same frequency whose instantaneous values are to be added algebraically. This statement follows from the fact that, after we have combined two of the functions in the above fashion, we can in the same manner combine a third with the resultant of the first two, then combine a fourth with the resultant of the first three, etc.

From all this discussion, we conclude that *if any number of sinusoidal functions of the same frequency* (having any amplitude relations and any phase relations) *combine in such a way that their instantaneous values add algebraically, they produce a sinusoidal function of the same frequency as the components, and the amplitude of the resultant function is obtained by vector addition of the amplitudes of the component functions.* This conclusion we shall call the sinusoidal theorem in the vector form and shall see that it is very important in the solution of a-c circuit problems. You should note clearly that the amplitude of a sinusoidal function is not a vector quantity in the same sense that force, velocity, acceleration, etc. are vector quantities. This statement is obvious from the fact that the amplitude of a sinusoidal function does not have a physical direction in space as do true vector quantities. However, by the above method, we assign directions to the amplitudes of sinusoidal functions such that they may be represented on a vector diagram at proper phase angles with respect to a reference line and with respect to other amplitudes. After assigning directions in this manner, we find that we may treat the amplitudes as if they were vector quantities and apply the usual method of vector addition to them. For this reason we shall refer to amplitudes as vector quantities when it is convenient to do so, but the above distinction must be kept in mind.

7–3 VECTOR METHODS FOR A-C SERIES CIRCUITS USING MAXIMUM VALUES

Using the results of Sec. 6–5, we may label a series circuit as shown in Fig. 7–3–1. As before, we assume that the applied line voltage has a constant maximum value. By Kirchhoff's second law we know that at every instant v is the algebraic sum of v_L, v_C, and v_R, or

$$v = v_L + v_C + v_R \qquad (7\text{–}3\text{–}1)$$

Hence from Fig. 7–3–1

$$v = I_m X_L \sin\left(\omega t + \frac{\pi}{2}\right) + I_m X_C \sin\left(\omega t - \frac{\pi}{2}\right) + I_m R \sin \omega t \qquad (7\text{–}3\text{–}2)$$

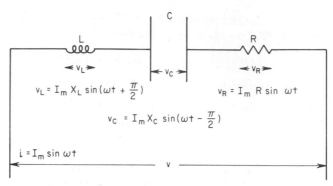

Figure 7–3–1. Alternating current series circuit.

In (7–3–2) we have the algebraic sum of three sinusoidal functions of the same frequency and these sinusoidal functions have constant values for their amplitudes and phase constants. Hence the sinusoidal theorem may be applied.

The sinusoidal theorem in the vector form says for (7–3–2) that the maximum value of the applied line voltage is the vector sum of $I_m X_L$, $I_m X_C$, and $I_m R$. In Fig. 7–3–2, let us draw a vector diagram like Fig. 7–2–2 for the case in (7–3–2). First, in Fig. 7–3–2, lay out a vector, whose length represents the magnitude of I_m, at an angle ωt with the X-axis. This vector is rotating with the constant angular velocity ω, and its projection on the Y-axis is the instantaneous current i flowing in the circuit, given by

$$i = I_m \sin \omega t \tag{7–3–3}$$

which is the same as (6–5–1). This vector for I_m is our reference line for phase differences.

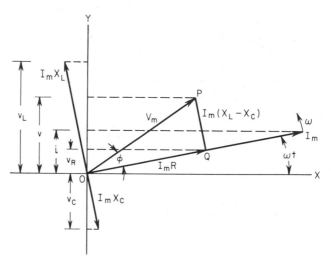

Figure 7–3–2. Vector diagram for the circuit in Fig. 7–3–1. The vector diagram is rotating with the constant angular velocity ω.

Next, in Fig. 7–3–2, lay out a vector whose length represents the magnitude of $I_m X_L$, the maximum potential difference across the inductor. This vector leads I_m by $\pi/2$, so it must be drawn 90° ahead of the vector for I_m. From the figure, the projection of this vector on the Y-axis gives the instantaneous potential difference across the inductance as a function of time expressed by the equation

$$v_L = I_m X_L \sin(\omega t + \pi/2) \qquad (7\text{–}3\text{–}4)$$

which is the same as (6–5–3).

Now, in Fig. 7–3–2, lay out a vector whose length represents the magnitude of $I_m X_C$, the maximum potential difference across the capacitor. This vector lags I_m by $\pi/2$, so it must be drawn 90° behind the vector for I_m. The scale for drawing $I_m X_C$ must, of course, be the same as the one adopted for drawing $I_m X_L$. From the figure, the projection of the vector that represents $I_m X_C$ on the Y-axis gives the instantaneous potential difference across the capacitor as a function of time expressed by the equation

$$v_C = I_m X_C \sin(\omega t - \pi/2) \qquad (7\text{–}3\text{–}5)$$

which is the same as (6–5–4).

Next lay out a vector whose length represents the magnitude of $I_m R$, the maximum potential difference across the resistor. The scale is, of course, the same as that for $I_m X_L$ and $I_m X_C$. The vector for $I_m R$ is in phase with I_m, so it is drawn along the I_m line. From the figure, the projection of the $I_m R$ vector on the Y-axis gives the instantaneous potential difference across the resistor as a function of time expressed by the equation

$$v_R = I_m R \sin \omega t \qquad (7\text{–}3\text{–}6)$$

which is the same as (6–5–5).

The maximum value of the applied line voltage is, as stated above, the vector sum of $I_m X_L$, $I_m X_C$, and $I_m R$. Since $I_m X_L$ and $I_m X_C$ are oppositely directed, their magnitudes may be subtracted, and a vector whose length represents $I_m(X_L - X_C)$ may be constructed at the end of the vector that represents $I_m R$. The vector that represents $I_m(X_L - X_C)$ must be at right angles to $I_m R$ and pointing in a direction parallel to $I_m X_L$ or $I_m X_C$, whichever is larger.

Draw the vector to represent the vector sum of $I_m R$ and $I_m(X_L - X_C)$. This vector sum is V_m, the maximum value of the applied line voltage. The projection of V_m on the Y-axis gives the instantaneous value v, of the applied line voltage. From the vector diagram, in Fig. 7–3–2, we have

$$v = V_m \sin(\omega t + \phi),$$

where
$$\phi = \tan^{-1}[I_m(X_L - X_C)/I_m R] = \tan^{-1}[(X_L - X_C)/R]$$

so
$$v = V_m \sin\{\omega t + \tan^{-1}[(X_L - X_C)/R]\} \qquad (7\text{–}3\text{–}7)$$

Equation (7–3–7) is the same as (6–5–2), as it must be for our method to be valid. Also from the right triangle OPQ,

$$I_m = V_m/\sqrt{R^2 + (X_L - X_C)^2} = V_m/z \qquad (7\text{–}3\text{–}8)$$

Equation (7–3–8) is the same as (6–3–9), and again it must be for our method to be valid.

Also the power factor for the circuit comes directly from the diagram as

$$\cos \phi = I_m R / V_m = I_m R / I_m z = R/z \qquad (7\text{–}3\text{–}9)$$

The rotating vector diagram of Fig. 7–3–2 thus contains a summary of many of the results that we have proved so far for sinusoidal a-c series circuits.

7–4 VECTOR METHODS FOR A-C SERIES CIRCUITS USING RMS VALUES OF CURRENT AND VOLTAGE

In general we make measurements on a-c circuits using a-c ammeters and voltmeters. Thus it is often much more convenient to do the calculations with regard to a-c circuits in terms of rms values of current and voltage, because these are the values that most a-c meters read.

The method of calculation, in terms of rms values of current and voltage, comes at once from the vector diagram of Fig. 7–3–2 and the results of Sec. 4–11. We simply divide each vector on the diagram by $\sqrt{2}$ and have the

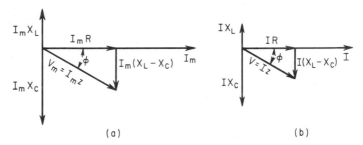

Figure 7–4–1. Vector diagram for a series circuit: (a) using maximum values of current and voltage, (b) using rms values of current and voltage.

smaller similar vector diagram in terms of rms values of current and voltage. Now, however, the projections of the vectors on the Y-axis have no meaning in terms of the corresponding instantaneous values. In those cases, however, where we are going to deal entirely in terms of rms values of current and voltage, we are not interested directly in instantaneous values, so we are not hampered by this loss of meaning in such cases.

Also, since the projections on the Y-axis have lost their meanings, there is no longer any use in thinking of the vector diagram as rotating. For a series circuit we may as well put the vector which represents the current along the X-axis and consider that it stays there. We put this vector along the X-axis merely as a matter of convenience, since it is the reference line for measuring phase angles for various voltages. Actually, the vector which represents the current could be drawn anywhere, as long as we still lay off the vectors which represent the voltages at the proper phase angles with respect to it.

Figure 7–4–1 shows the vector diagrams for a series circuit like the circuit in Fig. 7–3–1. In this case the potential difference across the capacitor happens to be larger than the potential difference across the inductor, but otherwise, Fig. 7–4–1 (a) is the same as Fig. 7–3–2, except that the vector, which represents the current, has been drawn along the X-axis as suggested above. Now divide each vector in Fig. 7–4–1 (a) by $\sqrt{2}$, thus giving rms value of current and voltage. Fig. 7–4–1 (b) is a replot of Fig. 7–4–1 (a) using the rms values of current and voltage to determine lengths of the vectors. The phase angle ϕ is, of course, the same in both.

From Fig. 7–4–1 (b),

$$V^2 = I^2 R^2 + I^2 (X_L - X_C)^2$$

or
$$I = V/\sqrt{R^2 + (X_L - X_C)^2} = V/z \qquad (7\text{–}4\text{–}1)$$

Also
$$\phi = \tan^{-1}[I(X_L - X_C)/IR] = \tan^{-1}[(X_L - X_C)/R] \qquad (7\text{–}4\text{–}2)$$

Further, from the figure,
$$\cos \phi = R/z \qquad (7\text{–}4\text{–}3)$$

which is the same as (7–3–9). As we shall see, these vector diagrams give us a powerful method for solving a-c circuits.

7–5 SERIES RESONANCE

In (7–4–2) we have the phase angle between the applied voltage and the current that flows in the circuit. From (7–4–2) we can see that:

1. The applied voltage leads the current if $X_L > X_C$.
2. The applied voltage lags the current if $X_L < X_C$.
3. The voltage and current are in phase if $X_L = X_C$. $\qquad (7\text{–}5\text{–}1)$

Case 3 is known as *series resonance*.

In general $z = \sqrt{R^2 + (X_L - X_C)^2}$, but at series resonance

$$X_L = X_C, \quad \text{so} \quad z = R \qquad (7\text{–}5\text{–}2)$$

and thus the only impedance in the circuit is the resistance. Hence, for a series circuit with fixed resistance but variable L or C, the greatest current, given by $I = V/R$, will flow under conditions of series resonance. The potential difference across the inductance is still IX_L and the potential difference across the capacitance is still IX_C, but these potential differences are equal and opposite in phase, so the vectors that represent them are of equal length and, of course, oppositely directed.

A series circuit near series resonance may be very dangerous both to the circuit elements and to you, because the potential difference across the capacitor and that across the inductor may be many times the applied line voltage. Before tuning a series circuit to resonance when that circuit is attached to a power line, be sure that the capacitor can withstand the maximum potential difference, which will be applied across its plates, and that the insulation of the coil will not break down under the maximum potential difference across its terminals, and between layers of turns. *As you tune the circuit to series resonance, keep away from the terminals of the capacitor and the terminals of the coil.* If you touch the terminals of the capacitor or the coil you will alter the circuit because you have made your body a parallel conducting path across this circuit element, but you may be in no condition to display an interest in the resulting changes in the circuit.

Series resonance is to be avoided in power transmission lines and most circuits. The power company does not wish maximum current flowing in the transmission line because this condition yields maximum I^2R power loss as heat on the line. In order to minimize this I^2R loss, the power company prefers that the line current be the minimum possible for a given power transmitted to the load. We shall see later in Sec. 7–12 how parallel resonance is used to achieve this objective. In general the user of electric power does not wish series resonance in his circuits because of the dangerous features mentioned above.

In the antenna circuit of a radio receiving set, however, series resonance is often used to select the broadcasting station desired. In such a case, the antenna circuit consists of R, L, and C in series, and C is varied until the antenna circuit is in series resonance with the carrier frequency f, of the selected broadcasting station. For this frequency f, the emf induced in the antenna causes a large current to flow through the antenna circuit and thus produces a large potential difference across the capacitor and across the inductor. One of these large potential differences, usually that across the capacitor, is used to actuate the remainder of the receiving circuit. The antenna circuit is not in resonance with the emf's induced in the antenna by other broadcasting stations with different frequencies, and thus these emf's send only negligibly small currents through the antenna circuit.

We have seen that the condition for series resonance is $X_L = X_C$ or $2\pi fL = 1/(2\pi fC)$. From this equation we may solve for the frequency of the applied voltage that will put the circuit in series resonance. We obtain

$$f_0 = \sqrt{1/LC}/2\pi \qquad (7\text{–}5\text{–}3)$$

where we use f_0 for the resonance frequency. In Chapter VI, where an oscillating circuit was considered, the value of f_0 in (7–5–3) is called the *natural* frequency of the circuit provided that the R of the circuit is small [see (6–2–26) and discussion there].

The phenomenon* of resonance is one of the most important in physics, for one encounters it in all kinds of systems ranging from electric circuits to nuclei. Let us therefore look at the results we have found for series circuits with an eye to bringing out some of their general features. We shall consider the behavior of the steady-state current in a circuit having given values of R, L, and C, as the frequency of the applied voltage V is varied. We have seen that the minimum value of z, and thus the maximum value of I, occurs when $X_L = X_C$, that is, when the applied frequency is equal to the natural frequency, (7–5–3). Plots of the current as a function of the applied frequency f are given for fixed values of L and C and several different values of R in Fig. 7–5–1.

The significant feature here is the ratio of the curve's height to its width, which clearly varies inversely with the resistance. The height of each maximum

---

* The remainder of Sec. 7–5 was written by David Park, the author of Chapter XIX.

in the figure is V/R. To discuss the width, it proves most convenient to locate the "half-power points" of the curve, which are the frequencies at which, for a given magnitude of V, the power I^2R dissipated in the resistance takes on half its maximum value. Since I^2 varies inversely with z^2, these are the points at which z^2 becomes equal to twice its minimum value of R^2. Taking the angular frequency ω as unknown, we have, at the half-power points, $R^2 + (\omega L - 1/\omega C)^2 = 2R^2$ or $\omega L - 1/\omega C = \pm R$. The desired values of ω are the *positive* roots of the equation $L\omega^2 \mp \omega R - 1/C = 0$ which are readily found to be

$$\omega = (\sqrt{R^2 + 4L/C} \pm R)/2L \qquad (7\text{--}5\text{--}4)$$

The half-power width, often called the *bandwidth* of the resonance curve, is the difference between these two values and is given by the very simple formulas

$$\Delta\omega = R/L, \qquad \Delta f = R/2\pi L \qquad (7\text{--}5\text{--}5)$$

It is customary to express the width of a resonance curve in terms of the dimensionless ratio $\Delta\omega/\omega_0 = \Delta f/f_0$. Since resonant circuits are commonly used to single out an applied signal whose frequency is equal to the resonant value, and since the circuit which does this with the highest discrimination is the one with the smallest $\Delta\omega$, we shall write

$$f_0/\Delta f = \omega_0/\Delta\omega = \omega_0 L/R = Q \qquad (7\text{--}5\text{--}6)$$

which is referred to sometimes as the *quality factor*, but more often just as *the Q* of the circuit. The basic feature of resonant circuits, and indeed reso-

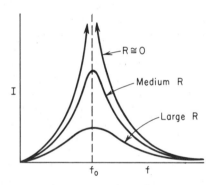

Figure 7–5–1. Resonance curves.

nant systems generally, is that Q varies inversely with R: The smaller the R, and consequently the smaller the energy dissipation in the circuit, the sharper is the resonance.

Other features of a resonant circuit are conveniently summarized in terms of Q. For example, we have mentioned above that voltages far greater than the applied voltage can be encountered in a resonant circuit. The rms voltage across the capacitor C is given by $V_C = I/\omega C = V/\omega_0 CR$ at resonance. The use of (7–5–3) to eliminate C gives

$$V_C = \omega_0 LV/R = QV \qquad (7\text{--}5\text{--}7)$$

which, with Q's in the neighborhood of several hundred readily available, can produce an unpleasant surprise as we mentioned above.

Let us turn back now to the purely transient properties of R–L–C circuits discussed in Sec. 6–2. It was found that the current in an underdamped circuit oscillates at a frequency given by (6–2–22) and (6–2–24) and that at the same time its amplitude decreases exponentially. For convenience, let us consider a circuit of low resistance in which the value of η is close to ω_0 so that we can write from (6–2–24)

$$i(t) = \mathscr{E}e^{-Rt/2L}(\sin \omega_0 t)/\omega_0 L \qquad (7\text{–}5\text{–}8)$$

The period T of the oscillation is equal to $2\pi/\omega_0$, and in this time the current undergoes a fractional decrease given by

$$i(t + T)/i(t) = e^{-R(t+T)/2L} [\sin \omega_0(t + T)]/e^{-Rt/2L} \sin \omega_0 t = e^{-RT/2L}$$

It is customary to denote the exponent as

$$\lambda = RT/2L = -\ln [i(t + T)/i(t)]$$

and it is called the logarithmic decrement of the circuit (see Sec. 13–6 for logarithmic decrement of a ballistic galvanometer). In terms of Q, it is given by

$$\lambda = 2\pi R/2L\omega_0 = \pi/Q \qquad (7\text{–}5\text{–}9)$$

The importance of (7–5–9) is that it relates the responses of a circuit under two different conditions of use. One may energize the circuit by charging the capacitor and watch its decaying oscillations characterized by the logarithmic decrement λ, or one may measure its bandwidth Δf when a signal in the neighborhood of the resonant frequency is applied. It should be noted that these two modes of investigation tend to complement each other rather than to overlap. Suppose for example that one wishes to measure the Q of a circuit in which it has such a high value that one encounters problems of frequency discrimination and of control in attempting to measure Δf. This very circuit will have a small value of λ which may be measured easily. The time required for the rms value of the current in the initially energized circuit to fall to $1/e$ of its original value is

$$\tau = 2L/R = 2Q/\omega_0 \qquad (7\text{–}5\text{–}10)$$

by (7–5–8). Thus the larger Q is, the more readily it can be determined by measuring ω_0 and τ and by then using (7–5–10). Conversely, if one has a high-frequency circuit in which the decay time τ is too short to be measured conveniently, one may find it by measuring $\Delta\omega$ and using (7–5–6) to give

$$\tau = 2/\Delta\omega \qquad (7\text{–}5\text{–}11)$$

These results have important applications in measuring the lifetimes of short-lived nuclear energy states.*

7–6 APPLICATION OF THE SINUSOIDAL THEOREM TO BRANCHES IN PARALLEL ON A SINUSOIDAL A-C LINE, STEADY-STATE CONDITIONS ONLY

Consider the circuit shown in Fig. 7–6–1, where there are two branches in parallel, and the parallel combination is connected to a sinusoidal a-c line. Let us call the lower branch the number one branch. This branch may have a capacitor as well as an inductor in series in the branch, but the inductive

* See Bethe and Morrison, *Elementary Nuclear Theory*, 2d ed. (New York: John Wiley & Sons, Inc., 1955), chap. 20.

reactance predominates, as shown by the symbol for an inductor in this branch. In other words the equivalent reactance X_1 for this branch is given by $X_1 = X_{L1} - X_{C1}$, and X_{L1} happens to be the larger. Let R_1 be the total resistance of this branch. Let i_1 represent the instantaneous current in this branch, I_{1m} represent the maximum value of the current, and I_1 the rms value of the current in this branch.

The upper branch, in Fig. 7–6–1, is called the number two branch. This branch probably also has inductive reactance in series in it, but the capacitive reactance predominates, as shown by the symbol for a capacitor in the branch. In other words, the equivalent reactance X_2 for this branch is given by $X_2 = X_{L2} - X_{C2}$, and X_{C2} happens to be the larger. Let R_2 be the total resistance of this branch. Let i_2 represent the instantaneous current, I_{2m} represent the maximum value of the current, and I_2 the rms value of the current in this branch.

Let v represent the instantaneous applied voltage, V_m the maximum value of the applied voltage, and V the rms value of the applied voltage. This voltage is applied between points A and B, and is the same for both branches.

Let i be the instantaneous line current, I_m the maximum value, and I the rms value of the line current.

By Kirchhoff's first law we know that at every instant

$$i = i_1 + i_2 \qquad (7\text{–}6\text{–}1)$$

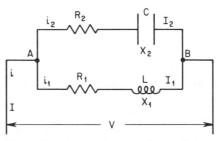

Figure 7–6–1. Two branches in parallel on a sinusoidal a-c line.

The currents flowing in the branches are sinusoidal, so we may represent them by the equations

$$i_1 = I_{1m} \sin (\omega t + \alpha_1) \quad (7\text{–}6\text{–}2)$$
$$i_2 = I_{2m} \sin (\omega t + \alpha_2) \quad (7\text{–}6\text{–}3)$$

where α_1 and α_2 are the phase constants. Substitute (7–6–2) and (7–6–3) into (7–6–1) and we have

$$i = I_{1m} \sin (\omega t + \alpha_1) + I_{2m} \sin (\omega t + \alpha_2) \qquad (7\text{–}6\text{–}4)$$

In (7–6–4) we have two sinusoidal functions of the same frequency, whose instantaneous values are added algebraically in order to satisfy Kirchhoff's first law. Also these sinusoidal functions have constant values for amplitudes and phase constants. The conditions, specified for the sinusoidal theorem in Sec. 7–1, are satisfied here, so the results of the theorem may be applied. Equation (7–1–9) applied to this case gives

$$i = I_m \sin (\omega t + \theta) \qquad (7\text{–}6\text{–}5)$$

where, by (7–1–8),

$$I_m^2 = I_{1m}^2 + I_{2m}^2 + 2I_{1m}I_{2m} \cos (\alpha_2 - \alpha_1) \qquad (7\text{–}6\text{–}6)$$

and by (7–1–7)

$$\tan \theta = \frac{I_{1m} \sin \alpha_1 + I_{2m} \sin \alpha_2}{I_{1m} \cos \alpha_1 + I_{2m} \cos \alpha_2} \qquad (7\text{–}6\text{–}7)$$

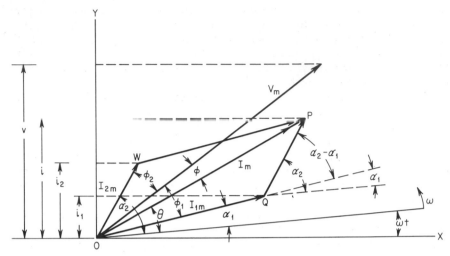

Figure 7–6–2. Rotating vector diagram for the circuit in Fig. 7–6–1.

Here I_m is, of course, the maximum value of the line current, and θ gives, by means of (7–6–7), the phase relationship of I_m to I_{1m} and I_{2m}.

The above results mean, as we have shown for the sinusoidal theorem in Sec. 7–2, that I_m *is the vector sum of* I_{1m} *and* I_{2m}. Let us draw, in Fig. 7–6–2, the vector diagram, which this theorem requires, for (7–6–2) through (7–6–7), This needs no explanation beyond that associated with Fig. 7–2–2 (a) since (7–6–2) and (7–6–3) are identical in form with (7–1–1) and (7–1–2). Reread the explanation associated with the construction of Fig. 7–2–2 (a), making the following obvious mental substitutions: $i_1 = y_1$, $i_2 = y_2$, $I_{1m} = A_1$, $I_{2m} = A_2$, $i = y$, $I_m = A$, $\theta = \theta'$, (7–6–2) for (7–1–1), (7–6–3) for (7–1–2), and Fig. 7–6–2 for Fig. 7–2–2 (a).

We know from the circuit in Fig. 7–6–1 that

$$I_{1m} \text{ lags } V_m \text{ by } \quad \phi_1 = \tan^{-1}\frac{X_1}{R_1} \qquad (7\text{–}6\text{–}8)$$

because branch 1 has R and L in series. Also

$$I_{2m} \text{ leads } V_m \text{ by } \quad \phi_2 = \tan^{-1}\frac{X_2}{R_2} \qquad (7\text{–}6\text{–}9)$$

because branch 2 has R and C in series. In.Fig. 7–6–2, draw the vector for V_m, leading the vector for I_{1m} by ϕ_1, and lagging the vector for I_{2m} by ϕ_2. Here V_m is represented by the same vector for both branches. Label the angles ϕ_1 and ϕ_2 on the vector diagram. Let ϕ be the phase angle between the maximum line current I_m and the maximum line voltage V_m. Label the angle ϕ on the diagram. With i_1 and i_2 expressed as they are in (7–6–2) and (7–6–3), and i expressed as it is in (7–6–5), the equation for the line voltage as a function of time must be written

$$v = V_m \sin (\omega t + \theta + \phi) \qquad (7\text{–}6\text{–}10)$$

as we can see most readily from the vector diagram in Fig. 7–6–2.

Since V_m is the same for both branches, it would be much more convenient, if we were to use it as the reference for measuring phase differences, and write it

$$v = V_m \sin \omega t \qquad (7\text{–}6\text{–}11)$$

Equation (7–6–11) means that, in drawing the vector diagram, we start by placing the vector that represents V_m along the ωt line, and then let (7–6–8) and (7–6–9) tell us the angles between V_m and I_{1m} and between V_m and I_{2m}. Since the vector for V_m is along the ωt line, α_1 becomes the same as ϕ_1, α_2 the same as ϕ_2, and θ the same as ϕ. In Fig. 7–6–3, let us redraw Fig. 7–6–2, making these changes.

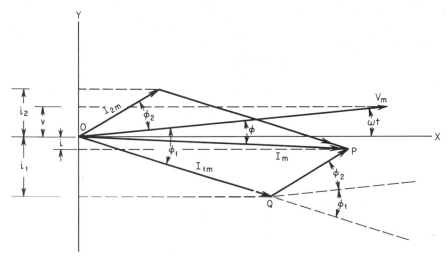

Figure 7–6–3. Rotating vector diagram for the circuit in Fig. 7–6–1. This diagram is the one in Fig. 7–6–2 but redrawn with V_m along the ωt line.

Apply (7–6–6) to the vector diagram in Fig. 7–6–3 and we have,

$$I_m^2 = I_{1m}^2 + I_{2m}^2 + 2I_{1m}I_{2m} \cos (\phi_2 - \phi_1) \qquad (7\text{–}6\text{–}12)$$

Note that in this diagram ϕ_1 happens to be a negative angle. Thus when we substitute a number for ϕ_1 we must include the minus sign on the number so that in (7–6–12) we have $\cos (\phi_2 + |\phi_1|)$, as we would expect from Fig. 7–6–3.

Divide both sides of (7–6–12) by 2, and obtain

$$I^2 = I_1^2 + I_2^2 + 2I_1I_2 \cos (\phi_2 - \phi_1) \qquad (7\text{–}6\text{–}13)$$

Equation (7–6–13) says that we may divide each vector in Fig. 7–6–3 by $\sqrt{2}$ and have the smaller similar vector diagram which applies to rms or effective values of current and voltage. Now, however, the projections of the vectors on the Y-axis lose their meanings in terms of instantaneous currents and voltages. Hence, when we draw the vector diagram for rms values, we may as well put the line voltage vector along the X-axis, and consider that the vector diagram is standing still.

This method may, as we have shown in Sec. 7–2, be extended to any number of sinusoidal functions of the same frequency, so it may be extended to any number of branches in parallel.

The conclusion from all this is: *For any number of branches in parallel on a sinusoidal a-c line the rms value of the line current is the vector sum of the rms values of the branch currents.*

7–7 INTRODUCTION TO USE OF COMPLEX NUMBERS IN SERIES CIRCUITS

We have seen earlier in this chapter that we may treat either maximum values or rms values of current and voltage in a sinusoidal a-c circuit as vector quantities. That is, we may obtain proper answers by vector methods. Current and voltage are not vector quantities in the same sense as are displacement, force, velocity, etc., because they do not have a physical direction in space as do true vector quantities. However, by the methods used in Secs. 7–2, 7–3, and 7–6, we assign directions to current and voltage vectors such that Kirchhoff's laws are satisfied through the sinusoidal theorem; then we apply vector methods. This gives us a powerful tool for solving sinusoidal a-c circuit problems when we are interested in either maximum or rms values of current and voltage.

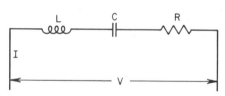

Figure 7–7–1. Alternating current series circuit. I is the rms value of the current flowing, V is the rms value of the applied voltage.

Having pointed out above that I and V are not true physical vector quantities, we shall now refer to them as *vector quantities* without qualifying the statement each time that we use the term vector.

The vector diagrams for a-c circuits are confined to a plane. We have seen in Sec. 6–1 that the algebra of complex numbers can be looked upon as a vector algebra when the vectors are confined to a plane. We shall now proceed to use the algebra of complex numbers as a very important tool for the solution of sinusoidal a-c circuit problems.

Let us adopt a more convenient notation than the one that we used in Sec. 6–1 in the summary of the algebra of complex numbers. When we refer to the full vector properties (i.e., both magnitude and direction) of a current or voltage we shall put a *dot* under the symbol used. When we refer to the magnitude only of a current or voltage (without reference to direction) we shall omit the dot under the symbol. This convention will avoid the absolute magnitude signs used earlier and will fit right in with the notation used in previous chapters, because previous to this all symbols for current or voltage have referred to magnitude only. Thus our present addition to notation is the use of a dot under the symbols I and V when we wish to express the full vector properties of the current or the voltage.

Consider now the series circuit shown in Fig. 7–7–1, which is the same one shown in Fig. 7–3–1, and discussed in detail there in the process of introducing the vector method of dealing with a-c circuits.

As before, let $X = X_L - X_C$ be the resultant reactance of the circuit and let us assume that X is positive, i.e., that $X_L > X_C$. The opposite assumption would do equally well, but we must use one or the other in order to draw a vector diagram. Let us draw the vectors to represent the current I and the voltage vector V in the complex plane.

At this point we have a perfectly free choice. We may put the vector that represents the current in any direction that we select in the complex plane. Once we draw the vector for the current, the circuit constants immediately tell us the direction that the vector for the voltage must have, because the voltage vector leads the current vector by ϕ, where

$$\phi = \tan^{-1}(X/R) \qquad (7\text{–}7\text{–}1)$$

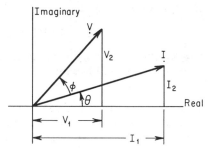

Conversely, we could have selected any direction for the vector that represents the voltage and then drawn the vector that represents the current lagging the vector for the voltage by the angle given in (7–7–1). However, let us stick to our original plan and draw I at an angle θ with respect to the positive axis of reals, where θ may be any arbitrarily selected angle. The vectors are drawn in Fig. 7–7–2 with θ less than 90°. However, θ need not be less than 90°.

Let I_1 be the component of I along the axis of reals and I_2 be the component of I along the axis of imaginaries.

Figure 7–7–2. Vector diagram for the circuit in Figure 7–7–1. The vector which represents I is drawn at any arbitrary angle θ with respect to the positive axis of reals. The circuit determines the angle ϕ between the vectors which represent I and V.

Similarly V_1 and V_2 are, respectively, the real and imaginary components of V (see Fig. 7–7–2). Using this notation, we may write I and V in the algebraic form as

$$I = I_1 + jI_2 \quad \text{and} \quad V = V_1 + jV_2 \qquad (7\text{–}7\text{–}2)$$

or in the exponential form as

$$I = Ie^{j\theta}; \qquad V = Ve^{j(\theta + \phi)} \qquad (7\text{–}7\text{–}3)$$

where, of course, $I = \sqrt{I_1^2 + I_2^2}$ and $V = \sqrt{V_1^2 + V_2^2}$. Here I is the magnitude of the current as read by an ammeter in series in the circuit, and V is the magnitude of the applied voltage as read by a voltmeter across the line.

It is obvious from Fig. 7–7–2 that the lengths of the real and imaginary components (I_1 and I_2) of I depend on the arbitrary choice of θ. However the magnitude I depends only on the circuit constants since the length of I must be such that, by means of the current scale, it represents the ammeter reading.

Once θ is chosen and I is drawn, the direction of V is immediately established by (7–7–1). Nevertheless the lengths of V_1 and V_2 depend upon the choice of θ. The choice of θ does not, however, influence the magnitude V, since V depends only on the applied line voltage. The length of V must be such that, by means of the voltage scale, it represents the voltmeter reading.

Let us now define a new quantity that we shall call *complex impedance* and shall represent by the symbol Z. Notice that this is a capital Z and remember that earlier we used a small z for magnitude of impedance. Here Z is defined as the quotient obtained when the vector expression for V is divided by the vector expression for I, so the defining equation is

$$Z = V/I \qquad (7\text{–}7\text{–}4)$$

Let us now evaluate Z by inserting the vector expressions for V and I from (7–7–3) into (7–7–4).

$$Z = Ve^{j(\theta + \phi)}/Ie^{j\theta} \quad \text{or} \quad Z = (V/I)e^{j\phi} \qquad (7\text{–}7\text{–}5)$$

We recognize V/I as the magnitude z of the impedance [see for example (7–4–1)], so (7–7–5) becomes

$$Z = ze^{j\phi} \qquad (7\text{–}7\text{–}6)$$

Equation (7–7–6) is the kind of expression that we should expect for complex impedance. This is a very interesting result, however, since the angle θ canceled out of the complex expression for the impedance, and thus *the expression for Z is independent of the orientation of I in the complex plane.* This result puts Z on a very different footing from I and V, since the complex expressions for I and V *do* depend on the orientation of I in the complex plane. Hence, while we shall call I and V vector quantities, we shall *not* call Z a vector quantity but shall call it complex impedance as we did when we introduced it. Note that, to emphasize this distinction, we do *not* put a dot under Z, and that we use a small z for its magnitude.

Let us explore further to see just what it is that the complex expression for impedance does depend upon. Write (7–7–6) in the trigonometric form

$$Z = z(\cos \phi + j \sin \phi) = z \cos \phi + jz \sin \phi$$

From (7–4–3) we know that $R = z \cos \phi$, and from Fig. 7–4–1, $X = z \sin \phi$ for a series circuit. Hence

$$Z = R + jX = R + j(X_L - X_C) \qquad (7\text{–}7\text{–}7)$$

for a series circuit. Thus we conclude that, for a fixed frequency circuit, *the complex expression for impedance depends only on the resistance and reactance of a series circuit or series part of a circuit, and not at all on the arbitrary choice of orientation of I in the complex plane.*

If we have a series circuit, or a series part of a circuit, where the resistance and reactance are known we may write down at once the complex expression for the impedance, since it is determined by the circuit constants (including frequency) only. In Problem 7–8 you are asked to prove this same fact, using the algebraic vector expressions for V and I as given in (7–7–2) rather than the exponential expressions given in (7–7–3).

From the definition of Z in (7–7–4) we see that

$$V = IZ \qquad (7\text{–}7\text{–}8)$$

which is often called Ohm's law in the complex form for an a-c series circuit or a series part of a circuit.

We have seen that, in the algebra of complex numbers -1 may be looked upon as an operator which, when it operates on a quantity, rotates that quantity through $180°$. In this same scheme we have introduced j as an operator which, when it operates on a quantity, rotates that quantity through $90°$. Using Ohm's law in the complex form $V = IZ$, we may think of Z as an operator which, when it operates on I, rotates the vector which represents I into coincidence with the vector which represents V and produces a vector which has the same magnitude as the vector which represents V.

7-8 DEFINITION OF COMPLEX ADMITTANCE. RULE OF SIGNS FOR COMPLEX IMPEDANCE AND COMPLEX ADMITTANCE

Let us define complex admittance as the reciprocal of complex impedance. We shall represent complex admittance by a capital Y and its magnitude by small y.

1. R AND L IN SERIES. With R and L in series, we see from (7–7–7) that the complex impedance is

$$Z = R + jX_L \qquad (7\text{–}7\text{–}9)$$

RULE: *Use the plus sign for inductive reactance in the expression for complex impedance.* From the definition for complex admittance we have

$$Y = 1/Z = 1/(R + jX_L)$$

Rationalize, i.e., multiply the numerator and denominator by the conjugate of the denominator.

$$Y = \frac{1}{R + jX_L} \cdot \frac{R - jX_L}{R - jX_L} = \frac{R}{R^2 + X_L^2} - j\frac{X_L}{R^2 + X_L^2} \qquad (7\text{–}7\text{–}10)$$

The combination of symbols $R/(R^2 + X_L^2)$ occurs frequently, is given the name *conductance*, and is represented by the symbol G. Similarly $X_L/(R^2 + X_L^2)$ is given the name *susceptance* and is represented by the symbol B_L. Thus we have the defining equations

$$G = R/(R^2 + X_L^2) \quad \text{and} \quad B_L = X_L/(R^2 + X_L^2) \qquad (7\text{–}7\text{–}11)$$

and (7–7–10) becomes

$$Y = G - jB_L \qquad (7\text{–}7\text{–}12)$$

RULE: *Use the minus sign for inductive susceptance in the expression for complex admittance.* From (7–7–12) the magnitude of admittance is given by

$$y = \sqrt{G^2 + B_L^2} \qquad (7\text{–}7\text{–}13)$$

Since Y is defined as the reciprocal of Z, the expression [such as the one in (7–7–12)] for complex admittance is independent of the orientation of I in the complex plane and depends only on the circuit constants. Also since $I = V/Z$ and $Y = 1/Z$,

$$I = VY = VG - jVB_L \qquad (7\text{-}7\text{-}14)$$

2. R AND C IN SERIES. With R and C in series, we see from (7–7–7) that

$$Z = R - jX_C \qquad (7\text{-}7\text{-}15)$$

RULE: *Use the minus sign for capacitive reactance in the expression for complex impedance.* From the definition of Y,

$$Y = \frac{1}{Z} = \frac{1}{R - jX_C} = \frac{R}{R^2 + X_C^2} + j\frac{X_C}{R^2 + X_C^2}$$

or

$$Y = G + jB_C \qquad (7\text{-}7\text{-}16)$$

RULE: *Use the plus sign for capacitive susceptance in the expression for complex admittance.* From (7–7–16)

$$y = \sqrt{G^2 + B_C^2} \qquad (7\text{-}7\text{-}17)$$

For this case (7–7–14)

$$I = VY = VG + jVB_C \qquad (7\text{-}7\text{-}18)$$

7–9 NUMERICAL EXAMPLES OF SERIES CIRCUITS

EXAMPLE (A). Find the value of V and the power factor for the circuit in Fig. 7–9–1.

Complex impedances in series add directly, so the total complex impedance Z for the circuit is

$$Z = Z_1 + Z_2 + Z_3 = R_1 + jX_1 + R_2 - jX_2 + R_3 - jX_3$$
$$Z = (R_1 + R_2 + R_3) + j(X_1 - X_2 - X_3) \qquad (7\text{-}9\text{-}1)$$

We can see that (7–9–1) automatically handles resistances and reactances in series in just the way that is required, so this justifies the statement that complex impedances in series add directly. Substitute numerical values from the circuit into (7–9–1).

$$Z = 28 - j10$$

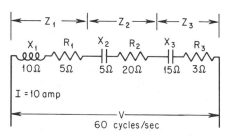

Figure 7–9–1. Application of complex numbers to a series circuit.

At this point we must make a choice as to orientation of I in the complex plane. It will be recalled that this is an entirely free choice. With the choice a free one we may as well make the problem as simple as possible by placing the vector that represents I along the positive axis of reals. With this choice, $I = 10 + j0$. Then V is given by

$$V = IZ = (10 + j0)(28 - j10) = 280 - j100$$

and

$$V = \sqrt{(280)^2 + (100)^2} = 297 \text{ v.}$$

Thus a voltmeter across the line would read 297 v.

Since the vector that represents I is along the positive axis of reals, the phase angle ϕ between the current and voltage is the angle between the axis of reals and the vector that represents the voltage. The power factor is then the cosine of this angle, and this cosine equals the real component of V divided by the magnitude of V. Note that this is a special case because we took I along the positive axis of reals. Thus in this special case $\cos \phi = 280/297 = .943$.

EXAMPLE (B). A long power transmission line has appreciable distributed self-inductance, because the changing magnetic field of each wire induces an emf of self-induction in the wire itself and in the neighboring wire.

Also such a transmission line has an appreciable distributed capacitance because the wires of the line act as the plates of a capacitor. Actually this capacitance is in parallel with any loads across the line. However, it can be treated as an equivalent series capacitance.

While we shall not go into any detail with respect to transmission lines, they make excellent examples for calculation of series circuits, if we use their equivalent series reactances. Their virtue as examples arises from the fact that the vector diagram for the circuit can be a primary guide in the method to be used in solving the problem presented.

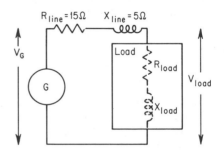

Figure 7–9–2 shows a generating station G, supplying power to a factory load over a transmission line. The equivalent series reactance of the line is distributed along the length of the line and is both inductive and capacitive. However, in this case, the inductive reactance of the line predominates, and the equivalent inductive reactance

Figure 7–9–2. A 60 cycles/sec generating station G supplying power to a factory load over a transmission line.

can be considered as concentrated in one place as shown by X_{line} in Fig. 7–9–2, since there is only one load on the line. Also the resistance of the line is distributed along the wires of the line, but again, since there is only one load, it may be considered as concentrated in one place as shown by R_{line}.

We are told that at the generating station the following meter readings are recorded: voltmeter, $V_G = 33.0$ kv; ammeter, $I = 200$ amp; wattmeter, $P_G = 4850$ kw; phase angle meter, line current is lagging V_G by $41°\,25'$. The transmission line has a resistance of 15.0 ohms and an inductive reactance of 5.00 ohms. There is a single factory load on the line and we are asked to find current, voltage, power, and phase angle at the load.

Let us elect to put the vector that represents I along the positive axis of reals, so

$$I = 200 + j0 \tag{1}$$

Since V_G leads I by $41°\,25'$ and the vector for I is along the positive axis of reals, the vector for V_G leads the axis of reals by $41°\,25'$. With the angle given, it is most convenient to express V_G in the trigonometric form as

$$V_G = V_G(\cos\phi + j\sin\phi) \qquad (2)$$

$$\cos\phi = 0.750 \quad \text{and} \quad \sin\phi = 0.662. \qquad (3)$$

Thus $\quad V_G = 33{,}000\,(0.75 + j0.662) = 24{,}800 + j21{,}800. \qquad (4)$

$$V_{\text{line}} = IZ_{\text{line}} = (200 + j0)(15 + j5)$$
$$= 3000 + j1000 \qquad (5)$$

$$V_{\text{load}} = V_G - V_{\text{line}} = 24{,}800 + j21{,}800 - 3000 - j1000$$
$$= 21{,}800 + j20{,}800 \qquad (6)$$

$$V_{\text{load}} = \sqrt{(21{,}800)^2 + (20{,}800)^2} = 30{,}100 \text{ v.} \qquad (7)$$

Hence a voltmeter across the line at the load end would read 30.1 kv. Since the vector that represents I is along the positive axis of reals, the phase angle between line current and load voltage is the angle between the axis of reals and the vector that represents V_{load}. The cosine of this angle is the real component of V_{load} divided by V_{load}, or

$$\cos\phi_{\text{load}} = \frac{21{,}800}{30{,}100} = 0.724$$

$$P_{\text{load}} = IV_{\text{load}}\cos\phi_{\text{load}}$$
$$= 200 \times 30{,}100 \times 0.724 = 4{,}350{,}000 \text{ w.}$$

Hence a wattmeter at the load end of the line would read 4,350 kw. A phase-angle meter at the load end of the line would show the current lagging the voltage by ϕ_{load}, where $\phi_{\text{load}} = \cos^{-1} 0.724 = 43°\,37'$.

7–10 INTRODUCTION TO PARALLEL CIRCUIT PROBLEMS

Assume that we know the resistance, reactance, conductance, and susceptance of each branch in Fig. 7–10–1, as well as the line voltage V. We have seen that the choice of orientation of the vector diagram in the complex plane is an entirely free one. Hence, let us elect to put the vector which represents the applied line voltage V along the positive axis of reals, as shown in Fig. 7–10–2, since V is the same for all three branches. Then the vector expression for V, with this special choice, is

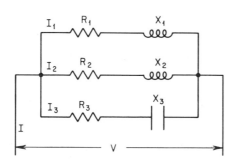

Figure 7–10–1. Three branches in parallel on a sinusoidal a-c line.

$$V = V + j0 \qquad (7\text{–}10\text{–}1)$$

The vector expression for the current in branch 1 is, by (7–7–14), (7–7–12), and (7–10–1),

$$I_1 = VY_1 = V(G_1 - jB_1) = VG_1 - jVB_1 \qquad (7\text{–}10\text{–}2)$$

From this equation we see that VG_1 is the component of I_1, which is in phase with the line voltage, and VB_1 is the component of I_1 which is 90° out of phase with the line voltage.

Similarly we may write for the currents in branches 2 and 3:

$$I_2 = VY_2 = V(G_2 - jB_2) = VG_2 - jVB_2 \qquad (7\text{--}10\text{--}3)$$

and
$$I_3 = VY_3 = V(G_3 + jB_3) = VG_3 + jVB_3 \qquad (7\text{--}10\text{--}4)$$

and we can make similar statements about the meanings of VG_2, VG_3, VB_2, and VB_3.

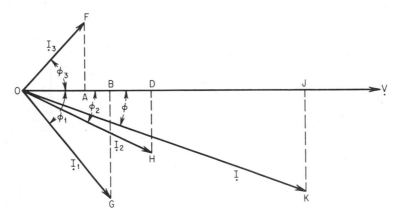

Figure 7–10–2. Vector diagram for the circuit in Fig. 7–10–1; I is the vector sum of I_1, I_2, and I_3.

From Sec. 7–6, we know that I is the vector sum of I_1, I_2, and I_3, so we may write

$$I = I_1 + I_2 + I_3 \qquad (7\text{--}10\text{--}5)$$

or, using (7–10–2), (7–10–3), and (7–10–4),

$$I = V[(G_1 + G_2 + G_3) + j(-B_1 - B_2 + B_3)] \qquad (7\text{--}10\text{--}6)$$

Let us define the equivalent admittance Y of the three branches in parallel as

$$Y = Y_1 + Y_2 + Y_3 = (G_1 + G_2 + G_3) + j(-B_1 - B_2 + B_3) \qquad (7\text{--}10\text{--}7)$$

and
$$I = VY \qquad (7\text{--}10\text{--}8)$$

This argument can be extended to any number of branches in parallel.

We now see the virtue of conductance, susceptance, and admittance, because

(1) Conductances in parallel add arithmetically to give the equivalent conductance of the parallel combination.
(2) Susceptances in parallel add algebraically to give the equivalent susceptance of the parallel combination.
(3) Complex admittances in parallel add algebraically *as complex numbers* to give the equivalent complex admittance of the parallel combination.

Also we see from Fig. 7–10–2 that, for any particular part of a circuit or for the whole circuit,

$$\cos \phi = G/y \qquad (7\text{--}10\text{--}9)$$

7–11 NUMERICAL EXAMPLES OF PARALLEL CIRCUITS

EXAMPLE (A). Let us solve the circuit problem presented in Fig. 7–11–1. (a) Write the expressions for complex admittance of each branch and find the R and X of each branch.

$$Y_1 = G_1 + jB_1 = 0.0520 + j0.0980$$
$$Z_1 = 1/Y_1 = 1/(0.052 + j0.098) = 4.23 - j7.96$$

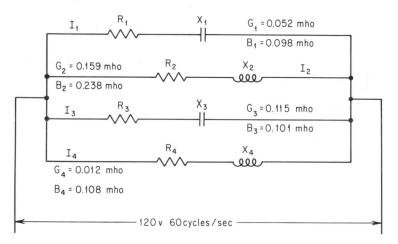

Figure 7–11–1. Four branches in parallel on a sinusoidal a-c line.

Hence $R_1 = 4.23$ ohms and $X_1 = 7.96$ ohms capacitive.

$$Y_2 = G_2 - jB_2 = 0.159 - j0.238$$
$$Z_2 = 1/Y_2 = 1/(0.159 - j0.238) = 1.94 + j2.92$$

Hence $R_2 = 1.94$ ohms and $X_2 = 2.92$ ohms inductive. By similar methods we obtain $R_3 = 4.94$ ohms, $X_3 = 4.34$ ohms capacitive, $R_4 = 1.02$ ohms, and $X_4 = 9.16$ ohms capacitive.

(b) Find the equivalent admittance of the four branches in parallel. Let Y = equivalent admittance.

$$Y = Y_1 + Y_2 + Y_3 + Y_4 = 0.338 - j0.147$$

(c) Find the vector expressions for the current in each branch and the current in the line. Since the applied line voltage is known and is the same for all four branches, let us elect to put the vector that represents this voltage along the positive axis of reals. Note that this is a free choice, and that at this point we must make some choice in order to progress with the problem.

Since V is to be along the positive axis of reals, its vector expression is

$$V = 120 + j0$$
$$I_1 = VY_1 = (120 + j0)(0.052 + j0.098)$$
$$I_1 = 6.24 + j11.8$$
$$I_2 = VY_2 = 19.1 - j28.6$$
$$I_3 = VY_3 = 13.8 + j12.1$$
$$I_4 = VY_4 = 1.44 - j13.0$$

Note that these could just as well have been computed from $I_1 = V/Z_1$, $I_2 = V/Z_2$, etc. If the R's and X's had been given in the problem, instead of the G's and B's, this would have been the easy way to compute the branch currents.

$$I = VY = (120 + j0)(0.338 - j0.147) = 40.6 - j17.6$$

(d) Find what ammeters would read if one were connected in series in each branch and one in series in the line. $I_1 = \sqrt{(6.24)^2 + (11.8)^2} = 13.3$ amp. By the same method we obtain $I_2 = 34.4$ amp, $I_3 = 18.2$ amp, $I_4 = 13.1$ amp, and $I = 44.3$ amp.

(e) Draw the vector diagram of currents and voltage to scale. First adopt two scales, one for current vectors and the other for voltage vectors. Next, lay off a vector to represent the applied voltage of 120 v along the positive axis of reals, using the voltage scale to determine the length of the vector to be drawn. Then, using the current scale, lay off the real and imaginary components for each vector that represents a current and draw the vector to represent that current. These vectors have been drawn in Fig. 7–11–2.

As a check we may make use of the fact that the line current is the vector sum of the branch currents, or $I = I_1 + I_2 + I_3 + I_4$. Substitute the vector expressions for the branch currents and obtain $I = 40.6 - j17.7$, which checks within slide-rule error.

(f) What is the equivalent series circuit diagram? From the value of the equivalent admittance Y which we obtained early in part (b), we may compute the equivalent impedance of the circuit at once. Let Z represent the equivalent complex impedance, and

$$Z = 1/Y = 1/(0.338 - j0.147) = 2.49 + j1.08$$

The fact that the sign in front of the j is positive tells us that the equivalent reactance is inductive. Hence the equivalent circuit is a resistance of 2.49 ohms in series with an inductive reactance of 1.08 ohms.

EXAMPLE (B). Frequently we are confronted with a problem where there are only two branches in parallel, the resistances and reactances are known, and we need to know the equivalent impedance. An easy method of calculation stems from the following.

We have seen that complex admittances in parallel add directly. Let Y equal the equivalent admittance for Y_1 and Y_2 in parallel, and

$$Y = Y_1 + Y_2 \quad \text{so} \quad 1/Z = 1/Z_1 + 1/Z_2 \qquad (7\text{–}11\text{–}1)$$

which may be transformed into

$$Z = Z_1 Z_2/(Z_1 + Z_2) \qquad (7\text{–}11\text{–}2)$$

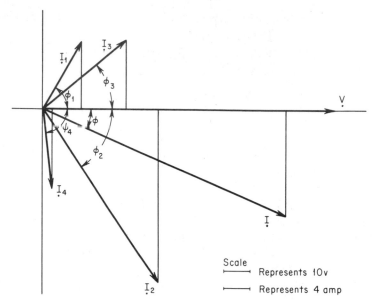

Figure 7–11–2. Vector diagram, for the circuit in Fig. 7–11–1, with the applied voltage taken along the positive axis of reals.

Equation (7–11–2) is a convenient form for the equivalent complex impedance in the case we are considering because it saves the calculation of admittances from known resistances and reactances. To illustrate, consider the circuit in Fig. 7–11–3.

(a) Find the equivalent impedance for the circuit in Fig. 7–11–3. Assume that the numerical values given on the circuit diagram are all known to three significant figures.

$$Z = \frac{Z_1 Z_2}{Z_1 + Z_2} = \frac{(4 + j3)(6 - j8)}{4 + j3 + 6 - j8} = \frac{48 - j14}{10 - j5}$$

Rationalize, and

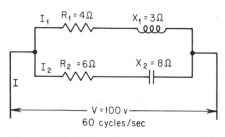

$$Z = \frac{48 - j14}{10 - j5} \frac{10 + j5}{10 + j5}$$

$$= 4.40 + j0.800$$

Hence the equivalent circuit would be made up of a resistance of 4.40 ohms in series with an inductive reactance of 0.800 ohm.

(b) Find the line current, the power factor, and the power supplied by the line to the circuit.

Figure 7–11–3. Two branches in parallel.

Elect to put the vector that represents V along the plus axis of reals so, $V = 100 + j0$. Then $I = V/Z = (100 + j0)/(4.4 + j0.8) = 22.0 - j4.00$ and $I = \sqrt{(22)^2 + (4)^2} = 22.4$ amp.

Since V is along the positive axis of reals, ϕ is the angle between I and the positive axis of reals. Hence $\cos \phi = 22.0/22.4 = 0.982$ and $P = IV \cos \phi = 2200$ w.

7–12 PARALLEL RESONANCE OR ANTIRESONANCE

(A) *Special case where $R_2 = 0$, and where R_1 is not small compared with X_1.* Consider the circuit in Fig. 7–12–1. Since $R_2 = 0$, then $G_2 = 0$, and the magnitude of the square of the admittance of the two branches in parallel is given by

$$y^2 = (G_1 + G_2)^2 + (-B_1 + B_2)^2$$
$$= [R_1/(R_1^2 + X_1^2)]^2 + [-X_1/(R_1^2 + X_1^2) + 1/X_2]^2$$

or $\qquad y^2 = 1/(R_1^2 + X_1^2) - [2X_1/(R_1^2 + X_1^2)]/X_2 + 1/X_2^2 \qquad$ (7–12–1)

Let us assume that R_1, X_1, and V are fixed, but X_2 is variable, and *define parallel resonance in this case as the condition that permits minimum line current.* In order to have minimum line current, we must adjust X_2, in (7–12–1), to such a value that the admittance y of the two branches in parallel will be a minimum. Minimum admittance, of course, means maximum impedance.

Obviously y will be a minimum if y^2 is a minimum, so let us take $d(y^2)/dX_2$ in (7–12–1), and equate the derivative to zero.

$$d(y^2)/dX_2$$
$$= [2X_1/(R_1^2 + X_1^2)]/X_2^2 - 2/X_2^3$$
(7–12–2)

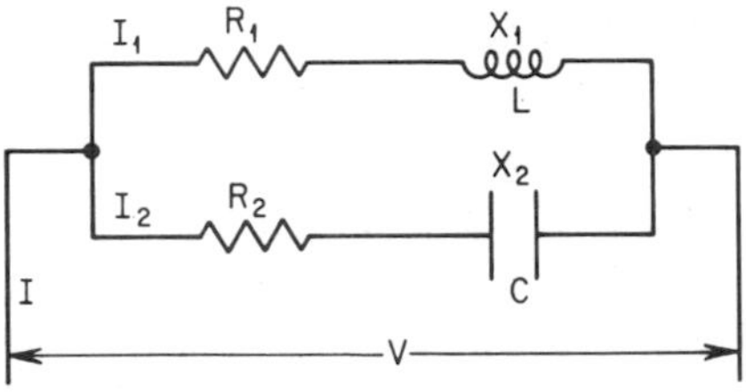

Equate the derivative to zero and solve for X_2.

$$X_2 = (R_1^2 + X_1^2)/X_1 \quad (7–12–3)$$

Figure 7–12–1. Two branches in parallel. Parallel resonance.

The usual tests of calculus will show that this gives a minimum, not a maximum, for y.

Equation (7–12–3) gives the value which the reactance X_2 of the capacitor must have in order that the two parallel branches shall offer a minimum admittance (maximum impedance), and thus is the condition for minimum line current.

Put the value of X_2 in (7–12–3) into (7–12–1), and obtain an expression for the admittance of the two branches in parallel when they are in parallel resonance.

$$y = R_1/(R_1^2 + X_1^2) \qquad (7–12–4)$$

We see that y is equal to the conductance of the inductive branch, which is also the conductance of the two branches in parallel, since $R_2 = 0$.

The line current I is given by Vy, so at parallel resonance

$$I = VR_1/(R_1^2 + X_1^2) \qquad (7–12–5)$$

and we have seen that this is the minimum line current for fixed values of R_1, X_1, and V. From (7–12–3), $X_1X_2 = R_1^2 + X_1^2$, so (7–12–5) may be written

$$I = VR_1/X_1X_2 \qquad (7–12–6)$$

Here, we have the interesting and unusual situation that the line current is directly proportional to the resistance in the inductive branch.

From the condition for parallel resonance in (7–12–3), let us compute the frequency that gives parallel resonance in this case.

$$1/C\omega = (R_1^2 + L^2\omega^2)/L\omega, \quad \text{or} \quad \omega = \sqrt{1/LC - R_1^2/L^2}$$

But $\omega = 2\pi f$, so

$$f = \sqrt{1/LC - R_1^2/L^2}/2\pi \quad (7–12–7)$$

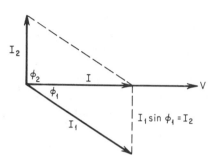

Figure 7–12–2. Line current I and branch currents I_1 and I_2 at parallel resonance of the circuit in Fig. 7–12–1 under conditions that $R_2 = 0$ but R_1 may have any value. I is the vector sum of I_1 and I_2.

The power factor for the line current and line voltage is $\cos\phi = G/y$. In (7–12–4) we saw that, at parallel resonance, the admittance y, of the two branches in parallel, is equal to the conductance G, of the two branches in parallel, so

$$\cos\phi = 1 \quad (7–12–8)$$

Thus in this case *at parallel resonance, the line current is in phase with the line voltage,* as well as the line current being a minimum. The vector diagram for this case is shown in Fig. 7–12–2.

Special case (A) is an important practical one for the reason that it reduces the line current to a minimum, for fixed values of R_1, X_1, and V, and puts the line current in phase with the line voltage. This importance can be best illustrated by a numerical example. Most commercial loads involve machines such as motors, whose induct-ance causes the line current to lag the line voltage. Suppose that we have such a load in Fig. 7–12–3. It is a complicated load but we may represent it by its equi-valent circuit diagram as shown. Calcu-late the line current I, the power factor of the load, and the power input to the load. The constants of the circuit are known to three significant figures.

Let us elect to put the line voltage vector along the positive axis of reals

Figure 7–12–3. Inductive load on a transmission line.

so $V_{\text{load}} = 550 + j0$. Then $I_{\text{load}} = 550/(3.00 + j5.00) = 48.5 - j81.0$, from which $I_{\text{load}} = 94.4$ amp. From the circuit diagram, the magnitude of the impedance of the load is given by $z_{\text{load}} = \sqrt{(5.00)^2 + (3.00)^2} = 5.83$ ohms, so $\cos\phi_{\text{load}} = R_{\text{load}}/z_{\text{load}} = 0.514$. Then the power input from the line to the load is given as

$$P_{\text{load}} = IV_{\text{load}} \cos\phi_{\text{load}} = 94.4 \times 550 \times 0.514 = 26{,}700 \text{ w}$$

Suppose the transmission line has a resistance of 1 ohm. The power loss on the line is

$$P_{\text{line}} = I^2 R_{\text{line}} = (94.4)^2 1.00 = 8920 \text{ w}$$

or the power loss on the line is about one-third of the power used by the load. If the watthour meter is located at the load, the power company is paid for the energy used by the load, but is not paid for the energy loss on the line. Hence, this situation is not to the liking of a power company. Power companies usually fix their rates to penalize industrial consumers for such low power factors, or take other steps to correct this kind of a situation.

Suppose that the situation is to be corrected by placing a capacitor across the line at the load. The capacitor is to be selected so that it will put the load and capacitor in parallel resonance. The load requires the same line voltage, and the same power input, after the change as before. Hence, the power company will adjust the line so that the line voltage at the load is 550 v after the change. The current through the load will thus remain 94.4 amp. After the selected capacitor has been installed, the circuit diagram will be as shown in Fig. 7–12–4.

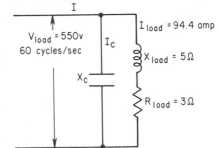

The vector diagram in Fig. 7–12–2 may now be considered to be the diagram for this circuit in Fig. 7–12–4. From this vector diagram we see that the current through the capacitor branch must have such a value that the vector sum of I_C and I_{load} will be in phase with V. Thus $I = I_C + 48.5 - j81.0$ or $I_C = j81.0$. But $V = I_C X_C$

Figure 7–12–4. Capacitor added in parallel with load in Fig. 7–12–3. Capacitor selected so that the two branches are in parallel resonance.

so $X_C = V/I_C = (550 + j0)/j81.0 = -j6.79$ from which $X_C = 6.79$ ohms. From this we can compute the capacitance required as

$$C = \frac{1}{2\pi f X_C} = \frac{1}{6.28 \times 60 \times 6.79} = 0.391 \times 10^{-3} \text{ farad} = 391 \text{ } \mu\text{f}$$

This gives the capacitance of the capacitor that must be used, and it must be a very well-designed capacitor for this kind of service.

From Fig. 7–12–2, the line current is given by $I = I_C + I_{\text{load}} = 48.5 + j0$, so $I = 48.5$ amp.

The power loss on the line is now

$$P_{\text{line}} = I^2 R_{\text{line}} = (48.5)^2 1.00 = 2350 \text{ w}$$

which is about one-quarter of the line loss prior to the installation of the capacitor, and the same power is being transmitted to the load. It is becoming fairly common practice to correct the power factors of inductive loads in this fashion. Frequently, however, the capacitor will be selected to give only partial power factor correction, because of the cost of a capacitor that will give complete correction. This is an economic question, which must be settled for individual installations.

(B) *Special case where* $R_2 = 0$ *and* $R_1 \ll X_1$. In this special case the condition for parallel resonance given in (7–12–3) reduces to

$$X_2 = X_1 \quad \text{or} \quad X_L = X_C \qquad (7\text{–}12\text{–}9)$$

From (7–12–9) we see that, in this extra special case, the condition for parallel resonance is the same as the one for series resonance. However, series resonance produces maximum line current whereas parallel resonance results in minimum line current. You can show that in this special case (B), the line current and line voltage are in phase as before and that the vector diagram is the one shown in Fig. 7–12–5.

From Fig. 7–12–5, we see that the current in each branch may be many times as large as the line current. This is possible because the line current is the vector sum of the branch currents, and the branch currents are almost 180° out of phase.

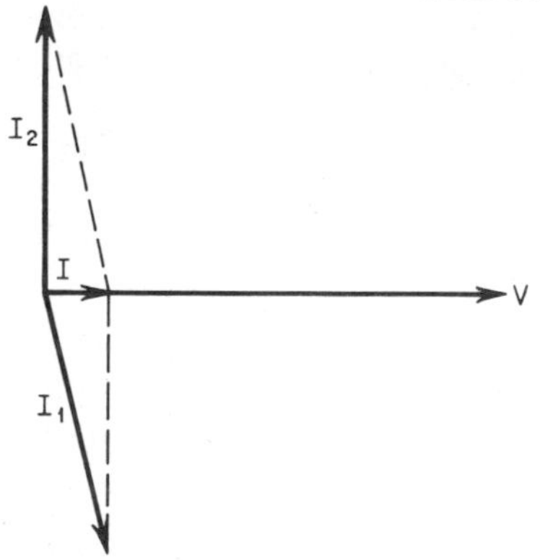

The capacitor has maximum energy stored in it when it has a maximum potential difference across its plates. By (4–5–4) this maximum energy W_{Cm}, stored in the capacitor is given by

$$W_{Cm} = \tfrac{1}{2}CV_m^2 \qquad (7\text{–}12\text{–}10)$$

where V_m is the maximum value of the line voltage (since there is no resistance in the capacitor branch). The energy stored in the capacitor will rise and fall in phase with v, the instantaneous applied line voltage. Thus, on the vector diagram in Fig. 7–12–5, the energy stored in the capacitor is in phase with the vector that represents V, although of course energy is not a vector quantity.

Figure 7–12–5. Line current I and branch currents I_1 and I_2 at parallel resonance of the circuit in Fig. 7–12–1 under conditions that $R_2 = 0$ and $R_1 \ll X_1$. I is the vector sum of I_1 and I_2.

The inductor has a maximum energy stored in its magnetic field when the current through the inductor is a maximum. By (5–1–9) this maximum energy W_{Lm} stored in the magnetic field of the inductor is given by

$$W_{Lm} = \tfrac{1}{2}LI_{1m}^2 \qquad (7\text{–}12\text{–}11)$$

where I_{1m} is the maximum current through the inductor branch. The energy stored in the magnetic field of the inductor will rise and fall in phase with i_1, the instantaneous current in the inductor branch. Thus, on the vector diagram in Fig. 7–12–5, the energy stored in the magnetic field of the inductor is in phase with the vector that represents I_1.

For the special case considered here, I_1 and V are very nearly 90° out of phase. Thus, the energy stored on the capacitor is zero when the energy stored in the magnetic field of the inductor is maximum, and conversely, the energy stored on the capacitor is maximum, when the energy stored in the magnetic field of the inductor is zero.

At parallel resonance, W_{Lm} of (7–12–11) is equal to W_{Cm} of (7–12–10), as we can see from the following. From the circuit in Fig. 7–12–1, $I_{1m} = V_m/$

$\sqrt{R_1^2 + X_1^2}$, but in this special case $R_1^2 \ll X_1^2$ so $I_{1m} = V_m/X_1$. Substitute this value of I_{1m} into (7-12-11) and obtain $W_{Lm} = LV_m^2/2X_1^2 = LV_m^2/2L\omega X_1 = V_m^2/2\omega X_1$. From (7-12-9) the condition for parallel resonance in this special case is $X_1 = X_2$ so we have

$$W_{Lm} = V_m^2/2\omega X_2 = V_m^2 C\omega/2\omega \quad \text{or} \quad W_{Lm} = \tfrac{1}{2}CV_m^2 \qquad (7\text{-}12\text{-}12)$$

which is the same as W_{Cm} in (7-12-10).

From this result, we can explain, from an energy point of view, what is happening at parallel resonance. As the current in the inductor decreases, the energy in its magnetic field is fed back into the circuit, and all goes into branch 2 to charge the capacitor. As the capacitor discharges, its energy is fed back into the circuit, and all goes to branch 1 to build up the magnetic field about the inductor. Thus, the energy to charge the capacitor, and the energy to build up the magnetic field about the inductor, is simply handed back and forth between the two branches, and the line need supply only the energy converted into heat in the resistance R_1. Hence, there is a big oscillatory current in the branches, but only a small line current.

With a parallel combination, such as this, there is some handing back and forth of energy whether the circuit is in parallel resonance or not. When, however, the capacitor is adjusted to parallel resonance, it is adjusted to such a capacitance that the capacitor stores the same maximum energy during one part of the cycle, that the inductor is going to need, during the next part of the cycle. Then it delivers this energy to the inductor, only to have it returned for delivery next time.

When the resistor R_1 in the inductive branch is not negligibly small compared to X_1, as is the situation in special case (A), this energy explanation becomes much more complicated with regard to phase. This statement means that the reactive energy is not handed directly back and forth between the inductor and capacitor. (Solve Problem 7-36 here.) However, the net result is physically the same, and at parallel resonance, the line current can be a minimum for a given power delivered to the inductive load because the maximum values of the reactive powers required by C and L are equal (as you will prove in Problem 7-37).

PROBLEMS

7-1 Prove that

$$y = A \sin (\omega t + \theta) \qquad (7\text{-}1\text{-}9)$$

is the same as

$$y = A_1 \sin (\omega t + \alpha_1) + A_2 \sin (\omega t + \alpha_2) \qquad (1)$$

where the values of A and θ are given by (7-1-8) and (7-1-7), respectively. To do this, expand (7-1-9), using the formula for the sine of the sum of two angles, substitue into this expanded formula the values of A and θ and show that the result will reduce to (1) above. This problem is an alternative proof of the sinusoidal theorem, to the one given in the text by the argument associated with (7-1-1) through (7-1-9). Explain briefly why it is an alternate proof.

7-2 Two generators, whose emfs are given by $e_1 = \mathscr{E}_{1m} \sin \omega t$ and $e_2 = \mathscr{E}_{2m} \sin (\omega t + \pi/3)$, are connected in series in a circuit. The value of $\mathscr{E}_{1m}$ is 50.0 v and that of $\mathscr{E}_{2m}$ is 40.0 v. What is the equation for the equivalent emf applied to the circuit as a function of time?

7-3 In Problem 4–21, use the method of Sec. 7–1 and Sec. 7–6 to write the equation for the line current i as a function of time and show that you get the same equation as the one you obtained in part (c) of Problem 4–21.

7-4 Repeat Problem 7–3 but use the conditions described in Problem 4–22. Show that you arrive at the same answer as the one you obtained in Problem 4–22.

7-5 In Problem 4–29 you had the equations $i = I_m \sin \omega t$, $v_R = V_{Rm} \sin \omega t$, and $v_c = V_{cm} \sin (\omega t - \pi/2)$ where $I_m = 1.00$ amp, $V_{Rm} = 72.0$ v, $V_{Cm} = 50.4$ v, and $\omega = 2\pi$ 100 sec^{-1} (refer to the statement of Problem 4–29). (a) Using the method of Sec. 7–1, find the equation for the applied line voltage as a function of time and then compare it with your answer to part (b) of Problem 4–29. (b) What would an a-c ammeter read if it were connected in series in this circuit? What would an a-c voltmeter read if it were connected across the line?

7-6 Consider Problem 5–17 and repeat Problem 7–5.

7-7 A coil with an inductance of 0.0200 henry and a resistance of 10.0 ohms is connected to a 100 cycle/sec a-c power line. (a) What is the expression for the complex impedance of the coil? What is the magnitude of the impedance of the coil? [*Ans: z = *16.1 ohms.] (b) What is the phase angle between the current and the applied line voltage? [*Ans: 51° 29′.*]

7-8 Starting with the definition of Z as given in (7–7–4) and using the algebraic complex expressions for I and V as given in (7–7–2), prove that the complex expression for impedance is independent of the angle θ in Fig. 7–7–2, and is given by $Z = R + jX$. Do this proof without using the exponential expression for a complex number.

In the following problems the currents and voltages given are rms values unless the problem explicitly states to the contrary. All currents and voltages are sinusoidal.

Make a circuit diagram and a vector diagram in solving these problems. If the problem tells you to *plot* the vector diagram, it must be drawn to scale and the scale stated, otherwise you may simply sketch the vector diagram. Use complex-number vector methods, not instantaneous methods, in solving these problems.

7-9 A circuit has a complex impedance given by $7 + j10$. The current flowing in this circuit is $10 + j6$. All circuit constants are known to three significant figures. (a) What is the vector expression for the applied voltage? [*Ans: 10 + j142.*] What would a voltmeter read if connected across the source of applied voltage? [*Ans: 143 v.*] (b) Draw the circuit diagram, labeling it to show voltmeter reading, ammeter reading, resistance, and reactance. (c) Plot the current and voltage vector diagram to scale with the proper orientation in the complex plane. Calculate the phase angle between the current and voltage and label it on the vector diagram. (d) Find the component of V that is in phase with I and the component of V that is 90° out of phase with I.

7–10 Repeat Problem 7–9 for a complex impedance of $7 - j10$ and the same current of $10 + j6$.

7–11 Repeat Problem 7–9 with the single change that the vector that represents the current is to be along the positive axis of reals. The ammeter reading is the same as in Problems 7–9.

7–12 A voltage of $30.0 + j24.0$ is applied to a circuit whose impedance is $5.00 + j4.00$. (a) Find the vector expression for the current. [*Ans:* 6.00 + *j*0.] (b) Draw the circuit diagram, labeling it to show voltmeter and ammeter readings, resistance, and reactance. (c) Find the real and imaginary components of I. (d) Sketch the current and voltage vector diagram with the correct orientation in the complex plane. (e) Find the component of I in phase with V and the component of I that is 90° out of phase with V. (f) Find the power used by the circuit.

7–13 A voltage of $30.0 + j24.0$ is applied to a circuit whose impedance is $5.00 - j4.00$. Answer the questions asked in Problem 7–12. [*Ans:* (a) 1.32 + *j*5.85, (e) 4.68 amp, 3.78 amp.]

7–14 A voltage of $120 + j0$ is applied to a circuit that has 9.00 ohms resistance and 6.00 ohms inductive reactance in series. Find: (a) The vector expression for the current. (b) The magnitude of the current. (c) The power factor for the circuit. (d) Sketch a vector diagram of V and I.

7–15 A coil of 0.100 henry inductance and 20.0 ohms resistance is connected to a 25 cycle/sec 220 v a-c line. (a) What is a suitable vector expression for the current? What would an ammeter read if connected in series in the circuit? [*Ans:* $I = 6.81 - j5.34$, 8.65 amp.] (b) What power is being used by the circuit?

7–16 A capacitor of 40.0 μf, a resistor of 30.0 ohms, and an ammeter are connected in series and the series combination is connected to a 60 cycle/sec sinusoidal a-c line. The ammeter reads 1.65 amp. (a) What is a suitable vector expression for the applied line voltage? What would a voltmeter read if connected across the line? [*Ans:* $V = 49.5 - j109$, 120 v.] (b) What is the phase angle between I and V and which one is ahead in phase? [*Ans:* I leads V by 65° 35′.]

7–17 A capacitor whose reactance at 60 cycles/sec is 20.0 ohms, a coil whose resistance is 10.0 ohms and whose inductive reactance at the same frequency is 15.0 ohms, and an ammeter are connected in series and the combination is connected to a 220 v 60 cycle/sec a-c line. (a) If you elect to represent the line voltage with the vector expression $V = 99.0 + j197$, what is the vector expression for the current? What does the ammeter read? [*Ans:* $I = j19.7$, 19.7 amp.] (b) What is the phase relationship between I and V? [*Ans:* I leads V by 26° 35′.]

7–18 A capacitor of 15.0 μf capacitance, an inductor of 0.200 henry inductance and of 50.0 ohms resistance, and an ammeter are connected in series to a 220 v 60 cycle/sec power line. (a) What is a suitable vector expression for the current? What does the ammeter read? [*Ans:* 0.851 + *j*1.74, 1.94 amp.] (b) What is the power factor for the circuit and what power is the circuit using? [*Ans:* 0.440, 188 w.]

7–19 The 0.200 henry inductor of Problem 7–18 is removed from the circuit and replaced with one, of the same resistance, which puts the circuit in series resonance. (a) What is the inductance, in henrys, of the new inductor? (b) What is now a suitable vector expression for the current and the ammeter reading? [*Ans:* $I = 4.40 + j0.$] (c) A commercial capacitor usually has a voltage rating printed on it. This is the maximum instantaneous voltage that it is safe to apply across the capacitor. A higher voltage may cause the dielectric in the capacitor to break down, because a spark passes between the plates, and the capacitor is ruined if its dielectric is a solid. What must be the minimum voltage rating of the capacitor in this circuit if one is to be sure that it will not break down? [*Ans:* 1100 v.]

7–20 A voltmeter across an a-c circuit reads 550 v, an ammeter in series in the circuit reads 50.0 amp, and a phase angle meter shows that the current lags the voltage by 20.0°. (a) What are suitable vector expressions for the voltage and current? What is the component of I in phase with V? [*Ans:* 47.0 amp.] What is the component of I which is 90° out of phase with V? [*Ans:* 17.2 amp.] (b) What is the complex expression for the impedance of the circuit? Draw and label the equivalent circuit diagram. [*Ans:* $Z = 10.3 + j3.77.$]

7–21 An a-c motor is drawing 25.0 amp from a 220 v line and the voltage leads the current by 15.0°. (a) Put the current vector along the positive axis of imaginaries and write a suitable vector expression for the voltage vector. (b) Find the complex expression for the equivalent impedance of the motor and draw and label the equivalent circuit diagram. [*Ans:* $Z = 8.48 + j2.28.$]

7–22 A series circuit has 10.0 ohms resistance, 10.0 μf capacitance, and 0.702 henry inductance. (a) What is the frequency of a 120 v a-c line on which the circuit is in series resonance? (b) What steady-state current would flow if this circuit were connected to a 120 v d-c line?

7–23 A coil draws 20.0 amp from a 220 v d-c line. When connected to a 220 v 60 cycle/sec a-c line, the current through the coil is 11.0 amp. What is the inductance of the coil? [*Ans:* 0.0443 henry.]

7–24 A certain factory load is equivalent to 200 ohms resistance and 150 ohms inductive reactance at 60 cycles/sec, the frequency of the line which supplies the factory. The transmission line has 5.00 ohms resistance and a distributed reactance equivalent to 6.00 ohms inductive reactance in series. A voltmeter across the line at the load end reads 10,000 v. (a) Elect to put the load voltage along the positive axis of reals and write a suitable vector expression for the line current. What would an ammeter in series in the line read? [*Ans:* $I = 32.0 - j23.9$, 40.0 amp.] (b) What is the power factor of the load and what power is the load using? (c) What is the vector expression for the voltage across the line at the generator end of the line? (d) What is the power factor at the generator and what power does the generator deliver? [*Ans:* 328 kw.]

7–25 Power is transmitted to a load by a 60 cycle/sec transmission line whose resistance is 50.0 ohms and whose equivalent series reactance is 60.0 ohms inductive. The meters at the generator end show readings as follows: wattmeter, 3000 kw; voltmeter, 50.0 kv; ammeter, 80.0 amp; phase angle meter, current lags voltage. What would corresponding meters read at the load end of the line? Elect to put the vector which represents the current along the positive axis of reals. [*Ans:* $V_{\text{load}} = 33{,}500 + j28{,}300$; $V_{\text{load}} = 43.9$ kv.]

7-26 (a) Explain clearly why vector methods may be used to solve sinusoidal a-c *series* circuits when dealing with ammeter and voltmeter readings. (b) Explain clearly why vector methods may be used to solve sinusoidal a-c *parallel* circuits when dealing with ammeter and voltmeter readings.
Note: In answering (a) and (b) above, state clearly any laws, theorems, and equations needed for the explanations, but *do not* take time to prove the theorems or derive the equations. Make the logic of your argument clear, precise, brief, and to the point.

7-27 The potential difference across a load is given by $400 + j175$, and the current through the load is given by $25 - j15$. Find: (a) The equivalent resistance of the load. (b) The equivalent reactance of the load. (c) The power factor for the load. (d) The power used by the load.

7-28 A 60 cycles/sec 100 v potential difference is applied to a circuit, and a current of 5 amp, lagging 60° behind the voltage results. Find: (a) Complex expression for the impedance. [*Ans:* $Z = 10 + j17.3$.] (b) Magnitude of the impedance. (c) Resistance and reactance. (d) Inductance in henrys.

7-29 Two branches are connected in parallel and the combination is connected across a 220 v a-c line. Branch 1 has a current of 10.0 amp leading the line voltage by 20.0°. Branch 2 has a current of 15.0 amp lagging the line voltage by 10.0°. Elect to put the line voltage along the positive axis of reals. (a) What are the vector expressions for the currents in the branches? What would an ammeter read if it were in series in the line? [*Ans:* 24.2 amp.] (b) Write the expressions for the complex impedance of each branch. Draw the circuit diagram in detail and label each resistance and reactance with its magnitude. Be sure that you show the right kind of reactance in each branch.

7-30 Two branches are connected in parallel and the combination is connected across a 150 v 60 cycle/sec a-c line. Branch 1 has a resistance of 10.0 ohms and an inductive reactance of 15.0 ohms. Branch 2 has a resistance of 12.0 ohms and an inductive reactance of 7.00 ohms. The reactances are for $f = 60$ cycles/sec. (a) What is the expression for the complex admittance of each branch and of the equivalent for the two branches in parallel? What is the equation for the equivalent complex impedance of the two branches in parallel? [*Ans:* $Z = 6.02 + j5.34$.] (b) What is a suitable vector expression for the line current? [*Ans:* $I = 14.0 - j12.4$.]

7-31 Three branches are connected in parallel and the combination is connected to a 120 v 60 cycles/sec a-c line. For branch 1: $G_1 = 0.055$ mho, $B_1 = -0.043$ mho. For branch 2: $G_2 = 0.034$ mho, $B_2 = +0.063$ mho. For branch 3: $G_3 = 0.071$ mho, $B_3 = -0.093$ mho. The values of G and B are for $f = 60$ cycles/sec. (a) Draw the circuit diagram, being sure that you have the correct type of reactance in each branch. (b) Find the equation for the equivalent complex impedance of the three branches in parallel. (c) What would an ammeter read if connected in series in the line? [*Ans:* 21.1 amp.]

7-32 In Problem 7-24 it is desired to correct the power factor of the line at the load to unity and, at the same time, reduce the line current to a minimum.

The factory load is to remain the same and the line is to be so adjusted that there will again be 10,000 v across the line at the load. (a) Tell quantitatively how this power factor correction can be made. Include a schematic circuit diagram with numerical values on the circuit elements. (b) What is the power loss on the line after the change you propose has been made? [*Ans:* 5.12 kw.]

7–33 A complicated load has an equivalent circuit of 15.0 ohms resistance in series with 10.0 ohms inductive reactance at 60 cycles/sec. It is connected to a 220 v 60 cycle/sec line. The power factor of the line at the load is to be corrected to unity by the installation of a capacitor in parallel across the load. The line voltage is to be adjusted after the installation of the capacitor so that the voltage at the load is again 220 v. Find the capacitance of the capacitor which must be installed. [*Ans:* 81.3 µf.]

7–34 A capacitor is to be installed across the line at the load in Problem 7–25 in order to correct the line power factor at the load to unity. After the capacitor is installed the generator is to be adjusted so that the voltage at the load will again be given by $V_{load} = 33,500 + j28,300$, with the load current vector still along the positive axis of reals, and thus the magnitude of the voltage across the load will be 43.9 kv as before. (a) What is the vector expression for the current in the capacitor branch? What capacitance must be used and what minimum voltage rating must the capacitor have? [*Ans:* $I_c = -33.4 + j39.4$, 3.14 µf, 62 kv.] (b) What was the power loss on the line before the capacitor was installed? After the capacitor was installed? (c) What was the power delivered to the load before the capacitor was installed? After the capacitor was installed? What was the reading of the wattmeter at the generator before and after C was installed?

7–35 A capacitor of capacitance C is shunted by a resistor of resistance R. What are the equivalent series resistance and capacitance of the combination in terms of C, R, and ω?

7–36 Refer to the circuit in Fig. 7–12–1 and the conditions of special case (A) where $R_2 = 0$ but R_1 is not small compared to X_1. Write the applied line voltage as $v = V_m \sin \omega t$. The two branches have been adjusted so the circuit is in parallel resonance. (a) Show that the instantaneous power input p_c to the capacitor is given by $p_c = (CV_m^2\omega/2) \sin 2\omega t$. (b) Show that the instantaneous power input p_L to the magnetic field of the inductor is given by $p_L = (LI_{1m}^2\omega/2) \sin (2\omega t - 2\phi_1)$ where ϕ_1 is the phase angle for branch 1. (c) Show that the instantaneous power input p_R to the resistor in branch 1 is given by $p_R = I_{1m}^2 R_1/2 - (I_{1m}^2 R_1/2) \cos (2\omega t - 2\phi_1)$ (d) Show that the total instantaneous power input p from the line to the two branches is given by $p = (I_m V_m/2) (1 - \cos 2\omega t)$.

7–37 Consider again the conditions stated in Problem 7–36 and in Sec. 7–12 special case (A). Prove that the maximum energy $CV_m^2/2$ stored on the capacitor is equal to the maximum energy $LI_{1m}^2/2$ stored in the magnetic field of the inductor under conditions of parallel resonance. These two do not occur at the same time, of course. [Note that this same fact for special case (B) is proved in equations (7–12–10) to (7–12–12).]

7–38 Prove that the impedance of a series R–L–C circuit can be written in terms of R and dimensionless variable as $z = R\sqrt{1 + Q^2[(f/f_0) - (f_0/f)]^2}$. For frequencies well above the resonant frequency f_0 this becomes roughly equal to $z = QRf/f_0$.

7-39 Prove that the phase angle ϕ can be written as $\phi = \tan^{-1} Q[(f/f_0) - (f_0/f)]$. For frequencies in the neighborhood of f_0 show that this can be represented by the approximate formula $\phi = \tan^{-1}[2Q(f-f_0)/f_0]$.

SOME ALTERNATING

CURRENT NETWORKS

8–I SOLUTION OF A SERIES-PARALLEL COMBINATION. REDUCTION TO AN EQUIVALENT SERIES CIRCUIT

The method employed in this kind of a problem is an application of the principles already studied. For this reason let us solve a numerical problem

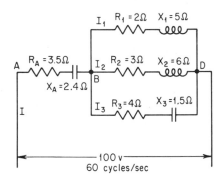

Figure 8–1–1. A series-parallel combination. The circuit constants are known to three significant figures.

as we point out the technique to be employed. Consider the problem posed by the circuit in Fig. 8–1–1. (a) Find the equivalent series circuit between points B and D, i.e., the equivalent series circuit for the three branches in parallel.

$$Y_1 = \frac{1}{Z_1} = \frac{1}{2 + j5}\frac{2 - j5}{2 - j5} = 0.069 - j0.172 \qquad (1)$$

$$Y_2 = \frac{1}{Z_2} = \frac{1}{3 + j6} \frac{3 - j6}{3 - j6} = 0.0667 - j0.134 \qquad (2)$$

$$Y_3 = \frac{1}{Z_3} = \frac{1}{4 - j1.5} \frac{4 + j1.5}{4 + j1.5} = 0.220 + j0.0823 \qquad (3)$$

Let Y_{BD} be the equivalent admittance between B and D, and

$$Y_{BD} = Y_1 + Y_2 + Y_3 = 0.356 - j0.224 \qquad (4)$$

Let Z_{BD} be the equivalent impedance between B and D, and

$$Z_{BD} = \frac{1}{Y_{BD}} = \frac{1}{0.356 - j0.224} = 2.01 + j1.27 \qquad (5)$$

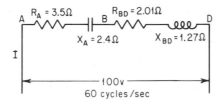

Figure 8–1–2. Equivalent series circuit for the series-parallel combination shown in Fig. 8–1–1.

Thus the equivalent series circuit between B and D is a resistance of 2.01 ohms and an inductive reactance of 1.27 ohms.

(b) Draw the equivalent series circuit A to D and compute the equivalent series impedance. This equivalent series circuit is shown in Fig. 8–1–2.

Let Z be the total impedance from A to D. Complex impedances in series add directly so, from Fig. 8–1–2,

$$Z = Z_{BD} + Z_{AB} = 2.01 + j1.27 + 3.5 - j2.4 = 5.51 - j1.13 \qquad (6)$$

(c) Compute the vector expression for the line current, and each of the branch currents.

At this point in the solution we must make a choice as to orientation of our vector diagram in the complex plane. This is an entirely free choice, but with V known it would be reasonable to put the vector that represents V along the positive axis of reals. Having made this choice, we express V as

$$V = 100 + j0 \qquad (7)$$

Then

$$I = V/Z = (100 + j0)/(5.51 - j1.13) = 17.4 + j3.56 \qquad (8)$$

In order to compute the branch currents we must know the vector expression for the potential difference V_{BD} between B and D.

$$V_{BD} = IZ_{BD} = (17.4 + j3.56)(2.01 + j1.27) = 30.5 + j29.3 \qquad (9)$$

Now we may compute the branch currents.

$$I_1 = V_{BD} Y_1 = (30.5 + j29.3)(0.069 - j0.172) = 7.15 - j3.22 \qquad (10)$$

$$I_2 = V_{BD} Y_2 = 5.97 - j2.14 \qquad (11)$$

$$I_3 = V_{BD} Y_3 = 4.29 + j8.95 \qquad (12)$$

As a check we may use the fact that

$$I = I_1 + I_2 + I_3 \qquad (13)$$

and substitution of the values of I_1, I_2, and I_3 from (10), (11), and (12), respectively, into (13) will give a value of I that checks with the value in (8) within slide rule error.

(d) Compute the vector expression for the potential difference between A and B. Find what a voltmeter would read if connected between A and B, between B and D.

$$V_{AB} = IZ_{AB} = (17.4 + j3.56)(3.5 - j2.4) = 69.3 - j29.3 \qquad (14)$$

As a check we may make use of the fact that

$$V = V_{AB} + V_{BD} \qquad (15)$$

and substitution of the values of V_{AB} from (14) and V_{BD} from (9) into (15) will give a value of V that checks with the value in (7) within slide rule error. From (14)

$$V_{AB} = \sqrt{(69.3)^2 + (29.3)^2} = 75.2 \text{ v}$$

and this is the reading of a voltmeter if it were connected to A and B. From (9)

$$V_{BD} = \sqrt{(30.5)^2 + (29.3)^2} = 42.3 \text{ v.}$$

This is the reading of a voltmeter if it were connected to B and D.

(e) Find what ammeters would read if one were connected in series in each branch and one in the line.

From (10), (11), (12), and (8), $I_1 = \sqrt{(7.15)^2 + (3.22)^2} = 7.84$ amp and, similarly, $I_2 = 6.35$ amp, $I_3 = 9.92$ amp, and $I = 17.7$ amp.

(f) Draw the vector diagram showing all currents and voltages. Show the phase angle for each current with respect to its appropriate voltage.

This vector diagram is shown in Fig. 8–1–3.

(g) Compute the power factors, phase angles, and power used in each part of the circuit and the power input from the line.

The phase angles for the various parts of the circuit are shown in Fig. 8–1–3 and it will be noted that only one, ϕ_{line}, is measured with respect to V and thus with respect to the positive axis of reals. Hence this is the only one

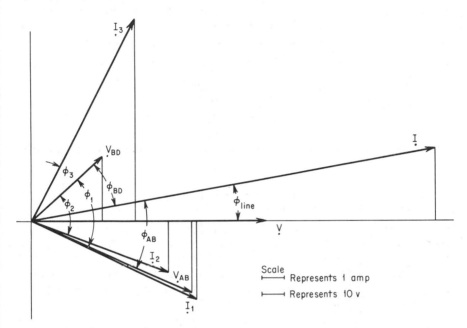

Figure 8–1–3. Vector diagram for the circuit in Fig. 8–1–1, with the applied voltage along the positive axis of reals.

where it is convenient to use the vector diagram for the computation of the power factor. For this one,

$$\cos \phi_{\text{line}} = \frac{\text{real component of } I}{\text{magnitude of } I} = \frac{17.4}{17.7} = 0.984; \phi_{\text{line}} = 10° 15'$$

So the power input from the line to the circuit is $P_{\text{total}} = IV \cos \phi_{\text{line}} = 17.7 \times 100 \times 0.984 = 1740$ w. This same result may also be computed by using the equivalent total resistance between A and D, which, as given in (6), is 5.51 ohms. Such a method is valid since resistance is the only element in this circuit that converts electrical energy irreversibly into some other form, so

$$P_{\text{total}} = I^2 R_{AD} = (17.7)^2 \times 5.51 = 1740 \text{ w}$$

For calculation of all other power factors (and thus phase angles if they are required) it is well to use $\cos \phi = R/z$ from (7–4–3) or $\cos \phi = G/y$ from (7–10–9).

$$\cos \phi_1 = R_1/z_1 = 2/5.38 = 0.374, \quad \text{so} \quad \phi_1 = 68° \, 2'$$

$$P_1 = I_1 V_{BD} \cos \phi_1 = 7.84 \times 42.3 \times 0.374 = 124 \text{ w}$$

or $\qquad P_1 = I_1^2 R_1 = (7.84)^2 \times 2 = 123 \text{ w}$

which agrees within slide rule error. In similar fashion, you may make the computations and obtain: $\cos \phi_2 = 0.447$, $\phi_2 = 63° \, 26'$, $P_2 = 120$ w; $\cos \phi_3 = 0.937$, $\phi_3 = 20° \, 27'$, and $P_3 = 393$ w.

$$\cos \phi_{AB} = R_A/z_{AB} = 3.5/4.25 = 0.824, \quad \text{so} \quad \phi_{AB} = 34° \, 30'$$

$$P_{AB} = IV_{AB} \cos \phi_{AB} = 17.7 \times 75.2 \times 0.824 = 1100 \text{ w}$$

or $\qquad P_{AB} = I^2 R_A = (17.7)^2 \times 3.5 = 1100 \text{ w}$

As a check,

$$P_{\text{total}} = P_1 + P_2 + P_3 + P_{AB}$$

and substitution of the corresponding numbers shows that this checks within slide rule error.

8–2 KIRCHHOFF'S LAWS IN THE COMPLEX FORM. A SELF-INDUCTANCE BRIDGE

From the discussion in Chapter VII and so far in this chapter, it is clear that the following statements of Kirchhoff's two laws are valid for sinusoidal a-c networks when currents and voltages are expressed as vector quantities and impedance is in the complex form. Compare these statements with the ones given in Sec. 2–1 where instantaneous values of current and voltage are considered.

1. KIRCHHOFF'S FIRST LAW. The *algebraic sum of the vector expressions for all currents meeting at a point in a network is zero.*

2. KIRCHHOFF'S SECOND LAW

　　(a) First statement. *The potential difference, expressed in vector form, between two points in a network is the same regardless of the path followed between the two points.*

　　(b) Second statement. *In any closed loop in a network the algebraic sum of the emfs, expressed in vector form, is equal to the algebraic sum of the IZ terms in the same loop.*

　　A SELF-INDUCTANCE BRIDGE. The previous examples given in Chapter VII and in this chapter have applied the above laws. As a further example let us consider a Wheatstone type bridge that is used for the measurement of an unknown self-inductance in terms of a known self-inductance and known resistances. This type of bridge is commonly assembled by students in an electrical measurements laboratory and used for the determination of the self-inductances of coils with cores that are not ferromagnetic. For this purpose, standard noninductive resistance boxes and a calibrated variable self-inductor are used. This circuit also serves as the basic starting point for some commercial types of self-inductance bridges. The circuit is shown schematically in Fig. 8–2–1.

In the circuit in Fig. 8–2–1, L_1 is the self-inductance of the variable calibrated inductor (see Sec. 8–6); L_2 is the unknown self-inductance that is to be measured; R_3 and R_4 are the resistances of calibrated variable noninductive resistors; R_1 is the resistance of the L_1 inductor plus the resistance of a calibrated variable noninductive resistor; R_2 is the resistance of the L_2 inductor plus the resistance of a calibrated variable noninductive resistor; $\mathcal{E}$ is a source of sinusoidal alternating emf with a frequency in the audible range (it is common practice to use 1000 cycles/sec for this frequency); D is a pair of very sensitive headphones used as the detector.

The bridge is balanced by adjusting L_1, R_1, R_2, R_3, and R_4 to the condition

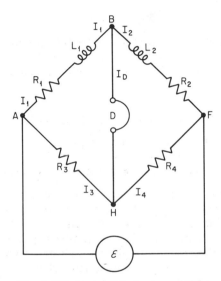

Figure 8–2–1. A self-inductance bridge.

that no sound is heard in the headphones. With a good set of phones and in a quiet room this is a very sensitive balance. When balance is achieved, I_D is zero, so B and H are at the same potential. This statement is true at every instant as well as on the average, because if there were a part of each cycle during which B and H differed in potential there would be current through the phones during this part of each cycle and a sound would be heard. The fact that no sound is heard in the phones guarantees that B and H rise and fall in potential as if they were the same point.

From Kirchhoff's second law as stated above, it follows that

$$V_{AB} = V_{AH} \quad \text{and} \quad V_{BF} = V_{HF} \tag{8–2–1}$$

Let ω be the angular frequency of the source, so that $L_1\omega = X_1$ is the

inductive reactance of number 1 arm, and $L_2\omega = X_2$ is the inductive reactance of the number 2 arm. From (8–2–1),

$$I_1(R_1 + jX_1) = I_3R_3 \quad \text{and} \quad I_2(R_2 + jX_2) = I_4R_4$$

from which

$$I_1(R_1 + jX_1)/[I_2(R_2 + jX_2)] = I_3R_3/I_4R_4 \tag{8–2–2}$$

From Kirchhoff's first law and the fact that $I_D = 0$, $I_1 = I_2$ and $I_3 = I_4$.
Clear fractions

$$R_1R_4 + jR_4X_1 = R_2R_3 + jR_3X_2 \tag{8–2–3}$$

When two complex numbers are equal, the reals are equal and the imaginaries
are equal. Equating reals in (8–2–3),

$$R_1R_4 = R_2R_3, \quad \text{or} \quad R_1/R_2 = R_3/R_4 \tag{8–2–4}$$

Equating imaginaries in (8–2–3),

$$R_4X_1 = R_3X_2, \quad \text{or} \quad X_1/X_2 = R_3/R_4 \tag{8–2–5}$$

Equations (8–2–4) and (8–2–5) are the two balance conditions, and both must
be satisfied when there is no sound in the phones. Equation (8–2–4) may be
used to find the resistance of the unknown inductor if the resistance of the L_1
inductor is known.

Using (8–2–5),

$$L_1\omega/L_2\omega = R_3/R_4, \quad \text{or} \quad L_1/L_2 = R_3/R_4 \tag{8–2–6}$$

With L_1, R_3, and R_4 known, L_2 may be computed.*

8–3 AN IMPERFECT CAPACITOR. A CAPACITANCE BRIDGE

We have considered all capacitors so far as perfect capacitors, i.e., we have
assumed that all energy fed into the capacitor during the charging of the
capacitor is returned to the electric circuit during the discharge of the capacitor. This assumption is not true for any actual capacitor because there is
always some flow of current through the dielectric from one plate to the
other, and thus electrical energy is converted irreversibly into heat energy.
Also, on alternating current, work is done in turning the dielectric molecules
back and forth as the potential difference between the plates alternates, and
the energy for this work is supplied by the electric circuit and is converted
irreversibly into heat. This dissipation of electrical energy into heat energy is
called dielectric loss.

The net result is that the voltage across the capacitor is not 90° out of
phase with the current in the wires leading to the plates and the power factor
is not zero.

An actual capacitor may be treated by means of an equivalent circuit
diagram. By equivalent, here, we mean the same concept that we have used
extensively earlier, i.e., the current, voltage, and power factor shall be the
same in the equivalent circuit as in the actual circuit.

* For greater detail about a-c bridges of this type see Melville B. Stout, *Basic Electrical Measurements* (New York: Prentice-Hall, Inc., 1950), Chap. 9, especially pp. 179–
184.

The equivalent circuit for an actual, or imperfect capacitor may be either a parallel combination of a perfect capacitor and a resistor, or, in an a-c circuit, a series combination of a perfect capacitor and resistor. The resistances will, of course, be very different in the two cases. We have seen how to convert a parallel combination into an equivalent series combination and the process may be reversed.

Since an actual capacitor may be treated by either of these two kinds of equivalent circuits and since we have learned how to handle perfect capacitors either in series or in parallel with resistors, we need only modify our view of an actual capacitor and continue to use the same methods. For high frequencies, the distributed inductive reactance* of a capacitor needs to be considered also, but at power frequencies it is usually negligible.

For our purpose here it will be more convenient to represent an actual capacitor by means of a perfect capacitor in series with a noninductive resistor. The resistance r must be of such magnitude that $I^2 r$ equals the power loss in the actual capacitor, but this will be satisfied when we make the power factor satisfy the requirements of an equivalent circuit.

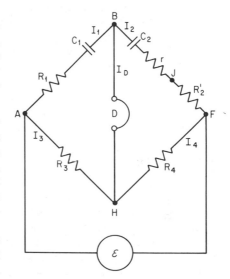

Figure 8–3–1. A capacitance bridge.

CAPACITANCE BRIDGE. As another illustration of the use of Kirchhoff's laws let us consider the Wheatstone type of capacitance bridge shown in Fig. 8–3–1. This bridge will also permit us to measure the equivalent series resistance of an actual imperfect capacitor.

In the circuit in Fig. 8–3–1, C_1 is the capacitance of a variable calibrated capacitor. It is a sufficiently good capacitor so that its equivalent series resistance may be considered to be zero. This means that it is very well made and the dielectric has been selected as one which gives negligible dielectric loss. Variable air capacitors are often used for this purpose. The section from B to J in the diagram represents the equivalent circuit of the actual capacitor whose properties are to be measured. It shows a perfect capacitance C_2 in series with an equivalent resistance r. Resistance R_2' is that of a calibrated variable noninductive resistor. The remainder of the symbols in the diagram have the same meaning as they did in Fig. 8–2–1.

The bridge is balanced by adjusting C_1, R_1, R_2', R_3, and R_4 to a condition such that there is no sound in the headphone. The same comments that were made about the inductance bridge now apply and we may derive

* See, for example, Melville B. Stout, *Basic Electrical Measurements* (New York: Prentice-Hall, Inc., 1950), pp. 293–94.

the balance conditions as we did there. Let $R_2 = r + R_2'$, $X_1 = 1/C_1\omega$, and $X_2 = 1/C_2\omega$.

From Kirchhoff's second law $I_1(R_1 - jX_1) = I_3R_3$ and $I_2(R_2 - jX_2) = I_4R_4$. Also from Kirchhoff's first law $I_1 = I_2$ and $I_3 = I_4$, since $I_D = 0$. You can solve these equations and obtain

$$R_1/R_2 = R_3/R_4 \tag{8-3-1}$$

and

$$X_1/X_2 = R_3/R_4 \quad \text{oo} \quad C_2/C_1 = R_3/R_4 \tag{8-3-2}$$

From (8–3–1), R_2 may be computed and then from $R_2 = r + R_2'$, r may be computed. Hence we know the equivalent perfect capacitance C_2 and the equivalent series resistance r for the actual capacitor measured. We may now compute its phase angle for sinusoidal a-c wave form from (4–7–10), as $\phi = \tan^{-1}(1/rC_2\omega)$, and thus its power factor is expressed as $\cos\phi = rC_2\omega/\sqrt{1 + r^2C_2^2\omega^2}$. In general the smaller the power factor the better the capacitor, because a small power factor means small power loss. For most purposes, if the capacitor is good enough so that it can be used, $r^2C_2^2\omega^2$ must be small compared with unity, and in such cases the power factor is given by

$$\cos\phi = rC_2\omega \tag{8-3-3}$$

Some commercial capacitance bridges give the product $rC_2\omega$, as well as C_2, as part of the reading after balance has been attained. This quantity $rC_2\omega$ is called the *dissipation factor* for the capacitor and is represented by D.

8–4 MUTUAL INDUCTANCE M

At this point you should review Secs. 3–4, 3–5, 3–8, and 3–9, for we wish to extend the discussion there to a consideration of mutual inductance.

We have pointed out that whenever the magnetic flux through a circuit changes an emf is always induced. If the current in a coil of wire is changing, its magnetic field is changing. If there is a second coil near the first one the magnetic flux linkages with the second coil change as the current in the first coil changes, and thus an emf is induced in the second coil. This emf is referred to as an emf of mutual induction to distinguish it from the emf of self-induction. Hence a changing current in a coil of wire induces an emf of self-induction in itself and an emf of mutual induction in a neighboring coil.

There is said to be mutual inductance between coils 1 and 2 and we wish to define the term mutual inductance. The coil in which the current is changing is called the primary, and the coil in which the emf of mutual induction is established is called the secondary. We shall now define mutual inductance under the conditions of Fig. 8–4–1 where coil 1 is the primary and coil 2 is the secondary. This mutual inductance is represented by the symbol M_{12}. The subscript on M is read "one, two" (not "twelve") and means the mutual inductance between coils 1 and 2 when coil 1 is the primary and coil 2 is the secondary. Note that the first subscript tells which coil is the primary and the second subscript tells which coil is the secondary.

The mutual inductance M_{12} is defined as the number of magnetic flux linkages with coil 2 for unit current in coil 1. Let $n_{12} =$ number of magnetic flux linkages with 2 for a current i_1 flowing in 1, where n_{12} is in weber turns in the mks system. Hence from the definition of M_{12},

$$M_{12} = n_{12}/i_1, \quad \text{or} \quad n_{12} = M_{12}i_1 \qquad (8\text{–}4\text{–}1)$$

If there is no ferromagnetic material in the core [see discussion just prior to (3–7–1)] we may differentiate (8–4–1) with respect to time as follows.

$$dn_{12}/dt = M_{12}\, di_1/dt \qquad (8\text{–}4\text{–}2)$$

Let e_2 = emf induced in 2 due to the rate of change of the magnetic flux linkages with 2. Then, from (3–8–2) and (8–4–2),

$$e_2 = -dn_{12}/dt = -M_{12}\, di_1/dt \qquad (8\text{–}4\text{–}3)$$

or $$M_{12} = -e_2/(di_1/dt) \qquad (8\text{–}4\text{–}4)$$

From (8–4–4) we may state an equivalent definition for the mutual inductance, between two coils that do not have a ferromagnetic core, as follows. *The mutual inductance M_{12} is equal to the emf induced in coil 2 when the current in coil 1 is changing at the rate of one ampere per second.*

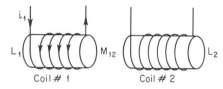

The henry is used as a unit of mutual inductance as well as a unit of self-inductance. From (8–4–4), two coils have, by definition, *a mutual inductance of one henry if an emf of one volt is induced in the secondary due to a primary current changing at the rate of one ampere per second.* From this the unit of the henry is given by the following equivalence:

Coil # 1   Coil # 2

Figure 8–4–1. Changing current in coil 1 produces a change in the number of magnetic flux linkages with coil 2 and thus induces an emf of mutual induction in coil 2.

$$1 \text{ henry} = \frac{\text{volt}}{1 \text{ ampere/sec}} = 1\,\frac{\text{volt sec}}{\text{ampere}}$$

This equivalence yields the same unit for the henry of mutual inductance as for the henry of self-inductance (see Sec. 3–7) and is also the same unit for the henry as we would obtain from (8–4–1) if we used the fact that 1 weber = 1 volt sec.

Now let us start over again and consider that a current i_2 is flowing in coil 2 in Fig. 8–4–1 and no current is flowing in coil 1. Hence, now we are taking coil 2 as the primary and coil 1 as the secondary, so we now represent the mutual inductance between them as M_{21}. Following the same procedure as above, we proceed to define M_{21}. *The mutual inductance M_{21} is defined as the number of magnetic flux linkages with coil 1 for unit current in coil 2.*

Continuing the argument as above, we arrive at

$$M_{21} = n_{21}/i_2, \quad \text{and} \quad M_{21} = -e_1/(di_2/dt) \qquad (8\text{–}4\text{–}5)$$

8-5 PROOF THAT $M_{12} = M_{21}$

(A) Let us calculate the energy stored in the magnetic field about coils 1 and 2 when a current I_1 is flowing in 1 and a current I_2 is flowing in 2, and these two currents are flowing in such senses that their magnetic fields strengthen each other. We shall calculate this energy stored in the magnetic field by calculating the energy fed from the electric circuits into the magnetic field while the magnetic field was being established.

We know from (5-1-10) that, when the situation is as shown in Fig. 8-5-1, the energy W_1 which has been fed from the circuit into the magnetic field of coil 1 is given by

$$W_1 = \tfrac{1}{2}L_1 I_1^2 \qquad (8\text{-}5\text{-}1)$$

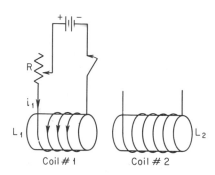

Figure 8-5-1. Current i_1 rises from 0 to I_1 establishing a magnetic field about coil 1. This magnetic field links coil 2.

In Fig. 8-5-1 no energy has been fed into the mutual field of the two coils because the emf induced in coil 2 does not see a complete circuit, and thus no secondary current flows.

Now in Fig. 8-5-2, close the switch S in circuit 2 and, by adjusting the rheostat R in circuit 1, keep I_1 constant while i_2 rises from zero to I_2. You will recall from elementary physics the rule for determining the direction of the magnetic field produced by a current flowing in a wire. The rule says, in imagination grasp the wire with the right hand pointing the thumb in the direction of the current, and the fingers, as they encircle the wire, will point in the direction of the magnetic field produced by the current. For a current flowing in a coil of wire, this rule can be restated as: in imagination grasp the coil of wire with the right hand pointing the fingers in the direction of the current, and the thumb will point in the direction of the magnetic field which the current produces inside the coil. Note that the currents flow in the two coils of Fig. 8-5-2 in such senses that both magnetic fields are directed from left

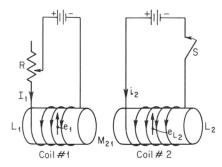

Figure 8-5-2. Current i_2 rises from 0 to I_2 while I_1 is kept constant.

to right inside the coils and thus the magnetic fields strengthen each other.

The energy W_2 in the magnetic field of coil 2 due to its self-inductance is given by

$$W_2 = \tfrac{1}{2}L_2 I_2^2 \qquad (8\text{-}5\text{-}2)$$

But in this case (8-5-2) does not tell the whole story. The emf e_1 induced in coil 1, due to the changing current in coil 2, is in the sense of the arrow marked

e_1 in Fig. 8–5–2. From this, and the fact that you adjust R in such a way that I_1 is kept constant, you can show in Problem 8–9 that the additional energy fed into the mutual magnetic field of the two coils is given by

$$W_{M21} = M_{21}I_1I_2 \qquad (8\text{–}5\text{–}3)$$

The symbol M_{21} is used in (8–5–3) because coil 2 is the primary and coil 1 is the secondary during the process of feeding energy from the electric circuit into the mutual field of the two coils.

The final total energy W_{21} in the magnetic field is the sum of the energies in (8–5–1), (8–5–2), and (8–5–3), so

$$W_{21} = \tfrac{1}{2}L_1I_1^2 + \tfrac{1}{2}L_2I_2^2 + M_{21}I_1I_2 \qquad (8\text{–}5\text{–}4)$$

Now start the experiment over again with $i_1 = 0$ and $i_2 = 0$. Let i_2 rise from 0 to I_2 while i_1 is zero; then let i_1 rise from 0 to I_1 while I_2 is held constant. You can see that the result will be the same except that now coil 1 is the primary and coil 2 the secondary while energy is being fed from the electric circuit into the mutual magnetic field. Hence M_{12} must be used for the mutual inductance. In this case the final total energy W_{12} in the magnetic field is

$$W_{12} = \tfrac{1}{2}L_1I_1^2 + \tfrac{1}{2}L_2I_2^2 + M_{12}I_1I_2 \qquad (8\text{–}5\text{–}5)$$

The total energy stored in the magnetic field must be the same in (8–5–4) and (8–5–5) because the final state is the same in the two cases, i.e., the same current I_1 is flowing in circuit 1 in both cases, the same current I_2 is flowing in circuit 2 in both cases, and the geometrical arrangement is the same. In symbols $W_{12} = W_{21}$, so it follows from (8–5–4) and (8–5–5) that

$$M_{12} = M_{21} \qquad (8\text{–}5\text{–}6)$$

Thus the *mutual inductance M between two coils is the same whichever one is used as the primary.* From this and the definition of M in (8–4–1) it follows that *the number of magnetic flux linkages with coil 2 due to unit current in coil 1 is the same as the number of magnetic flux linkages with coil 1 due to unit current in coil 2.*

Now we may write either (8–5–4) or (8–5–5) as

$$W = \tfrac{1}{2}L_1I_1^2 + \tfrac{1}{2}L_2I_2^2 + MI_1I_2 \qquad (8\text{–}5\text{–}7)$$

(B) CALCULATION OF THE ENERGY STORED IN THE MAGNETIC FIELD OF THE TWO COILS IF THEIR CURRENTS FLOW IN SUCH SENSES THAT THEIR MAGNETIC FIELDS OPPOSE EACH OTHER.

In Problem 8–10 you are asked to prove that the equation

$$W = \tfrac{1}{2}L_1I_1^2 + \tfrac{1}{2}L_2I_2^2 - MI_1I_2 \qquad (8\text{–}5\text{–}8)$$

gives the energy stored in the magnetic field in this case.

8–6 SELF-INDUCTORS IN SERIES. THE VARIABLE SELF-INDUCTOR

So far, when dealing with self-inductors in series, we have taken the total self-inductance to be the sum of the separate self-inductances. This procedure assumes either that the self-inductors are far enough apart so that the mutual inductance between them is essentially zero or that the effect of the mutual inductance is included in the measured value of the self-inductance. In this latter case the geometry of arrangement of the two inductors must be kept constant.

Now we wish to inquire specifically into the influence of mutual inductance between two inductors in series, on the total self-inductance.

In Fig. 8–6–1 (a) two coils are shown so connected that the current flows in the same sense in both and thus their magnetic fields strengthen each other. The self-inductance of coil 1 alone is L_1 and of coil 2 alone is L_2. Let e_{L1} be the emf of self-induction set up in coil 1 due to the changing current in L_1, and e_{L2} be the emf of self-induction set up in coil 2 due to the changing current in L_2.

$$e_{L1} = L_1 \, di/dt \quad \text{and} \quad e_{L2} = L_2 \, di/dt \tag{8–6–1}$$

The minus sign that appears in the usual statement $e_L = -L \, di/dt$ is included to show the sense of e_L, i.e., e_L is in such a sense as to oppose the change in the current. In the present argument we shall take proper account of the senses of all the induced emf's by the way in which we used them in the

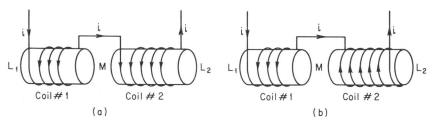

Coil # 1   Coil # 2   Coil # 1   Coil # 2

(a)   (b)

Figure 8–6–1. Two inductors in series: (a) connected so that their magnetic fields strengthen each other; (b) connected so that their magnetic fields oppose each other.

equations. Hence our terms $L \, di/dt$ and $M \, di/dt$ here mean the absolute magnitude of these quantities.

Let e_{M1} be the emf set up in coil 1 due to the changing current in coil 2, and let e_{M2} be the emf set up in coil 2 due to the changing current in coil 1; then

$$e_{M1} = M \, di/dt \quad \text{and} \quad e_{M2} = M \, di/dt \tag{8–6–2}$$

By analogy with the situation in Fig. 8–5–2 we can see that in Fig. 8–6–1 (a) the emf's of mutual induction will be in the same sense as the emf's of self-induction. Let e_L represent the total emf set up in the two coils due to the changing current. Then e_L will equal e_{L1} plus the emf of mutual induction set up in coil 1 plus e_{L2} plus the emf of mutual induction set up in coil 2, or, as an equation,

$$e_L = (L_1 + L_2 + 2M)(di/dt) \tag{8–6–3}$$

Let L equal the equivalent self-inductance of the two coils in series. From (8–6–3) we see that

$$L = L_1 + L_2 + 2M \tag{8–6–4}$$

when the two coils are wound in the same direction.

Consider Fig. 8–6–1 (b) where the two coils are wound in opposite directions. By reasoning similar to that in the solution of Problem 8–10 it can be seen that the emf of mutual induction in each coil will be in the opposite sense to that of the emf of self-induction, so in this case,

$$e_L = (L_1 + L_2 - 2M)(di/dt) \qquad (8\text{–}6\text{–}5)$$

so that
$$L = L_1 + L_2 - 2M \qquad (8\text{–}6\text{–}6)$$

when the coils are wound in opposite directions.

Equations (8–6–4) and (8–6–6) are the basis for the construction of a variable self-inductance such as the one referred to as L_1 in the inductance bridge circuit of Fig. 8–2–1. The two coils of Fig. 8–6–1 may be arranged mechanically so that one can be moved or rotated with respect to the other. In this manner the mutual inductance can be changed, with a resulting change in the equivalent self-inductance of the two coils in series. One type of variable self-inductor has coil 1 wound on the inside surface of a section of a sphere. Coil 2 is wound on the outside surface of a section of another sphere concentric with the first and of slightly smaller radius. The inner section of a sphere is mounted with an axis across a diameter so that it may be rotated through 180° relative to the outside spherical section. Thus the inner coil may be rotated from a position where the coils are oppositely wound and (8–6–6) applies, to a position where the coils are wound in the same direction and (8–6–4) applies. This makes the equivalent self-inductance continuously variable from $L_1 + L_2 - 2M$ to $L_1 + L_2 + 2M$. If such an inductor has a pointer and scale it may be calibrated against a standard and be used as a variable calibrated inductor.*

1. ONE METHOD FOR MEASUREMENT OF M. Equations (8–6–4) and (8–6–6) suggest a means of measuring the mutual inductance between two coils. Let L' be the equivalent self-inductance of the two coils when they are connected as in Fig. 8–6–1 (a), and $L' = L_1 + L_2 + 2M$. Measure L' by a bridge such as the one in Sec. 8–2. Now connect the two coils as in Fig. 8–6–1 (b), measure the equivalent self-inductance and represent it by L'', where $L'' = L_1 + L_2 - 2M$. From these two equations $M = (L' - L'')/4$, and M may be computed from the measured values of L'' and L'.

2. INDUCTORS THAT SATISFY VERY SPECIAL CONDITIONS. Suppose we have two coils so wound and located with respect to each other that all the magnetic flux lines from each coil link all its own turns of wire and all turns of the other coil. Let N_1 = number of turns of wire on coil 1; Φ_1 = number of magnetic flux lines set up in coil 1 due to a current i_1 in the coil; N_2 = number of turns of wire on coil 2; Φ_2 = number of magnetic flux lines set up in coil 2 due to a current i_2 in this coil. From (3–9–2), L is the number of magnetic flux linkages for unit current, so for this special condition where all flux lines link all turns, $L_1 = N_1\Phi_1/i_1$ and $L_2 = N_2\Phi_2/i_2$. From the definition of mutual inductance

---

* For more detail about standard inductors and other types of variable inductors see a book on electrical measurements, e.g., Melville B. Stout, *Basic Electrical Measurements* (Englewood Cliffs, N.J.: Prentice-Hall, Inc., 1950), pp. 280–87, and the references given there.

in (8–4–1) and the special condition that all flux lines from one coil link all turns of the other coil, $M = N_1\Phi_2/i_2 = N_2\Phi_1/i_1$ so $M^2 = (N_1\Phi_2/i_2)(N_2\Phi_1/i_1)$ $= (N_1\Phi_1/i_1)(N_2\Phi_2/i_2) = L_1L_2$

or $$M = \sqrt{L_1L_2} \tag{8–6–7}$$

for this very special case.

Now suppose further that the two coils are identical, so that $L_1 = L_2$; then, from (8–6–7),

$$M = L_1 = L_2, \quad \text{or}, \quad 2M = L_1 + L_2. \tag{8–6–8}$$

A variable inductor built to satisfy these very special and rigid requirements when the two coils are parallel (either when turned so that they are wound in the same direction or in opposite directions) could be variable from $L = 0$ to $L = 4L_1$. These conditions can never be completely satisfied in a variable inductor, so such an inductor can never have a self-inductance quite as small as zero or quite as large as $4L_1$. However the conditions are closely approximated in a good variable calibrated self-inductor.

Such a variable inductor may be used as a variable mutual inductor also. For such use the coils are not connected in series but one is used as the primary and the other as the secondary.

8–7 COUPLING AND COEFFICIENT OF COUPLING

Consider again (8–6–7) and the conditions under which it was derived. Under these ideal conditions the coils are said to have complete coupling. If most, but not all, of the flux lines from one coil link the other coil, the two coils are said to have *close coupling*. If only a few flux lines from one coil link the other coil, the two coils are said to have *loose coupling*. These are qualitative concepts that are often useful. We may make the concept quantitative by defining a term, called the *coefficient of coupling K*, by the equation

$$M = K\sqrt{L_1L_2}, \quad \text{or} \quad K = M/\sqrt{L_1L_2} \tag{8–7–1}$$

where K has the value of unity if the coils are completely coupled as they were for the derivation of (8–6–7). The looser the coupling the smaller the value of K.

8–8 REPRESENTATION OF THE EMF OF MUTUAL INDUCTION AS A COMPLEX NUMBER. HEYDWEILLER BRIDGE FOR MUTUAL INDUCTANCE

The emf e_2 of mutual induction in the secondary is given by $e_2 = M(di_1/dt)$, where i_1 is the instantaneous current in the primary. If i_1 is sinusoidal we may write $i_1 = I_{1m}\sin\omega t$, so

$$e_2 = M\,di_1/dt = MI_{1m}\omega\cos\omega t = MI_{1m}\omega\sin(\omega t + \pi/2)$$

Let $\mathscr{E}_{2m}$ be the maximum emf induced in the secondary, and $\mathscr{E}_{2m} = I_{1m}M\omega$ where $\mathscr{E}_{2m}$ is 90° out of phase with the current I_{1m}. We have seen that we may represent this 90° phase difference between current and voltage by the operator j. Thus we may write

$$\mathscr{E}_{2m} = jI_{1m}M\omega \qquad (8\text{-}8\text{-}1)$$

to represent both the magnitude and phase of $\mathscr{E}_{2m}$ relative to I_{1m}. Divide both sides of (8-8-1) by $\sqrt{2}$ in order to have rms values of current and voltage, and we have

$$\mathscr{E}_2 = jI_1M\omega \qquad (8\text{-}8\text{-}2)$$

We see that (8-8-2) is analogous to the use of $jIL\omega = jIX_L$ to take account of the emf of self-induction, which is 90° out of phase with the current. Here $M\omega$ is sometimes called *mutual reactance* and represented by X_M.

The sign to be used with $jI_1M\omega$ depends on the circuit connections. We shall not have time to consider this question in any detail,* but shall illustrate it with one more example, using Kirchhoff's laws in the complex form.

HEYDWEILLER'S NETWORK FOR MEASURING MUTUAL INDUCTANCE. Figure 8-8-1 shows one of the many types of networks used for the measurement of mutual inductance. It permits the measurement of M in terms of the known capacitance of a capacitor and of known resistances. In the figure, M is the mutual inductance to be measured, and is the mutual inductance between the primary coil P and the secondary coil S. The circuit diagram symbol used here is the usual one for a mutual inductor that does not have a ferromagnetic core. In this circuit

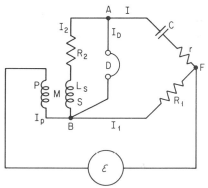

Figure 8-8-1. Heydweiller's network for mutual inductance.

diagram, L_S is the self-inductance of the secondary coil S; R_2 is the known resistance of S plus a calibrated variable noninductive resistor; C is a calibrated variable capacitor of sufficiently high quality so that its equivalent series resistance may be considered to be zero; R_1 and r are calibrated variable noninductive resistors; D is a sensitive headphone; $\mathscr{E}$ is a source of sinusoidal alternating emf of audible frequency.

The network is balanced by adjusting R_2, C, r, and R_1 to a condition such that no sound is heard in the phone, thus indicating that A and B are at the same potential. Since A and B are at the same potential, there is a zero net potential difference along the path from B through S and R_2 to A. In order for this latter condition to be possible, the emf of mutual induction set up in S, due to the changing current in P, must be directed oppositely to the emf of self-induction set up in S by the changing current in S. This in turn requires that P and S must be connected, at B, in such a way that they are oppositely

---

* For more detail see engineering books on alternating current networks, e.g., R. M. Kerchner and G. F. Corcoran, *Alternating Current Circuits* (New York: John Wiley & Sons, Inc., 1943), pp. 193–96.

wound, as illustrated in Fig. 8–6–1 (b). Then, P and S are said to be negatively coupled, and this condition must be satisfied or a balance cannot be obtained.

We may express the fact that there is a zero net potential drop along the path BSR_2A by the complex equation

$$I_2(R_2 + jL_S\omega) - jI_PM\omega = 0 \qquad (8\text{–}8\text{–}3)$$

Equation (8–8–3) illustrates the usual rule that the negative sign is used on $jIM\omega$ of (8–8–2) if the emf of mutual induction is opposite to the emf of self-induction in a particular winding, and conversely for the positive sign.

Also, from the fact that A and B are at the same potential, we may write

$$I(r - jX_C) = I_1R_1 \qquad (8\text{–}8\text{–}4)$$

From Kirchhoff's first law, since $I_D = 0$,

$$I_2 = I \quad \text{and} \quad I_P = I_1 + I_2 \qquad (8\text{–}8\text{–}5)$$

Put this value of I_P into (8–8–3), and we have

$$I_2(R_2 + jL_S\omega) - jI_2M\omega = jI_1M\omega \qquad (8\text{–}8\text{–}6)$$

Put the value of I from (8–8–5) into (8–8–4), and obtain

$$I_2(r - jX_C) = I_1R_1 \qquad (8\text{–}8\text{–}7)$$

Divide (8–8–6) by (8–8–7) and cancel the currents, then clear fractions.

$$R_1R_2 + j\omega R_1(L_S - M) = M\omega X_C + jM\omega r \qquad (8\text{–}8\text{–}8)$$

Equate reals, use the fact that $X_C = 1/C\omega$, and solve for M.

$$M = R_1R_2C \qquad (8\text{–}8\text{–}9)$$

which is one balance condition. Equate imaginaries in (8–8–8) and solve for M.

$$M = \frac{R_1}{r + R_1} L_S \qquad (8\text{–}8\text{–}10)$$

which is the second balance condition, and both balance conditions must be satisfied simultaneously. Note, from (8–8–10), that L_S must be larger than M in order for a balance to be possible. If this is not satisfied by the secondary alone, an additional self-inductor is needed in series with the secondary.

Since R_2 and C appear in the balance condition in (8–8–9) and not in the other one, whereas r appears in (8–8–10) and not in (8–8–9), the balance may be achieved by alternate adjustment of R_2 or C and r.

PROBLEMS

8–1 Coils 1 and 2 are connected in parallel. Coil 1 has a resistance of 8 ohms and an inductive reactance of 6 ohms. Coil 2 has a resistance of 5 ohms and an inductive reactance of 4 ohms. Coil 3 is connected in series with the parallel combination of coils 1 and 2. Coil 3 has a resistance of 4.5 ohms and an inductive reactance of 3.6 ohms. The reactances are all for f = 60 cycles/sec. This series-parallel combination is connected across a 110 v 60 cycles/sec

line. Take the vector which represents this line voltage along the positive axis of reals. Find: (a) The current flowing through each coil. [*Ans:* $I_1 =$ 4.45 amp, $I_2 = 6.95$ amp, $I = 11.4$ amp.] (b) The potential difference across each coil. (c) The line current.
(d) The line power factor. (e) How does it happen that the line current is (to three significant figures) the arithmetic sum of the currents in the branches? Is this true in general?

8–2 (a) Using complex numbers, find the currents I, I_B, and I_C in the circuit of Fig. 8–P–1. Express your answers in the complex form and find the magnitudes. (b) Draw a vector diagram showing V, I, I_B, and I_C, and from the diagram show that your answers for the currents are self-consistent. The resistances and reactances, on the diagram in Fig. 8–P–1, are in ohms for 60 cycles/sec alternating current.

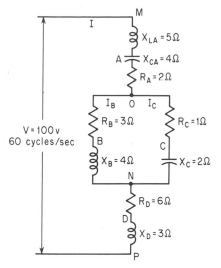

Figure 8–P–1.

8–3 (1) Prove that the circuits in (a) and (b) of Fig. 8–P–2 are equivalent if: $R_2 = (R_1^2 + X_1^2)/R_1$ and $X_2 = (R_1^2 + X_1^2)/X_1$; or if: $R_1 = R_2 X_2^2/(R_2^2 + X_2^2)$ and $X_1 = R_2^2 X_2/(R_2^2 + X_2^2)$. (2) Prove that the same formulas hold if inductive reactances replace X_1 and X_2 in the figures.

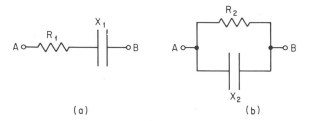

(a)

(b)

Figure 8–P–2.

8–4 With the applied line voltage along the positive axis of reals, find the vector expressions for the current I and I_2 in Fig. 8–P–3. [*Ans:* $I = 13.8 -$ $j13.9$, $I_2 = 8.32 - j4.85$.]

8–5 Find the vector expressions for the currents I_1, I_2, and I_3 in Fig. 8–P–4. The arrows show the assumed directions of the positive senses of the current vectors. [*Ans:* $I_1 = 1.07 - j0.435$, $I_2 = 3.83 + j5.04$.]

8–6 As an alternate calculation of the numerical example in Sec. 7–12 given in connection with Figs. 7–12–3 and 7–12–4, assume that the capacitor to be used for power factor correction of the line to unity is not perfect but is one whose power factor is 0.0369 [see Sec. 8–3 and equation (8–3–3)]. As in the illustrated example, the potential difference across the line at the load is reestablished at 550 v after the capacitor is installed. (a) What capacitance must the capacitor have in order to correct the line power factor to unity?

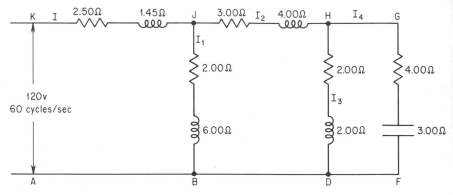

Figure 8–P–3.

(b) What is the equivalent series resistance of the capacitor and what is the power loss in the capacitor? [*Ans:* 0.251 ohm, 1670 w.] (c) What is the line current and what is the power loss on the line? [*Ans:* 51.5 amp, 2650 w.]

8–7 In Problem 8–6 in place of part (a), find the capacitance the capacitor must have in order that the line current shall lag the line voltage by 10.0° after the capacitor is installed. Such an installation gives partial power factor correction. The capacitor itself still has a power factor of 0.0369. [*Ans:* 347 μf.]

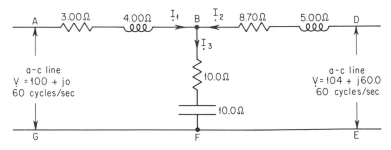

Figure 8–P–4.

8–8 In Problem 7–33 the capacitor to be installed has a power factor of 0.100 [see Sec. 8–3 and equation (8–3–3)] and the power factor of the line at the load is to be corrected to 0.966 (instead of unity) with the line current lagging the line voltage. The rest of the conditions of the problem are as stated in Problem 7–33. Find the capacitance of the capacitor that must be installed.

8–9 Solve the problem stated in Sec. 8–5 just prior to (8–5–3). First give an argument to show that e_1 is in the sense of the arrow marked e_1 in Fig. 8–5–2 and then derive (8–5–3).

8–10 Derive (8–5–8) under the conditions stated in heading (B) of Sec. 8–5.

8–11 The *Owen* bridge, shown in Fig. 8–P–5, is used to measure the unknown self-inductance L_x and its unknown resistance R_x in terms of the variable, standard capacitors C_1 and C_3, and the variable, standard, non-inductive resistors R_2 and R_3. The standard capacitors C_1 and C_3 are of high enough quality so their equivalent series resistances can be considered to be zero. The source $\mathscr{E}$ provides a sinusoidal alternating voltage of audible frequency ω and, at balance, no sound is heard in the headphone detector D. Derive the balance conditions $L_x = R_2 R_3 C_1$ and $R_x = R_2 C_1 / C_3$.

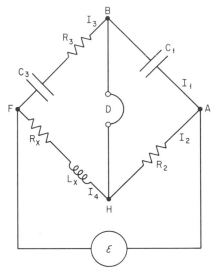

Figure 8–P–5. Owen bridge.

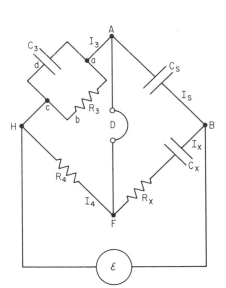

Figure 8–P–6. Schering bridge.

8–12 Figure 8–P–6 shows the *Schering* bridge which is used for measurement of capacitance. The unknown capacitor has a capacitance C_x and an equivalent series resistance R_x, as shown in the number two bridge arm. The standard variable capacitors C_s and C_3 are of high quality and their equivalent series resistances can be considered to be zero. The standard, variable, non-inductive resistors are R_3 and R_4. The source $\mathscr{E}$ supplies a sinusoidal alternating voltage of audible frequency ω and, at balance, no sound is heard in the headphone. Show that the balance conditions are $R_x = R_4 C_3 / C_s$ and $C_x = C_s R_3 / R_4$.

8–13 The *Anderson* bridge, shown in Fig. 8–P–7, is used to measure the unknown inductance L_X and unknown resistance R_X in terms of the standard variable resistors R_1, R_2, R_3, and R_5 and capacitor C_s. The source $\mathscr{E}$ supplies a sinusoidal alternating voltage of audible frequency ω. At balance, no sound is heard in the headphone detector D. Show that at balance $L_X = C_s R_2$ $(R_3 + R_5 + R_3 R_5/R_1)$ and $R_X = R_2 R_3/R_1$.

8–14 The *Heaviside* mutual inductance bridge is shown in Fig. 8–P–8 where M represents the unknown mutual inductance whose value is to be determined.

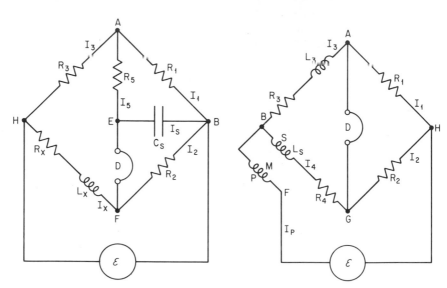

Figure 8–P–7. Anderson bridge.   **Figure 8–P–8.** Heaviside bridge.

The self-inductance of the secondary S is represented by L_s, and R_4 includes the resistance of S and the resistance of a standard, variable, non-inductive resistor. The self-inductance of a variable, standard inductor is shown as L_3, while R_3 represents the resistance of this inductor plus a variable, standard, non-inductive resistor. The resistors R_1 and R_2 are similar variable standards. The source $\mathcal{E}$ gives an audio frequency sinusoidal voltage and balance has been established when no sound is heard in the headphone detector D. Prove that the balance conditions are given by

$$R_4 = R_2 R_3/R_1$$

and

$$M = (R_2 L_3 - R_1 L_s)/(R_1 + R_2).$$

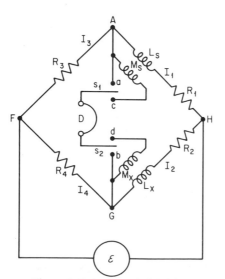

Figure 8–P–9. Campbell bridge.

8–15 Figure 8–P–9 shows the *Campbell* bridge for measurement of the unknown mutual inductance M_x in terms of the standard, variable

mutual inductance M_s and the resistances of the standard, variable resistors. The source $\mathscr{E}$ provides a sinusoidal voltage of audible freqeuncy ω
and, at balance, there is no sound in the headphone detector D. The
balancing has to be done in two stages:

(1) With switches S_1 and S_2 in contact with a and b respectively, adjust
the resistors so that there is no sound in the headphone. Prove that this
balance condition yields $R_1/R_2 = R_3/R_4 = L_s/L_x$.

(2) Next, move S_1 and S_2 so they make contact with c and d respectively,
and adjust M_s, with the resistors fixed, to such a setting that there is no
sound in D. The emf's induced in the two secondaries must be opposite in
phase, and it may be necessary to reverse the connection of one secondary
in order to achieve a balance. Prove that this balance condition yields
$M_s/M_x = R_3/R_4$.

THE ELECTROSTATIC FIELD

9–1 REVIEW OF SOME OF THE CONCEPTS OF ELECTROSTATICS

We introduced the subject of electricity, in the first eight chapters, by a study of electric currents and some of their properties. This was made possible by the fact that you had previously studied the subject in an elementary course and had learned something of the properties and laws of electric charges at rest and in motion. Now we wish to give further attention to the properties of electric charges at rest. At the start of this discussion we need to remind you of some of the concepts of electrostatics which you studied in elementary physics in order that we may build on these concepts. Electrostatics and current electricity are related parts of a unified theory as we shall see more clearly as the theory develops.

1. CHARGING BY FRICTION. One of the earliest observations of electricity had to do with electrification by "friction" or "rubbing". You learned in the laboratory or by lecture demonstration that, when a hard rubber rod is rubbed with fur (catskin is very good for this purpose), the rod develops an electric charge. The charge on the rubber rod was said to be a negative charge long before any one understood the nature of electric charges. Further, if a glass rod is rubbed with silk, the glass develops a charge. The glass rod is found to attract the rubber rod, whereas two charged rubber rods repel each other. Hence the glass rod was said to have an opposite kind of charge to that on the rubber rod and the charge on the glass rod was said to be positive. From this arose the knowledge that *there are two kinds of charge* and the law that *like charges repel each other, while unlike charges attract each other*. A little further experimentation shows that the force between charged bodies decreases as the distance between the bodies increases.

Much later in history when the electron was discovered it was found to have the same kind of charge as that on the rubber rod, so the electron is said to have a negative charge. The convention, of calling the charge on the electron negative, was pointed out in Sec. 1–1, and you are urged to review Chapter I at this point. We now think of the rubber rod as having a negative charge because electrons "rubbed off" onto it from the fur. If the process of rubbing the rubber rod with fur is carried out in such a manner that both are carefully insulated from the ground, you will find that the fur has a positive charge (i.e., it will attract a charged rubber rod and will repel a charged glass rod). Similarly the silk has a negative charge after it has rubbed the glass. This substantiates our theory that the rubbing process separates charge but does not create charge.

2. CHARGING BY INDUCTION. We observe experimentally that one of our charged rods will attract an uncharged body. To be explicit, let us consider the case where a charged rubber rod attracts a piece of metal and explain it by the electron theory.

Consider Fig. 9–1–1 in which a negatively charged rubber rod R is held close to one end of an insulated piece of metal MN, which at the outset is uncharged. The surplus electrons on the rubber rod repel the electrons in the metal. Hence, a few free electrons move from M to N, leaving a net positive charge at M and a net negative charge at N. Equilibrium will immediately be re-established with the charge distribution shown in Fig. 9–1–1 because the electrons cannot move on into the air beyond N. This leaves a positive charge at M that is closer to the negative charge on R than is the negative charge at N. Hence, there is a net attraction of R for the body MN, whose total charge is zero. The apparatus in Fig. 9–1–1 does not lend itself readily to the detection of this net force of attraction but you have observed the same phenomenon by the use of a metal-coated pith ball suspended by a silk thread. Either a charged rubber rod or a charged glass rod will attract such a pith ball.

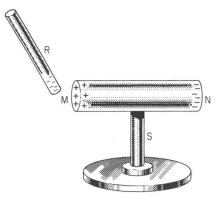

Figure 9–1–1. A metal cylinder MN on an insulating stand S with a charged rubber rod R nearby. Charging by induction.

(At this point answer Problems 9–1 through 9–4, which will help to clarify your thinking about the above explanation.)

Now imagine that a conductor, which has one end connected to ground, is brought in contact with cylinder MN at N in Fig. 9–1–1. This can be done conveniently by touching one's finger to MN, since the human body is a sufficiently good conductor for this purpose. The surplus electrons at N flow through the conductor to the ground, leaving MN with a net positive charge that is due to the close proximity of R. Next, break the ground connection, and remove the rubber rod R. Now MN has a net positive charge that distributes itself over MN (the free electrons move about to accomplish this). It is said that MN has been given a charge by induction. Note that the induced charge on MN is opposite in sign to the inducing charge on R. This is always true, i.e., *the induced charge is always opposite in sign to the inducing charge.*

You have observed experimentally that a charged body will attract an uncharged piece of insulator (or dielectric) but with a much smaller force than in the case of a conductor. By a similar discussion, we may explain this attraction of a dielectric on the basis of the electron theory, but we must remember that in a perfect dielectric there are no free electrons (see Sec. 1–2). Thus, in Fig. 9–1–1, if MN were a dielectric, there would be a shift of each nucleus toward M and a shift of the bound electrons toward N, but this shift would be within each atom. When the atoms are distorted in this fashion they are said to be polarized. This results in a positive charge at M that is closer to R than is the adjacent negative charge and, thus, a net attraction of R for the dielectric. The remainder of the process of charging by induction cannot be carried out in this case, however, for the negative charges are bound to their parent atoms and none can be conducted off to ground.

3. THE ELECTROPHORUS. The electrophorus is a device that is used to obtain useful amounts of charge by the process of induction. It is shown schematically in Fig. 9–1–2 (a). Here R_1 is a hard rubber plate which, at the outset, is charged negatively by rubbing it with fur; D is a metal disk mounted on the insulating handle A. The disk is placed on the surface of the rubber plate and touches it at only a few points of the rubber. Even though R_1 looks well polished to the unaided eye, microscopically it is a rough surface and neither R_1 nor D is completely flat. The high points that touch D are promptly discharged and their only future function is to support D whenever it is placed on R_1. The remainder of the surface of R_1 retains its negative charge.

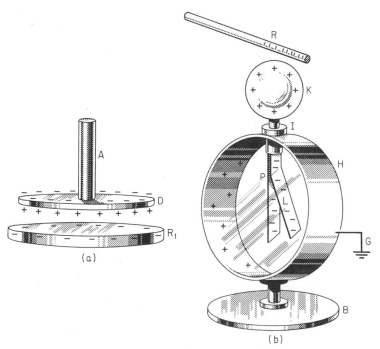

Figure 9–1–2. (a) An electrophorus; (b) a gold leaf electroscope.

With D resting on R_1, the lower surface of D becomes charged positively because some electrons are repelled to its upper surface. This is the situation shown in Fig. 9–1–2 (a). The upper surface of D is now grounded and the electrons flow from the upper surface to the ground. Next the ground connection is broken, and D is lifted off with its positive charge. This positive charge on D may be used to charge other bodies either by contact or by induction. The disk D may be recharged from R_1 by this process as many times as desired without loss of charge from R_1 (see Problem 9–7 for energy considerations in this process).

Refer to your elementary text for a discussion of the Wimshurst machine, which is another device for obtaining induced charges in usable quantities.

4. THE SIMPLE GOLD LEAF ELECTROSCOPE. You have used the electroscope for many purposes in elementary physics, but we shall review its principle briefly since we shall need it for a discussion that follows. The electroscope is constructed in many forms, but we shall describe only the simple gold leaf variety. Gold leaf is used because it is a conductor and also because a gold sheet can be beaten into extremely thin foil. This foil has low mass per unit area and is very flexible, hence it will respond quickly and vigorously to small electrostatic forces.

Figure 9–1–2 (b) shows a schematic diagram of one type of gold leaf electroscope. Here L is the gold leaf attached to a metal support post P; I is an insulator of high quality, usually sulfur or amber; P passes through the insulator and terminates in a metal knob K; H is a cylindrical metal housing that surrounds the gold leaf and serves as an electrostatic shield as well as a shield against air currents. The function of an electrostatic shield will be explained later (see Sec. 9–9). The housing H is electrically connected to ground as shown by the symbol at G. There are glass windows on the front and back ends of H so that the behavior of the leaf may be observed. The base on which the electroscope rests is shown at B.

The figure shows a charged rubber rod R located near K. The negative charge on the rod drives some free electrons down onto P and L. The mutual repulsion of the negative charges on P and L causes L to swing away from P and stand out at an angle as shown in the figure. In this position L is in equilibrium under the action of the force of gravity, the electric force of repulsion between the charges, and the tension in the leaf. The presence of the negative charges on P and L induces a positive charge on the inside of H by repelling an equal number of electrons to the outside of H and thence to ground through G.

If R is removed, the electrons on L and P return to K, neutralizing the positive charge there. At the same time electrons come from ground through the case and neutralize the positive charge on the inside of H. The electroscope is now everywhere electrically neutral, as it was before R was brought near K. See Problem 9–5, where you are asked to explain how the electroscope may be left with a positive charge on P, L, and K after R has been removed. The charge on P and L is usually referred to as the charge on the electroscope.

We see that, by the use of an electroscope, we can determine experimentally whether or not a body has a charge. If a body has a charge, and is brought near *K*, it will cause the leaf of the electroscope to swing out away from *P*. If the body has no charge, bringing it near *K* will not cause the leaf to move. We also observe that the closer a charged body is brought to *K*, the greater the deflection of the leaf.

If a battery with a large emf is connected to the electroscope, it may be connected either way and produce a deflection of the leaf. The electroscope has capacitance and the battery charges the electroscope in the same way that any capacitor is charged. The only distinction is that the electroscope leaf indicates the presence of a charge, while the capacitors that we discussed earlier had no such device for indicating the presence of a charge.

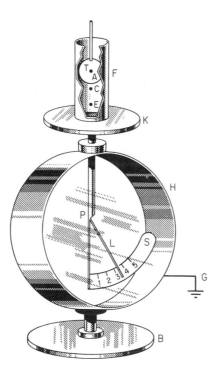

Figure 9–2–1. Electroscope of Fig. 9–1–2 (b) slightly modified, with Faraday's ice pail *F* standing on the metal plate *K*. *S* is a scale for reading the deflection of the leaf. *S* is behind the electroscope, and a light in front casts a shadow of the leaf on the scale.

9–2 FARADAY'S "ICE PAIL" EXPERIMENT

This experiment became known as Faraday's "ice pail" experiment because Faraday used his metal ice pail as an auxiliary piece of equipment in connection with the electroscope. In Fig. 9–2–1, the knob of the electroscope has been replaced by a flat metal plate *K*, and the ice pail *F* rests on this plate. Any metal can whose height is large compared to the diameter of its mouth will serve.

We have at hand several metal spheres on insulating handles. Two of the spheres are small and of the same diameter; the others are of various diameters. We also have an electrophorus at hand as a source of charge. We perform the following experiment in a very dry room so that there will be a minimum of leakage of charge over the insulating surfaces.

Charge the electrophorus disk *D* [see Fig. 9–1–2 (a)], and mount it in a clamp stand, being careful to touch only the insulating handle, so that *D* retains its positive charge. Have *D* far removed from the electroscope and ice pail.

Step 1. Charge one of the smallest spheres (call it sphere 1) by touching the sphere to plate *D* of the electrophorus. Always grasp any sphere by its insulating handle. Show, by lowering the sphere to various points in the pail, without touching the pail, that there is a maximum induced charge possible for a given charge on the inducing sphere and that we obtain the maximum deflection of the leaf if we lower the charge far enough into the ice pail.

Let us call the charge on sphere 1 *our arbitrary unit of charge and mark position* 1 *on the scale as the deflection produced by the arbitrary unit of charge.*

Remove sphere 1 from the ice pail and the leaf of the electroscope will fall back to zero on the scale.

Step 2. Charge the second of the two smallest spheres (call it sphere 2) by touching it to the disk *D* of the electrophorus. Insert sphere 2 to position *E* in the ice pail. If the electrophorus disk *D* has an area very large compared with the area of the surface of the sphere, it will be found that sphere 2 also causes the electroscope leaf to move out to position 1 on the scale, showing that sphere 2 also has a unit charge. Thus we really define two charges as equal in magnitude if they produce the same deflection.

With sphere 2 at position *E*, ground the ice pail, and the leaf will fall to zero. Then break the ground connection, and withdraw the sphere, When the sphere is withdrawn the leaf will deflect again, proving that we have left a charge of induction on the ice pail and electroscope.

Now reinsert sphere 2 and touch it to the pail. The leaf will be observed to fall to zero and remain there even though sphere 2 is withdrawn. This proves that the charge on sphere 2 was just the right magnitude to neutralize the charge that it had previously induced. This experiment leads to the well-established general proposition that *the induced charge is always equal in magnitude, as well as opposite in sign, to the inducing charge.*

In general, for every charge there is always an equal and opposite induced charge somewhere. In this experiment we inserted the inducing charge far enough into the ice pail so that the induced charge was all on the pail.

Step 3. Recharge sphere 2 with a unit charge and test to be sure that it has a unit charge as shown by the fact that the leaf of the electroscope deflects to position 1 on the scale when sphere 2 is at position *E* in the ice pail. Now insert sphere 1, which still has its unit charge, into the ice pail next to sphere 2. Note experimentally that the leaf deflects farther out on the scale, thus showing that the larger the charge held inside the ice pail the larger the deflection of the leaf. Thus the deflection of the leaf may be used as a measure of the magnitude of the charge on the body held inside the ice pail.

Since we now have in the ice pail a total charge whose magnitude is twice that of the arbitrary unit of charge, let us mark the position of the leaf on the scale as position 2. Thus in the future when a charge held inside the ice pail causes the leaf to deflect to position 2 on the scale, we know that the magnitude of the charge is twice that of our arbitrary unit charge. Continue this process until the scale is calibrated, in terms of the arbitrary unit of charge, over its whole length.

This calibrated electroscope with its ice pail is very important to us, since it permits measurement of the ratio of the magnitudes of two charges. Since the measurement is done by an induction process, we do not lose the charges in the process of comparing their magnitudes. The same electroscope and the same ice pail must be used for all future measurements in this experiment since we do not know how a change of geometry would influence the calibration.

Step 4. So far, we have experimented only with positive charges. Now we wish to deal with negative charges. You can readily devise an experiment which will justify the definition that the charges are equal in magnitude if, separately, they produce equal deflections of the electroscope leaf even though they are opposite in sign. This definition also permits us to use the calibration of the electroscope to compare magnitudes of either positive or negative charges by comparing deflections.

Step 5. Start with an uncharged rubber rod and a piece of fur. Using insulating tongs to hold the rod and the fur, rub the rod with the fur. Observe experimentally that if the rod alone is introduced into the ice pail, there is a certain deflection of the leaf. If the fur alone is introduced into the ice pail the same deflection of the leaf results. If both the fur and the rod are introduced at once there is zero deflection of the leaf. This experiment shows that the plus charge on the fur is equal in magnitude to the minus charge on the rod, and is in accord with our theory that the rubbing process transferred electrons from the fur to the rod.

9–3 COULOMB'S EXPERIMENTAL LAW OF FORCE BETWEEN POINT CHARGES

Coulomb's law deals with the force that one point charge exerts on another point charge. Strictly, a point charge should be one that is located on a body that is a mathematical point in size. We cannot deal experimentally with such small bodies, but the purpose is served well enough if the dimensions of the bodies are small compared with the distances between the bodies whose charges are exerting the forces being discussed and measured. Consequently, in the following we consider that these conditions are satisfied when force measurements are made. Any distribution of charges may be looked upon as equivalent to a distribution of point charges.

In 1785, Coulomb was the first to determine quantitatively the law relating the force between point charges and the distance between the charges. He used a torsion balance that employed the twist in an elastic fiber to measure the force between point charges. This experiment has been repeated, modified, and improved many times since, with the result that Coulomb's law is now firmly based on experiment.

The experiment should be performed in empty space because, in the presence of charged bodies, air molecules will become polarized and thus contribute their forces on the charged bodies. We are here interested in the force that one point charge exerts on a second point charge without any complications due to the presence of any other charges either bound, as in a dielectric, or free, as those on conductors. It has been found experimentally, however, that the presence of air contributes only a very tiny error, so we may consider that the experiment is performed in air if we wish.

1. EXPERIMENT AND RESULTS. *Step* 1. Charge two small metal spheres with charges of the same sign and locate them at a measured separation that is large compared with the diameter of either sphere. By use of the torsion balance measure the electric force of repulsion between the two spheres. Repeat this measurement for various measured separations, each being large

compared with the diameter of either sphere. Note that the charge on each sphere is kept constant during this measurement.

The experimental results of these measurements show that the force of repulsion between the charges is inversely proportional to the square of the distance between them, and the direction of the force is along the line joining the two charges. This relationship is called the "inverse square law" because the force varies inversely with the square of the distance.

Step 2. Charge the same two metal spheres with opposite charges, i.e., one positive and the other negative. Repeat the above experiment. The same result is obtained as in step 1, with the single change that the force is now one of attraction between the two charges.

Let F represent the force between the point charges. The direction of F is along the line joining the two charges. Force F is a force of repulsion if the charges have the same sign and a force of attraction if the charges have opposite signs.

Let r represent the distance from the center of one point charge to the center of the other point charge. The experimental results from steps 1 and 2 are summarized by

$$F \text{ is proportional to } 1/r^2 \qquad (9\text{–}3\text{–}1)$$

There are indirect methods of demonstrating the validity of this inverse square law that are more precise than direct measurements of forces.* Results by Plimpton and Lawton† in 1936 showed by experiment that if the exponent of r differs from 2, it does so by an additive constant whose absolute magnitude is less than 2×10^{-9}.

Rutherford's experiments,‡ in which he scattered alpha particles by atomic nuclei, showed that the inverse square law is valid for charged particles of nuclear dimensions, down to separations of about 10^{-12} cm. Nuclear experiments show that the forces between charged particles do not obey this law for smaller separations of the charges. From all this we may conclude that (9–3–1) is known experimentally with a high degree of accuracy. Further it applies over a wide range of separations of charges but it has limitations.

The experiments that we shall discuss and the theory that we shall derive apply to moderate magnitudes of charges interacting at moderate distances. Over this range the inverse square law is well established experimentally, as pointed out above. Outside of this range, however, the experimental evidence is scanty.

Step 3. Using the ice pail and electroscope calibrated in Sec. 9–2, Steps 3 and 4, measure the magnitude of the charges on two small spheres in terms of the arbitrary unit of charge. Set the two spheres at a measured separation r and measure the force.

By a systematic experiment, in which the magnitudes of the charges are

* James Clerk Maxwell, *A Treatise on Electricity and Magnetism*, Vol. 1 (London: Macmillan & Co., Ltd., Clarendon Press Series, 1873), Art. 74, pp. 74–77.

† S. J. Plimpton, and W. E. Lawton, "A Very Accurate Test of Coulomb's Law of Force Between Charges," *Phys. Rev.*, **50**, 1066 (1936).

‡ E. Rutherford, "The Scattering of α and β Particles by Matter and the Structure of the Atom." *Phil. Mag.*, **21**, 669 (1911).

varied, it is shown that *the force between two point charges is proportional to the product of the magnitudes of the charges.*

We have made these measurements in terms of an arbitrarily defined unit of charge but, of course, the proportionality expressed above would be valid regardless of the size of the unit adopted as long as the magnitudes of both charges were measured in terms of the same unit.

Let q_1 represent the magnitude of the charge on one of the charged bodies and q_2 represent the magnitude of the charge on the other charged body. Combining the result obtained here and the result expressed in (9–3–1) we have

$$|F| = k_0 \frac{|q_1||q_2|}{r^2} \tag{9–3–2}$$

where the absolute magnitude signs are used to express the fact that we take the quantities without reference to algebraic signs. In this equation k_0 is a constant of proportionality. The subscript zero on k is used to remind us that this formula is for empty space, and we shall use the subscript zero for other quantities when we refer to their values for empty space. As we have pointed out, the value of the constant of proportionality will not be very different if air is the medium surrounding the charged bodies.

Force F is a vector quantity, so that it is completely specified only if both its magnitude and direction are specified. Equation (9–3–2) gives only the magnitude for F. Force is a proper vector since it has a physical direction in space. This distinguishes it, and the class of physical vectors to which it belongs, from the so-called vectors I and V of a-c circuit analysis. For this reason we shall use boldface type for a symbol that represents a physical vector, instead of a dot as we have earlier. Thus, the symbol F indicates the full vector properties of F. If the boldface type is omitted, only the magnitude of the vector is being considered. Neither the teacher nor the student can write a boldfaced letter in ordinary handwriting,* so it is suggested that you put a bar under a symbol to take the place of boldface type in the text.

Let us adopt the following convention: If, on substitution of numbers with the appropriate algebraic signs for q_1 and q_2 in (9–3–2), the number for F is positive, a force of repulsion along the line of centers of the charged bodies is indicated. Conversely, if the number for F is negative, a force of attraction along the line of centers of the charged bodies is indicated. With this convention in mind we may write

$$F = k_0 \, q_1 q_2 / r^2 \tag{9–3–3}$$

This is Coulomb's experimental law of force between point charges, and is a basic law on which we build much of the structure of electrical theory. [See (9–6–15) where Coulomb's law is written in vector notation.]

Step 4. Measure the force on a charge q_1 due to a charge q_2 at a distance r.

---

* The author agrees with Professor Mark W. Zemansky in his argument against boldfaced letters. See "Alphabet Soup," *Physics Today*, **4**, p. 4 (1951). However, the practice of placing a bar under a symbol to replace boldface type in the text makes an easy substitute. In the illustrations, a bar is placed under each such symbol because the draftsman cannot conveniently letter in boldface either.

Keeping q_1 and q_2 in their original positions, measure the total force on q_1 when a third charge q_3 is brought to a fixed location in the vicinity of q_1. Analysis of the data shows that this total force on q_1 can be represented by the vector sum of the force that q_2 alone exerts on q_1 and the force that q_3 alone exerts on q_1.

Continue this procedure, introducing one charge at a time, until there are many charges exerting forces on q_1. After the introduction of each new charge the experimental data are satisfied if the total force on q_1 is computed as the vector sum of the separate forces due to the separate charges acting on q_1. Within the same broad limits as mentioned for the inverse square law, this experiment establishes a result known as the *principle of superposition* which may be stated as follows. *If a charge q_1 is acted upon simultaneously by the electric forces from charges q_2, q_3, q_4, etc., the total force on q_1 is the vector sum of the forces that q_1 would experience if the individual charges were to act on q_1 one at a time.**

Obviously, any one charge in the configuration may be looked upon as q_1. Thus we may compute the force on any charge in the configuration due to the action of all the other charges in the configuration.

Also if a body of large dimensions has a charge distributed on it, we may, in imagination, divide this distributed charge into an assembly of point charges each of magnitude dq. Then, by Coulomb's law, we may compute the force that each dq alone would exert on a point charge. This point charge may be a part of the distributed charge or it may be a separate charge entirely. Next, application of the principle of superposition permits us to compute the force that the distributed charge on the large body exerts on the point charge. The geometry may become difficult but the method is simple enough. Hence Coulomb's law, which applies to the forces between point charges, may be extended to the calculations of forces due to distributed charges.

9–4 UNITS IN COULOMB'S LAW

We have established Coulomb's law of (9–3–3) in terms of an arbitrarily chosen unit for measuring the magnitude of a charge and without stating the units in which F and r shall be measured. The only requirement was that we use the same units for charge for force and for distance throughout the experiment.

From (9–3–3) we see that whatever units are used, a unit charge will be one of such magnitude that it will repel a like charge (like as to magnitude and sign) at unit distance in empty space with a force equal to k_0.

* The wording of this statement is almost a direct quotation from the Report of the Coulomb's Law Committee of the American Association of Physics Teachers, "The Teaching of Electricity and Magnetism at the College Level," *Am. J. Phys.*, **18**, 6 (1950), heading (f); also **18**, 70 (1950).

The author is deeply indebted to the Coulomb's Law Committee for their recommendations and discussions, which have clarified his thinking on many points. Starting with Chapter IX, the organization and point of view of this text follows very closely the recommendations of the committee. The members of the Committee were Dr. W. F. Brown, Jr.; and Professors N. H. Frank; E. C. Kemble, Chairman; W. H. Michener; C. C. Murdock; and D. L. Webster.

1. BASIS FOR THE ELECTROSTATIC SYSTEM OF ELECTRICAL UNITS. The electrostatic system of electrical units (abbreviated esu) employs the centimeter, gram, second (abbreviated cgs) system of mechanical units, but uses Coulomb's law to define the unit charge. The unit charge in this system is called the statcoulomb and the choice is made that the statcoulomb shall be defined in such a way that k_0 of (9–3–3) shall have the value of unity and shall have no units. This is an extremely convenient choice for the solution of electrostatic problems but does not lead directly to the common units such as the coulomb, the ampere, the volt, etc.

Once the above choices are made, the statcoulomb must be defined from Coulomb's law as follows. *A statcoulomb of charge is a charge of such magnitude that, in a vacuum, it will repel a like charge* (like as to magnitude and sign) *at a distance of one centimeter with a force of one dyne.* It is assumed in this definition that the charges are located on bodies whose dimensions are small compared with 1 cm, so that the charges may be considered to be point charges.

The statcoulomb is the basic unit defined in the electrostatic system (see appendix A–1), and all other electrical units in the system are defined by reference to the statcoulomb and fundamental laws of electricity. The statcoulomb is also the basic electrical unit for the Gaussian system of units, because the Gaussian system uses the electrostatic system for its electrical units. You will encounter both the electrostatic and the Gaussian systems of units in many books on electricity as well as in journals that publish the results of research. In this book, however, we shall use these two systems only enough to give the student some familiarity with them, employing the mks system for most purposes.

Using the definition of the statcoulomb, as given above, Coulomb's law may be written in the simple form

$$F = q_1 q_2 / r^2 \qquad (9\text{–}4\text{–}1)$$

Equation (9–4–1) determines the units equivalent to the statcoulomb, since from this equation 1 statcoulomb^2 = 1 dyne cm^2, but 1 dyne = 1 gm cm/sec^2 so 1 statcoulomb = 1 gm$^{1/2}$ cm$^{3/2}$ sec^{-1}.

The measured charge on an electron is 4.80×10^{-10} statcoulomb, so there are 2.08×10^9 electrons per statcoulomb. This signifies that a body has 2.08×10^9 surplus electrons if it has a negative charge of one statcoulomb, and it has a deficiency of 2.08×10^9 electrons if it has a positive charge of one statcoulomb.

2. THE MKS SYSTEM OF UNITS AND COULOMB'S LAW. In Sec. 1–4 we defined the ampere as the unit of current in the mks system of units, and then we defined the coulomb, as the unit of quantity of electricity, from the ampere. The system should be designated mksa, since we use the definition of the ampere as the basic definition for introducing electrical units into the system. For simplicity we shall continue to call it the mks system.

As stated in Chapter I, and repeated here for emphasis, the coulomb is a very large quantity of charge when dealing with electrostatic cases, even though it is a small quantity of charge when dealing with the charge passing a point in a given length of time in a commercial circuit.

In the mks system we are confronted with a very different situation from that encountered in the electrostatic system. In the mks system the unit charge is previously defined and is to be the coulomb, the unit of force is the newton, and the unit of distance is the meter. These units are all defined without reference to Coulomb's law. With these units all previously determined, k_0 of (9–3–3) must be measured. In principle the experiment involves the measurement of the force, in newtons, between two point charges, whose magnitudes have been measured in coulombs, when the two charges are separated by one meter in empty space. In actual practice k_0 is determined indirectly, and the value is found to be

$$k_0 = 8.98776 \times 10^9 \text{ newton meters}^2/\text{coulomb}^2$$

the units being those required by (9–3–3).

The mks system as commonly used is one of the *rationalized* systems of electrical units. This has a very simple meaning even though it sounds impressive. It means that a factor of 4π is written explicitly in the denominator of Coulomb's law. The word *rationalized* here has nothing to do with the term as used in complex numbers. It was introduced by Oliver Heaviside* in 1893, when he devised a system of units so constructed that 4π appears in formulas where spherical symmetry exists in the geometry of the physical situation described; 2π occurs in formulas where there is circular or cylindrical symmetry; and there is no π where there is rectangular symmetry. A system of electrical units that will yield such formulas is said to be a *rational* one.

Further a new symbol ε_0 is introduced, is called the *permittivity of empty space*, and is defined by the equation

$$k_0 = 1/4\pi\varepsilon_0, \quad \text{or} \quad \varepsilon_0 = 1/4\pi k_0 \qquad (9\text{–}4\text{–}2)$$

This equation introduces the 4π in the fashion desired in order to make the system a rationalized one. Some authors use the mks system in the unrationalized form, but the rationalized form is the more common. When studying a book or article on electricity you must not only determine the system of units used by the author; you must also determine whether the

---

* In the preface to volume I of *Electromagnetic Theory* (London: "The Electrician" Printing and Publishing Company, Ltd., 1893), on pages x and xi, in talking about the "common electrical units" (his name for the unrationalized electrostatic and electromagnetic systems), Heaviside says, "It is not long since it was taken for granted that the common electrical units were correct. That curious and obtrusive constant 4π was considered by some to be a sort of blessed dispensation, without which all electrical theory would fall to pieces. I believe that this view is now nearly extinct, and that it is well recognized that the 4π was an unfortunate and mischievous mistake, the source of many evils. In plain English the common systems of electrical units involve an *irrationality* of the same kind as would be brought into the metric system of weights and measures, were we to define the unit area to be the area, not of a square with unit side, but a circle of unit diameter. The constant π would then obtrude itself into the area of a rectangle, and everywhere it should not be, and be a source of great confusion and inconvenience. So it is in the common electrical units, which are truly *irrational*." He expands this notion at considerable length on pages 116–27 of the same volume.

system is being used in the rationalized or unrationalized form. We *shall use the* mks *system in only the rationalized form in this text.*

Substitution of the value of k_0 into (9–4–2) yields the value* of ε_0.

$$\varepsilon_0 = 1/(4\pi \times 8.98776 \times 10^9) \text{ coulomb}^2/\text{newton m}^2 \qquad (9\text{–}4\text{–}3)$$

For most calculations one may use the approximate value

$$\varepsilon_0 = 8.85 \times 10^{-12} \text{ coulomb}^2/\text{newton m}^2 \qquad (9\text{–}4\text{–}4)$$

Put the value of k_0, in terms of ε_0, from (9–4–2) into (9–3–3).

$$F = q_1 q_2/4\pi\varepsilon_0 r^2 \qquad (9\text{–}4\text{–}5)$$

This is Coulomb's law in the form for the rationalized mks *system of units.*

Coulomb's law in the form (9–4–1), for the electrostatic system of units, or (9–4–5), for the rationalized mks system of units, *gives the direct force of one charge q_1 on another charge q_2 regardless of the medium in which the charges are immersed.*† If the charges q_1 and q_2 are located in a dielectric medium, the polarization charges of the medium will also exert forces on q_1 and q_2. Also there may be mechanical forces, of electrical origin, acting on q_1 and q_2. Hence in the general case the observable force acting on q_1 or q_2 will be the vector sum of these separate forces. We shall have more to say about this in the chapter on theory of dielectrics. For some time we shall be considering cases where there are no material dielectrics nearby, and thus need be concerned only with this *direct* force between two charges. We have pointed out, without any proof, so far, that the presence of air influences our experiments very little (about 1 part in 2000).

A given charge, expressed in coulombs, may be expressed in statcoulombs, or vice versa, by using the appropriate conversion factor given in Appendix A-3 and by following the instructions given there.

9–5 ELECTRIC FIELD INTENSITY, E

In Sec. 1–4, you were reminded of the definition of E as you learned it in an elementary course. Here we wish to expand this concept. As stated in Sec. 1–4, an electric field exists in a region if an electric charge placed in the region experiences a force of electrical origin. Since an electric charge experiences a force if it is in the vicinity of a charged body, there is an electric field surrounding any charged body.

By definition, *the magnitude E of the electric field intensity at a point in an electric field is the quotient obtained when the force acting on a test charge q' placed at that point is divided by the magnitude of the charge q' placed at the point. The direction of E at the point is the direction of the force that would act on a positive point charge placed at the point.*

---

* It is the value of ε_0 that is determined from experimental measurements (see J. A. Stratton, *Electromagnetic Theory* [New York: McGraw-Hill Book Co., Inc., 1941], p. 23) and k_0 may then be computed. See also pp. 368 and 512 of this book.

† For a more complete discussion see Report of the Coulomb's Law Committee of the A.A.P.T., "The Teaching of Electricity and Magnetism at the College Level," *Am. J. Phys.*, **18**, sec. 2–1, pp. 6–11 (1950).

From this, E is a *vector-point function* since it has a definite magnitude and direction at every point in the electric field. Force is a vector quantity, so if we consider that F is the force on a positive test charge at the point, the definition of E may be written in the equation

$$E = F/q' \qquad (9\text{-}5\text{-}1)$$

We consider that there is a definite value of E at every point in an electric field whether or not there is a charge at the point to experience a force due to the field. The experimental process of placing a positive test charge q' at a point P where E is to be determined, measuring the force on q', and then obtaining E from the quotient of F over q', is a scheme that, in principle at least, will permit us to determine E at the point P. The process of measuring a physical quantity must not alter the quantity that is being measured. Hence, when we measure E by the experimental process above, E must not be altered by the process of placing the test charge q' at P. This means that q' must be infinitesimal in magnitude so that its presence at P will not alter, by induction, the distribution of charges that set up the electric field. Also q' must be a point charge in the sense that we defined earlier, so that it may be considered to be

Figure 9–5–1. Point P is in the electric field of a point charge q. P is at a distance r from q.

located at P. When we speak of a test charge we mean one that satisfies these requirements.

The value of E at a point P in an electric field is independent of both the magnitude and sign of the test charge used for computing it, and depends only on the locations and magnitudes of the charges that produce the field.

From (9–5–1), the unit of E in the electrostatic system is dynes/stat-coulomb, and in the mks system is newtons/coulomb.

1. E DUE TO A POINT CHARGE. Let us compute the value of E at a point P in the field due to a point charge q.

In Fig. 9–5–1 we consider that the dimensions of the body on which q is located are small compared with r. Imagine a small positive test charge q' situated at P. By Coulomb's law in the mks system, the force on q' is $F = qq'/4\pi\varepsilon_0 r^2$. From the defining equation (9–5–1) for E

$$E = F/q' = q/4\pi\varepsilon_0 r^2 \qquad (9\text{-}5\text{-}2)$$

which is the equation that we desire. The direction of E is radially outward along r, since this is the direction of F on a positive point charge at P.

From the way in which E is defined, it follows at once that the principle of superposition (see Sec. 9–3, Step 4) may be used in solving for E at a point due to a distributed charge. The principle of superposition may be restated for E as follows. *The total E at a point P due to the combined influence of a distribution of point charges is the vector sum of the electric field intensities that the individual point charges would produce at P if each acted alone.*

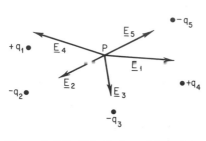

Thus, if we have a distribution of point charges as shown in Fig. 9–5–2, we may extend (9–5–2) to include this case. In Fig. 9–5–2, five point charges q_1, q_2, q_3, q_4, and q_5 are shown; P is a point in the combined field of these point charges. Let r_1 be the distance from q_1 to P, r_2 be the distance from q_2 to P, etc. The figure shows the electric field intensity E_1 at P due to q_1 alone, E_2 at P due to q_2 alone, etc. From the principle of superposition we may express the resultant E at P as the vector sum of E_1, E_2, E_3, E_4, and E_5. From (9–5–2) we may compute each individual E. Thus as an equation

Figure 9–5–2. Calculation of E at P in the field of a distribution of point charges.

$$E = (1/4\pi\varepsilon_0) \sum_{i=1}^{n} q_i/r_i^2 \quad \text{vector sum} \qquad (9\text{--}5\text{--}3)$$

where $n = 5$ in Fig. 9–5–2.

If the distribution is continuous on a body, the continuous distribution may be imagined to be broken up into infinitesimal point charges, each of magnitude dq, and then the vector summation of (9–5–3) performed. We may represent this as

$$E = \frac{1}{4\pi\varepsilon_0} \int \frac{dq}{r^2} \quad \text{vector sum} \qquad (9\text{--}5\text{--}4)$$

This is a symbolic notation, because ordinary integration is a scalar summation process and the above indicates a vector sum. We may, however, integrate separately the components of E along mutually perpendicular directions because components along a given direction add algebraically. Then we may find the resultant E as the vector sum of its components. See Problems 9–18, 9–19, and 9–20, which you are asked to solve by this method.

9–6 SOME CONCEPTS FROM VECTOR ANALYSIS

We have seen that electric field intensity E is a vector-point function; hence, at every point in an electric field E has a definite magnitude and direction. Thus, an equation that completely expresses E as a function of position in the electric field must be a vector equation. This means that it must be an equation into which we may substitute the coordinates of a point P, at which we desire the value of E, and the answer (after the substitution) must contain both the magnitude and direction of E at that point.

The equations that we have written for E so far have been scalar equations. When we substitute the coordinates of a point P into these scalar equations the answer gives only the magnitude of E at P. Then, in addition, we must make a separate statement concerning the direction of E at P. The statement as to the direction of E at P is not contained in a scalar equation.

The methods of vector analysis permit us to write vector equations of the type needed to express E (or any other proper physical space vector). We wish now to consider a few of the simple techniques of vector analysis.

We have already used complex numbers as a form of vector algebra and have found this algebra very useful in the solution of a-c circuit problems. It was very satisfactory for these problems because the vectors were confined to a plane. If, however, one extends this complex number algebra to three dimensions it is no longer simple or satisfactory. In this case the methods of vector analysis become much more useful. Some of you have studied vector analysis in considerable detail, and for you the following will be an elementary review. For the ones who have not studied vector analysis elsewhere, we shall give a sufficient background for the few concepts that we need in this course. We shall [as pointed out in Sec. 9–3, Step 3, following (9–3–2)], use boldface type for a symbol to designate the quantity as a vector quantity. As before, if the symbol for a vector quantity is set in italic, we refer only to the magnitude of the quantity.

1. COMPONENTS OF VECTORS AND UNIT VECTORS. In Fig. 9–6–1, let A be a vector whose components along the X, Y, and Z axes of the right-hand coordinate system are A_x, A_y, and A_z, respectively. The magnitude of A is given by

$$A = \sqrt{A_x^2 + A_y^2 + A_z^2} \quad (9\text{–}6\text{–}1)$$

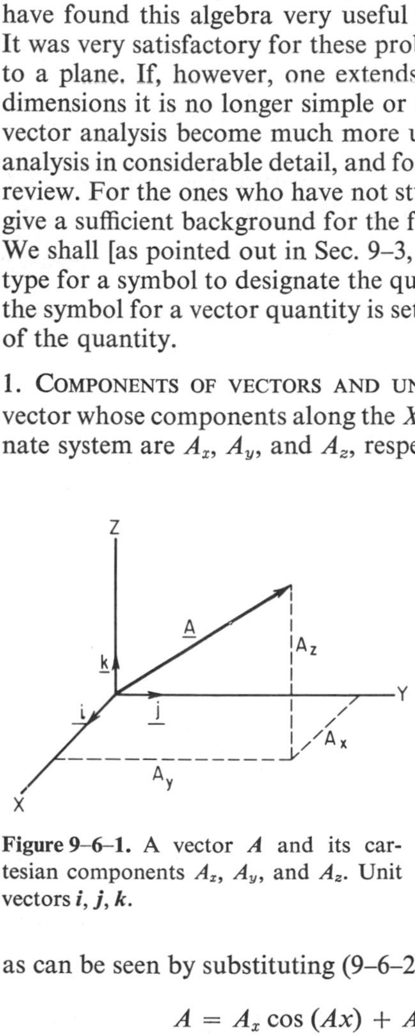

Let the angles that A makes with the X, Y, and Z axes be, respectively, (Ax), (Ay), (Az), The cosines of these angles are called the direction cosines of A, and as can be seen from Fig. 9–6–1,

$$\cos(Ax) = A_x/A$$
$$\cos(Ay) = A_y/A$$
$$\cos(Az) = A_z/A \quad (9\text{–}6\text{–}2)$$

Figure 9–6–1. A vector A and its cartesian components A_x, A_y, and A_z. Unit vectors i, j, k.

These direction cosines satisfy the relation

$$\cos^2(Ax) + \cos^2(Ay) + \cos^2(Az) = 1 \quad (9\text{–}6\text{–}3)$$

as can be seen by substituting (9–6–2) into (9–6–3). Also

$$A = A_x \cos(Ax) + A_y \cos(Ay) + A_z \cos(Az) \quad (9\text{–}6\text{–}4)$$

as can be seen by substituting the values of the direction cosines from (9–6–2) into (9–6–4) and then using (9–6–1).

Let i be a vector of unit length directed along the positive X-axis, j be a vector of unit length directed along the positive Y-axis, and k be a vector of unit length directed along the positive Z-axis. A negative sign before a unit vector means that the unit vector is directed in the negative sense along its associated axis. (Here j is not to be confused with j used earlier in complex numbers to represent $\sqrt{-1}$.) By iA_x we mean a vector whose length is A_x and whose direction is that of i, i.e., along the X-axis. Similar meanings are assigned to jA_y and kA_z along the directions of j and k, respectively, i.e., along the Y-axis and Z-axis, respectively.

With this notation, a convenient way to represent the vector A in Fig. 9–6–1 is the equation

$$A = iA_x + jA_y + kA_z \tag{9–6–5}$$

This expression means that A is the vector sum of $iA_x, jA_y,$ and kA_z, which in turn is just what one means by the components of a vector.

2. SCALAR PRODUCT OR DOT PRODUCT OF TWO VECTORS. The scalar product or dot product of two vectors is defined by the equation

$$A \cdot B = AB \cos \theta \tag{9–6–6}$$

This says that the scalar product of two vectors is a scalar with a magnitude equal to the product of the magnitudes of the two vectors and the cosine of the angle between them.

As an example of the use of a scalar product, consider the calculation of the work done by a force acting on a body and moving it through an element of distance. The work done is equal to the component of the force in the direction of the displacement times the displacement. Both force and displacement are vector quantities but work is a scalar quantity. Let F represent the force and dS the displacement. Then

$$\text{work} = F \cdot dS = F \, dS \cos \theta \tag{9–6–7}$$

where θ is the angle between the directions of F and dS.

Consider next the scalar product of the unit vectors

$$
\begin{array}{ll}
i \cdot i = \cos 0 = 1 & j \cdot j = \cos 0 = 1 \\
i \cdot j = \cos 90° = 0 & k \cdot k = \cos 0 = 1 \\
i \cdot k = \cos 90° = 0 & j \cdot k = \cos 90° = 0
\end{array} \tag{9–6–8}
$$

The dot product of identical unit vectors is unity and the dot product of unlike unit vectors is zero.

Now return to the vectors A and B in (9–6–6). Using (9–6–5), write them as

$$A = iA_x + jA_y + kA_z$$
$$B = iB_x + jB_y + kB_z \tag{9–6–9}$$

Take the scalar product

$$
\begin{aligned}
A \cdot B &= (iA_x + jA_y + kA_z) \cdot (iB_x + jB_y + kB_z) \\
&= A_x B_x + A_y B_y + A_z B_z
\end{aligned} \tag{9–6–10}
$$

as you can show by direct multiplication and the use of (9–6–8).

Return now to (9–6–7) and write

$$F = iF_x + jF_y + kF_z \qquad (9\text{–}6\text{–}11)$$
$$dS = i \, dx + j \, dy + k \, dz$$

where dx, dy, and dz are the x, y, and z components, respectively, of dS.

$$F \cdot dS = F \, dS \cos \theta = F_x \, dx + F_y \, dy + F_z \, dz \qquad (9\text{–}6\text{–}12)$$

When the force moves the body, we may think of each component of the force as doing work. The work done by F_x is $F_x \, dx$, that done by F_y is $F_y \, dy$, and that done by F_z is $F_z \, dz$. The total work done by all three components is the sum of the work done by the separate components, as stated in (9–6–12).

From the definition of a dot product as given in (9–6–6) it is evident that

$$A \cdot B = B \cdot A \qquad (9\text{–}6\text{–}13)$$

Also $$A \cdot (B + C) = A \cdot B + A \cdot C \qquad (9\text{–}6\text{–}14)$$

See Problem 9–25, where you are asked to prove (9–6–14).

3. COULOMB'S LAW IN VECTOR FORM. Consider Coulomb's law in the form for the rationalized mks system of units given in (9–4–5). Let us say that we are considering the force on q_1 due to q_2, and let i_r be a unit vector at q_1 directed away from q_2. Then in vector notation we write (9–4–5) as

$$F = q_1 q_2 i_r / 4\pi \varepsilon_0 r^2 \qquad (9\text{–}6\text{–}15)$$

Equation (9–6–15) shows, by the notation, that the terms on both sides are vector quantities. If q_1 and q_2 have the same sign, the coefficient of i_r is positive, and the F on q_1 is in the same direction as i_r, or away from q_2, i.e., repulsion. If the charges q_1 and q_2 have opposite signs, the coefficient of i_r is negative, and the direction of F on q_1 is opposite to that of i_r, or toward q_2, i.e., attraction.

4. DEFINING EQUATION FOR E. Consider next the defining equation (9–5–1) for electric field intensity $E = F/q'$ or the equation that results directly from it:

$$F = q'E \qquad (9\text{–}6\text{–}16)$$

We have already written this in the vector form, showing that F and E are both vectors. In (9–6–16) if q' is positive, F is in the same direction as E; if q' is negative, F is in a direction opposite to that of E.

5. FIELD OF A POINT CHARGE. Now consider the case of the electric field intensity due to a point charge q considered in Fig. 9–5–1 and imagine a spherical coordinate system with its origin at the center of the charged body that has the charge q on it. The result shows that E is a function of the coordinate r only and is independent of the other two spherical coordinates of the point P. Thus if we let i_r be a unit vector in the positive direction of r (directed along r away from the origin) we may write (9–5–2) as the vector equation

$$E = q i_r / 4\pi \varepsilon_0 r^2 \qquad (9\text{–}6\text{–}17)$$

If q is a positive charge, the coefficient of i_r is positive, and E at P is directed in the same direction as i_r, i.e., radially *outward* along r. If q is a negative charge, the coefficient of i_r is negative, and E at P is directed oppositely to i_r, i.e., radially *inward* along r. This, of course, we know to be the case since the direction of E is defined as the direction of the force on a positive test charge at P. All this is said in (9–6–17), and no supplementary statement as to the direction of E at P is needed.

6 FIELD DUE TO A DISTRIBUTION OF CHARGE. Refer to Fig. 9–5–2, and (9–5–3). Here, for convenience, we place the origin of a spherical coordinate system at P, the point where the field is to be computed. Again the result shows that the individual fields at P are functions of r_i only, and independent of the θ and ϕ spherical coordinates of the point where q_i is located. Define i_{ri} as a unit vector directed radially outward from the origin at P *away from* q_i. Then by the principle of superposition the resultant E at P is the vector sum of the E_i's, so we write

$$E = (1/4\pi\varepsilon_0) \sum_{i=1}^{n} q_i i_{ri}/r_i^2 \qquad (9\text{–}6\text{–}18)$$

We do not need to say "vector sum" as we did in (9–5–3) because this is made implicit by the presence of the unit vector.

Continuing the discussion to the case of a continuous distribution of charges, we may write for (9–5–4)

$$E = (1/4\pi\varepsilon_0) \int dq\, i_r / r^2 \qquad (9\text{–}6\text{–}19)$$

9–7 ELECTRIC LINES OF FORCE

It is often convenient to represent an electric field graphically by drawing electric lines of force, a method of mapping introduced by Faraday. The lines are imaginary and are not to be considered as existing in the space around a charged body, but they are a great help in visualizing an electric field and in quantitative thinking about such a field. *The direction of an electric line of force at any point shall be parallel to the direction of the electric field intensity at that point.* Hence the direction of an electric line of force at any point shows the direction that a positive charge would tend to move if it were placed at that point. Arrowheads are placed on the lines of force to show this direction along the lines.

In order to make quantitative computations with lines of force we must have a quantitative convention to tell us how many lines of force we shall draw to represent an electric field. The quantitative convention that is usually adopted is: *The number of electric lines of force drawn through an imaginary unit area of surface perpendicular to the field shall be numerically equal to the electric intensity E of the field.* We use an imaginary unit area of surface here because we do not wish to have any electrical influence due to the atoms of a real surface. The unit area is taken perpendicular to the lines so that the number will be uniquely determined in a field of given intensity.

From this convention we see that the lines of force will be closely spaced in a region where E is large in magnitude and will be far apart in a region where E is small in magnitude.

We imagine that electric lines of force originate on positive charges because E is directed away from positive charges. Conversely we imagine that electric lines of force terminate on negative charges.

Let N represent the number of electric lines of force that pass through an imaginary surface of area A. If A is perpendicular to a uniform field of intensity E, then

$$N = EA \qquad (9\text{–}7\text{–}1)$$

By a uniform field we mean one that has the same magnitude and direction at all points under consideration.

If we are dealing with a nonuniform field we shall need, first, to consider an element of area dA over which E is uniform. If dA is perpendicular to E, the number dN of lines of force through dA is given by $dN = E\, dA$.

If E is not perpendicular to dA, we have the situation shown in Fig. 9–7–1. In this case we must take the projection of dA on a surface which is perpendicular to E. This projection is given by $dA \cos \phi$. Then E times the projection of dA on a surface that is perpendicular to E gives the number of lines of force that cut through dA.

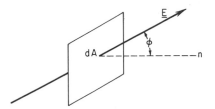

Hence $dN = E\, dA'$

(where $dA' = dA \cos \phi$)

or $dN = E \cos \phi\, dA \qquad (9\text{–}7\text{–}2)$

Figure 9–7–1. E passes through an imaginary element of area dA and E makes an angle ϕ with the normal, n, to dA.

Let us represent this normal component of E as E_n, so that $E_n = E \cos \phi$. Then

$$dN = E_n\, dA \qquad (9\text{–}7\text{–}3)$$

It is important to understand that $E_n\, dA$ gives the number of electric lines of force that cut through dA.

An element of area dA may be represented as a vector if we adopt a suitable convention for so representing it. The convention usually adopted says that the length of the vector shall be proportional to the area, and the direction of the vector shall be along the normal to the area. Thus, the infinitesimal vector dA completely specifies dA as to size and orientation. The shape is never important since dA is assumed infinitesimal. If the surface is a closed one, the outward normal is the one selected for the direction of the vector.

If we consider dA a vector, in the manner just defined, (9–7–2) or (9–7–3) obviously represent the scalar or dot product of E and dA and may be written

$$dN = E \cdot dA \qquad (9\text{–}7\text{–}4)$$

The scalar product of two vectors results in a scalar. Thus dN is a scalar since it is just the number of electric lines of force through dA.

If the imaginary surface is of finite area A, we must add up all such products, $E_n \, dA$ over the surface in order to calculate the total number of lines of force that cut through A. This may be represented symbolically by the notation

$$N = \int_A E_n \, dA = \int_A \boldsymbol{E} \cdot d\boldsymbol{A} \qquad (9\text{--}7\text{--}5)$$

which means that we carry out the mathematical process which is necessary in order to secure the summation of all of the $E_n \, dA$ products over the surface A. The process and limits of integration must be decided upon when the conditions of the problem are known.

At any point in an electric field, E can have one, and only one, direction. Thus, since lines of force are, at every point, parallel to E, lines of force cannot cross each other or even intersect.

NUMBER OF ELECTRIC LINES OF FORCE ORIGINATING ON A CHARGE $+q$. Using the quantitative convention that specifies the number of electric lines of force that shall be drawn to represent a field, let us compute the number of electric lines of force which originate on a positive point charge of magnitude q. Imagine that q is isolated, i.e., there is no other matter nearby.

Surround the point charge with an imaginary sphere of radius r. At every point on the surface of this sphere E is given by $E = q/4\pi\varepsilon_0 r^2$ and E is directed radially outward, so it is everywhere perpendicular to the surface of the sphere. Since E lines are drawn through unit area and the area of the surface of the sphere is $4\pi r^2$, the total number of lines of force that cut through the imaginary sphere is

$$N = q4\pi r^2/4\pi\varepsilon_0 r^2 = q/\varepsilon_0 \qquad (9\text{--}7\text{--}6)$$

These lines of force must have originated on the positive charge q, so q/ε_0 *lines of force originate on a positive charge q.* Had we placed a negative charge q at the center of the imaginary *sphere we could have shown that q/ε_0 lines of force terminate on a negative charge q.* Every line of force that originates on a positive charge terminates somewhere on a negative charge. Thus no charge is ever really isolated; it always has a charge of opposite sign somewhere that is associated with it.

It will be noted that the derivation of (9–7–6) was possible only because the field of a point charge obeys the inverse square law for distance, and thus the result $N = q/\varepsilon_0$ is independent of the radius of the sphere chosen. For any other law than the inverse square law for the field of a point charge, N would have been a function of the distance r from the point charge. Such a situation would have made useless the device of representing a field with lines of force.

9–8 GAUSS'S THEOREM

Gauss's theorem deals with the net number of electric lines of force that cut out through an *imaginary closed surface* when the surface surrounds a charge. As before we use an imaginary surface because we do not want any of the electrical properties of the atoms of a real surface to enter into the discussion.

(A) *One point charge of magnitude $+q$ enclosed in the surface.* In this case the answer is obvious. We have shown that q/ε_0 lines originate from a positive charge of magnitude q, and since there are no negative charges inside the imaginary surface on which the lines can terminate, they must all cut out through the surface. This is true regardless of the shape of the surface. There may be other charges near by as long as they are not inside the surface.

However, let us compute this result in a more formal fashion, since the method and result are useful in more complicated cases.

Figure 9–8–1 shows a *closed imaginary* surface A (called a Gaussian surface) that surrounds a point charge $+q$. The surface is, of course, three-dimensional although it is shown in two dimensions in the figure. The surface is of any shape. Let dA be an infinitesimal element of the surface area, and we can think of this element of area as being plane. Line n is the normal to dA, drawn from the mid-point P. The vector E represents the electric field intensity at P due to the charge $+q$ at a distance r from P. The surface dA' represents the projection of dA on a plane that is perpendicular to E.

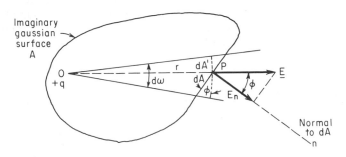

Figure 9–8–1. Gaussian surface enclosing a single point charge q.

As before, let dN represent the number of lines of force that cut through dA, and E_n represent the component of E that is along the normal to dA. From (9–7–2)

$$dN = E \, dA' \tag{9–8–1}$$

Using (9–5–2) for a point charge,

$$dN = q \, dA'/4\pi\varepsilon_0 r^2 \tag{9–8–2}$$

But also from (9–7–3), $dN = E_n \, dA$. Hence

$$E_n \, dA = q \, dA'/4\pi\varepsilon_0 r^2 \tag{9–8–3}$$

and either the right side or the left side represents the number of electric lines of force that cut through dA.

Let $d\omega$ equal the element of solid angle that dA subtends at q. Imagine now that the infinitesimal element of area dA', which we drew perpendicular to r, can be considered as an element of a spherical cap with the radius r. Then by definition of a solid angle,

$$d\omega = dA'/r^2 \tag{9–8–4}$$

Put (9–8–4) into (9–8–3).

$$E_n \, dA = q \, d\omega/4\pi\varepsilon_0 \tag{9–8–5}$$

Equation (9–8–5) tells us that the number of electric lines of force which cut out through dA is directly proportional to the solid angle which dA subtends at the charge, and that $q/4\pi\varepsilon_0$ is the constant of proportionality. It is important to note that this would not be true if Coulomb's law were not an inverse square law. Thus Gauss's theorem, which we shall see follows directly from (9–8–5), is valid only because Coulomb's law is an inverse square law.

Now, to obtain the total number of electric lines of force which cut out through the whole imaginary Gaussian surface A, we must add all such terms $E_n\,dA$ for all the dA's on the whole surface. We can do this by integrating $E_n\,dA$ over the surface. This is a surface integral, so it would have to be a double integral. However, to simplify the notation let us represent the process by $\int_A E_n\,dA$. By this notation we mean, carry out whatever mathematical process is necessary in order to add up all the products $E_n\,dA$ over the whole surface A.

In (9–8–5), if we integrate the left side over the surface, we must integrate the right side over the surface. Since the surface A completely surrounds the point 0, the surface A subtends the complete solid angle of 4π steradians. This can be written as $\int_A d\omega = 4\pi$, and (9–8–5) yields

$$\int_A E_n\,dA = q/\varepsilon_0 \quad \text{or} \quad \int_A \boldsymbol{E}\cdot d\boldsymbol{A} = q/\varepsilon_0 \qquad (9\text{–}8\text{–}6)$$

which is the result that we had before from the more elementary argument.

The quantity E_n is positive if it is directed outward along the normal to the surface and thus, of course, negative if it is directed inward along the normal to the surface. Note that (9–8–6) does not contain r, so it does not depend on the location of q as long as q is inside the Gaussian surface.

(B) *Any number of charges enclosed in the Gaussian surface.* First let us solve the problem when two point charges are enclosed in the imaginary Gaussian surface. Again we wish to calculate the total number of electric lines of force that originate on these two point charges and cut out through the Gaussian surface.

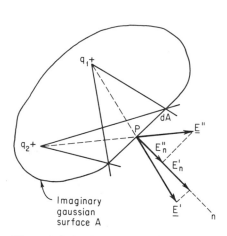

Figure 9–8–2. Gaussian surface enclosing two point charges q_1 and q_2.

Figure 9–8–2 shows an imaginary Gaussian surface A enclosing two point charges q_1 and q_2; dA is an element of surface area as before and P is the mid-point of dA; $\boldsymbol{E}'$ is the electric field intensity at P due to q_1 alone, and $\boldsymbol{E}''$ is the electric field intensity at P due to q_2 alone; n is the normal to dA drawn from P; E_n' is the component of $\boldsymbol{E}'$ along n, and E_n'' is the component of $\boldsymbol{E}''$ along n.

By the principle of superposition we may compute the resultant electric field intensity E at P due to the two charges q_1 and q_2 by taking the vector sum of E' and E''. Consequently, we may compute the component of E along the normal as the algebraic sum of E'_n and E''_n. Let E_n represent this normal component of E.

$$E_n = E'_n + E''_n \qquad (9\text{-}8\text{-}7)$$

As before, $E_n \, dA$ = number of electric lines of force that cut out through the element of surface dA, and $\int_A E_n \, dA$ = total number of electric lines of force that cut out through the whole Gaussian surface. Using (9-8-7),

$$\int_A E_n \, dA = \int_A E'_n \, dA + \int_A E''_n \, dA \qquad (9\text{-}8\text{-}8)$$

The value of each integral on the right side of (9-8-8) is given by (9-8-6), so

$$\int_A E_n \, dA = q_1/\varepsilon_0 + q_2/\varepsilon_0 = (q_1 + q_2)/\varepsilon_0 \qquad (9\text{-}8\text{-}9)$$

This can be extended by the same method to any number of charges enclosed in the surface and to any distribution of these charges inside the surface. If some of the charges are negative, the corresponding E_n's will be directed into the surface and will be subtracted from the E_n's that are directed out of the surface. This will result in minus signs on the corresponding values of q on the right side of (9-8-9). Hence, if we let q = algebraic sum of the charges enclosed in the Gaussian surface, and (9-8-9) becomes

$$\int_A E_n \, dA = q/\varepsilon_0 \quad \text{or} \quad \int_A E \cdot dA = q/\varepsilon_0 \qquad (9\text{-}8\text{-}10)$$

From (9-8-10) we may state Gauss's theorem in *empty space* as follows. *If an imaginary closed surface of any shape is constructed in an electric field, the net number of electric lines of force which cut across the surface in an outward direction is equal to $1/\varepsilon_0$ times the net positive charge which is enclosed in the surface, regardless of the way in which the charge is distributed inside the Gaussian surface.*

It follows from this, of course, that if the net charge enclosed in the Gaussian surface is negative, Gauss's theorem will give the net number of electric lines of force which cut across the surface in an inward direction. In this case q in (9-8-10) will be negative. It also follows that the net number of electric lines of force which cut across the Gaussian surface is zero if the net charge enclosed in the surface is zero.

9-9 ELECTRIC FIELD AND CHARGE WITHIN A CONDUCTOR THAT HAS A STATIC CHARGE

We have seen in the study of current electricity that a current flows in a conductor if an electric field is maintained in the conductor. Such an electric field may be maintained by connecting the conductor to the terminals of a source of emf such as a battery. We have pictured this current as the drift of the free electrons in the metallic conductor due to the force that the electric field exerts on them. The free electrons drift in the opposite direction to that of E because the direction of E is the direction of the force that the field exerts on a positive charge.

The free electrons of a conductor can, and will, move whenever there is an electric field in the conductor. But we are now considering cases where the conductor has a static charge. Hence it follows that *the electric field intensity must be zero inside the conducting material of a conductor that has a static charge.* When the charge was first given to the conductor, an electric field existed in the conductor momentarily, and the free electrons moved to distribute the charge over the conductor. But that process ended and the charge became static. When the charge is static it must be distributed over the conductor in such a way that E is zero inside the conducting material of the conductor.

Even under conditions where the conductor has a so-called static charge, the free electrons are not at rest, for they join in the thermal agitation of the atoms. This, however, is a completely random motion and in a finite time there is no net motion of charge across any cross section of the conductor. Thus no current flows. The net result is the same as if the charge were completely static and we shall so consider it.

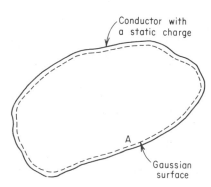

Knowing that E is zero inside a conductor with a static charge, we may use Gauss's theorem to prove that all the static charge is on the surface of the conductor. Consider Fig. 9–9–1, which shows a conductor of any shape. The conductor has a static charge. Inside the conductor but within an infinitesimal distance of its surface, describe a Gaussian surface. By Gauss's theorem, the total number of electric lines of force that cut through this Gaussian surface equals $1/\varepsilon_0$ times the charge q enclosed in the surface, or

Figure 9–9–1. A Gaussian surface A described an infinitesimal distance inside the surface of a conductor which has a static charge.

$$\int_A E_n \, dA = q/\varepsilon_0 \qquad (9\text{--}9\text{--}1)$$

But $E = 0$ everywhere inside the conductor, so $E_n = 0$ everywhere, including all positions on the Gaussian surface. Hence the left side of (9–9–1) is zero, or

$$0 = q/\varepsilon_0 \qquad (9\text{--}9\text{--}2)$$

Since ε_0 is not infinite, $q = 0$. Equation (9–9–2) says that there is no net charge enclosed in the Gaussian surface, so all the net charge on the conductor must be outside the Gaussian surface. But the Gaussian surface is within an infinitesimal distance of the surface of the conductor, so all the net charge must be on the surface of the conductor. Further, if we suspect any point inside the conductor of having a charge, we may surround that point with a Gaussian surface and use the above proof to show that the net charge at the point is zero, because E equals zero at all points inside the conducting material of a conductor. From this we conclude that *a conductor with a static charge has all its charge on its surface.*

The argument above cannot, of course, be extended beyond the surface of the conductor, because the field intensity is not zero outside the surface of the conductor. This raises the question: What is the magnitude and direction of E just outside the surface of a conductor with a static charge? Let us settle the question with regard to the direction of E first.

Figure 9–9–2 shows a conductor of any shape and with a static charge. At point B let us assume that the direction of E is at an angle ϕ with respect to the normal n to the surface at this point. With E in this direction, it has the component $E \sin \phi$ parallel to the surface, as shown in the figure. Thus the free electrons on the surface of the conductor would experience a force in the opposite direction to $E \sin \phi$. Since the free electrons are free to move parallel to the surface they would do so, and a current would flow if E were directed as shown in the figure. But there is no current flowing, the charge is static.

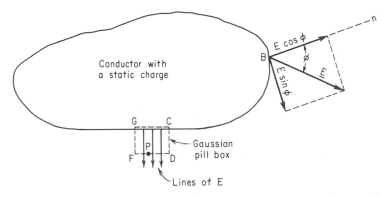

Figure 9–9–2. A conductor of any shape and with a static charge of surface density σ.

Hence the component $E \sin \phi$ parallel to the surface must be zero, and this can be satisfied only if ϕ is zero. *Thus, at every point, E is normal to the surface of a conductor that has a static charge.*

Now let us look into the magnitude of E just outside the surface of the conductor. Let σ represent the surface density of charge on the surface of the conductor. This means that σ is the charge per unit area on the surface of the conductor. Generally the charge on a conductor is not uniformly spread on its surface, so that we must consider a small area ΔA with a magnitude of charge Δq on it. Then σ at a point on the surface is given by

$$\sigma = \underset{\Delta A \to 0}{\text{limit}} \ \Delta q / \Delta A \qquad (9\text{–}9\text{–}3)$$

where ΔA shrinks to zero around the point under consideration. Thus σ has a value at every point on the surface. The units of σ are coulomb/meter^2 as required by (9–9–3).

We wish now to determine the magnitude of E just outside the surface of the conductor at P in Fig. 9–9–2. To do this, draw the imaginary closed surface (Gaussian surface) shown as $CDFG$ in Fig. 9–9–2. This is, of course, a three-dimensional closed surface and is often called a "Gaussian pill box" because it may be visualized as a small box such as the pharmacist uses when he fills a prescription for pills. Sides DC, GF, and the ones in front of the paper and behind the paper are perpendicular to the surface of the conductor and thus parallel to the lines of E. End CG is just inside the surface of the conductor, and end FD is parallel to the surface of the conductor. All sides of the Gaussian pill box are very small in length.

Let A_1 equal the area of the end of the box FD and of the end CG. Thus the charge on the surface of the conductor and enclosed in the pill box is σA_1.

Now apply Gauss's theorem of (9–8–6) to the pill box where q is the charge enclosed in the pill box and is thus the σA_1 above. The $\int_A E_n \, dA$ may be divided up into the integral over the sides plus the integral over end CG plus the integral over end FD.

$$\int_{\text{sides}} E_n \, dA + \int_{\text{end } CG} E_n \, dA + \int_{\text{end } FD} E_n \, dA = \sigma A_1/\varepsilon_0 \qquad (9\text{–}9\text{–}4)$$

On the sides, E is parallel with the surface of the pill box, so $E_n = 0$, hence the first integral is zero. On the end CG, $E = 0$ because it is inside the conductor, so $E_n = 0$ and the second integral is zero. On the end FD, E is normal to the surface, so $E = E_n$. Also, since the area of the end is very small, we may consider that the value of E is constant over the end. Hence E may be taken out in front of this integral sign. Thus (9–9–4) becomes

$$E \int_{\text{end } FD} dA = \sigma A_1/\varepsilon_0 \qquad (9\text{–}9\text{–}5)$$

But the $\int_{\text{end } FD} dA$ yields the area A_1 of the end. Hence

$$EA_1 = \sigma A_1/\varepsilon_0 \quad \text{or} \quad E = \sigma/\varepsilon_0 \qquad (9\text{–}9\text{–}6)$$

We can see that the units are proper in (9–9–6) since the units of ε_0 are coulomb²/ (newton m²) and the units of σ are coulomb/m².

From (9–9–6) we conclude that the magnitude of the electric field intensity in free space just outside a conductor with a static charge is σ/ε_0, and the direction of E is normal to the surface of the conductor. Here σ is the surface density of charge at a point on the conductor immediately adjacent to the point where the field is computed.

In general, the lines of force that leave the conductor normal to its surface continue normal to the surface only in special cases. Later we shall consider several such cases.

The fact that the charge is all on the *outside* surfaces of a conductor that has a static charge applies equally well to a hollow conductor, if no charge is enclosed in the interior of the hollow. (Solve Problem 9–26, where you are asked to prove this statement, and solve Problem 9–27.)

Now let us consider the case of a hollow conductor that has a static charge enclosed in the hollow as shown in Fig. 9–9–3. The negative charge q enclosed in the hollow must induce an equal positive charge on the inside surface of the conductor at the hollow so that all lines of force from q can terminate on this induced charge. Then, in turn, a negative charge, equal to q, must have appeared on the outside surface of the conductor, since none of this negative charge can remain in the interior of the conducting material.

Thus a charge outside a hollow conductor does not produce an electric field in the interior of the hollow; but a charge in the interior of the hollow does produce an electric field outside the conductor. The first of these two facts makes *electrostatic shielding* possible. Such shielding is used for various instruments and devices where an electric field due to external charges would cause undesirable behavior. The instrument is enclosed in a metal housing, and there is no electrostatic field inside of the housing as a result of static charges that are outside the housing. You will encounter in the laboratory numerous examples of this kind of shielding such as the one cited in Sec. 9–1 in connection with Fig. 9–1–2 for the electroscope. A familiar example is the

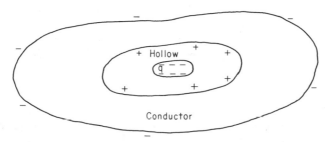

Figure 9–9–3. Hollow conductor with a static charge enclosed in the hollow.

metal can which is placed over a glass radio tube so that external electric fields will not influence the behavior of the electrons inside the tube. Many modern radio tubes have metal envelopes instead of glass envelopes. This metal envelope serves as the shield as well as the gastight container that permits the tube to be evacuated.

9–10 ELECTRIC FIELD INTENSITY DUE TO AN INFINITELY LONG ISOLATED CYLINDRICAL CONDUCTOR THAT HAS A STATIC CHARGE

In the first place we can see that it makes no difference whether the cylinder is hollow or solid, since we have shown that the static charge will all be on the outside surface in either case.

Figure 9–10–1 shows the cylinder with its uniform distribution of charge. Here P is the point at which we wish to compute the value of E due to the charge on the cylinder; P is at a distance r from the axis of the cylinder and must be in free space for the cylinder is isolated, i.e., there are no other charges nearby.

Assume the distributed charge on the cylinder to be divided into an infinite number of infinitesimal point charges and compute the field at P due to each point charge separately. A few of the vectors for these individual fields at P due to the individual point charges have been drawn in Fig. 9–10–1. Now apply the principle of superposition and compute the resultant field at P as the vector sum of these individual fields. Without actually doing the calculation called for above, two conclusions are obvious from the symmetry of the figure.

1. The resultant E will be directed radially outward from the cylinder, because for each component to the right in Fig. 9 10 1 there be an equal component to the left; and for each component out of the paper there will be an equal component into the paper. Thus all components perpendicular to r will cancel in pairs. All components along r will add arithmetically.

2. The magnitude of E will be the same at all points that are at the same distance r from the axis of the cylinder. This follows from the fact that the

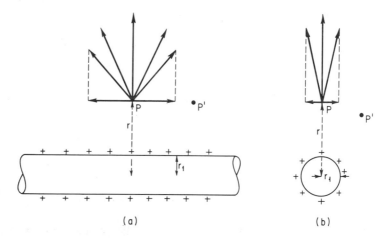

(a)   (b)

Figure 9–10–1. Infinitely long isolated cyclindrical conductor: (a) side view, (b) cross section. A static charge is uniformly distributed over the surface.

cylinder is infinitely long and any result obtained for the magnitude of E at P would also be obtained at P', which is at the same distance from the axis.

With these two conclusions at our disposal, let us now apply Gauss's theorem to obtain the answer. Gauss's theorem applies to an imaginary closed surface of any shape, so we select a surface that will make the solution as simple as possible. A cylinder, coaxial with the conducting cylinder and with flat ends perpendicular to the axis of the conducting cylinder, will be the easiest to deal with, since its cylindrical surface will be perpendicular to the electric lines of force and its ends will be parallel to the lines of force. Figure 9–10–2 shows the Gaussian surface enclosing a part of the conducting cylinder. Since the Gaussian surface is imaginary, there is no trouble passing its ends through the conducting cylinder. The cylindrical part of the Gaussian surface passes through the point P of Fig. 9–10–1.

Let b represent the charge per unit length on the conducting cylinder, and thus ba is the charge enclosed in the Gaussian surface. Apply Gauss's theorem.

$$\int_A E_n \, dA = ba/\varepsilon_0 \tag{9–10–1}$$

The integral over the Gaussian surface may be conveniently split into two parts, one over the cylindrical part of the Gaussian surface (let us call this part c) and one over the ends of the Gaussian surface. Thus, (9–10–1) becomes

$$\int_c E_n \, dA + \int_{\text{ends}} E_n \, dA = ba/\varepsilon_0 \tag{9–10–2}$$

Over the cylindrical part of the Gaussian surface E is everywhere normal to the surface from conclusion 1 above, so $E_n = E$. Also, the magnitude of E is the same at all points on the cylindrical part of the surface from conclusion number 2 above. Thus, E_n is constant over the cylindrical part of the Gaussian surface, and for the first integral, E_n may be taken out in front of the integral sign.

On the ends of the Gaussian surface, E_n is zero because E is parallel to

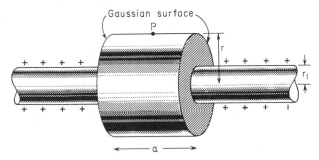

Figure 9–10–2. Gaussian surface enclosing a portion, of length a, of the charged conducting cylinder.

these ends, and thus has no component normal to the end surfaces. Hence the second integral is zero. From these two arguments (9–10–2) becomes

$$E \int_c dA = ba/\varepsilon_0 \tag{9–10–3}$$

where E is the magnitude of the electric field intensity at a distance r from the axis of the charged cylinder.

We need not bother to do the integration implied in $\int_c dA$ because we know that it will yield the area of the cylindrical part of the Gaussian surface and we also know that this area is $2\pi ra$. Thus (9–10–3) becomes

$$E2\pi ra = ba/\varepsilon_0, \quad \text{or} \quad E = b/2\pi\varepsilon_0 r \tag{9–10–4}$$

and E is directed radially outward. Note that the intensity of the field varies inversely as the *first* power of the radial distance from the axis of the charged conductor. This result applies, of course, only to points outside the charged cylinder. For points inside, $E = 0$.

In Problem 9–29 you are asked to solve a case similar to the one here except that a very fine wire replaces the conducting cylinder of this discussion. It will be noted for both cases that (9–10–4) gives the formula for the field intensity outside the conductor. This means that, for points outside the conducting cylinder, E is the same as if the charge on the conducting cylinder were distributed along the axis of the cylinder.

Let σ represent the surface density of charge on the cylinder and r_1 represent the radius of the cylinder. Then we may express σ in terms of the charge b per unit length (of 1 meter) of the cylinder as $b = 2\pi r_1 \times 1 \times \sigma$. Put this into (9–10–4) and we have

$$E = r_1\sigma/\varepsilon_0 r \qquad (9\text{–}10\text{–}5)$$

Just outside the surface of the cylinder where $r = r_1$, (9–10–5) becomes $E = \sigma/\varepsilon_0$, which agrees in this special case with the general case stated in (9–9–6) and the statement immediately following (9–9–6).

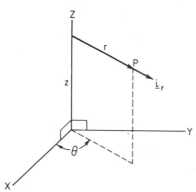

Now we wish to express (9–10–4) in vector form so that it will give a complete statement about E. In this case it is most convenient to consider cylindrical coordinates and locate the Z-axis along the axis of the charged cylinder. Locate the origin at any point on the axis of the charged cylinder, for instance at its center. Figure 9–10–3 shows the relationship between coordinate systems in the usual convention for cylindrical coordinates. Point P in Fig. 9–10–3 corresponds to point P in Fig. 9–10–1. With this orientation of the coordinate system, we note that the cylindrical coordinate r measures the radial distance from the axis of the charged cylinder to the point P where we wish to express the value of E.

Figure 9–10–3. Cylindrical coordinate system. The coordinates of the point P are r, θ, and z.

Let i_r be a unit vector along r and in the positive direction of r, i.e., radially outward from the Z-axis as shown in Fig. 9–10–3.

We see from (9–10–4) that the magnitude of E depends only on the r coordinate of the point P and is independent of the other two cylindrical coordinates. We may write (9–10–4) in vector notation as

$$E = bi_r/2\pi\varepsilon_0 r \qquad (9\text{–}10\text{–}6)$$

and the direction and magnitude of E are set forth by (9–10–6). If there is a positive charge on the cylinder, b is positive, and the coefficient of i_r is positive. This means that E at P is in the same direction as i_r, i.e., radially outward. If there is a negative charge on the cylinder, b is negative, and the coefficient of i_r is negative. This means that E is in the opposite direction to i_r, i.e., E at P is directed radially inward toward the cylinder. All of this is implicit in (9–10–6).

The problem considered in this section is not a practical one because one cannot have an isolated conducting cylinder of infinite length with nothing else in the universe. However, if a second conducting cylinder is placed around, outside and concentric with the charged cylinder, the induced negative charges are located on the inside surface of the outer cylinder. The situation between the two cylinders satisfies all the requirements of this derivation, and (9–10–6) gives the electric field intensity in the free space between the two cylinders. If the cylinders are of finite length, but with a length that is large compared with the distance between the two cylinders, the conditions for (9–10–6) will be satisfied except for points near the ends. At the ends, the lines of force do not follow radial lines from one cylinder to the other, and the lines are said to fringe.

We shall see that concentric conducting cylinders of this sort are important because of their capacitance.

9–11 ELECTRIC FIELD INTENSITY DUE TO AN ISOLATED SPHERICAL CONDUCTOR THAT HAS A STATIC CHARGE

At points inside the sphere, $E = 0$ as we have shown in general for any conductor with a static charge.

You have been asked to solve this problem in Problem 9–30 for points outside a conducting sphere that has a radius r_1 and a charge q. For a point at a distance r from the center of the charged sphere, where $r \geqq r_1$, the answer in free space is

$$E = qi_r/4\pi\varepsilon_0 r^2 \qquad\qquad (9\text{–}11\text{–}1)$$

with E directed radially outward, as shown by the formula.

If the charge on the surface of the sphere is expressed in terms of the surface density σ of charge, (9–11–1) becomes

$$E = \sigma r_1^2 i_r/\varepsilon_0 r^2 \qquad\qquad (9\text{–}11\text{–}2)$$

In (9–11–1) we see that the formula is the same as it would be if a point charge of magnitude q were located at the center of the sphere and the sphere were absent. Thus, for points outside the sphere, the field is the same as if the charge on the sphere were located at its center.

Equation (9–11–1) also gives the electric field intensity in the empty space between two concentric conducting spheres if the inner sphere has a charge q.

9–12 FORCE IN EMPTY SPACE BETWEEN TWO PARALLEL STRAIGHT WIRES THAT HAVE A UNIFORM DISTRIBUTION OF STATIC CHARGE

Figure 9–12–1 shows two straight fine wires stretched parallel to each other in otherwise empty space. We assume that the wires are infinitely long and that they are far enough apart, compared with the diameter of each, so that the distribution of charge on each is not altered by the presence of the other.

We wish to compute the force on the charges on a length L of wire 1 due to all the charges on wire 2. Obviously the force on a length L of wire 2 will be equal in magnitude and opposite in direction, by Newton's third law of motion, or by the same type of calculation as below.

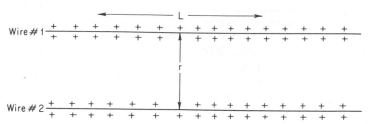

Wire # 1

r

Wire # 2

Figure 9–12–1. Two parallel straight wires with uniform distributions of static charge. The magnitude of the charge per unit length on wire 1 is b_1 and that on wire 2 is b_2.

From Problem 9–29 the electric field intensity at every point of wire 1 due to all the charges on wire 2 is given by

$$E = b_2/2\pi\varepsilon_0 r \qquad (9\text{–}12\text{–}1)$$

where r is the distance between the wires and b_2 is the magnitude of the charge per unit length on wire 2. Thus the force on a length L of wire 1 is

$$F = +b_1 b_2 L/2\pi\varepsilon_0 r \qquad (9\text{–}12\text{–}2)$$

where the + sign means a force of repulsion if the charges are of the same sign.

9–13 ELECTRIC FIELD INTENSITY IN THE EMPTY SPACE BETWEEN PARALLEL METAL PLATES THAT HAVE EQUAL AND OPPOSITE STATIC CHARGES

If the plates are far apart, the charges will be distributed over both surfaces of each plate. In this case the electric lines of force will have a very complicated configuration. As the plates are brought closer and closer together the charges will concentrate more and more on the surfaces of the plates that face each other. We know that, whatever the separation of the plates, the lines of force leave each plate in a direction normal to the face of the plate because these plates are conductors with static charges. If the negatively charged plate is near the positively charged plate, the lines of force that originate on the positive charges and leave the surface normally will continue straight across to the negatively charged plate where, of course, they must approach the plate along the normal to that plate. Thus, if the plates are parallel and separated by a distance that is very small compared with their linear dimensions, the

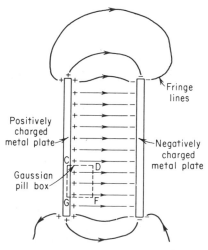

Figure 9–13–1. Oppositely charged parallel metal plates.

electric lines of force will be parallel straight lines except at the edges of the plates, where fringing will occur. When these conditions are satisfied, the device is called a parallel plate capacitor and we discussed the circuit behavior of such a capacitor in Sec. 4–1.

Figure 9–13–1 shows such a pair of parallel plates where the separation is to be considered small compared with the linear dimensions of either plate. The lines of force are shown with some fringing at the edges. We shall assume that the effect of fringing is negligibly small.

In Fig. 9–13–1 consider that the Y-axis is perpendicular to the two metal plates. In Problems 9–37 and 9–38 you are asked to prove that

$$E = \sigma j/\varepsilon_0 \qquad (9\text{–}13\text{–}1)$$

gives the uniform electric field intensity in any part of the region between the plates of a parallel plate capacitor where fringing may be neglected.

9–14 FORCE ON A CONDUCTOR DUE TO ITS OWN STATIC CHARGE

Consider the element of area dA between G and C on the piece of metal in Fig. 9–14–1. The static charge on this element of area produces an electric field intensity E_0 at P directed outward and an equal electric field intensity E_i at P_i directed inward, where P is an in- finitesimal distance outside the metal in empty space and P_i is an infinitesimal distance inside the metal. But we know that the net electric field intensity at P_i must be zero. Hence all the other charges on this body, plus the charges

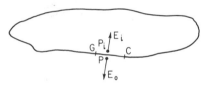

Figure 9–14–1. Metallic conductor with a positive static charge.

on other charged bodies that may be nearby, must produce at P_i an electric field intensity E_s which is equal and opposite to E_i. The point P is only an infinitesimal distance from P_i, so the direction and magnitude of E_s at P is equal to that at P_i. Hence E_s at P is equal to E_0, and the total field at P is $E_s + E_0 = 2E_s$. Let σ be the surface density of charge on the surface of the conductor between G and C and, from (9–9–6), we know that the resultant electric field intensity E at P is given by σ/ε_0. Hence $2E_s = \sigma/\varepsilon_0$, or

$$E_s = \sigma/2\varepsilon_0 \qquad (9\text{–}14\text{–}1)$$

Remember that E_s is the electric field intensity at P due to all charge except that on the element of area dA between G and C.

The infinitesimal charge $\sigma\,dA$ does not exert a force on itself, but all the other charges exert a force on it. Let df_s = force on the charge $\sigma\,dA$ and, since $F = Eq$, we have

$$df_s = \sigma\,dA\,E_s = \sigma^2\,dA/2\varepsilon_0 \qquad (9\text{–}14\text{–}2)$$

or, using $E = \sigma/\varepsilon_0$, we have

$$df_s = \varepsilon_0 E^2\,dA/2 \qquad (9\text{–}14\text{–}3)$$

and df_s is directed outward along the normal to the surface of the charged metallic conductor regardless of the sign of the charge on the body.

The element of force df_s is acting on the charge on the element dA of the surface of the conductor. But this charge is held to the conductor by atomic forces; so we can say that df_s acts on the element of surface area dA of the conductor itself. The resultant force on a finite region of the surface would be obtained by a vector sum of terms like the one given in (9–14–3), and the effect on the body would depend on whether or not it is deformable and on its elastic mechanical properties. In any event, these electric forces set up stresses in the body and, in some cases, very severe stresses.

PROBLEMS

9–1 Draw a diagram showing a metal-covered pith ball suspended by a silk thread with a charged glass rod nearby. Explain the attraction of the pith ball by the glass rod. What will happen if the pith ball touches the glass rod? Why?

9–2 Two metal plates, insulated from each other, are set up and given a charge as shown in Fig. 9–13–1. The plates are then disconnected from the charging source. A metal-covered pith ball, suspended on a long insulating silk thread, is given a negative charge and then, by use of a stiff insulating handle, is lowered into the region between the metal plates and released. The diameter of the ball is much less than the distance between the plates. Tell what horizontal motion the pith ball will enjoy and why it will execute this motion. What is the source of the energy for the motion? What are the conditions when the motion of the pith ball ceases?

9–3 Two metal-covered pith balls are suspended on insulating silk threads from a common point. Initially both are uncharged and they hang down together in contact. (a) A negatively-charged hard-rubber rod is brought near the two pith balls and it is observed that one pith ball moves toward the rod while the other moves away. Neither one is permitted to touch the rod. By means of sketches, show the situation and explain the behavior very briefly. (b) On a second try, both pith balls move toward the charged rod. Again neither one is permitted to touch the rod. By means of a sketch show this situation and why it differs from the above.

9–4 In Fig. 9–1–1, imagine that a second metal cylinder on its own insulating stand is brought in contact with N of cylinder MN. The apparatus of Fig. 9–1–1 remains as shown. The second metal cylinder is now moved some distance away from MN. In all of this the second cylinder is kept insulated from its surroundings, except for the momentary contact at N, so it is moved about by using one's hands on the insulating stand only. Explain how experimental tests of the charges on the two cylinders could further verify the explanation given in connection with Fig. 9–1–1 in the text.

9–5 Refer to Fig. 9–1–2 (b). Explain, with the aid of diagrams, how an electroscope may be left with a positive charge after the charging rod has been removed. The process of charging by induction is to be used.

9–6 Repeat Problem 9–5 with the single change that the electroscope is to be left with a negative charge after the charging rod has been removed. As in Problem 9–5 the process of charging by induction is to be used.

9-7 Refer to the electrophorus in Fig. 9–1–2 (a). After D has been charged by induction from R_1 and taken away from R_1, disk D has energy due to its charge. This can be shown by the fact that a spark will jump from D to a neighboring grounded conductor and the energy will make itself evident by the light and heat of the spark. Also, D may be charged from R_1 by induction as many times as one wishes, and each time that the above experiment is repeated it will cause a spark to jump, showing that it had energy before the spark jumped. What is the source of this energy?

9-8 An electroscope has a positive charge. The charge is known to be positive because the electroscope was charged by induction from a negatively charged rod. Explain how this charged electroscope may be used to determine the unknown sign of the charge on some other body.

9-9 A certain electroscope, with a scale like the one in Fig. 9–2–1, has a capacitance of 2.00 μμf. It is calibrated by use of a variable-voltage d-c power supply with the positive terminal connected to K and the negative terminal connected to the case H. The following data are obtained.

Applied voltage	Leaf deflection	Applied voltage	Leaf deflection
volts	cm	volts	cm
0	0.00	3000	4.15
500	0.25	3500	4.90
1000	0.85	4000	5.58
1500	1.62	4500	6.48
2000	2.50	5000	7.20
2500	3.30		

(a) Draw a charge calibration curve for this electroscope, plotting charge as abscissa and deflection as ordinate. (b) With the leaf at 7.20 cm on the scale and the power supply disconnected, a resistor of 5.65×10^{12} ohm is connected between K and H. What is the reading of the leaf on the scale 12.0 sec after the resistor is connected? [*Ans:* 2.02 cm.]

9-10 (a) Two positive point charges are 25.0 cm apart. Each point charge has a magnitude of 5.00 statcoulombs. Compute the force of repulsion on each point charge. (b) Convert the charges to coulombs and the distance to meters, and compute the force of repulsion in newtons. Check the answer in (a) against the answer in (b). Use the table of conversion factors in Appendix A–3 as needed.

9-11 A negative point charge $q_1 = 33.3 \times 10^{-10}$ coulomb is at a distance of 0.200 m from a negative point charge $q_2 = 133 \times 10^{-10}$ coulomb. (a) What is the electric field intensity at the mid-point of the line joining the two charges? [*Ans:* 9000 newtons/coulomb.] (b) At what point on the line joining the two charges is E equal to zero? What does the second solution of the quadratic represent? [*Ans:* 0.0667 m from q_1 toward q_2.]

9-12 Three points X, Y, Z lie at the vertices of a right traingle. It is 6.00 m from X to Y, 8.00 m from Y to Z, and 10.0 m from X to Z. A positive point charge of 64.0×10^{-10} coulomb is located at Y, and a positive point charge of 100×10^{-10} coulomb is located at X. What is the magnitude and direction of the electric field intensity at Z? [*Ans:* 1.71 newtons/coulomb at an angle of $18\frac{1}{2}°$ with line YZ extended.]

9–13 In Problem 9–12, convert the magnitudes of the charges to statcoulombs, the distances to centimeters, and solve the problem in electrostatic units. Substitute units with numerical quantities, and show that the units of E in the electrostatic system come out dynes/statcoulomb, as one would expect from the definition of E.

9 14 Two small metal coated spherical pith balls of the same diameter are suspended by fine silk fibers from a common point on a stand so that they hang vertically downward when uncharged. Each pith ball weighs 3.00×10^{-5} newton, and each is given the same magnitude of positive charge. After the pith balls are given the charge they move apart and reach equilibrium at a horizontal separation of 10.0 cm. Each silk fiber is 10.0 cm long. What is the charge on each pith ball in coulombs? in statcoulombs? [*Ans:* 4.38×10^{-9} coulomb.]

9–15 A charge $q_1 = 5.00 \times 10^{-8}$ coulomb is located at the origin of coordinates and a charge $q_2 = -3.00 \times 10^{-8}$ coulomb is located at 5.00 m from the origin on the Y-axis. At what point is $E = 0$? If a very small body with a positive charge is placed at this point, is it in stable equilibrium? [*Ans:* 22.2 m.]

9–16 Bohr's model of the hydrogen atom describes this atom as a single electron revolving about a single proton in such a way that the electrostatic attraction of the proton for the electron furnishes just the centripetal force required to keep the electron in its orbit. From Bohr's theory it is shown that, for circular orbits, the allowed electron orbit which is closest to the proton has a radius of about 53.0×10^{-12} m. What is the linear speed of the electron in this orbit? What is its angular velocity? [*Ans:* 2.19×10^6 m/sec; 4.13×10^{16} radians/sec.]

9–17 What is the electric field intensity due to the proton at the location of the electron in Problem 9–16 [*Ans:* 5.13×10^{11} newtons/coulomb.]

9–18 In Fig. 9–P–1, AB is a fine wire of infinite length in otherwise empty space. The wire has a negative charge uniformly spread along its length. Consider

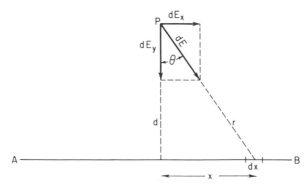

Figure 9–P–1. A fine wire with a uniformly distributed charge.

that the wire is fine enough so that the charge is distributed on a mathematical line. Let b represent the charge per unit length of the wire. Find the electric field intensity at P, where P is a distance d from the wire. Use Coulomb's law and the principle of superposition for this calculation. [*Ans:* $E = - j\,b/2\pi\varepsilon_0 d$ with origin at P.]

9–19 In Fig. 9–P–1, assume that the wire is of length d (not infinitely long) with one end situated at the point where the perpendicular from P meets the line AB and the other end is at a distance d to the right of this point. The wire has uniform *positive* charge distribution along it. Otherwise the conditions are as stated in Problem 9–18. Prove, by the use of Coulomb's law and the principle of superposition, that the magnitude of the electric field intensity at P is given by $E = 0.765b/4\pi\varepsilon_0 d$ and that the vector equation for E is $E = - i(0.293b)/4\pi\varepsilon_0 d + j(0.707b)/4\pi\varepsilon_0 d$.

9–20 In Fig. 9–P–2, BC is a very fine copper wire whose length $2d$ is vertical. It has a uniform positive charge distribution b per unit length. P is a metal-coated pith ball of weight w, whose diameter is small compared to d, which has a positive charge q. This charge q is small enough so it can be assumed that it does not alter the uniform charge distribution on the wire. The pith ball is suspended by a very fine silk thread from a point A which is a distance $5d$ vertically above the midpoint of wire BC, and the force of electrostatic repulsion makes the pith ball stand out a distance d from the mid-point of the wire. Prove by use of Coulomb's law and the principle of superposition that the magnitude of E at P, due to the charge on the wire, is given by $E = \sqrt{2}b/4\pi\varepsilon_0 d$ and that the charge on the pith ball can be computed from $q = 4\pi\varepsilon_0 Wd/7.07b$.

Figure 9–P–2.

9–21 Find the vector sum, and the magnitude of the vector sum of (a) $A = 5i + 10j - 6k$, and $B = - 2i + 4j + k$. [*Ans:* $3i + 14j - 5k,\ 15.2$.] (b) $A = 2i - 3j + 4k$, and $B = - 9i + 4j - 3k$, and $C = 4i - 2j + 2k$.

9–22 Find the scalar product $A \cdot B$ where $A = 2i - 3j + 4k$, and $B = - 9i + 4j - 3k$. [*Ans:* $- 42$.]

9–23 Find the scalar product $A \cdot B$ where $A = i + 4j + 3k$ and $B = 4i + 2j - 4k$ and prove that A and B are perpendicular to each other.

9–24 A force given by $F = 3i + 4j + 5k$ newtons acts through a displacement given by $S = 4i + 2j + k$ meters. What work does the force perform? [*Ans:* 25 joules.]

9–25 Prove that (9–6–14) is valid, i.e., that the left side equals the right side. To do this: (1) write the vectors in terms of their Cartesian components, (2) form the dot products of $A \cdot B$ and $A \cdot C$ and add the results, (3) add B and C and then form the dot product $A \cdot (B + C)$.

9–26 Prove the statement, located three paragraphs below (9–9–6), by use of an argument similar to the one associated with Fig. 9–9–1. The statement you are to prove can be restated in the form: Charge is all on the *outside* surface of a hollow conductor with a static charge provided that no charge, on an insulated body, is enclosed in the interior of the hollow.

9–27 Describe an experiment you could perform in order to secure an approximate test of the validity of the statement in Problem 9–26 when no charge is enclosed in the hollow. Tell how you can make the experiment progressively more convincing and thus make the statement creditable in the limit.

9–28 Describe an experiment you could perform to demonstrate the validity of the statement concerning Fig. 9–9–3, namely: A charge on an insulated body enclosed in an insulated hollow conductor produces an induced charge of the same sign on the outside surface of the hollow conductor.

9–29 Solve the problem presented in Problem 9–18 by use of Gauss's theorem instead of by direct application of Coulomb's law and the principle of superposition. For this solution use the method of Sec. 9–10. Include a clear discussion of the conclusions that may be arrived at from symmetry arguments before applying Gauss's theorem. In this case let r represent the radial distance from the wire to the point P, i.e., let r represent the same quantity that d represents in Fig. 9–P–1. [*Ans: $E = b/2\pi\varepsilon_0 r$, and E is directed radially inward toward the wire.*]

9–30 Consider an isolated metal sphere of radius r_1 that has a positive static charge q on it. The charge is uniformly spread over the surface of the sphere so that the surface density σ of charge is uniform. (a) By the use of Gauss's theorem, find the formula for the electric field intensity at a point outside the sphere at a distance r from its center. Apply appropriate symmetry arguments, similar to those in the first part of Sec. 9–10, and arrive at conclusions similar to 1 and 2. Select a shape of Gaussian surface that will take full advantage of the spherical symmetry. (See Sec. 9–11 for answer.) (b) Sketch a curve showing the magnitude of E, plotted as ordinate, against the distance from the center of the sphere, plotted as abscissa. Start the curve at the center of the sphere.

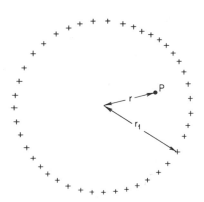

Figure 9–P–3. Continuous uniform distribution of positive charge in the form of a spherical shell in otherwise empty space.

9–31 Consider the discussion near the end of Sec. 9–10 and explain how the conditions required in Problem 9–30 may be satisfied in the laboratory and still have other bodies near the charged sphere. Will there be any fringing of lines of force in this case?

9–32 Imagine that Fig. 9–P–3 represents a continuous distribution of positive point charges in the form of a spherical shell. The shell has a radius r_1. The rest of space, both inside and outside the shell, is empty. The surface density of charge on the shell is σ. We shall not attempt to say how a distribution of charges could be held in this configuration. Apply Gauss's theorem to prove that $E = 0$ at any point P at a distance r from the center of the shell, where $r < r_1$. First, secure conclusions from the symmetry of the problem, similar to numbers 1 and 2 in the first part of Sec. 9–10. This problem proves that a spherical shell of charge cannot produce an electric field inside itself. Of course for points outside, the formula for E will be the same as it is for a spherical conductor with a static charge, and thus is the same as if the charge on the shell were concentrated at the center.

9–33 Imagine that electrons are uniformly distributed throughout the volume of a sphere of radius r_1, the volume density of charge being ρ. All space is empty except for these charges. Such a configuration might exist, but not with such nice symmetry, in the space charge of a radio tube. (a) Using the result from Problem 9–32 prove that E inside the sphere at a distance r from the center is given by $E = r\rho/3\varepsilon_0$ for $r \gtrless r_1$. What is the direction of E? (b) Find the force on one of the electrons at a distance r from the center. What is the direction of this force? (c) Sketch a graph showing E as a function of r both inside and outside the sphere. Plot E as ordinate and r as abscissa.

9–34 A Gaussian surface is drawn in a region of empty space where there is an electric field. There are no charges enclosed in the Gaussian surface, so $\int_A E_n\, dA = 0$. Explain, qualitatively, why this can be true when E is not zero.

9–35 Suppose in Problem 9–33 that ρ is not uniform but is given by $\rho = cr$. Solve parts (a) and (c) of Problem 9–33 for this situation. [*Ans:* for (a), $E = cr^2/4\varepsilon_0$.]

9–36 Consider the problem of the force between two parallel straight wires with static charges as discussed in Sec. 9–12. Write (9–12–2) as a vector equation. State your choice of coordinate system to be used and the location of the origin of coordinates. Show that your vector equation contains implicitly the rule for the direction of the force as stated immediately following (9–12–2).

9–37 Prove that E in the empty space between the plates of a parallel plate capacitor [see definition in Sec. 9–13] is given by $E = \sigma j/\varepsilon_0$ [as stated in (9–13–1)] where the Y-axis is taken along a line perpendicular to the two plates. The surface charge density is σ on each of the surfaces facing each other. In this proof, use Gauss's theorem, the Gaussian pill box $CGFD$ of Fig. 9–13–1, and a method of argument like the one used with (9–9–4) to derive (9–9–6). Explain why (9–13–1) for the parallel plate capacitor is less restricted in its region of application than is (9–9–6).

9–38 By application of Coulomb's law, the principle of superposition, and direct integration, show that the magnitude of E at a point O in the empty space between the plates of a parallel plate capacitor, (see definition in Sec. 9–13) where O is far removed from any edge, is given by $E = \sigma/\varepsilon_0$. The charge density is σ on each of the surfaces facing each other. In the course of the proof, demonstrate that half of the magnitude of E is due to the charge on each of the plates. Reference to Fig. 9–P–4 will help you to carry out the analysis. Consider the test charge to be located at O (i.e., this is the point where E is to be computed) and consider first the force on the test charge at O due to the charge on the ring of radius r and width dr. Then sum for all such rings from $r = O$ to $r = \infty$.

9–39 A uniformly charged circular ring of wire, with a total positive charge q and a charge per unit length b, is situated in empty space. The wire has a negligible cross-section and the radius of the ring is a. The Y-axis of a Cartesian coordinate system is along the axis of the ring and the origin is

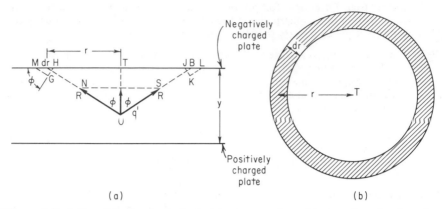

Figure 9–P–4. Parallel plate capacitor; (a) cross section, (b) top view showing the imaginary ring of radius r and width dr drawn on the under surface of the top plate.

at the center of the ring. (a) Prove that the electric field at a point P on the Y-axis at a distance y from the plane of the ring is given by $E = jqy/ 4\pi\varepsilon_0(y^2 + a^2)^{3/2}$. In this proof use Coulomb's law, the principle of superposition, and direct integration. (b) Explain why this vector formula for E is correct along both the positive and negative Y-axis out from the ring. (c) Explain why this vector formula is also correct for a negative charge on the wire ring.

9–40 (a) In Problem 9–39, reduce the answer for E to its value at the origin of coordinates and explain physically why this is a correct value. (b) In this same problem, reduce the answer for E to its value at points on the Y-axis where $y \gg a$ and again explain physically why your answer is a correct one.

9–41 A metal disk, of radius R and negligible thickness, has a uniform positive charge density σ on each of its faces. The Y-axis of a Cartesian coordinate system is along the axis of the disk with the origin at the center of the disk, so the disk lies in the X-Z plane. (a) Prove that for points on the Y-axis, $E = j [1-y(R^2 + y^2)^{-1/2}]\sigma/\varepsilon_0$. (b) Show that for very small and very large values of y (but constant values of R and σ) this formula reduces to appropriate formulas for the physical situations approached in the two cases.

ELECTRIC POTENTIAL

10–1 POTENTIAL ENERGY OF A CHARGE IN AN ELECTRIC FIELD

In Fig. 10–1–1, we visualize an electric field all through the region. We imagine a positive test charge q' at B, and we wish to compute the change in potential energy of this test charge when we move it from B to A. With the lines of force and the positions of A and B as shown in Fig. 10–1–1, we see that we must do work against the field to move q' from B to A.

From the usual concept of potential energy, the increase in potential

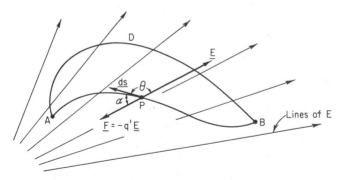

Figure 10–1–1. Two points, A and B, in an electric field. A positive test charge q' is moved along the path BPA from B to A.

energy of q', when we move it from B to A, is the work that we (an external agency) must do on q' in the moving process. Conversely, if the field were allowed to move q' from A to B, the decrease in potential energy of q' would be the work that the field would do on q'. Thus, work done on a charge by an *external* agency increases the potential energy of the charge; and work done by the electric field on the charge is done at the expense of the potential energy of the charge. For simplicity of notation, let us represent potential energy by the symbol PE. We must first select a particular path along which we propose to move q' from B to A. Let us select the path shown by the curved line BPA

in Fig. 10–1–1. Here P represents any point on this path. At P, draw the vector that represents E, and draw an element of path length ds which is directed along the path from B toward A, since this is the direction of motion of q'. In the figure, θ represents the angle between E and ds.

From the convention that we have previously adopted for the direction of E, the force which the electric field exerts on a positive charge q' is $q'E$. Hence, if we wish to hold the charge q' at rest at the point P, we must exert a force F which is equal to $-q'E$ and is shown in the figure. Newton's second law of motion says, among other things, that if there is no acceleration there is no unbalanced force. Thus, we must exert the force $F = -q'E$ when we move q', without acceleration, from B to A along the path BPA. The magnitude and direction of E at the point P depend on the position of P on the line. Consequently, we must take these functional relationships into account when we compute the work required to move q' from B to A along the path. We are now ready to indicate the method by which we can compute the change in PE of q'.

Let dW represent the element of work that we (an external agency) must do in order to move the test charge through the element of distance ds. Let α represent the angle between F and ds as shown in Fig. 10–1–1. We exert the force F, but only the component $F \cos \alpha$ is parallel to the motion, so this is the only component which does work. Hence, $dW = F \cos \alpha\, ds$. But α is the supplement of θ, so $\cos \alpha = -\cos \theta$, and $dW = -F \cos \theta\, ds$. In this equation, F and ds are the magnitudes only of the force and displacement, because we already took their directions into account properly when we took the component of F along ds. In the vector formula $F = -q'E$, the minus sign is included to show that F has a direction opposite to that of E. Thus, the magnitude of F equals $q'E$, and we write

$$dW = -q'E \cos \theta\, ds = -q'E \cdot ds \qquad (10\text{–}1\text{–}1)$$

Note carefully that E and ds are magnitudes only in (10–1–1) and are therefore positive. In the case shown in Fig. 10–1–1, the angle θ is greater than $90°$, so $\cos \theta$ contains a minus sign hidden in it. Thus, since q' is considered to be a positive charge, a numerical calculation using (10–1–1) would yield a positive number for dW. This is as it should be, for we must do a positive amount of work against the field in order to move q' against the field and thus increase the potential energy of q'.

In passing, note also that (10–1–1) would give a negative numerical value for dW if ds were oppositely directed (motion of q' from A toward B), since θ would be less than $90°$. Such a result would be proper in this case, since we would be doing negative work, i.e., the field would be doing work for us at the expense of the potential energy of the charge. You can readily reason that (10–1–1) also yields proper results for motion in either direction when q' is a negative charge.

Now let us return to our original problem, namely, the computation of the increase in potential energy of a positive test charge q' when we move q' from B to A. For this purpose, imagine the path B to P to A split up into a series of short straight line segments as shown in Fig. 10–1–2. Let ΔW_i represent the work required from an external agency to carry the charge q' a distance Δs_i

in the direction B toward A, where the ith line segment is any one along the path. By the argument above, $\Delta W_i = -q'E_i \cos \theta_i \, \Delta s_i$, so the total work required to carry q' from B to A is

$$W = \lim_{n=\infty} \sum_{i=1}^{n} -q'E_i \cos \theta_i \, \Delta s_i \qquad (10\text{–}1\text{–}2)$$

In the limit this sum becomes the integral

$$W = -q' \int_{(B)}^{(A)} E \cos \theta \, ds \qquad (10\text{–}1\text{–}3)$$

which is the one that would have been obtained by direct integration of (10–1–1). Equation (10–1–2) and its associated argument simply fill in some

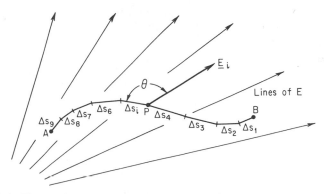

Figure 10–1–2. Figure 10–1–1 redrawn with the path BPA split up into n short straight line segments. The ith line segment is any one along the path.

of the thinking between (10–1–1) and (10–1–3). Since W in (10–1–3) is the increase in the PE of q' when it is moved from B to A,

$$PE_A - PE_B = -q' \int_{(B)}^{(A)} E \cos \theta \, ds = -q' \int_{(B)}^{(A)} \mathbf{E} \cdot \mathbf{ds} \qquad (10\text{–}1\text{–}4)$$

Change of PE is, of course, a scalar quantity.

   The integral in (10–1–4) is called a line integral, because it is to be evaluated along the line of the path from B to P to A in the manner suggested by Fig. 10–1–2 and (10–1–2). Since (B) and (A) are merely symbolic limits indicating the end points of the path, we enclose them in parentheses to distinguish them from actual numerical limits. Numerical limits can be inserted in place of (B) and (A) for a particular problem only after the geometry of the particular problem has been stated. Note that the lower limit is at the point from which the motion starts, and the upper limit is at the point where the motion ends. Also note that the first term on the left is associated with the upper limit, and the second term on the left is associated with the lower limit. As is the case with any definite integral, the sign is changed if the limits are interchanged. Thus, in (10–1–4) we may, when there is a need, calculate $PE_B - PE_A$ by interchanging the limits.

1. ILLUSTRATIONS OF THE EVALUATION OF A LINE INTEGRAL IN SAMPLE PROBLEMS

Example (A), Problem: In a limited region near the origin and in the *XY*-plane, a certain electric field can be represented by the vector equation

$$E = k(iy + jx) \qquad (10\text{–}1\text{–}5)$$

where $k = 1$ newton/coulomb meter, the units of k being those required to make (10–1–5) dimensionally correct. Find the increase in the potential energy of a positive test charge of 3.20×10^{-19} coulomb when the test charge is carried from *B* by a straight line path directly to *A*. Point *B* has coordinates $x = 3.00$ m, $y = 4.00$ m, and *A* is at the origin.

Solution. In Fig. 10–1–3, draw the coordinate axes, locate the points *B* and *A*, draw the straight line path from *B* to *A*, and draw a representative vector for *E* at any point on the path.

Equation (10–1–5) tells us that the x and y components of *E* are $E_x = ky$ and $E_y = kx$. Thus, the x component of *E* at a point *P* is directly proportional to the y coordinate of *P*, and the y component of *E* is directly proportional to the x coordinate of *P*. Figure 10–1–3 shows these two components of *E* at the point *P* on the path *BPA*. The coordinates of *P* are (x, y).

At *P* draw an element of path length *ds*, which must be directed toward *A*, since the motion of q' is from *B* to *A*. Here θ is the angle between *E* and *ds* in order to meet the requirements of Fig. 10–1–1, and it is thus the angle shown as θ in Fig. 10–1–3.

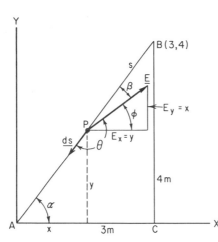

Figure 10–1–3. Path *BA* for the solution of Example (A).

We wish to evaluate the integral on the right of (10–1–4), so we must express *E* and cos θ as functions of *s*.

The distance *s* must be measured from the starting point of the motion at *B* so, on the diagram, *s* is the distance from *B* to *P* along the straight path *BPA*. First we shall find the functional relationship between *E* and *s*.

From the diagram in Fig. 10–1–3

$$s = 5 \text{ meters} - \sqrt{x^2 + y^2}, \quad \text{or} \quad \sqrt{x^2 + y^2} = 5 \text{ meters} - s \qquad (10\text{–}1\text{–}6)$$

where x and y are the coordinates of any point *P* on the line *BPA*. From (10–1–5), the magnitude of *E* is $k\sqrt{x^2 + y^2}$

$$\sqrt{x^2 + y^2} = E/k \qquad (10\text{–}1\text{–}7)$$

Substitute (10–1–7) into (10–1–6) and solve for *E*

$$E = 5k \text{ meters} - ks \qquad (10\text{–}1\text{–}8)$$

This gives the functional relationship between E and s that we need for substitution into the integral of (10–1–4).

Next, find the functional relationship between $\cos\theta$ and s. From the diagram, $\beta = \alpha - \phi$, so $\cos\beta = \cos\alpha\cos\phi + \sin\alpha\sin\phi$. Evaluate, from the diagram, the sines and cosines on the right, and make use of (10–1–6) to obtain

$$\cos\beta = (3y + 4x)/5(5 \text{ meters} - s) \qquad (10\text{–}1\text{–}9)$$

The straight line path APB may be represented by the equation $y = 4x/3$ which, with (10–1–9), yields

$$\cos\beta = 8x/5(5 \text{ meters} - s) \qquad (10\text{–}1\text{–}10)$$

Put $y = 4x/3$ into (10–1–6) and substitute the value of x obtained into (10–1–10). The result is $\cos\beta = 24/25$. But $\cos\theta = -\cos\beta$, so

$$\cos\theta = -24/25 \qquad (10\text{–}1\text{–}11)$$

Equation (10–1–11) gives the functional relationship between $\cos\theta$ and s, and it shows that $\cos\theta$ is constant along this path and thus independent of s.

In (10–1–8) and (10–1–11), we have the two necessary functional relationships relating E and $\cos\theta$ to the variable of integration s in (10–1–4). Hence,

$$PE_A - PE_B = -q' \int_{(B)}^{(A)} (5k \text{ meters} - ks)(-24/25)\, ds$$

We must replace the symbolic limits (A) and (B) by numerical limits expressed in terms of the variable of integration. At B, $s = 0$ and at A, $s = 5$ m. Hence we have

$$PE_A - PE_B = (24/25)\, q' \int_0^{5m} (5k \text{ meters} - ks)\, ds$$

Integrate and substitute the limits of integration

$$PE_A - PE_B = 12q' \text{ joules/coulomb} \qquad (10\text{–}1\text{–}12)$$

Note that $PE_A - PE_B$ is positive, since q' is positive, as it must be, for the PE of q' at A is greater than the PE of q' at B, i,e., we have done work against the field in moving q' from B to A.

Now, to obtain the answer, substitute the value of q' into (10–1–12) and obtain

$$PE_A - PE_B = 38.4 \times 10^{-19} \text{ joule} \qquad (10\text{–}1\text{–}13)$$

Solve Problem 10–1 at this point.

As an important side light on this example, let us inquire about the shape of the electric lines of force for a field that is given by (10–1–5) in the XY-plane. As we pointed out when we adopted the convention for drawing lines of force to represent an electric field, a line of force is drawn so that, at every point on the line, E is tangent to the line. Thus, an equation for a line of force must satisfy the requirement that its slope at every point is parallel to E. In the XY-plane, this requirement may be stated by the equation

$$dy/dx = E_y/E_x \qquad (10\text{–}1\text{–}14)$$

Apply this requirement to the special case of a field represented in the XY-plane by (10–1–5), and we have $dy/dx = x/y$. The solution of this differential equation gives the family of equations for the lines of force of the field. It is an equation where the variables are immediately separable, so $x\,dx = y\,dy$. Integrate and let C represent the constant of integration.

$$y^2 = x^2 + 2C \qquad (10\text{--}1\text{--}15)$$

Constant C may have any value, positive or negative, within the region of the XY-plane where (10–1–5) is valid, so (10–1–15) represents a family of hyperbolas. The asymptotes are obtained by making $C = 0$, so

$$y = \pm x \qquad (10\text{--}1\text{--}16)$$

is the equation of the asymptotes. These are two 45° lines. Figure 10–1–4 shows the asymptotes and a few of the lines of force for this field in the vicinity of the origin. (Solve Problem 10–2 at this point.)

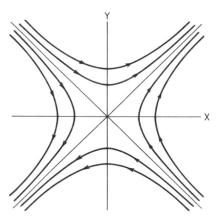

Figure 10–1–4. Some electric lines of force for the field

$$E = (iy + jx)\,\frac{1\ \text{newton}}{\text{coulomb meter}}.$$

2. $PE_A - PE_B$ IS THE SAME REGARDLESS OF THE PATH FOLLOWED BY q' FROM B TO A IN AN ELECTROSTATIC FIELD. To prove this point, imagine that q' follows the path B to D to A in Fig. 10–1–1, and imagine that $PE_A - PE_B$ is greater on this path than on the path B to P to A. Let us build a machine that will carry q' from B to A by the path BPA, doing work on q' in the process. Then, the machine is to let q' return to B by the path ADB. In this return part of the path, the field will do work on the machine through the force that the field exerts on q'. If $PE_A - PE_B$ is greater by the path ADB than by the path BPA, the charge will do more work on the machine than the work that the machine does on the charge. In other words, we shall derive a net amount of work from the machine for each trip that q' makes around the closed path $BPADB$. But this is an electrostatic field, and there is no outside agency that can feed energy into the system by means of the field. Hence, energy would be created by the machine. This is impossible by the law of conservation of energy. A converse argument will show that $PE_A - PE_B$ cannot be greater along the path BPA than along the path BDA. These two paths are any two paths; *hence, $PE_A - PE_B$ must be the same regardless of the path along which q' is moved from B to A.* A field that satisfies this requirement is said to be a *conservative* field, and all electrostatic fields are conservative. In Problems 10–1 and 10–4 you observed this path independence, because the fields given were conservative.

3. POTENTIAL ENERGY OF q' AT A POINT. In order to state the total PE of q' when it is at A in Fig. 10–1–1, we must select a reference frame in terms of which we shall measure potential energy. The choice of the zero for this reference frame is arbitrary. Whatever place we select for the zero, we say that q' has zero PE when it is at this place.

This is much the same problem as the one encountered in selecting a reference level for measuring the PE of a mass in the earth's gravitational field. We may select the level of the top of the table in the laboratory as the zero and say that the mass has zero PE when it is on the table top, positive PE when it is above the table top, and negative PE when it is below the table top. With equal validity, we could select the level of the floor in the laboratory as the zero level, or we could select sea level as the zero level or the bottom of the deepest mine.

In electrostatic problems, it is often convenient to say that a charge has a potential energy equal to zero when it is located at an infinite distance from us. The convenience arises from the fact that the electric field intensity, due to the charged bodies which set up the field, is zero infinitely far from the charged bodies. We shall adopt this convention concerning the zero of PE for the present consideration and for numerous problems in the future. However, this is an arbitrary choice and, as pointed out later, other choices are more convenient in other problems. For example, in some problems the earth is arbitrarily taken as the place where a charge has zero PE.

In Fig. 10–1–1, let us say that q' has zero PE when it is infinitely far from the charges that produced the electric field under consideration. We assume that these charges, which are responsible for the field, lie within a certain finite volume and that there are no charges outside this volume. We may now indicate how to compute the PE of q' at A by the method in (10–1–4). All we need do is to consider that B is infinitely far away, and we have from (10–1–4)

$$PE_A = -q' \int_{(\infty)}^{(A)} E \cos \theta \, ds = -q' \int_{(\infty)}^{(A)} \boldsymbol{E} \cdot \boldsymbol{ds} \qquad (10\text{–}1\text{–}17)$$

Remember that (∞) and (A) denote, respectively, the beginning and end points of the path. The symbol (∞) means that we are to take the limit of the integral in (10–1–4) as the initial point B, of the path, recedes to infinity.

This equation says that *the potential energy of a test charge at a point in an electric field is the work required to bring the test charge from infinity to the point against the electric forces exerted on it by the field.* (Solve Problems 10–5 and 10–6 at this point.)

10–2 POTENTIAL DIFFERENCE BETWEEN POINTS AND POTENTIAL AT A POINT IN AN ELECTROSTATIC FIELD

1. POTENTIAL DIFFERENCE BETWEEN TWO POINTS. *The potential difference between two points is defined as the change in potential energy of a test charge, when it is moved between the two points, divided by the magnitude and sign of the test charge.* Since change of PE and q' are both scalars, potential difference is a scalar quantity.

In Sec. 10–1 we learned how to compute the change in PE of a test charge when the test charge is moved from one point to another in an electrostatic field. Hence, using the preceding definition, we may at once convert the discussion in Sec. 10–1 into a discussion of potential. For example (refer to Fig. 10–1–1), Eq. (10–1–1) yields at once the important equation for the element of potential difference dV along the element of path length ds as follows. From the preceding definition, $dV = dW/q'$. So $dV = -q'E \cos \theta \, ds/q'$, or

$$dV = E \cos \theta \, ds \qquad E \, ds \qquad (10\text{–}2\text{–}1)$$

Since the magnitude and sign of q' appear in both the numerator and denominator, dV is independent of the magnitude and sign of q' and depends only on the field.

Similarly, we may convert (10–1–4) into an equation that yields the potential difference between B and A in Fig. 10–1–1 by dividing both sides of (10–1–4) by q'. Thus,

$$PE_A/q' - PE_B/q' = -(q'/q') \int_{(B)}^{(A)} E \cos \theta \, ds$$

or $$V_A - V_B = - \int_{(B)}^{(A)} E \cos \theta \, ds = - \int_{(B)}^{(A)} \mathbf{E} \cdot \mathbf{ds} \qquad (10\text{–}2\text{–}2)$$

where $V_A - V_B$ is the potential difference between points A and B. Potential difference $V_A - V_B$ is positive, since we must do work to move a positive test charge from B to A in Fig. 10–1–1. As pointed out immediately following (10–1–1), $\cos \theta$ in Fig. 10–1–1 [and thus in (10–2–2)] contains a minus sign hidden in it, since θ is greater than 90°. Thus, the right side of (10–2–2) is positive, as it must be in this case.

When we divide change in potential energy by the magnitude of the charge whose potential energy is changed, we are computing work per unit charge. Here E is force per unit charge, and thus the right side of (10–2–2) is a calculation of the work required to move a unit charge from B to A (under the assumption that the presence of the unit charge does not alter the distribution of the charges which established the field being considered). Thus, the definition of potential difference between two points is often stated in the equivalent form: *the potential difference between two points is the work per unit charge required to carry a positive test charge from one point to the other.* We see that this is the same concept of potential difference introduced in Sec. 1–4. In the early part of the book, we applied this concept to electric circuits. Here we apply the same concept to electrostatic fields.

2. POTENTIAL DIFFERENCE IS INDEPENDENT OF PATH. In Sec. 10–1 we have shown that the difference, PE of q' at A minus PE of q' at B, is the same regardless of the path which q' follows in going from B to A. Thus, we may write that $PE_A/q' - PE_B/q'$ is independent of path followed from B to A. Since $PE_A/q' - PE_B/q' = V_A - V_B$ we may conclude that *the potential difference between two points in an electrostatic field is independent of the path followed between the two points.* We saw that Kirchhoff's second law arose from this fact when the fact was applied to an electric circuit.

We may express the same fact by saying that the potential difference is zero around any closed path in an electrostatic field. This statement is expressed by the equation

$$\oint E \cos \theta \, ds = \oint \boldsymbol{E} \cdot \boldsymbol{ds} = 0 \qquad (10\text{–}2\text{–}3)$$

The circle on the integral sign means that the integration of the line integral is to be carried around a *closed* path. We have seen that this may be any closed path in the electrostatic field.

3. POTENTIAL AT A POINT. By definition, *the potential V at a point in an electric field is the potential energy of a test charge at that point, divided by the magnitude and sign of the test charge.* To satisy this definition in a particular problem, we may select any place for the zero of potential that we like as long as it is the same place that we have used for the zero of potential energy in the same problem. Frequently it is convenient to consider that the earth is at zero potential, and we shall make this choice when convenience is served. In other cases, the problem under consideration is simplified by the choice made in the latter part of Sec. 10–1, and in such cases we shall consider that the zero of potential is at a place infinitely far away.

The above definition of potential may be expressed by the formula

$$V_A = \frac{PE \text{ of } q' \text{ at } A}{q'} \qquad (10\text{–}2\text{–}4)$$

Conversely, if the potential at a point is known, the *PE* of a charge q' at the point may be computed from

$$PE \text{ of } q' \text{ at } A = V_A \, q' \qquad (10\text{–}2\text{–}5)$$

Potential at a point is merely a special case of potential difference, since V_A in (10–2–4) expresses the potential difference between a point (A) and the place arbitrarily taken as the location of the zero of potential. Thus, (10–2–2) is used to compute potential V_A at a point by this simple device, namely, locate (B) at the place where the potential is considered to be zero, and V_B is then zero. Usually the word "potential" alone is used in place of the words "potential at a point."

Potential is a scalar quantity, and it has a value at every point in an electric field. This concept is usually stated by saying that *potential is a scalar-point function.* An equation that expresses the potential at every point in an electric field must be a scalar equation that expresses V as a function of the coordinates of points in the field. If we have such a formula for V in a certain electric field and wish to know the potential at a particular point, we need only substitute the coordinates of that point into the formula. The answer will give the potential at the point in question.

4. UNITS OF POTENTIAL AND POTENTIAL DIFFERENCE. From the definitions of potential or potential difference, V has the units of work divided by charge.

In the electrostatic system of units, the erg is the unit of work and the statcoulomb is the unit of charge. Thus, the unit of V in this system is ergs/statcoulomb. This combination of units is given the name "statvolt." Thus, 1 statvolt = 1 erg/statcoulomb.

In the mks system, the unit of work is the newton meter or joule, and the unit of charge is the coulomb. Thus, the unit of V is joules/coulomb. As pointed out in Chapter I, this combination of units is given the name "volt." Thus, 1 volt = 1 joule/coulomb. See Appendix A–3 for the conversion factor relating the volt to the statvolt. (Solve Problems 10–7, 10–8, 10–9, and 10–10 at this point.)

10–3 POTENTIAL IN THE FIELD OF A POINT CHARGE

As an example of the derivation of a potential formula, let us take the very simple case of the electric field of an isolated positive point charge. In Problem 10–5, by reference to Fig. 10–P–2, you are asked to derive (10–P–2) as the increase in potential energy of a test charge q' when it is moved from B to A in the field set up by a positive point charge q. This formula can be transformed into one for potential difference between A and B merely by dividing both sides by q', so we have

$$V_A - V_B = \frac{q}{4\pi\varepsilon_0}\left(\frac{1}{r_A} - \frac{1}{r_B}\right) \tag{10–3–1}$$

Next we wish to get the potential at A. From (10–2–4) and (10–P–3), $V_A = PE_A/q' = q/4\pi\varepsilon_0 r_A$ or, dropping the subscripts since A is any point in the field,

$$V = q/4\pi\varepsilon_0 r \tag{10–3–2}$$

In (10–3–2), r is the radial distance from the point charge q to the point in the field where we wish to know the potential. If we consider that the origin of a spherical coordinate system is at the point charge q in Fig. 10–P–2, we see from (10–3–2) that the potential at a point is a function only of the r coordinate of that point. Equation (10–3–2) is a potential expression of the type described following (10–2–5). (Solve Problems 10–11 and 10–12.)

10–4 PRINCIPLE OF SUPERPOSITION FOR POTENTIAL

Let us consider the potential at a point in empty space in the electric field of two point charges. Figure 10–4–1 shows the two point charges q_1 and q_2 that are responsible for the field. By the usual method that we have used so much let us indicate the computation of the potential difference between A and B along the path BPA. Figure 10–4–1 shows the electric fields E_1 and E_2 at P due to the charges q_1 and q_2 separately. By the principle of superposition for electric fields, the resultant E at P is given by $E = E_1 + E_2$ and E is shown on the diagram. The component of E along the path is the sum of the components of E_1 and E_2 along the path, or $E\cos\theta = E_1\cos\theta_1 + E_2\cos\theta_2$ where θ is the angle that E makes with the path.

Now apply (10–2–2).

$$V_A - V_B = -\int_{(B)}^{(A)} E\cos\theta\, ds$$

$$= -\int_{(B)}^{(A)} E_1\cos\theta_1\, ds - \int_{(B)}^{(A)} E_2\cos\theta_2\, ds$$

But each of the integrals on the far right applies to a single one of the point charges, so we know from (10–3–1) that the result will be

$$V_A - V_B = q_1(1/r_{1A} - 1/r_{1B})/4\pi\varepsilon_0 + q_2(1/r_{2A} - 1/r_{2B})/4\pi\varepsilon_0$$

where r_{1B} and r_{2B} are the distances from q_1 to B and q_2 to B, respectively. This equation shows that potential differences are additive.

Now let B recede to infinity so that $r_{1B} \to \infty$ and $r_{2B} \to \infty$, and we have

$$V_A = q_1/4\pi\varepsilon_0 r_{1A} + q_2/4\pi\varepsilon_0 r_{2A}$$

This equation tells us that the potential at A due to two charges is the scalar sum of the potentials which each would produce at A alone.

This result may be extended by the same method to any number of point

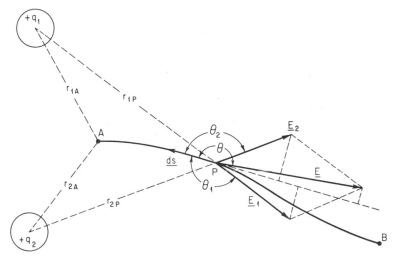

Figure 10–4–1. Potential difference between two points in the electric field of two point charges.

charges making up the configuration that produces the field. Since A is any point in the field, we may as well drop the A subscript on V. Extend the argument to the general case of n charges (see Fig. 9–5–2) making up the configuration that produces the field, and we have

$$V = (1/4\pi\varepsilon_0) \sum_{i=1}^{n} q_i/r_i \qquad (10\text{--}4\text{--}1)$$

where r_i is the distance from q_i to the point for which the potential is being computed. Equation (10–4–1) is a *scalar* sum, and the sign of each charge will determine the sign of the term in the sum that represents it.

From the above, we may state the principle of superposition for potential as follows. *For any configuration of charges, the potential at a point in an electric field is the algebraic sum of the potentials that each charge alone would produce at the point.* It is implicit in our derivation of this result that the potential is zero at an infinite distance from all the charges that contribute to the field.

A continuous distribution of charges, over the surfaces and throughout the volumes of bodies may be considered to be made up of an assembly of point charges each of magnitude dq. In such cases it may be convenient to express the sum in (10–4–1) as the integral

$$V = (1/4\pi\varepsilon_0) \int dq/r \qquad (10\text{–}4\text{–}2)$$

where r is the distance from dq to the point for which the potential is being computed. Equation (10–4–2) is really a symbolic notation because the integration would be double integrations for surfaces and triple integrations for volumes. Equation (10–4–2) means that we are to carry out the mathematical processes necessary in order to sum all the dq/r terms for all charges which contribute to the field.

It is usually much easier to evaluate scalar sums than it is to evaluate vector sums. The sums for potential in (10–4–1) and (10–4–2) are scalar sums, as contrasted with the vector sums in (9–5–3) and (9–5–4) for electric field intensity. Thus in a complicated problem it is often much easier to compute the potential function directly than it is to compute the field intensity function. [See the example in Sec. 10–8 for an illustration of the use of (10–4–2) in a simple problem.]

10–5 POTENTIAL DIFFERENCE BETWEEN THE PLATES OF A PARALLEL PLATE CAPACITOR WITH EMPTY SPACE BETWEEN THE PLATES

In Sec. 9–13 we discussed the electric field in empty space between the plates of a parallel plate capacitor, and in Fig. 9–13–1 some of the electric lines of force are shown. We derived the formula for the magnitude of the electric field intensity between the plates in the region where fringing may be neglected. The result is given in (9–13–1) as $E = \sigma/\varepsilon_0$, where σ is the surface density of charge on either plate.

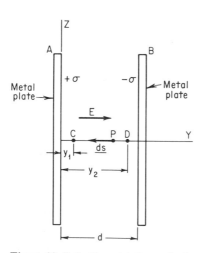

Figure 10–5–1. Computation of the potential difference between the plates of a parallel plate capacitor. Plate A is positively charged, and Plate B is negatively charged.

Let us again assume that the plates are so close together that their separation d is small compared with the linear dimensions of either plate and, thus, that fringing may be neglected. Assume that a set of Cartesian coordinates is set up as indicated in Sec. 9–13 for this problem, so that the Y-axis is perpendicular to the metal plates and thus parallel to the lines of force. The situation is shown in Fig. 10–5–1.

Each plate of the capacitor is a conductor with a static charge, so $E = 0$

everywhere inside either plate. Thus, no work against electric forces is required to carry a test charge from one point to another in either plate and, hence, each plate must have the same potential at all points. It is the potential difference between the two plates that we wish to compute.

The potential difference between the plates is independent of the path followed between the plates, so let us carry out the computation along the Y-axis from plate B to plate A and between any two points D and C on the path.

At all points on the path, E is in the opposite direction to ds, so $\theta = 180°$ and $\cos \theta = -1$. Using this fact and (9–13–1), Eq. (10–2–2) becomes

$$V_C - V_D = - \int_{(D)}^{(C)} \frac{\sigma}{\varepsilon_0} (-1) \, ds$$

But at D, $s = 0$ and at C, $s = y_2 - y_1$, so

$$V_C - V_D = \frac{\sigma}{\varepsilon_0} \int_0^{y_2 - y_1} ds = \frac{\sigma}{\varepsilon_0} (y_2 - y_1) \qquad (10\text{–}5\text{–}1)$$

Since σ is a constant in this case, we see from (10–5–1) that the potential difference is a linear function of the distance, parallel to the Y-axis, between the two points.

For the special case where $y_1 = 0$ and $y_2 = d$,

$$V_A - V_B = \sigma d / \varepsilon_0 \qquad (10\text{–}5\text{–}2)$$

which is the potential difference between the plates. If we replace σ/ε_0 in (10–5–2) by its equivalent E, we have $V_A - V_B = Ed$ or

$$E = (V_A - V_B)/d \qquad (10\text{–}5\text{–}3)$$

Equation (10–5–3) is often a more useful formula than is (9–13–1) for computation of E in the space between the plates of a parallel plate capacitor. This is due to the fact that the potential difference and distance between the plates are quantities that are readily measurable in many physical experiments, whereas σ may not be so easily measured.

Equation (10–5–3) gives volt/meter as the unit of E. You can show that 1 volt/meter = 1 newton/coulomb. The volt/meter is the common unit for E, and we shall see why from a general relationship that we shall derive shortly [see discussion following (10–8–12)].

10-6 POTENTIAL DIFFERENCE BETWEEN COAXIAL CONDUCTING CYLINDERS UNDER CONDITIONS WHERE FRINGING MAY BE NEGLECTED

Figure 10–6–1 shows the two metal cylinders in cross section. The inner cylinder has a positive charge b per unit length, and the outer cylinder has an equal negative charge per unit length on its inner surface.

We have discussed the problem of the field in the empty space between the two cylinders in Sec. 9–10 and, in the conclusion at the end of the section, have shown that (9–10–6) gives the electric field intensity at a point that is at a

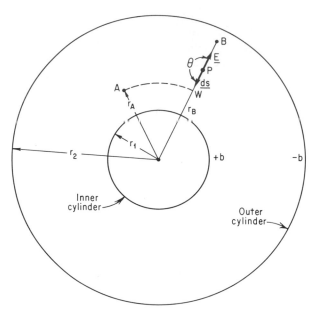

Figure 10–6–1. Coaxial metal cylinders shown in cross section. Calculation of the potential difference between any two points A and B in the empty space between the cylinders.

distance r from their common axis. At all points between the cylinders, E is directed radially outward as shown by (9–10–6).

Let A and B be any two points between the cylinders at radial distances r_A and r_B, respectively, from the common axis. First we shall compute the potential difference $V_A - V_B$ and, since the potential difference is the same regardless of path, let us take the path BWA. This may be split into the two parts B to W and W to A, where WA is an arc of a circle of radius r_A. At all points on the W to A part of the path, E is perpendicular to the path, so no work is done in moving a test charge from W to A. Hence, $V_A - V_B = V_W - V_B$, and all we need compute is $V_W - V_B$.

Along the path B to W, E is in a direction opposite to that of ds, so $\theta = 180°$ and $\cos \theta = -1$. Using this fact and the magnitude of E from (9–10–6), Eq. (10–2–2) becomes

$$V_A - V_B = - \int_{(B)}^{(A)} E \cos \theta \, ds = - \int_{(B)}^{(W)} \frac{1}{2\pi\varepsilon_0} \frac{b}{r} (-1) \, ds$$

At B, $s = 0$ and at W, $s = r_B - r_A$. Here r is the radial distance to any point P between B and W, and $r = r_B - s$. Hence,

$$V_A - V_B = \frac{-b}{2\pi\varepsilon_0} \int_0^{r_B - r_A} \frac{-ds}{r_B - s} = - \frac{b}{2\pi\varepsilon_0} \left[\ln (r_B - s) \right]_0^{r_B - r_A}$$

$$V_A - V_B = \frac{b}{2\pi\varepsilon_0} \ln \frac{r_B}{r_A} \qquad (10\text{–}6\text{–}1)$$

As a special case of (10–6–1), consider that B in Fig. 10–6–1 is located on the outer cylinder, and A is located on the inner cylinder. Then $r_A = r_1$ and $r_B = r_2$, and (10–6–1) becomes

$$V_1 - V_2 = \frac{b}{2\pi\varepsilon_0} \ln \frac{r_2}{r_1} \qquad (10\text{–}6\text{–}2)$$

Equation (10–6–2) gives the potential difference between the metal cylinders.

Since $E = 0$ inside the inner cylinder, no additional work per unit charge would be required to carry a test charge inside the inner cylinder. Thus, all the inner cylinder is at the same potential as its surface.

10-7 EQUIPOTENTIAL SURFACES

An equipotential line is a line so drawn that all points on it are at the same potential. Thus, no work against electric forces is required to move a test charge along such a line. We have seen that the circular arc WA in Fig. 10–6–1 is an equipotential line, and the argument by which we reach this conclusion can be extended to all points on a circle of radius r_A. Hence, this is an equipotential circle.

Similarly, the argument is equally valid for all points on an imaginary cylinder, perpendicular to Fig. 10–6–1, of which the circle of radius r_A is a cross section. This cylindrical surface is called an *equipotential surface*.

In general, an equipotential surface, as the name implies, is a surface so drawn that all points are at the same potential. Thus, no work against electric forces is required to move a test charge over an equipotential surface. We can see from the above that E *must be everywhere normal to an equipotential surface* so that θ will be 90° and cos θ will be zero. Equipotential surfaces are often referred to simply as *equipotentials*.

In Fig. 10–6–1, let us take the potential of the outer metal cylinder as the zero of potential. Between the two metal cylinders we may draw any number of cylinders, concentric with the metal cylinders, and each one that we draw will be an equipotential surface. However, the greater the radius of one of these equipotential surfaces the smaller will be the potential of its cylindrical surface. The inner metal cylinder is one of the equipotential surfaces and, as pointed out at the end of Sec. 10–6, $E = 0$ inside this inner metal cylinder, so this inner metal cylinder is an equipotential volume. By the same argument, *any conductor with a static charge will be an equipotential volume.*

Since E is everywhere normal to every equipotential surface, the electric lines of force are everywhere normal to every equipotential surface. Thus, if the lines of force have been drawn, equipotential surfaces may be drawn at once. Conversely, if the equipotential surfaces are known, lines of force may be drawn at once. When mapping an electric field by means of equipotential surfaces, it is conventional to space the equipotentials so that there is the same potential difference between any two adjacent ones.

1. EQUIPOTENTIAL SURFACES FOR A PARALLEL PLATE CAPACITOR. As an example of the mapping of an electric field by the use of equipotential surfaces and lines of force, let us map the field between the plates of a parallel plate capacitor. In Sec. 10–5 we computed the potential difference between any two

points in the field between the plates, under the conditions that fringing may be neglected.

Let us take the potential of the positively charged plate as the zero of potential. In Fig. 10–5–1, move C to the positively charged plate, so $y_1 = 0$. Then (10–5–1) becomes

$$0 - V_D = \sigma y_2/\varepsilon_0, \quad \text{or} \quad V_D = -\sigma y_2/\varepsilon_0 \qquad (10\text{–}7\text{–}1)$$

for the potential at any point D between the plates. This shows that the potential at any point between the plates is a linear function of the distance y_2 from the point to the plate and is a function of this distance only, since σ is constant. Thus the equipotential surfaces are planes parallel to the metal

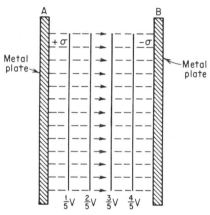

Figure 10–7–1. Parallel plate capacitor with metal plates A and B. Equipotential planes parallel with the metal plates.

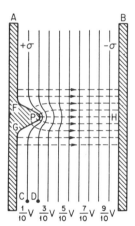

Figure 10–7–2. Equipotential surfaces and lines of force for a projection on a conductor with a static charge.

plates. Further, if the equipotential surfaces are equally spaced with respect to potential, they will be equally spaced with respect to distance.

Figure 10–7–1 shows the cross section, in the plane of the paper, of the metal plates A and B and of the equipotential planes. The dashed lines show some representative lines of force. Each line of force is, of course, perpendicular to all equipotential surfaces including the surfaces of the metal plates. In the figure, the equipotential planes are represented by lines parallel with the plates. The space between the plates is divided, in this case, into five equal divisions. Thus, if we let V represent the potential difference between the plates, each equipotential surface differs in potential by $V/5$ from its neighbors. There is some fringing of lines of force at the edges of the plates, even under the most nearly ideal conditions that can be realized experimentally, but the equipotentials and lines of force have not been shown in the region where fringing occurs.

2. CHARGE DENSITY AT SHARP POINTS ON CONDUCTORS. The method of mapping fields by means of equipotential surfaces can often yield qualitative answers to problems that would be difficult, or impossible, to solve quantitatively. Let us consider one example of such a problem.

A metal body has a static charge, and at one place its surface has a small radius of curvature that approximates a sharp point on the body. We wish to determine qualitatively the charge density at this point relative to the charge density on parts of the surface that have larger radii of curvature. This problem can be solved quantitatively* under favorable geometrical conditions, but the solution is not easy. We shall arrive at a qualitative answer by the use of equipotential surfaces.

For this purpose imagine that one metal plate of the parallel plate capacitor in Fig. 10–7–1 has a projection on it which sticks out into the region between the plates. This projection is shown at P in Fig. 10–7–2, where the size of the projection is exaggerated with respect to the size of the plates and to the distance between the plates. In the region above and below P in the figure, we assume that the presence of the projection has no influence and that the field is uniform.

Now let us draw equipotential surfaces. Divide the potential difference between the metal plates A and B by 10. At C, one-tenth of the distance between the plates, draw a plane upward parallel to plate A. This will continue as a plane until it approaches P, where it will have to bulge outward to the right in order to follow the contour of P. We do not know just how to draw it, but we know that it must bulge to the right and that, beyond P, it must come back to the same plane parallel to A that it followed below P. We mark this equipotential surface $\frac{1}{10}V$.

From D, two-tenths of the distance from A to B draw a second equipotential surface in the same fashion except that it bulges less at P. Continue this construction for the remainder of the equipotentials shown. Near plate B the equipotentials will be planes parallel to B and without bulges.

Next let us draw lines of force between the plates. From (9–7–6), $1/\varepsilon_0$ lines of force originate from a unit positive charge and terminate on a unit negative charge. On plate B there are σ unit negative charges on unit area, and let us assume that σ is uniform on this plate. Because of the projection P on plate A, σ is not uniform on plate B, but the assumption is sufficiently accurate for our qualitative argument. Thus, σ/ε_0 lines of force terminate on each unit area of plate B. Therefore, let us draw σ/ε_0 lines of force from unit area of B and go backward along each line of force toward plate A. A line of force must cross each equipotential at right angles, and this is our guide for drawing the lines of force. As shown in the figure, since the equipotentials bulge outward around P, the lines of force must converge toward the tip of P. The result is a concentration of lines of force just outside P, and these lines must have originated on points close together at the tip of P. But in a region where lines of force are close together, E is larger than it is where lines of force are farther apart. Hence E_P, just outside of P, is larger than E any other place between the plates. But just outside of any conductor with a static charge

* See, for example, J. H. Jeans, *Electricity and Magnetism*, 2d ed. (London: Cambridge University Press, 1911), pp. 59–62.

$E = \sigma/\varepsilon_0$. Let σ_P be the charge density on P, so that $E_P = \sigma_P/\varepsilon_0$. But E_P is larger than E any other place between the plates, so σ_P is larger than σ at any other place on the surface of the plates. Thus charge has concentrated on the sharp point P and produces a large electric field intensity just outside the point. We arrived at this conclusion by assuming that the σ is uniform on plate B even though the projection P is present on plate A. We can now see that the concentration of charge on P will, by induction, concentrate charge on B in a region H opposite P. This in turn requires more lines of force to be drawn from H and, thus, a still greater density of lines near P, which merely augments the qualitative argument.

We have carried out the argument above for the special case of a sharp point on one plate of a parallel plate capacitor, but it is generally true that the smaller the radius of curvature of a convex part of a charged conductor, the greater the charge density on that part; and the greater the radius of curvature of a convex part of a charged conductor, the smaller the charge density on that part. For a concave part of a charged conductor, the charge density decreases markedly. We can see this latter statement illustrated at F and G of Fig. 10–7–2, where the lines of force are far apart and, thus, the charge density is small.

As pointed out before, when a conductor has a static charge, all points on the surface and inside the conductor must be at the same potential. This is the fundamental requirement, and the charge must be distributed on the conductor in such a way that the requirement is satisfied. In turn this requirement says that, for all points of the conductor the sum in (10–4–1) must give a constant for the answer. Such a line of argument, however, is not the easy one to use directly for qualitative reasoning about the preceding problem.

3. CORONA. You will probably recall the lecture demonstration, in elementary physics, in which a metal body with a sharp point was connected to a high voltage machine. In a darkened room you observed light in the air around the sharp point and were shown that the high voltage machine was being discharged by the flow of electricity from the sharp point into the air. This phenomenon is called discharge of electricity from a point.

We may explain the discharge from points by the following description. There are always some free electrons and positive ions present in the air due to cosmic radiation and local radioactivity. In the presence of an electric field, these electrons and positive ions will be accelerated, the former in the opposite direction to the field and the latter in the direction of the field. Usually the energy that the electrons and ions receive from the field will be dissipated as heat due to their elastic collisions with neutral air molecules. If, however, the electric field intensity is high enough, an electron receives enough energy in one mean free path so that it can ionize an air molecule in an inelastic collision at the end of the free path. Under this condition the electron will produce further ions and electrons. These freed electrons in turn will produce further ions, and the air becomes conducting. In the immediate vicinity of a charged point, the field may be great enough to cause such conduction even though the field near other parts of the conductor is not great enough. If the point is positively charged, for example, the electrons in the air will move to the point

Figure 10–7–3. A General Electric Company research transmission line showing corona clearly all along the single wires. Dr. P. A. Abetti, the manager for General Electric Company in this research project says "Briefly, corona will be suppressed either by using a tube or a conductor of very large diameter, or else by using several conductors of normal diameter in a bundle. In the corona picture (above) you will notice that in the front there are four conductors in a bundle per phase and no corona can be seen on these conductors although they are operating at 720,000 volts.   There is corona on the single conductor 2.32 inches in diameter because this conductor was designed for use on 460,000-volt transmission lines."

By courtesy of the General Electric Company.

and neutralize the charge. Similarly, if the point is negatively charged the positive ions in the air will move to the point and neutralize the charge.

With a supply of electrons and positive ions present in the air near the point, there will be some direct recombination of electrons and positive ions. When this occurs, energy is radiated, and some of the radiation is in the visible part of the spectrum. Such radiation, if sufficiently intense, is seen by the eye, and this is the explanation of the light seen near the point in the lecture demonstration. In general, recombination will be greatest where the supply of ions and electrons is greatest, and thus most of the light is radiated from such regions. By this secondary effect we "see" the discharge from points in air as we did in the demonstration, and the phenomenon is called *corona*. You will also recall from elementary physics that discharge from points is employed in such machines as the Wimshurst and Van de Graaff generators for transfer of charge through a gas. Lightning rods owe their effectiveness to the discharge from points.

The construction of high voltage transmission lines must be such that sharp points and corners are avoided in order to avoid loss of energy by corona discharge. If the potential difference between the wires of the lines, or between the wires and ground, is very large, the electric field intensity just outside the cylindrical wires may be large enough to cause corona even though there are no points. This causes the wires of such transmission lines to be surrounded by a faint glow that can sometimes be seen at night and, of course, there is a power loss. This loss is known as the *corona loss*. Figure 10–7–3 shows dramatically the corona around a research transmission line of the General Electric Company where the potential difference between the wires has, for test purposes, been made about 1.6 times as big as the voltage for which the line was designed.

We have seen in (9–10–4) that the electric field intensity just outside a cylindrical conductor varies inversely with the radius of the conductor. Hence, if the corona loss is prohibitive, conductors of larger radius must be used. In order to keep the weight of the larger conductors reasonable, aluminum (instead of copper) cable is commonly used and it is steel reinforced in order to secure the required strength. As pointed out in the caption of Fig. 10–7–3, other methods can be employed which prevent the electric field around the conductors from reaching the value of E which will produce corona.

10–8 RELATIONSHIP BETWEEN ELECTRIC FIELD INTENSITY AND POTENTIAL GRADIENT

So far in this chapter we have been using the integral relationship between electric field intensity and potential. Now we wish to secure a differential relationship between these two quantities that will permit us to compute the formula for electric field intensity when we know the formula for potential.

As in Sec. 10–2, let dV represent the element of potential difference along an element of path length ds, and θ represent the angle between E and ds. We have seen in (10–2–1) that $dV = -E \cos \theta \, ds = -E \cdot ds$ from the definition of potential difference. We may write (10–2–1) as

$$E \cos \theta = -dV/ds \qquad (10\text{–}8\text{–}1)$$

which tells us that *the component of the electric field intensity in any direction*
s is equal to the negative space rate of change of potential taken in the s direction.
Equation (10–8–1) is a special case of a general proposition which states that,
if a body is held at rest in any kind of a field, the component of the force on
the body in any direction *s* is equal to the negative space rate of change of
the potential energy of the body if it were moved in the *s* direction.

We wish to put the relationship in (10–8–1) into a more useful form for
calculation. The methods of vector analysis are the simplest for the purpose.
We shall now extend our earlier introduction to vector analysis in order to
develop the few additional techniques that we require here.

Let us assume that in a particular electrostatic problem we are using
Cartesian coordinates and have expressed V as a function of x, y, and z, i.e.,

$$V = F(x, y, z) \qquad (10\text{–}8\text{–}2)$$

This means [as pointed out in Sec. 10–2 near (10–2–5)] that we have an
equation relating V to position in the field and may compute the value of V
at any point by substituting into (10–8–2) the numerical values of the Cartesian coordinates of the point. The total differential of V is (see a calculus
book*)

$$dV = \frac{\partial V}{\partial x}\, dx + \frac{\partial V}{\partial y}\, dy + \frac{\partial V}{\partial z}\, dz \qquad (10\text{–}8\text{–}3)$$

From (9–6–7), (9–6–11), and (9–6–12), we see that (10–8–3) suggests a
scalar product of two vectors. One of these vectors would be ds, which we
have seen has dx, dy, dz as its x, y, and z components, respectively. The other
vector would be one whose x, y, and z components are $\partial V/\partial x$, $\partial V/\partial y$, and
$\partial V/\partial z$, respectively. Let us introduce such a vector, call it gradient of V, and
write it as $grad\ V$. Then by definition $grad\ V$ is the vector

$$\boldsymbol{grad}\ V = \boldsymbol{i}\ \partial V/\partial x + \boldsymbol{j}\ \partial V/\partial y + \boldsymbol{k}\ \partial V/\partial z \qquad (10\text{–}8\text{–}4)$$

The vector ds mentioned above is

$$\boldsymbol{ds} = \boldsymbol{i}\ dx + \boldsymbol{j}\ dy + \boldsymbol{k}\ dz \qquad (10\text{–}8\text{–}5)$$

The scalar product of (10–8–4) and (10–8–5) gives

$$\boldsymbol{grad}\ V\cdot\boldsymbol{ds} = (\partial V/\partial x)\, dx + (\partial V/\partial y)\, dy + (\partial V/\partial z)\, dz \qquad (10\text{–}8\text{–}6)$$

The right sides of (10–8–3) and (10–8–6) are the same, so

$$dV = \boldsymbol{grad}\ V\cdot\boldsymbol{ds} \qquad (10\text{–}8\text{–}7)$$

But from (10–2–1), $$dV = -\boldsymbol{E}\cdot\boldsymbol{ds},$$

so $$\boldsymbol{E} = -\boldsymbol{grad}\ V \qquad (10\text{–}8\text{–}8)$$

and (10–8–8) expresses the desired relationship between E and the space rate
of change of V.

---

* For example, L. M. Kells, *Analytical Geometry and Calculus* (Englewood Cliffs,
N.J.: Prentice-Hall Inc., 1950), pp. 415–17, particularly Eq. (35) and (38).

If we write E in terms of its Cartesian components we have

$$E = iE_x + jE_y + kE_z$$

so (10–8–8) becomes [by the use of (10–8–4) for **grad** V]

$$iE_x + jE_y + kE_z = -i\,\partial V/\partial x - j\,\partial V/\partial y - k\,\partial V/\partial z$$

from which

$$E_x = -\partial V/\partial x, \quad E_y = -\partial V/\partial y, \quad E_z = -\partial V/\partial z \qquad (10\text{–}8\text{–}9)$$

Thus the x, y, and z components of E may be computed by the use of (10–8–9) if V is known as a function of x, y, and z. We can immediately see the connection between (10–8–9) and the statement following (10–8–1) as follows. In the first equation of (10–8–9) we have taken the direction s of (10–8–1) to be parallel to the X-axis as shown by the subscript on E and the partial derivative of V with respect to x. Then the equation tells us that the component parallel to the X-axis of the force per unit charge on an infinitesimal test charge is equal to the negative space rate of change of potential energy per unit charge when the space rate of change is taken parallel to the X-axis. You can readily make similar statements about the second two equations in (10–8–9).

As discussed in Sec. 10–7, an equipotential surface is a surface along which there is no change in potential. Suppose that in (10–8–7), ds is directed along such a surface. Then dV is zero because there is no change of potential from point to point on an equipotential surface, so in this special case (10–8–7) becomes $0 = $ **grad** $V \cdot ds$. But **grad** V is not in general zero, and ds is not zero, so this equation must mean that the angle between **grad** V and ds is $90°$, or **grad** V is normal to any equipotential surface.

Also from (10–8–1) the space rate of change of potential is greatest when s is parallel to E so that $\theta = 0$ or $180°$. But the direction of E is the direction of decreasing potential, and we know from the minus sign in (10–8–8) that the direction of **grad** V is opposite to that of E. Hence, the *direction of* **grad** V *in the electric field is normal to any equipotential surface, and in the direction in which the potential is increasing most rapidly*, i.e., **grad** V is directed "uphill" for potential. It is from this fact that the term "gradient of V" arises.

Another notation is often used in vector analysis in which the differential operator ∇ (read "nabla" or "del") is introduced by the definition

$$\nabla = i\frac{\partial}{\partial x} + j\frac{\partial}{\partial y} + k\frac{\partial}{\partial z} \qquad (10\text{–}8\text{–}10)$$

and turns out to be a fundamentally important operator. It has no meaning, however, until it has something on which to operate. You are familiar with other operators such as sine, cosine, d/dx etc., which also have no meaning until they have something on which to operate. We can see from (10–8–4) that when ∇ operates on V we have

$$\nabla V = \mathbf{grad}\ V = i\frac{\partial V}{\partial x} + j\frac{\partial V}{\partial y} + k\frac{\partial V}{\partial z} \qquad (10\text{–}8\text{–}11)$$

Hence we may write (10–8–8) in the equivalent form

$$E = -\nabla V = -\,grad\,V = -\left(i\frac{\partial V}{\partial x} + j\frac{\partial V}{\partial y} + k\frac{\partial V}{\partial z}\right) \quad (10\text{–}8\text{–}12)$$

Equation (10–8–8) [or its equivalent (10–8–12)] *is the fundamentally important differential relationship between E and V, and tells us that E equals the negative space rate of change of potential taken along the direction in which the potential is changing most rapidly.* To repeat for emphasis, the positive direction of **E** is the direction in which a positive charge would tend to move due to the force of the electric field. But this is the direction from high potential toward low potential. Thus the minus sign in (10–8–8) or (10–8–12) indicates mathematically the fact that the direction of **E** is the direction of decreasing potential.

In the mks system, the unit of space rate of change of V is volts/meter.

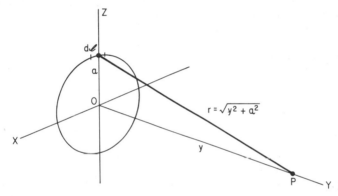

Figure 10–8–1. Circular ring of charge in the *XZ*-plane with its center at the origin. The *Y*-axis is the axis of the ring.

Since *E* is equal to the space rate of change of *V*, the common unit for *E* in the mks system is volts/meter. This explains the statement at the end of Sec. 10–5.

As pointed out before, since *V* is a scalar it is often easier in a particular problem to derive a formula for the potential function than it is to derive a formula for **E**. Once the potential function is known, the formula for **E** may be obtained by the use of (10–8–8), or the components of **E** may be obtained from (10–8–9).

Example. As an example of the use of (10–4–2) and (10–8–8), let us find the potential function and electric field intensity on the axis of a circular ring of wire with a uniform distribution of static positive charge on it and situated in empty space.

Figure 10–8–1 shows a ring, in the *XZ* plane, with a uniform distribution of positive charge on the ring. Let λ be the charge per unit length on the ring where λ is constant. The center of the ring is at the origin of coordinates, and the *Y*-axis is the axis of the ring. The radius of the ring is *a*.

Using (10–4–2), let us set up an expression for the potential at *P*. Let *dV* be the element of potential at P due to the element of charge dq on the infinitesimal length dl of the ring.

$$dV = dq/4\pi\varepsilon_0 r = \lambda \, dl/4\pi\varepsilon_0 \sqrt{y^2 + a^2} \qquad (10\text{--}8\text{--}13)$$

Let V be the potential at P due to the charge on the whole ring:

$$V = (\lambda/4\pi\varepsilon_0) \int_0^{2\pi a} dl/\sqrt{y^2 + a^2}$$

Since y and a are constant, as the integration is carried around the ring, and $q = 2\pi a\lambda$ is the total charge on the ring, then

$$V = q/4\pi\varepsilon_0 \sqrt{y^2 + a^2} \qquad (10\text{--}8\text{--}14)$$

This, of course, is a special case, since (10–8–14) is valid only for points on the Y-axis. However, it gives the desired potential function for points on the axis of the ring.

To compute the electric field intensity E at P let ∇ operate on V, i.e., apply (10–8–12). In this special case, x and z do not appear in the function for V, because it was derived for points where $x = z = 0$,

$$\partial V/\partial x = \partial V/\partial z = 0$$

so
$$\mathbf{E} = -\mathbf{j} \, \partial V/\partial y = \mathbf{j} \, qy/4\pi\varepsilon_0(y^2 + a^2)^{3/2} \qquad (10\text{--}8\text{--}15)$$

This equation tells us that E is directed along the positive Y-axis. Refer to Problem 9–39 where you were asked to solve this same problem by use of Coulomb's law and the principle of superposition applied to E.

Along the negative Y-axis a negative number would be substituted for y, and E would be negative. This indicates that on the left side of the ring in Fig. 10–8–1, E would be directed along the negative Y-axis. Hence, on either side of the ring, E is directed away from the ring as we would expect, since the ring has a positive charge.

10-9 POTENTIAL GRADIENT EXPRESSED IN SPHERICAL COORDINATES

Figure 10–9–1 shows a point P located in space by its x, y, z coordinates of the Cartesian system and also by its r, θ, ϕ coordinates of the spherical system. As usual r is the radial distance from the origin to P and is thus the radius of the sphere on which P lies, θ is the colatitude angle on the sphere, and ϕ is the longitude or azimuth angle on the sphere. From Fig. 10–9–1 it is seen that

$$\begin{aligned}
x &= r \sin\theta \cos\phi \\
y &= r \sin\theta \sin\phi \\
z &= r \cos\theta
\end{aligned} \qquad (10\text{--}9\text{--}1)$$

In Fig. 10–9–1 let $\mathbf{i}_r$ be a unit vector in the direction of increasing r, $\mathbf{i}_\theta$ be a unit vector perpendicular to r in the direction of increasing θ (ϕ constant),

i_ϕ be a unit vector perpendicular to r in the direction of increasing ϕ (θ constant). **Grad** V can be shown* to be, in spherical coordinates,

$$grad\ V = i_r \frac{\partial V}{\partial r} + i_\theta \frac{1}{r}\frac{\partial V}{\partial \theta} + i_\phi \frac{1}{r\sin\theta}\frac{\partial V}{\partial \phi} \qquad (10\text{-}9\text{-}2)$$

From (10-9-2) and the fact that $E = -grad\ V$ we may write

$$E = -\left(i_r \frac{\partial V}{\partial r} + i_\theta \frac{1}{r}\frac{\partial V}{\partial \theta} + i_\phi \frac{1}{r\sin\theta}\frac{\partial V}{\partial \phi}\right) \qquad (10\text{-}9\text{-}3)$$

and from this the components of E are

$$E_r = -\frac{\partial V}{\partial r}; \qquad E_\theta = -\frac{1}{r}\frac{\partial V}{\partial \theta}; \qquad E_\phi = -\frac{1}{r\sin\theta}\frac{\partial V}{\partial \phi} \qquad (10\text{-}9\text{-}4)$$

Equation (10-9-4) is the fundamental differential relationship between E and V expressed for use when V is written in terms of spherical coordinates.

Example. Potential and electric field intensity due to an isolated positive point charge q in empty space.

Consider the point charge to be located at the origin of coordinates in Fig. 10-9-1. We have shown in (10-3-2) that the potential function for an isolated point charge in empty space is given by $V = q/4\pi\varepsilon_0 r$, where r is the radial distance from the charge to the point being considered.

Apply (10-9-3) to the potential function in (10-3-2). Here V is independent of θ and ϕ, so $\partial V/\partial\theta = \partial V/\partial\phi = 0$ and

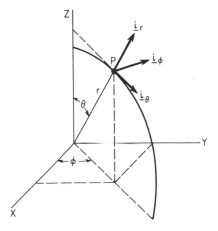

Figure 10-9-1. Spherical coordinate system.

$$E = -i_r \frac{\partial V}{\partial r} = -i_r \frac{q}{4\pi\varepsilon_0}\frac{\partial}{\partial r}\frac{1}{r} = i_r \frac{1}{4\pi\varepsilon_0}\frac{q}{r^2} \qquad (10\text{-}9\text{-}5)$$

This says that E is directed radially outward from q and has a magnitude $q/4\pi\varepsilon_0 r^2$. Equation (10-9-5) is the same equation as (9-6-17).

It does not prove anything new when we arrive at (10-9-5) from (10-3-2) because we derived (10-3-2) from the fact that E for a positive point charge is directed radially outward and has a magnitude at any point given by $q/4\pi\varepsilon_0 r^2$. This does show, however, how the machinery works in reverse.

---

* See a text on advanced calculus or vector analysis, e.g., Hildebrand, *Advanced Calculus for Engineers* (Englewood Cliffs, N.J.: Prentice-Hall, Inc. 1949), pp. 321-29, particularly pp. 328-29.

10–10 POTENTIAL AND ELECTRIC FIELD INTENSITY DUE TO AN ISOLATED DIPOLE

Two point charges of equal magnitudes but opposite signs are referred to as an *electric dipole*. The two charges must not be at the same point in space or they will neutralize each other and there will be no resultant electric field. However, we wish to consider that special case in which the distance between the two charges is small compared with the distance from either charge to the point in their field where the values of E and V are to be computed. This special case is an important one, since rarely when a dipole appears in a physical problem is it necessary to consider the general case.

Figure 10–10–1 shows an electric dipole with its axis along the Z-axis and with a separation l between the charges. The mid-point between the charges is at the origin of coordinates. Imagine Fig. 10–10–1 to be in the YZ-plane of Fig. 10–9–1, so that in Fig. 10–10–1 the positive X-axis projects out of the paper. We wish to derive a formula for the potential due to the

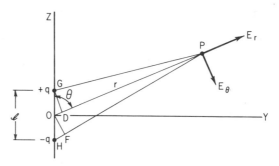

Figure 10–10–1. Field of an electric dipole.

dipole at any point, such as P in Fig. 10–10–1, under the special conditions stated above, namely, that r is very large compared with l. Then from this potential formula we wish to derive a formula for the electric field intensity at any point such as P. We shall use spherical coordinates for this purpose.

With P as a center, draw the arcs GD and OF. Since r is large compared with l, these arcs may be considered to be straight lines, and triangles DOG and OHF may be considered to be right triangles. Then, approximately,

$$HP = r + l(\cos \theta)/2 \quad \text{and} \quad GP = r - l(\cos \theta)/2$$

Let V be the potential at P due to both charges of the dipole. By the principle of superposition for potential,

$$V = q/4\pi\varepsilon_0 GP - q/4\pi\varepsilon_0 HP$$
$$= [q/(r - (l/2)\cos \theta) - q/(r + (l/2)\cos \theta)]/4\pi\varepsilon_0 \qquad (10\text{–}10\text{–}1)$$

If P moves so that ϕ changes, without a change of r or θ, the distances GP and HP remain constant, so V is independent of ϕ. Hence, this expression holds for all points in space as well as for points in the YZ-plane, and (10–10–1) is the desired potential function, valid for all points in space where r is large compared with l. In Fig. 10–10–1, r is not large compared with l, so the approximation involved is very evident.

Let us simplify (10–10–1) by securing a common denominator for the term in the square bracket, and make use of the fact that r is large compared with l, so we may neglect $(l^2/4) \cos^2 \theta$ with respect to r^2, and V becomes

$$V = ql (\cos \theta)/4\pi\varepsilon_0 r^2 \qquad (10\text{–}10\text{–}2)$$

The magnitude p of the dipole moment of an electric dipole is defined as the product of one of the charges and the distance between the charges. Hence, by this definition, $p = ql$. In terms of p, (10–10–2) becomes

$$V = p (\cos \theta)/4\pi\varepsilon_0 r^2 \qquad (10\text{–}10\text{–}3)$$

Electric dipole moment may be considered as a vector quantity and, when it is so considered, p is defined as a vector whose direction is parallel to l and in the direction from the negative charge to the positive charge. Hence, l is considered to be a vector quantity directed from the negative charge toward the positive charge. Thus, the definition of p would be

$$\boldsymbol{p} = q\boldsymbol{l} \qquad (10\text{–}10\text{–}4)$$

Since $\boldsymbol{i}_r$ has been defined above as a unit vector along r in Fig. 10–10–1, $ql \cos \theta$ is the scalar product of ql and $\boldsymbol{i}_r$, or

$$ql \cos \theta = q\boldsymbol{l}\cdot\boldsymbol{i}_r = \boldsymbol{p}\cdot\boldsymbol{i}_r \qquad (10\text{–}10\text{–}5)$$

Then the potential equation (10–10–3) may be written

$$V = \boldsymbol{p}\cdot\boldsymbol{i}_r/4\pi\varepsilon_0 r^2 \qquad (10\text{–}10\text{–}6)$$

However, it will serve our purpose here to use the potential equation in the form given in (10–10–3).

Next we wish to secure the equation for the electric field intensity E at any point. Apply (10–9–3) to (10–10–3). Since ϕ does not appear in the potential function, $\partial V/\partial \phi = 0$ and we obtain

$$\boldsymbol{E} = \boldsymbol{i}_r 2p (\cos \theta)/4\pi\varepsilon_0 r^3 + \boldsymbol{i}_\theta p (\sin \theta)/4\pi\varepsilon_0 r^3 \qquad (10\text{–}10\text{–}7)$$

Equation (10–10–7) is valid for any point P (whose coordinates are r and θ) in the three-dimensional field surrounding the electric dipole, as long as the point is sufficiently far from the dipole so that r is large compared with l. This approximation is not seriously limiting if the dipole is a polarized molecule, so that l is of atomic dimensions; i.e., 10^{-10} m or less. In such a case, r does not need to be very large in order to have the approximation be a good one.

Let us now compute the magnitude of E, which is given by $\sqrt{E_r^2 + E_\theta^2}$. You can show that this becomes

$$E = p\sqrt{1 + 3\cos^2 \theta}/4\pi\varepsilon_0 r^3 \qquad (10\text{–}10\text{–}8)$$

Equation (10–10–8) gives the magnitude of the electric field intensity at any point P whose coordinates are r and θ (but only for positions where r is large compared with l).

We wish now to find a simple means of expressing the direction of E at a selected point in the field. Consider Fig. 10–10–2, which is Fig. 10–10–1 redrawn with the resultant E added. From Fig. 10–10–2 we can see that $\tan \alpha = E_\theta/E_r$. Substitute the values of E_r and E_θ from (10–10–7) and we have

$$\tan \alpha = \tfrac{1}{2} \tan \theta \tag{10–10–9}$$

Thus, the direction of E at P can be computed at once, since the θ coordinate of the point P is known. Note again that we have oriented the dipole so that p points in the positive Z direction and that, as usual in spherical coordinates, θ is the angle between the positive Z-axis and the radius to the point P.

From (10–10–7) we can tell the directions of the components E_r and E_θ for any point P. For example, for points where $\cos \theta$ is positive, E_r is directed outward along r, and for points where $\cos \theta$ is negative, E_r is directed inward (toward the origin) along r. Similarly for points where $\sin \theta$ is positive, E_θ is

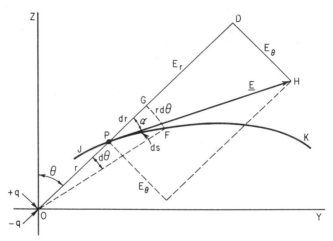

Figure 10–10–2. Direction of the resultant E at P for an electric dipole. *JFK* is a section of a line of force through P.

directed in the direction of increasing θ, or clockwise in Fig. 10–10–2. Conversely, for points where $\sin \theta$ is negative, E_θ is directed in the direction of decreasing θ, or counterclockwise.

At any point in the field where $r \gg l$, (10–10–8) may be used to compute the magnitude of E, and (10–10–9) may be used to compute the direction of E. The field is, of course, three-dimensional. However, since E is independent of the spherical coordinate ϕ, maps of the lines of force in all planes that contain the Z-axis will be the same.

1. LINES OF FORCE OF A DIPOLE. At every point on a line of force, E is tangent to the line. This requirement follows from the convention for drawing lines of force. Hence, as pointed out in Example A in Sec. 10–1, an equation which represents a line of force must satisfy the requirement that at every point the tangent is parallel to E. We have seen that a representative map of the lines of force may be drawn in any plane which contains the Z-axis, so let us draw

such a map in the YZ-plane. Refer to Fig. 10–10–2, where $JPFK$ represents a possible line of force through P. This line $JPFK$ is correct at P because E is tangent to the line, and thus at P the line satisfies the only requirement. In Fig. 10–10–2, ds represents an infinitesimal length along the line of force with dr and $r\,d\theta$ as its r and θ components, respectively. From the similar triangles PGF and PDH you can see that

$$dr/r\,d\theta = E_r/E_\theta \qquad (10\text{–}10\text{–}10)$$

Note that this is the same argument that we used in (10–1–14) except that here we are using spherical coordinates and there we used Cartesian coordinates.

Use the values of E_r and E_θ from (10–10–7), and we have,

$$dr/r = 2\,(\cos\theta)\,d\theta/\sin\theta$$

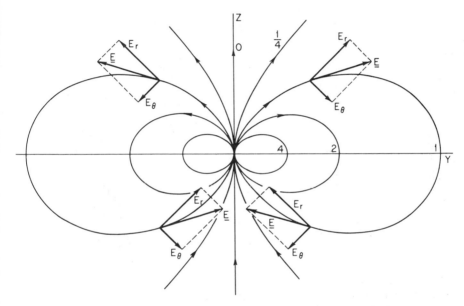

Figure 10–10–3. Some of the lines of force of an electric dipole.

This is the differential equation which we must solve in order to secure the equation for the line of force. Note that the variables are separated and that on each side the numerator is a differential of the denominator. Thus, letting $\ln C$ represent the constant of integration, we have on integration

$$\ln r + \ln C = 2\ln(\sin\theta) \quad \text{or} \quad \ln rC = \ln(\sin^2\theta)$$

or $$C = (\sin^2\theta)/r \qquad (10\text{–}10\text{–}11)$$

Various lines of force result from various selections of values of C. Figure 10–10–3 shows some lines of force for the dipole that we are considering, and each line shown is a plot of (10–10–11). The number written adjacent to a line of force shows the corresponding value of C for that line. Figure 10–10–3 also shows the directions of E, E_r, and E_θ in each quadrant of the YZ-plane.

10–11 POISSON'S AND LAPLACE'S EQUATIONS

In Figure 10–11–1, assume that there is an electric field all through the region and that a Cartesian coordinate system is set up in the field as shown. Let us assume that we know E as a function of the coordinates at a point P in the field where P has the coordinates (x, y, z). Starting at P, draw an imaginary box whose sides are of infinitesimal lengths dx, dy, dz, and whose faces are parallel to the coordinate planes of the Cartesian system. We assume that positive charge is distributed throughout the region so that there is charge enclosed in the box. Thus, there are more electric lines of force coming out of the box than going into the box, because electric lines of force originate on the enclosed charges. (If negative charges were distributed through the region

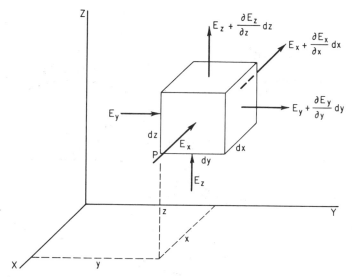

Figure 10–11–1. Infinitesimal cubical volume used for the calculation of the net number of electric lines of force cutting outward from the volume.

there would be more lines of force going into the box than coming out of the box because lines of force would terminate on the enclosed charges, but the result would be the same.) We wish first to compute the net number of lines of force which comes out of the box.

Let E_y be the component of E on the left face of the box. Then $\partial E_y/\partial y$ is the space rate of change of E_y in the y direction, so $(\partial E_y/\partial y)\, dy$ is the change in E_y from the left face of the box to the right face of the box. Here we must use the partial derivative of E_y with respect to y because E_y is a function of x and z as well as y, and we wish the space rate of change of E_y in the y direction only (x and z are constant in this change). From the above, the value of the y component of E on the right face of the box is $E_y + (\partial E_y/\partial y)\, dy$. [In the limit, as the dimensions of the box approach zero, the error in this expression becomes arbitrarily small compared with $(\partial E_y/\partial y)\, dy$.]

The number of lines of force through the left face of the box is E_y times the area of the left face of the box because the area is infinitesimal, and E_y may be considered constant over this area. Also, of course, E_y is the component of E that is normal to this area. Because these lines enter the box, we must use the negative sign, so the number of lines that leave the left face is $-E_y\,dx\,dz$.

The number of lines of force that leave the right face of the box is by the same reasoning

$$[E_y + (\partial E_y/\partial y)\,dy]\,dx\,dz$$

Hence, the net number of lines of force cutting out through the left and right faces of the box is

$$E_y\,dx\,dz + (\partial E_y/\partial y)\,dx\,dy\,dz - E_y\,dx\,dz = (\partial E_y/\partial y)\,dx\,dy\,dz \quad (10\text{--}11\text{--}1)$$

Similarly, the net number of lines of force cutting out through the front and back faces of the box is

$$(\partial E_x/\partial x)\,dx\,dy\,dz \qquad\qquad (10\text{--}11\text{--}2)$$

Also, the net number of lines of force cutting out through the top and bottom faces of the box is

$$(\partial E_z/\partial z)\,dx\,dy\,dz \qquad\qquad (10\text{--}11\text{--}3)$$

From (10–11–1), (10–11–2), and (10–11–3) the net number of lines of force cutting out through the whole surface of the box can be computed.

But from Gauss's theorem the net number of electric lines of force that cut out through any imaginary closed surface is $1/\varepsilon_0$ times the net charge enclosed in the surface. Let ρ represent the net volume density of charge inside the box, so that $\rho\,dx\,dy\,dz$ is the net charge enclosed in the box. Then, from Gauss's theorem,

$$(\partial E_x/\partial x + \partial E_y/\partial y + \partial E_z/\partial z)\,dx\,dy\,dz = \rho\,dx\,dy\,dz/\varepsilon_0$$

or $\qquad\qquad\qquad \partial E_x/\partial x + \partial E_y/\partial y + \partial E_z/\partial z = \rho/\varepsilon_0 \qquad (10\text{--}11\text{--}4)$

Equation (10–11–4) is true at any point P in the field. Of course, ρ is in general a function of x, y, and z, and it is the value of ρ at the point P that must appear on the right side of (10–11–4).

In vector analysis the *divergence* of a vector can be represented* by

$$\partial A_x/\partial x + \partial A_y/\partial y + \partial A_z/\partial z = \text{div } A \qquad (10\text{--}11\text{--}5)$$

where A_x, A_y, and A_z are the x, y, z components, respectively, of the vector A. The definition of div A will be given in Sec. 19–2, equation (19–2–7). Then using this shorthand notation, (10–11–4) may be written

$$\text{div } E = \rho/\varepsilon_0 \qquad\qquad (10\text{--}11\text{--}6)$$

From the definition of ∇ in (10–8–10) and the method of computing a scalar product of two vectors as given in (9–6–10), we can see that the left side of

* See Sec. 19–2, the argument associated with (19–2–9).

(10–11–4) is $\nabla \cdot E$. Hence, div $E = \nabla \cdot E$ and (10–11–6) is often written in the equivalent form

$$\nabla \cdot E = \rho/\varepsilon_0 \tag{10–11–7}$$

Using (10–8–9), we see that (10–11–4) may be written

$$\partial^2 V/\partial x^2 + \partial^2 V/\partial y^2 + \partial^2 V/\partial z^2 = -\rho/\varepsilon_0 \tag{10–11–8}$$

This is Poisson's equation.

In (10–8–10), we defined the ∇ operator. Now let us define the operator ∇^2 as

$$\nabla^2 = \nabla \cdot \nabla \tag{10–11–9}$$

and ∇^2 is often called the Laplacian operator. Equation (10–11–9) says that ∇^2 is the scalar product of ∇ with itself, so by (9–6–10) and (10–8–10) we may write

$$\nabla^2 = \frac{\partial}{\partial x}\frac{\partial}{\partial x} + \frac{\partial}{\partial y}\frac{\partial}{\partial y} + \frac{\partial}{\partial z}\frac{\partial}{\partial z} = \frac{\partial^2}{\partial x^2} + \frac{\partial^2}{\partial y^2} + \frac{\partial^2}{\partial z^2}$$

Now let ∇^2 operate on V.

$$\nabla^2 V = \partial^2 V/\partial x^2 + \partial^2 V/\partial y^2 + \partial^2 V/\partial z^2 \tag{10–11–10}$$

From this, (10–11–8) may be written

$$\nabla^2 V = -\rho/\varepsilon_0 \tag{10–11–11}$$

This is the form in which Poisson's equation is most often encountered.

In the special case where no charge is enclosed in the box in Fig. 10–11–1, $\rho = 0$, and Poisson's equation becomes

$$\nabla^2 V = 0 \tag{10–11–12}$$

This is known as Laplace's equation.

The process of solving many problems in electrostatics resolves itself into the solution of one or the other of these second-order partial differential equations (10–11–11) or (10–11–12). The solution must satisfy the boundary conditions of the particular problem being considered. The methods of finding such solutions is the subject of potential theory, and a discussion will be found in more advanced texts.

10–12 FURTHER COMMENTS ON THE CALCULATIONS OF POTENTIAL DIFFERENCE

We have seen that the potential difference between two points in an electric field is given by the line integral on the right side of (10–2–2). In all the examples that we have solved so far in the text, we have solved (10–2–2) as a line integral, i.e., we have expressed E and $\cos \theta$ as functions of s along the prescribed path, and thus kept s as the variable of integration. Also, we have recognized that $s = 0$ at the starting point (B) for the integration and have then expressed the position of (A) in terms of s in order to secure the numerical value of the upper limit of the integration. Further, we have pointed out that s and ds are always positive when the direction of progression along the line is that indicated by the limits of integration, i.e., progression from the place designated by the lower limit to the place designated by the upper limit.

It is often easier, in a particular problem, to compute the potential difference between two points in terms of the coordinates of a coordinate system than it is to evaluate the line integral in terms of s. This is particularly true in those cases where the coordinate system can be oriented so that one of the coordinate axes is parallel to E. In such a case we make a change of variable from s to the variable associated with the coordinate axis that is parallel to E. We must watch the sign conventions closely, but this is the only troublesome point.

As an example, let us calculate the potential difference between the two

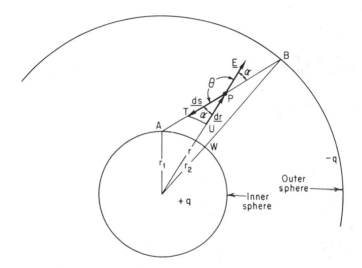

Figure 10–12–1. Two charged concentric spheres.

charged metal spheres shown in Fig. 10–12–1. The inner sphere is charged positively with a charge of magnitude q. The outer sphere has an equal negative induced charge. In the empty space between the spheres we know that E is given by $E = q/4\pi\varepsilon_0 r^2$ and is directed radially outward. Let us say, tentatively at least, that we intend to follow the straight line path $BPTA$ from B to A. At any point P, at a distance r from the center, draw an element of path length ds directed from B toward A, since this is the direction of motion. Instead of integrating in terms of s, let us change to the variable r, where r is the radial coordinate of a spherical coordinate system whose origin is at the common center of the two spheres. We make this choice because r is parallel to E.

From the figure, $|dr| = ds \cos \alpha$ and it is here that the sticky problem with regard to sign arises. Positive dr is in the direction of increasing r, since any positive differential of a coordinate is in the direction of increase of the variable of that coordinate. Thus in the figure, dr is directed radially outward, but ds is in an inward direction. Thus

$$dr = -ds \cos \alpha \qquad (10\text{–}12\text{–}1)$$

However, $\cos \alpha = -\cos \theta$, so

$$dr = ds \cos \theta \qquad (10\text{–}12\text{–}2)$$

Put (10–12–2) into (10–2–2), and we have

$$V_A - V_B = \int_{(B)}^{(A)} E \, dr \qquad (10\ 12\ 3)$$

with r as the variable of integration. We must now express the limits of integration in terms of the variable of integration. At B, $r = r_2$; and at A, $r = r_1$, so (10–12–3) becomes

$$V_A - V_B = -\int_{r_2}^{r_1} E \, dr \qquad (10\text{–}12\text{–}4)$$

Note that we are not integrating along the path $BPTA$ but along the path B to W. This is satisfactory because W is at the same potential as A (since the inner sphere is an equipotential) and the potential difference between two points is independent of the path followed between the two points.

We know E as a function of r since $E = q/4\pi\varepsilon_0 r^2$, so (10–12–4) immediately yields

$$V_A - V_B = (q/4\pi\varepsilon_0)(1/r_1 - 1/r_2) \qquad (10\text{–}12\text{–}5)$$

Radius $r_1 < r_2$, so $1/r_1 > 1/r_2$ and $V_A - V_B$ is positive, as required by the problem pictured in Fig. 10–12–1.

The integration of (10–12–4) is much easier than the evaluation of the line integral along the path $BPTA$, and such is often the case when a particular problem is to be solved.

The important point here is the following. The potential difference between two points is the work per unit charge required to carry an infinitesimal test charge from one point to the other. In a particular problem when you are to compute the potential difference between two points, compute the work required to carry a unit charge between the two points and do the calculation in the way best suited to the problem at hand. When you arrive at your answer you may find that the sign is obviously wrong as judged by the physics of the problem being solved. If such is the case you can go back over the solution and find the place [like the one in this example, just prior to (10–12–1)] where the sticky problem with regard to sign arises, and straighten it out.

PROBLEMS

10–1 Refer to Example A, Sec. 10–1, and Fig. 10–1–3. Calculate the work that you must do in order to carry a charge of 3.2×10^{-19} coulomb from B to A by the path B to C to A in Fig. 10–1–3. Split this path into two parts, one from B to C parallel to the Y-axis and the other C to A along the X-axis. Along these paths evaluate $-q' \int E \cos \theta \, ds$ in the formal fashion of

Example A, remembering that s is measured from the starting point of the motion for each section of path. Next point out an easier way to find $PE_C - PE_B$, based on the fact that E_z is everywhere normal to the path BC. [*Ans:* Same value of $PE_A - PE_B$ as the one given in the text for Example A.]

10–2 Using (10–1–15), plot lines of force for the electric field given by (10–1–5). Plot a line for each of the following values of $2C$: ± 2, ± 10, ± 100, ± 225, ± 400.

As stated in Example A, Sec. 10–1, this equation for E is approximately valid in a limited region, in the XY-plane, near the origin. Let us say that it is valid in the region covered by your plot. Make a qualitative sketch showing a charge distribution that could give the lines of force in your plot. Sketch freehand several lines of force required by your charge distribution in the region outside the scope of the plot.

10–3 In a limited region near the origin, a certain electric field may be represented by the equation

$$E = [iyz^2 + j(xz^2 - 1 \text{ m}^3) + k2(xyz - 1 \text{ m}^3)]\frac{1 \text{ newton}}{\text{coulomb m}^3} \quad (10\text{–P–}1)$$

Find the increase in the potential energy of a positive test charge of 3.20×10^{-19} coulomb when the test charge is carried from B to A. The coordinates of B are $x = 1.00$ m, $y = 2.00$ m, $z = 3.00$ m, and A is at the origin. The path is to be parallel to the Z-axis from B to a point C in the XY-plane, then from C parallel to the Y-axis to a point D on the X-axis, then along the X-axis to the origin. See Fig. 10–P–1. [*Ans:* 3.20×10^{-18} joule.]

10–4 Refer to Problem 10–3. Compute $PE_A - PE_B$ by following the path from B parallel to the Y-axis to a point G in the XZ-plane, then from G parallel to the X-axis to a point H on the Z-axis, then from H to A along the Z-axis. [*Ans:* 3.2×10^{-18} joule, the same as for the path followed in Problem 10–3.]

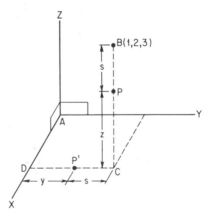

Figure 10–P–1. Coordinate axes and location of points for Problem 10–3.

10–5 Figure 10–P–2 shows a positive point charge q, in otherwise empty space (see Fig. 9–5–1), and one line of force outward from q. By the use of (9–5–2) and (10–1–4), compute the increase in potential energy of a positive test charge q', when q' is moved from B to A in Fig. 10–P–2, and show that this increase of PE is given by

$$PE_A - PE_B = (q'q/4\pi\varepsilon_0)(1/r_A - 1/r_B) \quad (10\text{–P–}2)$$

Then from (10–P–2), show that the potential energy of q' at A is given by

$$PE_A = q'q/4\pi\varepsilon_0 r_A \quad (10\text{–P–}3)$$

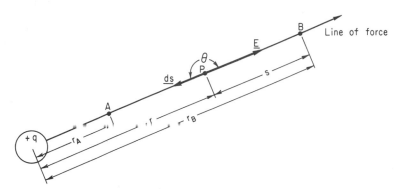

Figure 10–P–2. Calculation of the potential energy of a test charge q' in the field of a point charge q.

10–6 Consult Fig. 10–P–2 and your derivation of (10–P–2), in Problem 10–4, and consider that the point charge q is *negative*. Under these circumstances, show mathematically that a positive test charge at A will have a negative potential energy, and that a negative test charge at A will have a positive potential energy. Justify this result with a physical argument. Note that (10–1–4) just as it is written (with the negative sign on the right), takes account of this possibility as well as the one you treated in Problem 10–5 where q was positive.

10–7 In Problem 10–6, show that the potential at point A is negative and that this is independent of the sign of the test charge that is placed at A to determine the potential. Refer to the definition of potential at a point as it is given in Sec. 10–2.

10–8 By definition, the direction of E is the direction that a positive charge will tend to move. A negative charge will tend to move in an opposite direction to that of E. Potential decreases as one moves in the direction of E; thus the direction of E is the direction of decreasing potential.

From these two facts, positive charges tend to move from regions of high potential to regions of lower potential. Conversely, electrons tend to move from regions of lower potential to regions of higher potential. If a conducting path is offered, electrons *will* move from regions of lower potential to regions of higher potential.

As mentioned earlier (Sec. 10–2) the ground is often considered to be at zero potential. From this, bodies with potentials above that of the earth are said to be at positive potentials and those with potentials below that of the earth are said to be at negative potentials. We can often decide, in a particular case, whether electrons would tend to flow from a body to ground, or from ground to the body, or would remain at rest. In such a case we can say that the body is at a negative potential, or at a positive potential with respect to ground, or at ground (zero) potential.

Refer to Problem 9–5. Using the above criteria, explain each step of the process of charging the electroscope by induction in terms of potential. State whether K and L have positive or negative or zero potential in each step. Also point out each occasion when K and L have a difference of potential. Remember that for a conductor with a *static* charge all points of the conductor must be at the same potential. Illustrate clearly the function of the metal case that surrounds the leaf and serves as an electrostatic shield for the leaf.

10–9 Figure 10–P–3 shows some electric lines of force in an electrostatic field. Two points, C and D, are designated in the field. (a) Which of these two points is at the higher potential? Why? (b) What is the formula for computing $V_C - V_D$? What additional information must you have in order to carry out this computation? (c) If the lines of force shown, and others like them above and below the figure, are converging toward a common point P that is to the right of the figure, what sign of charge must be located at the point P toward which they are converging?

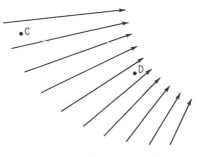

Figure 10–P–3. Some electric lines of force in an electrostatic field.

Imagine that each of these lines of force is extended as a *straight* line. If these extended straight lines are directed toward a common point P, what is the shape of the charged body located at P?

10–10 An electron of charge e and mass m leaves the cathode (heated filament) of a radio tube with zero velocity and is accelerated toward the plate by the electric field between the cathode and plate. The potential difference between the cathode and the plate is V with the plate at the higher potential. (a) What is the potential energy, with respect to the plate, of the electron as it leaves the cathode? (b) Assuming that the electron travels through empty space and thus makes no collision on the way, what is the kinetic energy of the electron just before it hits the plate? (c) Derive a formula for computing the velocity of such an electron, just before it hits the plate. [*Ans:* $v = \sqrt{2Ve/m}$.] Show that the units on the right are the correct ones for velocity. (d) If the potential difference V is 2000 v, what is the velocity of the electron when it arrives at the plate? [*Ans:* 2.65×10^7 m/sec.] (e) It should be pointed out that the mass of a body increases as the velocity of the body increases. This is the so-called relativity change of mass with velocity. As a rough rule of thumb for calculation, it is considered that the mass of a body may be considered to be constant at its "rest mass" for velocities less than about one-tenth the velocity of light. The velocity of light is 3×10^8 m/sec. The calculation above in (c) and (d) assumes that the mass is constant. What is the maximum potential difference that could be applied across this ratio tube and still have this type of calculation give a good approximation for the velocity of an electron? [*Ans:* 2560 v,]

10–11 Using Fig. 10–P–2, derive (10–3–1) by starting with a positive test charge q' at A and letting the field do work on it to move it to B. Next evaluate the result if B recedes to infinity. Remember that with the motion of q' from A toward B, ds is directed from A toward B.

10–12 Equations (10–3–1) and (10–3–2) were derived by carrying a positive test charge from B to A along a straight line path which is a line of force from a point charge q in Fig. 10–P–2. For practice in the evaluation of a line integral along a curved path you are asked in this problem to derive equations (10–3–1) and (10–3–2) by carrying the positive test charge from A to B along the curved line of the spiral of Fig. 10–P–5, where the positive point charge q, which produces the field, is at the origin of the spiral. The particular spiral chosen in Fig. 10–P–5 is one, known in analytical geometry as the logarithmic spiral, in which the tangent to the curve at every point makes a constant angle α with the normal to the radius vector at the point. Figure 10–P–4 shows as PU an infinitesimal element of path length

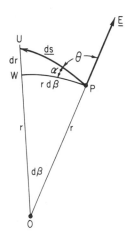

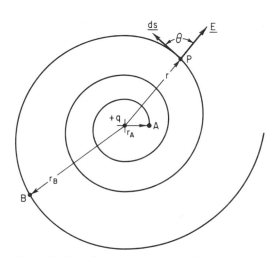

Figure 10–P–4. An element of length ds of the logarithmic spiral. ds subtends an element of angle $d\beta$ at the origin.

Figure 10–P–5. Logarithmic spiral. A point charge $+q$ is located at the origin of coordinates.

ds along the spiral. We shall write the equation of the spiral in polar coordinates and let β represent the angular polar coordinate and r the radial coordinate. In Fig. 10–P–4, PW is an arc of a circle of radius r drawn from P to W, and the length of the arc is $r\,d\beta$. Thus, dr is the infinitesimal change in r when β changes by $d\beta$, and α is the angle that the tangent to the spiral makes with the normal to the radius. From the figure, $\tan \alpha = dr/r\,d\beta$, and the condition on the spiral is that α shall be constant, so $\tan \alpha$ is constant. Let us represent the constant value of $\tan \alpha$ by K.

$$K = dr/r\,d\beta \tag{1}$$

From (1) show that the equation of the spiral is

$$r = r_A e^{K\beta} \tag{2}$$

Starting with (10–2–2) and being sure to treat it as a line integral (not as a coordinate integral), derive (10–3–1) by computing the work per unit charge that the field would do in moving a positive test charge q' from A to B *along the spiral*. The variable s, measured along the curved line of the spiral, is the distance from A to any point P between A and B. Note, as shown in the figures, that the angle θ between E and ds is less than $\pi/2$ at all points on the spiral. Next, let B recede to infinity and derive (10–3–2) from (10–3–1).

10–13 An alpha particle (helium nucleus) has a mass of approximately 6.68×10^{-27} kg and a charge of 2 protons. In a certain experiment, it is found that a beam of alpha particles can be brought to rest by making them travel through a potential difference of 5000 v against the lines of force of an electric field. What is the velocity of the alpha particles when they enter the electric field? [*Ans:* 6.91×10^5 m/sec.]

10–14 In the surface photoelectric effect, light is incident on an appropriate metal surface and the light ejects electrons from the surface. In a certain photoelectric experiment, it is the desire of the experimenter to find the velocity of the fastest electrons. To do this he has the light pass through a small hole in a large metal sphere and be incident on a smaller metal sphere that is concentric with the larger one. The spheres are located in an envelope from which the air has been evacuated. He finds that he can just stop the fastest electrons when the potential difference between the spheres is 2 v, with the outer sphere at the lower potential. What is the velocity of the electrons as they leave the inner sphere? [*Ans:* 8.37×10^5 m/sec.]

10–15 Consider the Bohr atom model of Problem 9–16. (a) Considering that the potential is zero at infinity, what is the potential in the hydrogen atom at a point on the allowed orbit which is closest to the nucleus? [*Ans:* 27.2 v.] (b) What is the *PE* of the electron in this orbit? What does the minus sign mean physically? [*Ans:* -43.5×10^{-19} joule.] (c) What is the kinetic energy of the electron in this orbit? [*Ans:* 21.8×10^{-19} joule.] (d) What is the total energy of the electron in this orbit? [*Ans:* -21.7×10^{-19} joule.] (e) In the above and in Problem 9–16 we considered that there is empty space between the proton and the electron in the hydrogen atom and for an appreciable distance beyond the electron (i.e., away from the nucleus). Was this an approximation for the region between the proton and electron? If this hydrogen atom is one of many hydrogen atoms in an atomic hydrogen gas at low pressure, would you expect that the approximation would be a good one for an appreciable distance beyond the electron?

10–16 The *electron volt* is defined as an *energy* unit and, by definition, is the kinetic energy that an electron acquires when it rises through a 1.000 v difference in potential. The abbreviation for electron volt is ev. (a) Calculate the conversion factor from joules to electron volts. [*Ans:* 1.60×10^{-19} joule/ev.] (b) In Problem 10–15, calculate in electron volts the potential energy, kinetic energy, and total energy of the electron in the hydrogen atom.

10–17 Consider the isolated charged spherical conductor of Problem 9–30. Let A and B be any two points in the electric field outside the sphere, with A closer to the sphere than B. (a) Adapt the results of Problem 10–11 to show that

$$V_A - V_B = (q/4\pi\varepsilon_0)(1/r_A - 1/r_B)$$

(b) What is the potential at point A? (c) What is the potential at the surface of the sphere? (d) What is the potential inside the sphere? [*Ans:* $V = q/4\pi\varepsilon_0 r_1$.] (e) Sketch a curve showing V plotted as ordinate, against the distance from the center of the sphere, plotted as abscissa. Start the curve at the center of the sphere.

10–18 An isolated metal sphere in empty space has a charge of 2.22×10^{-10} coulomb. The sphere's radius is 0.100 meter. Adopt a convenient scale, such as 10 cm on the drawing represents 1 m in space, and draw a cross section of the sphere in the plane of the paper. (a) Compute the distances from the center of the sphere to points where the potential is 18, 16, 14, 12, 10, 8, 6, 4, 2 v respectively. Using the same scale adopted above, draw a cross section, in the plane of the paper, of an equipotential surface through each of these points. What is the shape, in space, of each of these equipotential surfaces? What is the distance from the center of the sphere to a point where the potential is 0.0100 v? Zero? (b) Draw a few representative lines of force from the metal sphere. Is there any relationship between the density of lines of force and the density of equipotential surfaces that are spaced with equal increments of potential?

10–19 Two metal spheres are concentric, with empty space between them. The inner sphere is 10.0 cm in radius and has a negative charge of 5.00×10^{-9} coulomb. The outer sphere is 20.0 cm in radius and is grounded. (a) Point B is 12.0 cm from the common center of the two spheres and point A is 18.0 cm from the same center. What is the potential difference $V_B - V_A$? [*Ans:* $-$ 125 v.] (b) What is the potential difference between the two spheres? [*Ans:* 225 v.]

10–20 In Problem 10–14, the inner sphere is 2.00 cm in radius and the outer concentric sphere is 10.0 cm in radius. (a) Considering that the inner sphere is grounded and thus is at zero potential, what is the potential at a point P, 4.00 cm from the common center point of the two spheres? [*Ans:* $-$ 1.25 v.] (b) What is the velocity of one of the fastest electrons when it passes P? [*Ans:* 5.12×10^5 m/sec.] (c) What is the charge on the inner sphere? [*Ans:* 5.56×10^{-12} coulomb.]

10–21 Two round flat metal disks, each with a radius of 20.0 cm, are placed with the flat faces parallel to each other and 1.00 mm apart. One plate is connected to the positive terminal of a battery whose emf is 500 v, and the other plate is connected to the negative terminal of the battery and to ground. (a) What is the electric field intensity in the empty space between the plates? (b) What is the charge density and the charge on each plate? [*Ans:* $q = 5.56 \times 10^{-7}$ coulomb.] (c) What force would an electron experience at the mid-point between the plates? [*Ans:* 8.00×10^{-14} newton.]

10–22 Two long straight wires are stretched parallel to each other with a separation l between their centers. Each wire has a radius of r_1 and each has a static charge of b per unit length. One wire is positively charged and the other is negatively charged. Assume that the charge is uniformly distributed over the surface of each wire and thus that the distribution is not affected by the presence of the charge on the other wire. Also consider that there are no other charges near that can influence the electric field.

Using the principle of superposition for electric fields and (10–2–2), derive the formula

$$V_A - V_D = (b/2\pi\varepsilon_0) \ln [r_D (l - r_1)/r_1 (l - r_D)]$$

where D is any point between the two wires on a line joining their centers, A is a point on the surface of the positively charged wire, and r_D is the distance from the center of the positively charged wire to D.

10–23 The two long straight wires of Problem 10–22 are separated by a distance of 1.00 m between their centers. Each wire is 0.00200 m in radius and each has a static charge per unit length of 1.00×10^{-7} coulomb/m. Assume that the conditions stated in Problem 10–22 are satisfied. (a) Calculate the potential difference between the positively charged wire and point D, on the line joining the centers of the two wires, for the following values of r_D in meters: $r_D = 0.002, 0.006, 0.01, 0.05, 0.1, 0.2, 0.3, 0.4, 0.5, 0.6, 0.7,$ 0.8, 0.9, 0.98, 0.99, and 0.998. Assume that each distance is given to three significant figures. [*Ans:* At $r_D = 0.998$, $V_A - V_D = 22{,}300$ v.] (b) Plot a graph with $V_A - V_D$ as ordinate and r_D as abscissa. Continue the curve from the center of one wire to the center of the other wire. From your graph list the values of r_D for the points where equipotential surfaces, spaced at 2000 v intervals for $V_A - V_D$, would cross the line joining the centers of the wires.

10–24 Two metal spheres, each of radius r_1, are located so that there is a distance l between their centers. Sphere 1 has a positive charge q, and sphere 2 has a negative charge of the same magnitude. Assume that the charge on each sphere is uniformly distributed over its surface and thus that the distribution is not affected by the presence of the charge on the other sphere. Also consider that there are no other charges near that can influence the electric field. (a) Using the principle of superposition for electric fields and (10–2–2), derive the formula

$$V_A - V_D = (q/4\pi\varepsilon_0)\,[1/r_1 - 1/r_D + 1/(l - r_D) - 1/(l - r_1)]$$

where D is any point between the two spheres on a line joining their centers and at a distance r_D from the center of sphere 1, and A is a point on the surface of sphere 1. (b) Considering the zero of potential to be at infinity, compute the potentials at A and D due to each sphere separately, using (10–3–2). Next apply the principle of superposition for potentials to compute $V_A - V_D$ and obtain the same result as in part (a).

10–25 Consider the metal spheres in Problem 10–24 and assume that the conditions stated there apply. Each sphere has a radius of 0.00200 m and each has a charge of 1.00×10^{-10} coulomb. Sphere 1 is positive and sphere 2 is negative. The distance between the centers of the spheres is 1.00 m. (a) Calculate the potential difference $V_A - V_D$ for the following values of r_D in meters: 0.002, 0.003, 0.004, 0.005, 0.006, 0.008, 0.01, 0.02, 0.05, 0.1, 0.5, 0.9, 0.95, 0.98, 0.99, 0.992, 0.994, 0.995, 0.996, 0.997, and 0.998. Assume that each distance is given to three significant figures.

What is the potential difference $V_A - V_2$ between the spheres? [*Ans:* 898 v.] (b) Plot a graph with $V_A - V_D$ as ordinate and r_D as abscissa. On another piece of graph paper plot an enlarged section of the graph from $r_D = 0$ to $r_D = 0.0200$ m. From you graphs list the values of r_D for the points where equipotential surfaces spaced at 100 v intervals for $V_A - V_D$ would cross the line joining the centers of the spheres.

10–26 Describe an experiment which you could perform to show qualitatively that the charge density on a metal body with a static charge is greatest where the radius of curvature of the metal body is least.

10-27 Consider the physical problem described in Problem 9–41. By direct use of (10–4–2), derive a formula for the potential at a point P on the axis of the charged disk where P is at a distance y from the origin. Then apply (10–8–8) to your potential formula and show that the answer for E given for part (a) of Problem 9–41, results.

10-28 Consider the physical problem described in Problem 9–41. Point A is on the Y-axis at a distance y_2 from the center of the disk and point B is on the same axis at a distance y_1 from the center of the disk with $y_1 > y_2$. (a) By direct use of (10–2–2) as a line integral and of the formula for E derived in Problem 9 41, show that the potential difference between A and B is given by

$$V_A - V_B = [\sqrt{R^2 + y_2^2} - \sqrt{R^2 + y_1^2} - (y_2 - y_1)]\, \sigma/\varepsilon_0$$

(b) Let point B recede to infinity and show that the formula for V_A agrees with the one derived in Problem 10–27 by use of (10–4–2).

10-29 The potential function for a certain electric field can be represented in a limited region in the first quadrant by the equation $V = -Ax - By$, where $A = 2.00$ volt/m and $B = 4.00$ volt/m. (a) What is the vector expression for the electric field intensity E in this region? (b) Through what angle and in what direction must the X-axis be rotated in order that the same field may be represented by the expression $E = i\,4.47$? [*Ans:* $63\frac{1}{2}°$ counterclockwise.] (c) What kind of a configuration of charged conductors could produce this field? How must the conductors be oriented with respect to the axis in order that the equation in (b) shall represent the field?

10-30 In a limited region in the first quadrant, the potential function for a certain electric field can be represented by $V = Ax^2 + By^2$, where $A = 2.00$ volt/m² and $B = 4.00$ volt/m². (a) What is the vector expression for E in this region? (b) What is the magnitude and direction of E at the point $x = 2$, $y = 1.5$? [*Ans:* 14.4 v/m at an angle of $56\frac{1}{2}°$ with the X-axis.]

10-31 In a limited region near the origin of a polar coordinate system, the potential function of a certain electric field can be represented by the formula $V = A(\sin\theta)/r^3 + B/r^2$ where $A = 4.00$ volt m³ and $B = 3.00$ volt m². (a) What is the vector expression for E in this region? (b) What is the magnitude and direction of E at the point $r = 2$, $\theta = 40°$? [*Ans:* 1.25 v/m at an angle of $8°\,50'$ with the radius vector to the point.]

10-32 Two positive charges, each of magnitude q, lie on the X-axis. One is at a distance d to the right of the origin and the other is at the same distance to the left of the origin. There are no other charges about to contribute to the field. (a) Write the potential function for any point in the XY-plane. Use Cartesian coordinates. (b) Find the vector expression for the electric field intensity at any point in the XY-plane. [*Ans:*

$$E = \frac{q}{4\pi\varepsilon_0}\left(i\left\{\frac{x+d}{[(x+d)^2 + y^2]^{3/2}} + \frac{x-d}{[(x-d)^2 + y^2]^{3/2}}\right\}\right.$$
$$\left. + j\left\{\frac{y}{[(x+d)^2 + y^2]^{3/2}} + \frac{y}{[(x-d)^2 + y^2]^{3/2}}\right\}\right).$$

(c) If $q = 1.00 \times 10^{-10}$ coulomb and $d = 0.400$ meter, using the vector equation, find the magnitude and direction of E at the origin; at the point $x = 5d$, $y = 0$; at the point $x = 0$, $y = 5d$; and the point $x = d$, $y = d$.

10–33 The potential function of a certain charge distribution is given approximately by $V = Ax^2 + Bxy + Cy^2$, for a limited region in the XY-plane. In this potential equation $A = 5.00$, $B = 3.00$, and $C = 2.00$, each in units of volt/m^2. A proton at rest at $x = 3.00$ m, $y = 4.00$ m, $z = 0$, is suddenly released. What is the vector expression for its initial acceleration? [*Ans:* $- i40.1 \times 10^8$ m/sec$^2 - j24.0 \times 10^8$m/sec^2.]

10–34 A fine metal wire of length l lies on the Y-axis with one end at the origin of coordinates. The wire has a static charge q uniformly distributed along its length. Show that, for values of $y > l$, the potential function for points on the Y-axis only is given by $V = q[\ln y - \ln (y - l)]/4\pi\varepsilon_0 l$ and from this potential function derive the vector expression for E on the Y-axis.

10–35 Consider the dipole discussed in Sec. 10–10 and shown in Fig. 10–10–1. Assume that each charge has a magnitude of 2.00×10^{-10} coulomb and that the separation of the two charges is 1.00×10^{-7} m. There are no other charges nearby. (a) Starting with (10–10–7) for the electric field intensity of a dipole, derive the potential equation (10–10–3). To do this use (10–2–2) and compute the work per unit charge that the field would do on an infinitesimal test charge in carrying it *from a point A to infinity*. Point A has coordinates (r_A, θ) in the YZ-plane and is any point in this plane. Note that θ in (10–2–2) is not the same angle as θ in Fig. 10–10–1, so replace θ in (10–2–2) by some other symbol for this problem. Compute the potential at A if A has the coordinates $r = 0.00100$ m, $\theta = 40°$. (b) What is the magnitude and direction of E at point A? Use a sketch to show the direction. [*Ans:* 299 v/m directed 22° 50′ below r.]

10–36 In Problem 10–35 what is the magnitude and direction of E at a point P' where $r = 0.00100$ m and $\theta = 140°$?

10–37 Use (10–10–11) to plot some of the lines of force of a dipole (where $r \gg l$) like the lines plotted in Fig. 10–10–3. Use the same values of C marked on the lines in this figure. Use an $8\frac{1}{2} \times 11$ in. sheet of polar coordinate graph paper and adopt the largest convenient scale that will permit you to plot the complete lines for $C \geq 1$.

This formula is a very good approximation only for points where $r \gg l$. What marked discrepancy does this produce in your plotted lines of force near the origin?

10–38 Refer to Sec. 10–6 and Fig. 10–6–1 for coaxial charged metal cyclinders with empty space in the region between the cylinders. Derive the formula $E = i_r (V_1 - V_2)/r \ln (r_2/r_1)$ for the electric field intensity in the space between the cylinders. What is the practical advantage of this formula for E over the one in (9–10–6)?

10–39 Refer to Example A, Sec. 10–1 in which we considered an electric field that is given by (10–1–5) as $E = (iy + jx)$ 1 newton/coulomb meter for a limited region in the XY-plane and near the origin of coordinates. Show that div $E = 0$. What does this prove concerning the amount of charge in the region where the above formula for E is valid? Does this agree with your conclusions in Problem 10–2?

10–40 The potential formula in the field of a point charge is given by (10–3–2) in spherical coordinates. Changed to Cartesian coordinates, (10–3–2) is

$$V = q/4\pi\varepsilon_0\sqrt{x^2 + y^2 + z^2} \qquad (10\text{–}3\text{–}2A)$$

Show that (10–3–2A) satisfies $\nabla^2 V = 0$ except at the origin. Use $\nabla^2 V$ in Cartesian coordinates.

10–41 For the electric field given in Problem 10–3, show that the charge density, in the region where this vector expression for E is valid, is given by $\rho = xy17.70 \times 10^{-12}$ coulomb/m^5.

PROPERTIES OF

DIELECTRICS

II-I QUALITATIVE DISCUSSION

Let us refer again to Sec. 4–1, where we discussed the process of charging a capacitor by the use of a battery. We made the capacitor of two large metal plates with faces parallel and with a separation that was small compared with the linear dimensions of either plate. Air filled the space between the plates. Next, we connected the positive terminal of a battery to one plate and the negative terminal of the battery to the other plate and discussed the flow of current in the wires of the circuit and the accumulation of charge q on the plates. We defined the capacitance C of the capacitor by the equation

$$C = q/V \qquad (11-1-1)$$

where V is the potential difference between the plates when the charge on *one* plate is q. When the flow of current ceased, V became equal to the emf of the battery.

Now we wish to make some additional observations on the behavior of the experimental capacitor. Assume that the capacitor has been connected to the battery for some time, the potential difference across its plates has reached the emf of the battery, and current no longer flows. We select a slab of glass that will just fill the space between the plates and place it between the plates. We observe that the potential difference between the plates suddenly decreases when the glass is inserted between the plates, and that current flows in such a direction that the charge q on the capacitor is increased. The flow ceases when the potential difference between the plates again reaches the emf of the battery. But now q is larger for the same V than it was when air filled the space between the plates. From (11–1–1) this can mean only that the capacitance of the capacitor is greater with glass between the plates than it is with air between the plates.

We repeat this experiment with various solid and liquid dielectrics. Each time we find that C is larger than it is with air between the plates and we also find, incidentally, that C is in general different for each different dielectric material.

If we were able to evacuate the space between the plates we should find that the capacitance of the capacitor is a little greater with air between the plates than it is with empty space between the plates.

We can summarize by saying that the capacitance of a capacitor is greater with a material dielectric between its plates than it is with empty space between its plates. By the use of the capacitance bridge which we studied in Sec. 8–3 we could obtain quantitative results to substantiate this conclusion.

We immediately ask ourselves: What is happening in a material dielectric that causes the capacitance of a given capacitor to be larger with a material dielectric between the plates than it is with empty space between the plates? We hinted at the answer to this question when we said that dielectric molecules become polarized in an electric field and talked briefly about the fact that polarization charges exert forces on conduction charges just as conduction charges exert forces on each other. But we did not enlarge on this notion.

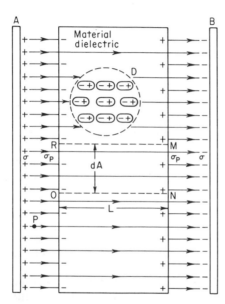

Now we wish to develop a picture of what happens inside and on the surface of a dielectric when that dielectric is in an electric field. We wish a model of a dielectric which will not only answer our questions qualitatively but which will give us a basis for quantitative calculations as well. We started the picture in Sec. 1–2 when we discussed the distinction between conductors and insulators, and continued it briefly in various parts of Sec. 9–1, particularly in the explanation of the attraction of an uncharged piece of dielectric by a charged body. Let us enlarge on this start by considering a slab of material dielectric between the plates of a capacitor. A parallel plate capacitor is a convenient one for this purpose because it has a uniform electric field between its plates in the region where there is no fringing. For the most part, we shall deal with a dielectric in a uniform electric field and thus our discussion will not be a general one. Many of the results, however, are general in their application although we shall derive them under restricted conditions.

Figure 11–1–1. Slab of material dielectric between the plates of a parallel plate capacitor.

Figure 11–1–1 shows a slab of material dielectric in the electric field between the charged plates A and B of a parallel plate capacitor. We have pointed out that a perfect dielectric has no free electrons (and we shall deal only with perfect dielectrics), but that the nucleus of each dielectric molecule experiences a force in the direction of E and the electrons in each molecule experience forces in the opposite direction. As a feature of our model of a dielectric, we consider that the electrons in a dielectric molecule are bound to the nucleus with elastic forces. The electric field will stretch or distort each dielectric molecule in Fig. 11–1–1 because the field will shift the nucleus a small distance in the direction of E and shift the electrons a small distance in the opposite direction. When a molecule is stretched in this manner it is said to be polarized. The shift of charges will cease when the elastic force binding the dielectric molecule together is equal and opposite to the force of the field on the charges of the molecule. If E is increased, each dielectric molecule will be stretched or polarized an additional amount against the elastic forces. If E is decreased, the elastic forces will draw the electrons back toward the nucleus. If E is decreased to zero, the electrons will return to their original symmetrical configuration about the nucleus, and the molecule is again unpolarized.

The dotted circle at D in Fig. 11–1–1 purports to show a section of the dielectric sufficiently magnified so that we may see individual molecules under conditions such that each molecule is polarized. Molecules are too small to be seen even under the highest magnification available, and the picture in the dotted circle is much too simple, but let us assume for the purposes of this discussion that the dielectric molecules behave as if this were a proper picture. The forces that bind the electrons to the nucleus are electric in nature, and a complete description of all forces involved would be very complicated. Again, however, let us assume for the purposes of our model of a dielectric, that it is sufficient to consider a simple elastic force binding the electrons to the nucleus. We might be even more pictorial and consider that each electron is bound to the nucleus by means of a spring but, of course, we must not take such a picture seriously.

In the dotted circle at D, we see that each dielectric molecule has become an induced dipole under the action of E. As defined in the previous chapter, the electric dipole moment p of a dielectric molecule is equal to the product of either charge and the distance between them. The dipole moment is a vector quantity directed from the minus charge toward the positive charge. When E is zero and the electrons are again symmetrically distributed around the nucleus, the dipole moment is zero.

So far we have been talking about the kind of dielectric molecules which are called *nonpolar*, i.e., the kind which have no dipole moment when E is zero. Other kinds of dielectric molecules are *polar*, and each such dielectric molecule has a *permanent dipole moment*. When an electric field is imposed on polar molecules, each dipole experiences a torque tending to align its dipole moment parallel with the field. The tendency toward alignment is opposed by the thermal motion of the molecules, but the greater the value of E the greater the alignment. A sufficiently intense field may even increase the dipole moment of each polar molecule. When E is removed, the thermal motion of the molecules quickly produces a random orientation of the dipoles and leaves no net external effect.

When an electric field is first applied to a dielectric, as in Fig. 11–1–1 when the charge is first put on the plates of the capacitor, there is a shift of negative charge toward the positive plate A and a shift of positive charge toward the negative plate B. Thus, there is motion of charge across any cross section of the dielectric which is perpendicular to E. This is true whether the dielectric is made up of polar or nonpolar molecules. Thus, negative polarization charges will appear on the surface of the dielectric near the positive plate A, and positive polarization charges will appear on the surface of the dielectric near the negative plate B. There results, then, a surface density of polarization charge on each face of the dielectric slab, and this is shown in Fig. 11–1–1 by the line of negative charge on the left face of the dielectric slab and the corresponding line of positive charges on the right face. The whole slab of dielectric is said to be polarized and contains an enormous number of tiny electric dipoles. We shall see that sometimes it is convenient to describe the effect of the dielectric in terms of the dipoles throughout its volume, and sometimes it is more convenient to use the surface density of polarization charge.

The polarization charge on the face of the dielectric is referred to as a *bound charge* because it cannot be conducted away by means of a conductor. This polarization charge is bound to the dielectric molecules and could not flow onto plates A or B even if the plates were in direct contact with the dielectric. Usually the plates of a capacitor are in direct contact with the dielectric. The charges on the plates A and B are called *free* or *conduction* charges because they can flow away on conductors. In fact, as we have seen, if a wire were connected from B to A the surplus electrons on B would flow through the wire and neutralize the positive charge on A.

11–2 MEANING OF E IN A DIELECTRIC

We learned in Secs. 9–5 and 9–6 how to compute E at a point in empty space when a distribution of conduction charges established the field being considered. The argument involved the use of coulomb's law and the principle of superposition for electric fields. The discussion leads to

$$E = (1/4\pi\varepsilon_0) \sum_{i=1}^{n} q_i \mathbf{i}_{ri}/r_i^2 \qquad (9\text{–}6\text{–}18)$$

and its equivalent for a continuous distribution,

$$E = (1/4\pi\varepsilon_0) \int dq\, \mathbf{i}_r/r^2 \qquad (9\text{–}6\text{–}19)$$

When we wish to compute E at a point in empty space due to a distribution of conduction charges, these equations tell us to compute the E at that point due to each conduction charge separately and then take the vector sum of the individual E vectors.

1. E AT A POINT IN EMPTY SPACE DUE TO CONDUCTION AND POLARIZATION CHARGES. Now visualize a situation where there is not only a distribution of conduction charges but also blocks of dielectric in the electric field of the conduction charges. The blocks of dielectric are, by our theory, polarized by the electric field in which they reside and thus have polarization charges on their surfaces. We wish to compute E, at a point, such as P in Fig. 11–1–1, in empty space, due to a distribution of both conduction and polarization charges. But physics knows only one species of positive and negative charge. The polarization charges differ from conduction charges only in that they are bound to molecules. Thus, each polarization charge exerts forces on other polarization charges and on conduction charges just as conduction charges

exert forces on each other. Hence, Coulomb's law and the principle of super-position apply and we may use the same methods of calculation that we used for conduction charges only. So E at P may be computed by the use of (9–6–18) or (9–6–19) [and also by equations which are derived from them], but now *we must include in the sum the terms for polarization charges as well as the terms for the conduction charges.* Thus, to repeat, each charge (both con-duction and polarization) exerts a force on a test charge at P as if there were no other charges about, and the total force on the test charge is the vector sum of the separate forces.

In Fig. 11–1–1 the polarization charge, inside the body of the dielectric, cancels over a volume containing many molecules because there are as many positive charges as negative charges. (We shall discuss this picture in more detail in Sec. 11–3.) Hence, the polarization charges at interior points in the dielectric contribute compensating terms to the sums in (9–6–18) or (9–6–19). However, the surface polarization charges do not contribute compensating terms to the sum because, in the specific example pictured in Fig. 11–1–1, the negative polarization charges on the left face of the dielectric are closer to P than are the positive polarization charges on the right face of the dielec-tric. The argument of this paragraph is strictly true only for dielectrics which are homogeneous throughout (see Sec. 11–8 where we discuss the situation in which the dielectric consists of two parts).

2. E INSIDE A MATERIAL DIELECTRIC. Next consider E inside a material dielectric. If the dielectric were a liquid or a gas, we could conceivably measure the force per unit charge on an infinitesimal test charge at a point inside the dielectric. However, if the dielectric is a solid, we cannot place a test charge at a point inside and measure the force on it. Hence, we shall *define E* at a point inside a dielectric rather than appeal to experiment. We shall adopt the definition of E for interior points that says: *E for points inside a dielectric shall be a vector quantity computed from the conduction and polarization charge distributions by the same rules that apply to points outside the dielectric.* Thus, (9–6–18) and (9–6–19) and others derived from them shall apply for interior points of the dielectric as well as for points outside.

This definition of E inside a dielectric makes E a theoretical tool rather than a measurable physical quantity. It turns out to be a useful tool because it leads to equations which can be checked against experiment with consider-able precision. As an aid to our thinking, we may continue to look upon E as force per unit charge on an infinitesimal test charge as long as we do not raise the question: How shall we measure it inside a solid dielectric? Every time this question arises we remember that E is defined by the italicized definition above and that we consider it force per unit charge only as an aid in using the tool.

The definition of E for interior points of a dielectric has great merit, because we may continue to use all the methods that we have learned for empty space. We simply have the added requirement that we must take the polarization charges into account.

3. E IS A SPACE AVERAGE. In our calculations which use polarization charges, we shall not calculate in terms of the individual molecular dipoles because the calculations would be too difficult. Rather we shall calculate in terms of average values over volumes which are large compared with the volume occupied by a molecule, although the volumes may be small in terms of ordinary dimensions. Consequently, when we compute E in a dielectric, it will be a space average of a function which is rapidly fluctuating from point to point in a molecule and between molecules. When we say, for example, that E is uniform in the dielectric between the plates of a parallel plate capacitor, it is this space average E which is uniform, not the microscopic field within molecular dimensions. Thus, the theory that we are developing here gives us no information about individual molecules but only about average effects due to many molecules. When we speak of the field at a point P in a dielectric, we do not mean a mathematical point but, rather, the average over a region around P that takes in several molecules. We shall not keep repeating these concepts, but shall understand that they are inherent in what follows except when we talk explicitly in terms of individual molecules.

4. ELECTRIC LINES OF FORCE AND POLARIZATION CHARGES. By the preceding definition of E in a dielectric, polarization charges are to enter into the calculation of E in exactly the same way as do conduction charges. Hence, we must think of electric lines of force as originating on positive polarization charges just as they do on positive conduction charges. Similarly, we must think of electric lines of force as terminating on negative polarization charges just as they do on negative conduction charges. Thus, in Fig. 11–1–1, some of the lines of force which originate on the positive conduction charges on the left plate of the capacitor will terminate on the negative polarization charges on the left face of the dielectric, leaving a reduced number of lines to go on through the dielectric. On the right side of the figure, lines of force will originate on the positive polarization charges and go over to terminate on the negative conduction charges on the right plate of the capacitor; this is shown in Fig. 11–1–1. At once we conclude that E in the dielectric is less than it is in the space between each plate and the adjacent face of the dielectric. Or, in other words, the surface polarization charges have reduced the field inside the dielectric.

11–3 DEFINITION OF THE POLARIZATION VECTOR P

We have seen that each molecule of a dielectric becomes an electric dipole when the dielectric is in an electric field. In (10–10–4) we defined the electric dipole moment p as a vector directed from the negative charge of the dipole toward the positive charge. The defining equation for p is

$$p = ql \qquad (10–10–4)$$

If q is the charge that is displaced in each atom by the electric field and l is the average distance that q is displaced, we may take (10–10–4) as the electric dipole moment of a polarized molecule.

Now let us define a new vector quantity which we shall represent by P and shall call the *polarization of the dielectric* or just *polarization*. Polarization P is *defined as the electric dipole moment per unit volume of the dielectric*. It is perhaps unfortunate that the term *polarization* is used in a general sense to describe what happens in a dielectric when the dielectric is subjected to an electric field, and is also used in this specific sense. But there is no confusion, since we can usually use P when the specific sense is the one meant.

Consider first the special case where there are n polarized molecules per unit volume of a dielectric and where all have the same dipole moment p and all dipole moments are parallel. Then, from the definition of P,

$$P = nql = np \qquad (11\text{–}3\text{–}1)$$

From (11–3–1), or from the definition of P,

$$\text{units of } P = \text{coulomb m/m}^3 = \text{coulomb/m}^2 \qquad (11\text{–}3\text{–}2)$$

Since P is a point function, in a case where the ideal situation above is not satisfied we would consider a small volume $\varDelta V$ throughout which all the p's are parallel and write the equation

$$P = \sum p/\varDelta V \qquad (11\text{–}3\text{–}3)$$

where $\varDelta V$ is large compared with a molecular volume but small compared with ordinary volumes. Thus, although P is a point function, it is a space average, as is E. The direction of P will, of course, be parallel to the vector sum of the dipole moments of the molecules within $\varDelta V$. In a case where the p's are not all parallel, as in a dielectric that has polar molecules, (11–3–3) is still the defining equation for P. We must remember that the summation in (11–3–3) is a vector summation as the equation indicates.

Consult Fig. 11–1–1, where we have a slab of dielectric between the plates of a parallel plate capacitor and thus have the dielectric in a uniform field. Also, we have the face of the slab parallel with the plates of the capacitor. Further let us assume that the dielectric is *ideal, homogeneous,* and *isotropic.* By *ideal* we mean that the dielectric has no free electrons and thus there is no conduction of electricity through the dielectric. By a *homogeneous* dielectric we mean one which is of the same kind all through the region being considered and thus has the same properties at all points. An *isotropic* dielectric is one which has the same properties in all directions. Generally, it is true that crystalline materials are nonisotropic and that noncrystalline materials are isotropic.

Now return to Fig. 11–1–1, and assume that all these conditions are satisfied. We have seen that the polarization of the dielectric results in a surface density of polarization charge on the face of the dielectric. Let us call this surface density of polarization charge σ_P. Note the rectangular block of dielectric marked $MNOR$ and let us first examine what happens to a molecule (or an atom) of the dielectric in this block when the field, directed toward the right, is first established. The molecule will become polarized, but we cannot be sure that the positive and negative parts of the atom will be displaced the same amount. So let us assume that, on the average, each positive charge is displaced a distance l_+ in the direction of the field, and each negative charge a distance l_- the other way. As before, q is the charge that is displaced in each molecule, positive q in one direction and negative q in the other, and we may picture the previously described polarization of a molecule as drawn in

Fig. 11–3–1 (a). The induced dipole moment per molecule is, by (10–10–4), $p = ql$, so

$$q(l_+ + l_-) = p$$

Now let us consider the block $MNOR$ before the E field was established and redraw it in Fig. 11–3–1 (b). In the absence of E, the total charge in regions d and b will be zero.

Next let us turn on E by placing charges on the plates of the capacitor. Positive charges within the distance l_+ of the right side of d will leave the region d, but will be replaced by those within the distance l_+ to the left of d. Figure 11–3–1 (c) attempts to picture this situation where, in the figure, we think of all positive charges in d as shifting to the right the distance l_+; the positive charges within the distance l_+ of the right face of d move into the space between the right face of d and the dotted line; and the positive charges in

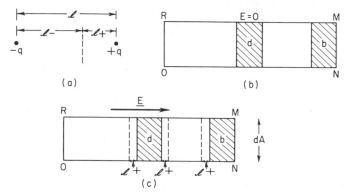

Figure 11–3–1. Polarization of a dielectric due to a uniform electric field: (a) polarization of an individual molecule; (b) block of the dielectric when no electric field is applied; (c) same block of the dielectric when an electric field is applied. The widths of the regions d and b are large compared to l.

the space between the dotted line on the left of d, and the left face of d moves into the region d. Similarly, for negative charges, some will move from the right into the region d to replace those that move to the left out of the region d, but in this case each charge moves a distance l_-. Thus, the region d still has a zero charge, as we pointed out in Sec. 11–2 from another point of view.

Now look at region b in Fig. 11–3–1 (c). When the E field is turned on, the positive charges within the distance l_+ of the right face MN will be forced toward the surface of the dielectric and be replaced by the positive charges within the distance l_+ to the left of region b (i.e., those between the dotted line and the left face of b). Thus, there will be a net increase of positive charge in the region b due to this motion of positive charges. If we let ρ represent the volume density of positive charge and dA represent the area of cross section of the block, the net increase in the positive charge in region b will be the positive charge originally in the space between the dotted line and the left face of b, i.e., the net increase in positive charge will be $\rho l_+ \, dA$. Similarly, negative charge within a distance l_- of the left face of b will move out of the region b, but there are no negative charges beyond MN to replace them. Thus, there will be a net decrease of $\rho l_- \, dA$ in the negative charge in the region b, where ρ is the same for positive and negative charges because the specimen was originally neutral. A decrease of $\rho l_- \, dA$ in the negative charge in b means a net increase of $\rho l_- \, dA$ in the positive charge in b. Thus, the total increase dQ in the positive charge in b is

$$dQ = \rho l_+ \, dA + \rho l_- \, dA = \rho(l_+ + l_-) \, dA$$

Since ρ is the density of positive charge per unit volume, $\rho = nq$, where n is the number of molecules per unit volume. Hence

$$dQ = nq(l_+ + l_-) \, dA = nql \, dA = np \, dA$$

from which $dQ/dA = np$. But dQ/dA is the surface density of polarization charge, which we have called σ_P, and by (11–3–1), $np = P$, so

$$P = \sigma_P \tag{11–3–4}$$

Of course, a similar argument at the left face of the dielectric would show that the surface density of $\sigma_P = -P$ of negative polarization charge appears on the left face of the dielectric.

Equation (11–3–4) tells us that the polarization, in this special case, is equal to the surface density of polarization charge. We see from (11–3–2) that the units are satisfactory in this equation. Equation (11–3–4) is a special case, because the conditions that we imposed above made P normal to the surface of the dielectric. It can be shown in the general case* that it is the component of P which is normal to the face of the dielectric and drawn *outward* from the dielectric which should appear here, or

$$P_n = \sigma_P \tag{11–3–5}$$

If we wish to describe polarization effects in terms of surface density of polarization charge we may use (11–3–4) or (11–3–5) to relate P and σ_P.

We now have four elements in our theory to describe the behavior of dielectrics. They are (1) the conduction charges on the conductors, for example on the capacitor plates in Fig. 11–1–1; (2) the electric field E which is caused by the conduction charges; (3) the polarization vector P which results from the resultant electric field in the dielectric, and (4) the surface density of polarization charge σ_P, which is directly related to P. The values of E inside the dielectric, of P, and of σ_P cannot be measured directly. They are tools of the theory which we have set up for the purpose of solving problems.

11–4 RELATIONSHIP BETWEEN P AND E

In order to advance the theory we must make an assumption regarding the relationship between the P that is produced in a dielectric and the E which produces it.

For simplicity in writing, we shall follow a common practice and call a

---

* See any advanced text, e.g., R. M. Whitmer, *Electromagnetics*, 1st ed. (Englewood Cliffs, N.J.: Prentice-Hall, Inc., 1952), p. 58.

certain class of dielectrics *class A dielectrics*. Class A dielectrics are those that are *ideal, homogeneous,* and *isotropic* (as defined in Sec. 11-3) and which in addition satisfy the assumption that we are about to make concerning the relationship between P and E. Many, but not all, common dielectrics fall in this class, or are very close approximations and may be treated as class A. We shall limit our discussion to class A dielectrics; for a more general discussion an advanced text should be consulted.

For class A dielectrics we shall assume that P is linearly proportional to E and in the same direction as E, where the constant of proportionality depends only on the kind of dielectric (at constant temperature). Let us write the constant of proportionality as $\varepsilon_0\eta$, where ε_0 is the permittivity of empty space as before. Thus the assumption may be written as the equation.

$$P = \varepsilon_0\eta E \qquad\qquad (11\text{-}4\text{-}1)$$

Here η is *called the electric susceptibility of the dielectric.*

From (11-4-1), $\eta = P/\varepsilon_0 E$, so the units of η are

$$\frac{\text{coulomb/m}^2}{\text{coulomb}^2/(\text{newton m}^2) \times \text{newton/coulomb}}$$

Thus, η is a dimensionless constant of proportionality whose value depends on the kind of dielectric. The greater the electric susceptibility η of a given dielectric, the greater the value of P which a given E will produce and thus, from (11-3-4), the greater the induced polarization charge. For most substances η has a value between 0 and 4.

You should remember that (11-4-1) is an assumption whose validity is tested by experimental tests of equations which are derived by its use. The assumption is found to be valid for class A dielectrics. Actually the reverse should be the statement made about it, namely, dielectrics for which (11-4-1) is found to be valid are called class A dielectrics. Some authors call such dielectrics linear dielectrics because (11-4-1) expresses a linear relationship between P and E. Equation (11-4-1) is found to be too simple an assumption for nonisotropic dielectrics.

11-5 RELATIVE DIELECTRIC CONSTANT ε_r AND PERMITTIVITY ε

In Fig. 11-5-1, let us redraw the parallel plate capacitor situation pictured in Fig. 11-1-1, but this time the slab of dielectric fills the space between the plates. However, in the figure, we have left a small gap between each plate and its adjacent dielectric face for clarity of picturing the detail. We assume that the conditions are such that fringing of lines of force may be neglected.

Let σ represent the surface density of free (or conduction) charges on the surface of each metal plate, and let σ_P represent the surface density of polarization (or bound) charges on each surface of the dielectric slab.

In Sec. 11-2 we have defined E inside a dielectric by saying that it shall be computed in the same way as it is for points outside the dielectric, but that we must take account of the polarization charge distribution as well as the conduction charge distribution. Thus, we may use Gauss's theorem in the way that we have previously, with the addition that any polarization charge inside the Gaussian surface must be taken into account in computing the net charge enclosed in the Gaussian surface.

Draw the Gaussian pill box $CDFG$ shown in Fig. 11–5–1 and apply Gauss's theorem to it.

$$\int_A E_n \, dA = q/\varepsilon_0 \qquad (11\text{--}5\text{--}1)$$

Here q is the net charge enclosed in the box and includes the conduction charge as well as the polarization charge. Thus,

$$q = (\sigma - \sigma_P)A_1 \qquad (11\text{--}5\text{--}2)$$

where A_1 is the area of face CG and of face DF of the pill box. Thus (11–5–1) becomes

$$\int_A E_n \, dA = (\sigma - \sigma_P)A_1/\varepsilon_0 \quad (11\text{--}5\text{--}3)$$

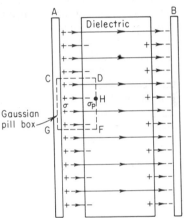

Apply the same reasoning used in Sec. 9–9 to derive (9–9–6), and (11–5–3) becomes

$$E = (\sigma/\varepsilon_0) - (\sigma_P/\varepsilon_0) \quad (11\text{--}5\text{--}4)$$

This is the value of E inside the dielectric at any point such as H in Fig. 11–5–1. Equation (11–5–4) tells us that the conduction charges set up an electric field intensity σ/ε_0 just as they did for empty space, but now the induced polarization charges set up an oppositely directed electric field intensity given by σ_P/ε_0, and thus the net value of E in the dielectric is the difference between the two fields.

Figure 11–5–1. Parallel plate capacitor with a slab of class A dielectric filling the space between the plates.

Equation (11–5–4) also agrees with the idea of regarding electric lines of force as expressed in the last part of Sec. 11–2. Applying this idea to Fig. 11–5–1, we think of σ/ε_0 lines of force as originating on the σ positive conduction charges per unit area of the left capacitor plate and σ_P/ε_0 of these lines terminating on the σ_P negative polarization charges per unit area on the left face of the dielectric. This leaves $\sigma/\varepsilon_0 - \sigma_P/\varepsilon_0$ lines of force per unit area to continue into the dielectric, and the number of lines of force per unit area is E. The lines of force are drawn in Fig. 11–5–1 as they were in Fig. 11–1–1. You can readily repeat the above argument on the right side of Fig. 11–5–1 and show that σ_P/ε_0 lines of force originate per unit area from the σ_P positive polarization charges on the right face of the dielectric and join the $\sigma/\varepsilon_0 - \sigma_P/\varepsilon_0$ lines per unit area that come through the dielectric. Thus there are σ/ε_0 lines of force per unit area that terminate on the σ negative conduction charges per unit area of the right capacitor plate.

We have shown in (11–3–4), for this special case where $\boldsymbol{P}$ is normal to the dielectric face, that $P = \sigma_P$, so (11–5–4) becomes

$$E = (\sigma/\varepsilon_0) - (P/\varepsilon_0) \qquad (11\text{--}5\text{--}5)$$

Replace P in (11–5–5) by the assumption regarding the relationship between P and E as given by (11–4–1) to obtain $E = (\sigma/\varepsilon_0) - (\varepsilon_0 \eta E/\varepsilon_0)$ and solve for E:

$$E = \sigma/\varepsilon_0(1 + \eta) \tag{11–5–6}$$

Now let us define a new quantity which we shall call *relative dielectric constant* and represent by ε_r. The defining equation for ε_r is

$$\varepsilon_r = 1 + \eta \tag{11–5–7}$$

The constant ε_r is called by various equivalent names in various books and tables of values. Some of the other names commonly used are *specific inductive capacity*, *dielectric constant*, and *dielectric coefficient*. We have introduced (11–5–7) in the course of a discussion of a parallel plate capacitor, but (11–5–7) is a general definition of ε_r.

Since electric susceptibility η is a dimensionless constant for class A dielectrics, ε_r is also a dimensionless constant for such dielectrics. For other dielectrics η and ε_r are not constant, but are functions of the magnitude of the electric field intensity and of the direction of the field through the dielectric. For many class A dielectrics, η and ε_r are functions of the temperature, but we shall confine our discussion to constant temperatures. For all material dielectrics, η is a positive number, and so ε_r is always greater than unity.

Put (11–5–7) into (11–5–6) and we have

$$E = \sigma/\varepsilon_r\varepsilon_0 \tag{11–5–8}$$

Equation (11–5–8) gives the electric field intensity inside the dielectric when the dielectric is between the plates of a parallel plate capacitor. If there were empty space between the plates of this capacitor, E would be given by

$$E = \sigma/\varepsilon_0 \tag{9–13–1}$$

Thus, if σ is kept constant, the introduction of a slab of material dielectric between the plates of a parallel plate capacitor reduces the electric field intensity to a value of $1/\varepsilon_r$ of its magnitude with empty space between the plates. Equations (11–5–8) and (11–5–4) contain the same physical information. Equation (11–5–4) expresses E inside the dielectric in terms of both conduction charge density and polarization charge density, whereas (11–5–8) expresses the same E in terms of conduction charge density and a constant ε_r which depends on the properties of the dielectric.

1. CAPACITANCE OF A PARALLEL PLATE CAPACITOR. In (10–5–2) we showed that, with empty space between the plates of a parallel plate capacitor, the potential difference $V_A - V_B$ between the plates is given by $V_A - V_B = \sigma d/\varepsilon_0$, where d is the distance between the plates. Let A = area of either plate, so that the charge on the capacitor is $q = \sigma A$. Then (10–5–2) becomes

$$V_A - V_B = qd/A\varepsilon_0 \tag{11–5–9}$$

But from (11–1–1)

$$C = q/(V_A - V_B) \tag{11–5–10}$$

so, using (11–5–9),

$$C_0 = A\varepsilon_0/d \tag{11–5–11}$$

Now apply the same reasoning used to derive (10–5–2), but this time apply it to Fig. 11–5–1, where a material dielectric fills the space between the plates and (11–5–8) is the formula for E. The reasoning gives

$$V_A - V_B = Ed = \sigma d / \varepsilon_r \varepsilon_0 = qd / A\varepsilon_r \varepsilon_0 \qquad (11\text{--}5\text{--}12)$$

Use this value of $V_A - V_B$ in (11–5–10) and obtain

$$C = A\varepsilon_r \varepsilon_0 / d \qquad (11\text{--}5\text{--}13)$$

A comparison of (11–5–11) and (11–5–13) indicates that the presence of the material dielectric has increased the capacitance of the capacitor by the factor ε_r or $\varepsilon_r = C/C_0$. Equation (11–5–11) is a special case of (11–5–13) because empty space has a relative dielectric constant of unity. In fact the term *relative dielectric constants* of material dielectrics arises because their dielectric constants are expressed relative to unity as the dielectric constant of empty space.

Equation (11–5–13) is a formula which permits us to compute the capacitance of a parallel plate capacitor in terms of the geometry of the capacitor and the relative dielectric constant of the material between its plates. Table 11–1 gives values of relative dielectric constants for a few commonly used dielectrics. Values for other dielectrics may be found in more complete tables of physical constants; for example see the reference handbook from which the values in Table 11–1 were taken.

TABLE 11–1*

Material	ε_r	Material	ε_r
Vacuum	1.000000		
Gases at 1 atm		Solids	
Air	1.000590	Amber	2.65
Argon	1.000545		
Carbon dioxide	1.000985	Beeswax, white	2.5
Hydrogen	1.000264	Glass	3.8 – 6.75
Neon	1.000127	Paraffin	2.1 – 2.5
Nitrogen	1.000580	Polystyrene	2.4 – 2.75
Oxygen	1.000523	Quartz, fused	3.7 – 4.1
Liquids			
Acetone	21.4	Rubber	2 – 3.5
Castor oil	4.67	Rubber, hard	3.0
Linseed oil	3.35		
Petroleum oil	2.13		
Transformer oil	2.24		
Water 0°C	88	Sulfur, amorphous	4.0
Water 20°C	80		
Water 100°C	48		

* From *Handbook of Chemistry and Physics*, 32d ed. (Cleveland: Chemical Rubber Publishing Co.), pp. 2107–13. Values at or near room temperature except as noted for water.

2. PERMITTIVITY ε. Since the produce $\varepsilon_r \varepsilon_0$, frequently appears in formulas as it does in (11–5–13), the product is called the *permittivity* of the dielectric whose relative dielectric constant is ε_r. Permittivity is represented by the symbol ε. Thus, the defining equation for the permittivity of a dielectric is

$$\varepsilon = \varepsilon_r \varepsilon_0 \tag{11–5–14}$$

In the case of empty space $\varepsilon_r = 1$ and $\varepsilon = \varepsilon_0$. Thus arises the name, "permittivity of empty space" or "permittivity of a vacuum," that we have been using for ε_0.

Combining (11–5–7) and (11–5–14) we have $\varepsilon = (1 + \eta)\varepsilon_0$

or

$$\varepsilon = \varepsilon_0 + \eta\varepsilon_0 \tag{11–5–15}$$

which is another useful relationship. Both (11–5–14) and (11–5–15) are general relationships, i.e., not limited to the special case of a parallel plate capacitor even though they arose first in our discussion of such a capacitor.

Note that we have more than the minimum number of quantities needed for the description of the behavior of a dielectric. The quantities that we have introduced for this purpose are: the polarization vector P, surface density of polarization charge σ_P, electric susceptibility η, relative dielectric constant ε_r, and permittivity ε. Of the last three, any one would be sufficient, for they are interrelated by the equations

$$\varepsilon_r = 1 + \eta \tag{11–5–7}$$

$$\varepsilon = \varepsilon_r \varepsilon_0 \tag{11–5–14}$$

$$\varepsilon = \varepsilon_0 + \eta\varepsilon_0 \tag{11–5–15}$$

However, all these (η, ε_r, and ε) are used, and you need to be familiar with all of them.

11-6 ELECTRIC DISPLACEMENT D

Let us define another vector-point function, which is called *electric displacement* (or just *displacement*) and is represented by the symbol D. The defining equation is

$$D = \varepsilon_0 E + P \tag{11–6–1}$$

Displacement D is another theoretical tool of the theory of dielectrics, and turns out to have very useful properties; it is not a directly measurable physical quantity any more than is E inside the dielectric.

In a class A dielectric, E and P are parallel, so the vector sum of (11–6–1) becomes a scalar sum for such dielectrics. In nonisotropic dielectrics, P and E are not parallel, so the vector sum of (11–6–1) must be used. As before, we shall confine our discussion to class A dielectrics, where we have the relationship between P and E given in (11–4–1). Put (11–4–1) into (11–6–1) and we have $D = \varepsilon_0 E + \varepsilon_0 \eta E = \varepsilon_0 E(1 + \eta)$. But from (11–5–7) $\varepsilon_r = 1 + \eta$, so

$$D = \varepsilon_r \varepsilon_0 E \tag{11–6–2}$$

As an alternate to (11–6–2) we may use $\varepsilon = \varepsilon_r \varepsilon_0$ from (11–5–14) and write

$$D = \varepsilon E \tag{11–6–3}$$

Thus, at any point in a class A dielectric, D has a magnitude which is ε times as large as the magnitude of E at that point.

From the defining equation (11–6–1), we obtain the unit of D as

$$\text{unit of } D = \text{coulomb/m}^2 \qquad (11\text{–}6\text{–}4)$$

The same units for D result, of course, from (11–6–3).

1. LINES OF D. It is convenient to represent D graphically by *lines of displacement*. A convention similar to the one for representing E by lines of force is used. The convention is: *lines of D shall be parallel to D at each point in a dielectric and the number of lines of D, drawn through an imaginary unit area perpendicular to D, shall be numerically equal to D.* We shall use the terms "lines of displacement" or "lines of D" when we refer to these lines, but you will often encounter the terms "electric lines of induction" and "electric flux lines" used for the same purpose. Note that lines of force refer to lines of E and you must not confuse lines of force with lines of displacement. From (11–6–3), at every point in a class A dielectric there are ε times as many lines of displacement as there are lines of force through a given area at right angles to the field. Even in empty space, where $\varepsilon = \varepsilon_0$, there are ε_0 times as many lines of D as lines of E.

2. LINES OF D ORIGINATE AND TERMINATE ONLY ON CONDUCTION CHARGES. By the application of Gauss's theorem to the Gaussian pill box in Fig. 11–5–1, we obtained in (11–5–8) the electric field in a dielectric between the plates of a parallel plate capacitor as $E = \sigma/\varepsilon_r\varepsilon_0$. Use (11–5–14) and this becomes $E = \sigma/\varepsilon$, or

$$\varepsilon E = \sigma \qquad (11\text{–}6\text{–}5)$$

But from (11–6–3), $D = \varepsilon E$, so

$$D = \sigma \qquad (11\text{–}6\text{–}6)$$

Remember that σ is the surface density of conduction charge on the metal plates of the parallel plate capacitor. Thus, from (11–6–6), the number of lines of D per unit area in the dielectric is equal to the conduction charge density on the plate without reference to the polarization charge. From this we have shown, for the special case of a parallel plate capacitor, that lines of D originate on positive free charges and do *not* terminate on negative polarization charges. A similar argument, at the right plate of the capacitor would show that lines of D do *not* originate on positive polarization charges but do terminate on negative conduction charges. Also from (11–6–6), D equals σ, so one line of D originates on each unit positive conduction charge and one terminates on each unit negative conduction charge. (This is to be contrasted with lines of E, of which about 10^{11} originate on a unit positive charge.)

We have proved the above in the special case of a class A dielectric between the plates of a parallel plate capacitor. However, it can be shown* to be true in general for any *isotropic* dielectric, and thus we may state that *lines of D*

* See any advanced text, e.g., R. M. Whitmer, *Electromagnetics*, 2d ed. (London: Prentice-Hall, International, 1962), pp. 74 and 78–79, where a proof is given for an isotropic dielectric.

originate and terminate only on conduction charges. Also the number of lines of D originating or terminating on a conduction charge is numerically equal to the magnitude of the conduction charge.

3. GAUSS'S THEOREM IN TERMS OF D. For Gauss's theorem in empty space we had, in (9–8–10), $\int_A E \cdot dA = q_C/\varepsilon_0$, where q_C is the conduction charge enclosed in the Gaussian surface, and, in empty space, conduction charge is the only charge we have. Thus we may write $\int_A \varepsilon_0 E \cdot dA = q_C$ or $\int_A D \cdot dA = q_C$. Now fill the volume of the Gaussian surface with a class A dielectric without disturbing the locations of the conduction charges. The dielectric becomes polarized, and polarization charges appear, due to the electric field. However, the *number* of lines of D cutting out through the Gaussian surface is not altered by the presence of the polarization charges, because lines of D originate and terminate on conduction charges only. Hence we have

$$\int_A D_n \, dA = q_C \tag{11–6–7}$$

where q_C is the total enclosed *conduction* charge. Equation (11–6–7) is Gauss's

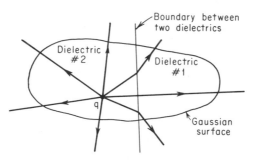

Figure 11–6–1. A Gaussian surface which contains a part of a boundary between two class A dielectrics. A conduction charge q is enclosed in the Gaussian surface. Lines of D are shown originating on q and cutting through the Gaussian surface.

theorem written in terms of D; it expresses one of the very useful properties of D, namely, the *total number of electric lines of displacement that cut out through an imaginary closed surface in an electric field is equal to the net conduction charge enclosed.*

Now we wish to show that (11–6–7) is valid even though there is a boundary between two class A dielectrics inside the Gaussian surface. Figure 11–6–1 shows the situation which we wish to consider, and the caption under the figure describes the situation. At the boundary interface between dielectrics 1 and 2 there will be surface polarization charges, but lines of D neither originate nor terminate on polarization charges. Thus the lines of D that originate on q will continue across the dielectric boundary without change in the number of lines. If there are no conduction charges inside the Gaussian surface on which the lines of D can terminate, the lines of D will continue outward and cut through the Gaussian surface. Hence the number of lines of D which cut out through the Gaussian surface is not altered by an interface between two class A dielectrics, and (11–6–7) is valid for the situation shown in Fig. 11–6–1. By the same argument, this may be extended to any number and any distribution of conduction charges inside the Gaussian surface, and the above italicized statement is valid.

The fact that the number of lines of D does not change at an interface between two dielectrics is often expressed by saying that *lines of D are continuous across the interface between two dielectrics*. This does *not* say that the lines of D continue *straight* across the boundary, and we shall consider this problem shortly in Sec. 11–8.

The number of lines of E does change at an interface between two dielectrics because lines of E originate and terminate on polarization charges.

11–7 RELATIONSHIP BETWEEN E AND V FOR POINTS INSIDE A DIELECTRIC

We have defined E inside a dielectric as a vector quantity that is calculated according to Coulomb's law for empty space, but now we must take due account of the distribution of polarization charges as well as conduction charges. From this it follows that the techniques and the results of Sec. 10–8 may be taken over directly for calculations inside dielectrics. Thus

$$E = -grad\ V \qquad (10\text{–}8\text{–}8)$$

is valid for points inside dielectrics, where E is the electric field intensity at a point inside a dielectric and $grad\ V$ is the space rate of change of potential at the same point.

Also, of course, the line integral relationship of Sec. 10–2, Eq. (10–2–2) is valid for points inside the dielectric, i.e.,

$$V_A - V_B = -\int_{(B)}^{(A)} E\cos\theta\ ds \qquad (10\text{–}2\text{–}2)$$

where E is the electric field intensity inside the dielectric. We have already used this fact in the derivation of (11–5–12) for a parallel plate capacitor.

Thus we may use the same methods that were learned in Chapter X for discussing the region inside a dielectric. Now, however, we must take proper account of the polarization charges when computing E.

11–8 BOUNDARY CONDITIONS AT THE INTERFACE BETWEEN TWO CLASS A DIELECTRICS

We wish to determine the relationships that E and D must satisfy at the interface between two class A dielectrics in an electric field. We shall see that there are two such relationships and they are commonly called the boundary conditions at the interface. We shall assume that there is only polarization charge at the interface (i.e., since the dielectrics are ideal they have no free electrons, and thus there is no conduction charge at the interface).

In Fig. 11–8–1, the rectangle represents a block of one kind of class A dielectric (call it M_2), with relative dielectric constant ε_{r2}, immersed in another class A dielectric (call it M_1) whose relative dielectric constant is ε_{r1}.

Imagine that a very small positive test charge q' is moved around the closed path *abcda* shown in the figure. This closed path is drawn so that the side *ab* is in dielectric M_1, is of length l, and is within an infinitesimal distance of the interface. Side *dc* is drawn in dielectric M_2, has the same length l, and is also within an infinitesimal distance of the interface. Hence sides *ad* and *bc* are each of infinitesimal length. Now compute the work to carry the small test charge q' completely around this path in the direction *abcda*.

To the left of the path in Fig. 11–8–1 are shown the vectors that represent E_1 and E_2, which are the electric field intensities in the two dielectrics. Let us assume that dielectric M_2 has the larger relative dielectric constant and thus larger susceptibility. Then we know that there will be more negative polarization charge on the surface of M_2 at the interface than there is positive polarization charge on the adjacent surface of M_1. Hence, more lines of force

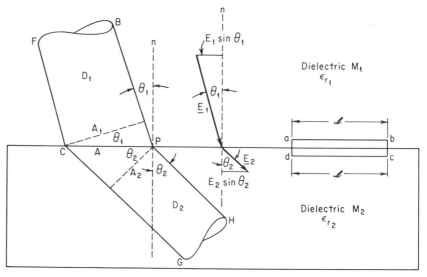

Figure 11–8–1. Refraction of lines of D at an interface between two class A dielectrics.

will terminate on the negative polarization charges on the face of M_2 than originate on the positive charges on the face of M_1, and E_2 will have a smaller magnitude than E_1. At the moment, we do not know whether or not E_2 has the same direction as E_1. Hence, let us draw E_2 at an angle θ_2 with respect to the normal n to the interface. In the figure, E_1 makes an angle θ_1 with the same normal. If it were to develop that E_1 and E_2 have the same direction, the derivation which follows would show that θ_2 is equal to θ_1 (we shall see that this is not the case).

In Fig. 11–8–1, we imagine that the vectors for E_1 and E_2 are at the same location as the rectangle *abcd*, but they have been drawn displaced to the left for clarity of the figure. Further, we have made l small enough so that we may consider that both E_1 and E_2 are uniform over the length l. Along the side *ab* the component, parallel to the path, of the force that the field exerts on q' is

$q'E_1 \sin \theta_1$, so the work done by the field in moving q' from a to b is $q'lE_1 \sin \theta_1$. Similarly the work done on q' against the field to move it from c to d is $q'lE_2 \sin \theta_2$. Since the distance bc is infinitesimal, the work done by the field in moving q' from b to c may be neglected. Similarly the work done against the field in moving q' the infinitesimal distance da is negligible. But in an electrostatic field the line integral of E around any closed path is zero,* so the work done by the field is equal to the work done against the field. Hence, we may write

$$q'lE_1 \sin \theta_1 = q'lE_2 \sin \theta_2 \qquad (11\text{--}8\text{--}1)$$

or $$E_1 \sin \theta_1 = E_2 \sin \theta_2 \qquad (11\text{--}8\text{--}2)$$

We have seen above that E_2 is not equal to E_1 so, from (11–8–2), θ_2 is not equal to θ_1 and thus E_2 does not have the same direction as E_1.

Equation (11–8–2) is one of the boundary conditions that we wished to secure; it says that *the tangential components of E are the same on the two sides of the boundary.*

With E_1 and θ_1 known, (11–8–2) does not give sufficient information to permit calculation of E_2 and θ_2 separately. Hence we need a second boundary condition. We shall secure the second boundary condition in terms of displacement D. As pointed out in Sec. 11–6, lines of displacement are continuous across a boundary between two dielectrics, i.e., lines of displacement do not begin or end on bound or polarization charges. Lines of D begin and end only on free charges. (Remember that we have assumed that there are only polarization charges at the interface between the two dielectrics.) The above does not necessarily mean that lines of D go straight across a boundary between two dielectrics. It does mean, however, that every line of D continues across the boundary even though it may be bent at the boundary.

For this derivation, let us use the concept of a Faraday tube of induction or displacement, where a Faraday tube of displacement is an imaginary sheath (or tube) which encloses the *same lines of displacement* all the way from the start of the lines on free positive charges to the termination of the lines on free negative charges. In order for this requirement on a tube of displacement to be satisfied, the sides of the tube must be parallel with D all along the tube, or else lines of D would cut out or in through the sides of the tube, and the same lines would not continue to be enclosed in the tube all along its length. The area of cross section of a tube of displacement varies from place to place in a nonuniform field in such a fashion that the above requirement is satisfied. A normal cross section of a tube of displacement is an imaginary surface which cuts across the tube in such a way that it is everywhere normal to the lines of displacement enclosed in the tube. If we let A be the area of cross section of the tube at any place, the number N of lines of D through the cross section is given by $N = \int_A D_n \, dA$ and this number is the same for all cross

---

* We could derive (11–8–2) without considering that E in the dielectric is force per unit charge. We know from the conclusions in Sec. 11–7 that for any closed path, such as $abcd$, $\oint E \sin \theta \, ds = 0$. This will give (11–8–2) if we recognize that the infinitesimal parts of the path bc and ad make negligible contributions to the line integral. By such an argument we would treat E only as a theoretical tool, and maintain formal agreement with our definition of E in Sec. 11–2 for points inside a dielectric.

sections of the tube, as we have seen. For the special case of a uniform field, this equation becomes $N = DA$. When solving a particular problem, usually we may take the area of cross section of the tube small enough so that D is essentially uniform across the cross section.

In Fig. 11–8–1, BP and FC represent the section, in the plane of the figure, of the sides of a tube of displacement as the tube is incident on the interface between the two dielectrics. The sides of the tube are parallel to the E_1 vector because D and E are parallel in a class A dielectric. We are to think of this tube as being incident at the place on the interface where the rectangle $abcd$ is located; it has been displaced to the left in the drawing only to save confusion. Area A_1 is the area of cross section of the tube in dielectric M_1, and the tube is considered to be small enough in cross section so that D may be looked upon as uniform in the tube. Let D_1 represent the magnitude of D in the tube in dielectric M_1.

Let PH and CG represent the sides of the tube as the tube enters dielectric M_2. By the same argument as used in M_1, the sides of the tube in M_2 are parallel to E_2. Let A_2 represent the area of cross section of the tube in M_2 and A represent the area of the interface that is enclosed in the tube.

As mentioned previously, the total number of lines of displacement enclosed in the tube is the same on the two sides of the boundary because there are no free charges, only polarization charges, at the interface. Hence, since D is the number of lines per unit area at right angles to D,

$$D_1 A_1 = D_2 A_2 \tag{11–8–3}$$

But $A_1 = A \cos \theta_1$, and $A_2 = A \cos \theta_2$, so

$$D_1 \cos \theta_1 = D_2 \cos \theta_2 \tag{11–8–4}$$

Here $D_1 \cos \theta_1$ is the component of D_1 along the normal to the interface and is called the *normal component* of D_1. Similarly, $D_2 \cos \theta_2$ is called the normal component of D_2. Equation (11–8–4) is the second boundary condition that we sought, and it tells us that the *normal component of D is the same on the two sides of the interface*.

Divide (11–8–2) by (11–8–4), use the fact that $D_1 = \varepsilon_{r1}\varepsilon_0 E_1$, and $D_2 = \varepsilon_{r2}\varepsilon_0 E_2$ and obtain

$$\tan \theta_1/\tan \theta_2 = \varepsilon_{r1}/\varepsilon_{r2} \tag{11–8–5}$$

Equation (11–8–5) gives the relationship between θ_1 and θ_2 which must be satisfied at the boundary, and from it we may compute the "refraction" of the electric lines of force or of the lines of displacement. As Fig. 11–8–1 is drawn, dielectric M_1 could be air and M_2 could be sulfur with a relative dielectric constant approximately four times that of air. Equation (11–8–5) permits us to compute θ_2 if θ_1 is known. Now we wish an equation which will permit us to compute E_2 if E_1 and θ_1 are known. From (11–8–2) and (11–8–5), you can show that (see Problem 11–14)

$$E_2 = E_1 \sqrt{\sin^2 \theta_1 + \varepsilon_{r1}^2 (\cos^2 \theta_1)/\varepsilon_{r2}^2} \tag{11–8–6}$$

and this is the desired formula. Note from (11–8–6) that as θ_1 approaches $90°$, E_2 approaches E_1, and in the limit when $\theta_1 = 90°$, $E_2 = E_1$. This is consistent with (11–8–2), since in this special case, the tangential component of E is equal to E.

We have just seen that, in general, an interface between two class A dielectrics produces bending of the lines of force as a result of the unequal polarization charges which accumulate on the two sides of the interface. We may look upon a nonhomogeneous dielectric as being one which has many such interfaces spread through its volume, because the susceptibility is changing from point to point in a nonhomogeneous dielectric. At each such interface there will be polarization charges which do not cancel. Thus, a non-homogeneous dielectric in an electric field has a distribution of polarization charges throughout its volume. This situation is in contrast with a homogeneous dielectric, which has its uncanceled polarization charges all on its faces. Also, the lines of force will be curved in a nonhomogeneous dielectric because, in general, they will be bent at each place where the susceptibility changes. Thus calculations for nonhomogeneous dielectrics become much more complicated than for homogeneous dielectrics. We leave such calculations for more advanced treatments.

11–9 NUMERICAL EXAMPLE

Let us now solve a numerical example which will illustrate the use of some of the theory presented so far in this chapter.

Figure 11–9–1 shows a parallel plate capacitor with two sheets of dielectric filling the space between its metal plates B and G. The dielectrics are paraffin and glass with relative dielectric constants of 2.40 and 4.00, respectively. Their thicknesses are shown in the figure, and their faces are parallel to the metal plates. Each metal plate has an area of 2.00 m² and, by connection to a battery, the left plate is given a positive conduction charge of 4.00×10^{-5} coulomb and the right plate is given a negative conduction charge of the same magnitude.

(a) What are the values of D, E, and P in each dielectric?

$$\sigma = q/A = 2.00 \times 10^{-5} \text{ coulomb/m}^2 \quad (1)$$

Now, σ lines of D originate on each unit area of plate G perpendicular to the plate and, since the face of the paraffin is parallel to the face of the plate, σ lines of D enter each unit area of the face of the paraffin. The number of lines of D per unit area perpendicular to D is equal to D, so D in the paraffin is equal to σ or

$$D = \sigma = 2.00 \times 10^{-5} \text{ coulomb/m}^2 \quad (2)$$

Also, D is normal to all dielectric interfaces;

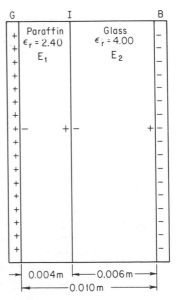

Figure 11–9–1. Parallel plate capacitor with two sheets of dielectric filling the space between the plates.

hence, as you can show from Fig. 11–8–1, $D_1 = D_2$ in such a case. Thus D has the same magnitude and direction in both dielectrics. From (11–6–2)

$$E = D/\varepsilon_r\varepsilon_0 \tag{3}$$

In the paraffin, let E_1 represent the electric field intensity, and substituting into (3) obtain

$$E_1 = 9.42 \times 10^5 \text{ newton/coulomb} \tag{4}$$

In the glass, let E_2 represent the electric field intensity, and again substitution into (3), gives

$$E_2 = 5.65 \times 10^5 \text{ newton/coulomb} \tag{5}$$

From (11–6–1),

$$P = D - \varepsilon_0 E \tag{6}$$

In the paraffin, using (6),

$$P_1 = 1.16 \times 10^{-5} \text{ coulomb/m}^2 \tag{7}$$

In the glass, again using (6)

$$P_2 = 1.50 \times 10^{-5} \text{ coulomb/m}^2 \tag{8}$$

(b) What is the surface density of polarization charge on each face of each dielectric?

Since P is parallel to D and E, then P is normal to all dielectric interfaces in this problem, so by (11–3–4) $\sigma_P = P$. Also, since P has the same value at all points in a given dielectric in this problem, the surface density on the left face of each dielectric is equal in magnitude to the surface density of polarization on the right face of the same dielectric. Hence on the left face of the paraffin, from (7) and (9)

$$\sigma_{P_1} = -1.16 \times 10^{-5} \text{ coulomb/m}^2 \tag{9}$$

and on the right face of the paraffin

$$\sigma_{P_1} = +1.16 \times 10^{-5} \text{ coulomb/m}^2 \tag{10}$$

Similarly on the left face of the glass, from (8),

$$\sigma_{P_2} = -1.50 \times 10^{-5} \text{ coulomb/m}^2 \tag{11}$$

and on the right face of the glass

$$\sigma_{P_2} = +1.50 \times 10^{-5} \text{ coulomb/m}^2 \tag{12}$$

(c) How many more lines of force per unit area, which approach the dielectric interface I (in Fig. 11–9–1) from the left, terminate on the negative polarization charges on the face of the glass than originate on positive polarization charges on the face of the paraffin? Evidently, σ_P/ε_0 lines of force per unit area originate or terminate on the σ_P polarization charges per unit area. Hence $\sigma_{P_2}/\varepsilon_0$ lines of force per unit area terminate on the glass and $\sigma_{P_1}/\varepsilon_0$ lines of force per unit area originate on the paraffin, so the difference is

$$\frac{1}{\varepsilon_0}\sigma_{P_2} - \frac{1}{\varepsilon_0}\sigma_{P_1} = \frac{1 \text{ newton m}^2}{8.85 \times 10^{-12} \text{ coulomb}^2}(1.50 - 1.16) \times 10^{-5} \frac{\text{coulomb}}{\text{m}^2}$$

$$= 3.80 \times 10^{-5} \text{ newton/coulomb} \tag{13}$$

As a check on arithmetic, this difference must equal $E_1 - E_2$, and from (4) and (5),

$$E_1 - E_2 = 3.77 \times 10^{-5} \text{ newton/coulomb} \qquad (14)$$

Thus, (13) and (14) check within slide rule error.

(d) What is the susceptibility of each dielectric?

From (11–4–1),

$$\eta = P/\varepsilon_0 E \qquad (15)$$

For paraffin, using (4), (7), and (15),

$$\eta_1 = \frac{1.16 \times 10^{-5} \text{ coulomb/m}^2}{8.85 \times 10^{-12} \dfrac{\text{coulomb}^2}{\text{newton m}^2} \times 9.42 \times 10^5 \dfrac{\text{newton}}{\text{coulomb}}}$$

$$= 1.40 \qquad (16)$$

or more simply, from (11–5–7), $\eta = \varepsilon_r - 1$

$$\eta_1 = 2.40 - 1 = 1.40 \qquad (17)$$

Similarly,
$$\eta_2 = 4.00 - 1 = 3.00 \qquad (18)$$

(e) What is the potential difference between the metal plates of the capacitor?

$$V_G - V_B = -\int_{(B)}^{(I)} E_2 \cos \theta \, ds - \int_{(I)}^{(G)} E_1 \cos \theta \, ds$$

For evaluation of these line integrals, select a path which is normal to both plates so the path will be parallel to the lines of force. Along this path, E_1 and E_2 are both constant, so the integrals reduce to

$$V_G - V_B = E_2 d_2 + E_1 d_1 = 5.65 \times 10^5 \text{ v/m} \times 6 \times 10^{-3} \text{ m} + 9.42$$
$$\times 10^5 \text{ v/m} \times 4 \times 10^{-3} \text{ m} = 7160 \text{ v} \quad (19)$$

This, of course, could be checked with a voltmeter with the charging battery still attached to the plates of the capacitor.

(f) What is the capacitance of the capacitor?

From (11–1–1) $C = q/V$. Hence from the value of q given in the problem and (19)

$$C = 4.00 \times 10^{-5} \text{ coulomb}/7.16 \times 10^3 \text{ v} = 55.9 \times 10^{-10} \text{ f} = 5590 \ \mu\mu\text{f}$$

This could be checked with the capacitance bridge discussed in Sec. 8–3.

11–10 DIELECTRIC STRENGTH

A gas is normally a good insulator or dielectric. That is, the electrons in a gas molecule are bound to the nucleus with elastic forces which permit polarization of the molecule but, under normal circumstances, the electrons are not freed from the nucleus by the force exerted on them by an electric field. However, in Sec. 10–7 under the discussion of corona, we have pointed out how a gas becomes a conductor when subjected to a sufficiently intense electric field. In the usual terminology, *dielectric breakdown* has occurred when a dielectric becomes conducting. This same term is applied whether the dielectric is a gas, a liquid, or a solid.

No dielectric is ideal, since all dielectrics have some free electrons. Thus, any dielectric will show some electric conduction whenever it is in an electric field. For good dielectrics, this type of conduction results in very tiny conduction currents, and the theory in this chapter is in error for real dielectrics to the extent that we have not taken such conduction currents into account. We have talked only about class A dielectrics, and you will recall that, among other things, a class A dielectric is ideal, i.e., it has no free electrons. In dielectric breakdown much larger conduction currents flow, due to the fact that many electrons are freed as a result of the force of the electric field in which the dielectric is placed. Dielectric breakdown occurs in all kinds of dielectrics and depends in a complicated fashion on a wide variety of variables such as the nature of the material, thickness of the material, temperature, humidity, presence of flaws, and length of time that the field is applied, as well as the electric field intensity to which the dielectric is subjected.

Our theory of dielectrics does not apply after dielectric breakdown has occurred so, for our purposes, dielectric breakdown is to be avoided.

The minimum magnitude of the electric field at which dielectric breakdown occurs, in an insulating material, is called the dielectric strength of that material. Thus, we are interested in the value of the dielectric strengths for the dielectrics that we use in order that we shall not impose electric fields as large as the dielectric strength. As indicated previously, many factors influence the dielectric strengths of gaseous, liquid, and solid dielectrics, and thus any values given in handbooks are average values which may or may not apply in a given set of circumstances. However, if we keep the electric field intensity well below the value of dielectric strength listed for the material under consideration, we can be reasonably sure that dielectric breakdown will not occur. Some representative values of dielectric strength for a few common dielectrics are listed in Table 11–2.

When dielectric breakdown occurs in a liquid or a gas and then the field is removed, the dielectric flows in and heals the break. There may be chemical changes in a liquid during the breakdown which lower the subsequent dielectric strength, but aside from this the insulation is restored once the break is healed.

TABLE 11–2*

Material	Dielectric strength (representative values) kilovolts/m
Air	3,000
Mica	100,000
Paraffin	10,000
Polystyrene	20,000
Porcelain	10,000
Rubber	40,000
Transformer oil	12,000

* See reference for Table 11–1.

In a solid dielectric, the breakdown makes a hole through the dielectric which is not subsequently healed. The dielectric strength then becomes that of the gas (usually air) which flows into the hole. Since the dielectric strength of the gas in the hole is usually less than that of the solid dielectric which it has replaced, dielectric breakdown will occur in the future at a lower value of the electric field intensity than it did on the first occasion.

PROBLEMS

Treat all dielectrics as class A dielectrics.

11–1 Calculate η and ε for all the solid dielectrics in Table 11–1 and present the results, including ε_r, in tabular form. Head each column with the proper units for the entries in that column.

11–2 A parallel plate capacitor is made of two metal disks each with a radius of 0.500 m. The disks are immersed in a tank of transformer oil and have a separation of 3.00 mm. The tank may be considered to be large enough so that it does not influence the field between the plates. By means of a battery the plates are charged to a potential difference of 100 v. (a) What is the capacitance of the capacitor? Show that the answer comes out in farads. [*Ans:* 5.19×10^{-9} f.] (b) What is the electric field intensity between the plates? Show that the answer comes out in newton/coulomb or volts/meter. (c) What is the polarization P of the dielectric? Calculate P in two ways as a check. [*Ans:* 36.5×10^{-8} coulomb/m².] (d) What is the surface density of polarization charge? What is the electric field intensity in the dielectric due to polarization charge alone? Due to the conduction charge alone? How are these two fields directed relative to each other?

11–3 A parallel plate capacitor has paraffin, with a relative dielectric constant of 2.50, filling the space between its plates. The electric field intensity in the paraffin is 1.00×10^5 v/m. The distance between the plates is 2.00 mm. Compute: (a) The displacement. (b) The surface density of free charge on the plates. [*Ans:* 22.1×10^{-7} coulomb/m².] (c) The surface density of polarization charge. [*Ans:* 13.25×10^{-7} coulomb/m².] (d) The polarization P. (e) The potential difference between the plates. [*Ans:* 200 v.]

11–4 The potential difference between the plates of a parallel plate capacitor is 1000 volts. The plates are separated by a distance of 1.56 mm and the space between the plates is filled with polystyrene with a relative dielectric constant of 2.45. What is the surface density of polarization charge on the face of the dielectric? [*Ans:* 8.23×10^{-6} coulomb/m².]

11–5 An ideal capacitor, with an ammeter in series, is connected across a sinusoidal 60 cycle/sec a-c line. A voltmeter is connected across the capacitor plates and reads the constant rms line voltage of 120 volts. With air between the capacitor plates the ammeter reads 5.35 ma, but when the space between the plates is filled with a class A dielectric oil, the ammeter reads 12.1 ma. What is the relative dielectric constant of the oil?

11–6 A parallel plate capacitor, with a class A dielectric of relative dielectric constant ε_r filling the space between the plates, is connected in series with a resistor of resistance R and the series combination is connected through a switch to a battery whose emf is $\mathscr{E}$. The area of each plate is A and the distance between the plates is d. Prove that the instantaneous polarization P of the dielectric is given by $P = a(1 - e^{-bt})$ where $a = \varepsilon_0(\varepsilon_r - 1)\mathscr{E}/d$ and $b = d/RA\varepsilon_r\varepsilon_0$.

11-7 For the capacitor and circuit described in Problem 11-6, prove that the instantaneous current i flowing in the wires of the circuit is related to the displacement D in the dielectric by the equation $i = A\, dD/dt$.

11-8 For the capacitor and circuit described in Problem 11-6, show that the instantaneous electric field intensity E in the dielectric between the plates of the capacitor is given as a function of time by $E = \mathscr{E}(1 - e^{-t/RC})/d$. Using this value of E, the value of P derived in Problem 11-6, and the definition of D given in (11-6-1) as $D = \varepsilon_0 E + P$, find the value of dD/dt. Put this value into the answer to Problem 11-7, namely $i = A\, dD/dt$, and derive an equation for i as a function of time. Show that this equation is the same as (4-3-11) derived earlier.

11-9 A parallel plate capacitor has 9.00 mm separation between its plates. A large flat slab of polystyrene 5.00 mm thick is centered in the space between the metal plates so that the faces of the slab are parallel with the metal plates. There is a gap of 2.00 mm on either side between the face of the polystyrene slab and the adjacent metal plate. The polystyrene has a relative dielectric constant of 2.70. Fringing of lines of force may be neglected.

By means of a battery, the plates of the capacitor are charged, and in the charging process 1.00×10^{-8} coulomb/m^2 of conduction charge accumulates on each plate. (a) What are the values of D and E both in the gaps and in the polystyrene? (b) What is the potential difference between the metal plates? [*Ans:* 6.60 v.] (c) What is the surface density of polarization charge on the face of the polystyrene? [*Ans:* 0.630×10^{-8} coulomb/m^2.]

11-10 Two metal plates, each with an area of 1.00 m^2, are used to make a parallel plate capacitor. Filling the space between the plates are two flat slabs of dielectric each one of which has its faces parallel with the metal plates of the capacitor. One dielectric slab is glass 1.00 mm thick and with a relative dielectric constant of 5.50. The other dielectric slab is hard rubber 4.00 mm thick and with a relative dielectric constant of 3.00.

By means of a battery, the right metal plate is given a positive conduction charge density of 1.00×10^{-6} coulomb/m^2, and the left metal plate is given an equal negative conduction charge density. Fringing of lines of force may be neglected. (a) What are the values of D and E in each dielectric? (b) What is the value of P in each dielectric? (c) What is the density of polarization charge on the face of each dielectric? [*Ans:* $\sigma_{P\text{glass}} = 0.818 \times 10^{-6}$ coulomb/m^2; $\sigma_{P\text{rubber}} = 0.667 \times 10^{-6}$ coulomb/m^2.] (d) What is the capacitance of the parallel plate capacitor? [*Ans:* 58.5×10^{-10} f.]

11-11 The space between two concentric spheres is filled with a single class A dielectric whose relative dielectric constant is ε_r. There is a conduction charge q on the inner sphere, and the radii of the inner and outer spheres are r_1 and r_2, respectively. (a) Apply Gauss's theorem in terms of D to derive the equation $D = q/4\pi r^2$ for any point between the spheres that is at a distance r from their common center. What is the direction of D?

(b) Express E as a function of r for the region between the spheres. (c) If $q = 5.00 \times 10^{-9}$ coulomb, $\varepsilon_r = 5.70$, $r_1 = 0.10$ m, and $r_2 = 0.200$ m, what is the potential difference between the spheres? [*Ans:* 39.5 v.]

11–12 A large class A dielectric sphere of radius r_d and of relative dielectric constant ε_r has a small concentric metal sphere of radius r_m at its center. There is a conduction charge q on the metal sphere. Prove that the surface density of polarization charge on the outside surface of the dielectric sphere is given by $\sigma_P = q(\varepsilon_r - 1)/4\pi r_d^2 \varepsilon_r$.

11–13 A parallel plate capacitor with empty space between the plates is connected to a battery and acquires a charge of 0.500×10^{-7} coulomb. While the battery is still connected to the capacitor, a slab of glass is inserted between the plates of the capacitor and completely fills this space. When the glass is inserted an additional charge of 2.00×10^{-7} coulomb flows onto the capacitor. What is the relative dielectric constant of the glass? [*Ans:* 5.00.]

11–14 Derive equation (11–8–6).

11–15 Derive the following formulas for the situation pictured in Fig. 11–8–1 and describe the kinds of physical problems for which they will be useful: $D_2 = D_1[(\varepsilon_{r2}^2/\varepsilon_{r1}^2)\sin^2\theta_1 + \cos^2\theta_1]^{1/2}$; if θ_1 is zero, $D_2 = D_1$ and $E_2 = (\varepsilon_{r1}/\varepsilon_{r2})E_1$. Why is this latter situation, where $\theta_1 = 0$, often important in capacitors?

11–16 In the discussion of Fig. 11–8–1 it is stated that the figure could represent the case of a block of sulfur immersed in air. (a) If θ_1 in this figure is 15°, what is the value of θ_2? (b) If the magnitude of D in the air is 5.00×10^{-7} coulomb/m², what are the magnitudes of E in the air and of D and E in the sulfur? [*Ans:* $D_{sulfur} = 7.08 \times 10^{-7}$ coulomb/m²; $E_{sulfur} = 2 \times 10^4$ v/m.]

11–17 What is the largest charge that can be retained by a metal sphere 1.00 cm in radius situated in air? [*Ans:* about 3×10^{-8} coulomb.]

11–18 What is the largest charge density that can be retained on the surface of any conductor in air? [*Ans:* about 26×10^{-6} coulomb/m².]

11–19 Consider the situation described in Problem 11–11. If the class A dielectric between the concentric spheres has a dielectric strength of 20,000 kv/m, what is the value of the potential difference between the spheres at which dielectric breakdown will occur? [*Ans:* 10^6 v.]

11–20 A metal sphere of radius 0.150 m is surrounded concentrically by a very thin metal spherical shell of radius 0.250 m, and the space between the spheres is filled with paraffin whose relative dielectric constant is 2.50. The outer spherical shell is given a positive charge of 5.00×10^{-8} coulomb and then, without any loss of charge from the outer sphere, the inner sphere is given a positive charge of 3.00×10^{-8} coulomb. Again without any loss of charge, the assembly is suspended in air with no other bodies nearby. What are the magnitudes of D and E at a point P, which is 0.200 m from the common center of the two spheres? At a point P', 0.300 meter from the common center? [*Ans:* $D_P = 5.96 \times 10^{-8}$ coulomb/m²; $E_P = 0.270 \times 10^4$ v/m; $D_{P'} = 7.08 \times 10^{-8}$ coulomb/m²; $E_{P'} = 0.800 \times 10^4$ v/m.]

11-21 Consider again part (b) of the numerical example solved in Sec. 11–9. We computed, by the use of certain equations, the polarization charge that accumulated on the surface of each dielectric at the interface between the two dielectrics. Explain, in words, the physical reason why polarization charge accumulated at the interface and why the polarization charge is greater on the surface of the glass than on the surface of the paraffin.

MORE ABOUT

CAPACITANCE

AND CAPACITORS

12-1 CAPACITANCE OF A CONDUCTOR AND OF A PARALLEL PLATE CAPACITOR

In Chapter IV we studied some of the properties of a capacitor as a circuit element. In Sec. 4–1 we indicated that later we would derive formulas which permit calculation of capacitance for a few types of capacitors (which have favorable geometries) in terms of the geometry and the kind of dielectric. In Sec. 4–1, and again in Sec. 11–1, we defined the capacitance C of a capacitor by the formula

$$C = q/V \qquad (12\text{--}1\text{--}1)$$

In this definition, q is the charge on one plate (there is an equal and opposite charge on the other plate) and V is the potential difference between the plates. We are now ready to use (12–1–1), and the information that we have about potential difference, to derive the type of formulas mentioned above.

1. CAPACITANCE OF A CONDUCTOR. We have seen that for every charge there is an equal and opposite induced charge somewhere, and thus that no charge is really isolated. If a charged conductor is far removed from other bodies, we may still look upon the charged conductor and its induced charge as being a capacitor and define its capacitance by (12–1–1). In such a case, V is the potential of the body, which in turn means that it is the potential difference between the body and the place that is considered to be at zero potential. The induced charge then is looked upon as being at the place considered to be at zero potential.

As a specific example, let us consider an isolated charged conducting sphere in empty space and consider that the zero of potential is infinitely far away. Let q represent the charge on the sphere, and since the sphere is isolated, the equal induced charge is at infinity. In Problem 10–17 you showed, for this case, that the potential of the sphere is given by

$$V = q/4\pi\varepsilon_0 r_1 \qquad (12\text{--}1\text{--}2)$$

where r_1 is the radius of the sphere. We may now compute the capacitance of the sphere directly by substituting (12–1–2) into (12–1–1) and obtain

$$C = 4\pi\varepsilon_0 r_1 \qquad (12\text{--}1\text{--}3)$$

Thus the capacitance of an isolated conducting sphere is directly proportional to the radius of the sphere. (Solve Problem 12–5 for the capacitance of a conducting sphere immersed in an infinite class A fluid dielectric.)

In a similar fashion, the capacitance of any isolated conductor may be computed if it is possible to compute the potential formula for the conductor.

2. PARALLEL PLATE CAPACITOR. In Sec. 11–5 we derived the formula

$$C = A\varepsilon_r\varepsilon_0/d = A\varepsilon/d \qquad (12\text{–}1\text{–}4)$$

for the capacitance of a parallel plate capacitor if the construction is such that fringing of the lines of force may be neglected. As before, A is the area of one plate and the other plate has the same area, d is the distance between the plates, and ε_r is the relative dielectric constant of the dielectric which *fills* the space between the plates.

We pointed out, by comparison of (11–5–11) and (11–5–13), that the relative dielectric constant of the material dielectric which *fills* the space between the parallel plates is given by

$$\varepsilon_r = C/C_0 \qquad (12\text{–}1\text{–}5)$$

where C_0 is the capacitance of the same capacitor with empty space between its plates. Thus, we measure ε_r by measuring C and computing C_0 from the dimensions of the capacitor.

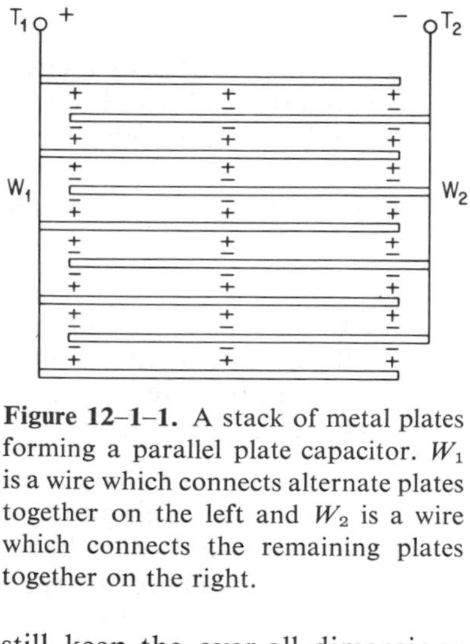

If in the construction of a parallel plate capacitor we use a single pair of plates, we find by calculation with (12–1–4) that A must be very large and d very small in order to secure an appreciable capacitance. Such a capacitor would be large and awkward for installation in most equipment. However, a stack of plates as shown in Fig. 12–1–1 may be used to secure a large area and still keep the over-all dimensions reasonable. The metal plates are shown in the figure connected to the wires W_1 and W_2, which in turn are connected to the capacitor terminals T_1 and T_2. The white areas between the plates represent the sheets of dielectric. You can observe from the distribution of charge that both sides of all metal plates, except the top and bottom ones, contribute to the area A for the capacitor.

Figure 12–1–1. A stack of metal plates forming a parallel plate capacitor. W_1 is a wire which connects alternate plates together on the left and W_2 is a wire which connects the remaining plates together on the right.

A common construction* uses a metal foil, such as aluminum foil, for the plates and paraffin impregnated paper for the dielectric. The stack is pressed firmly together and thus d is decreased to a minimum. In many cases the stack

---

* For the details of construction and the characteristics of various types of capacitors, see a book on electrical measurements such as Melville B. Stout, *Basic Electrical Measurements* (Englewood Cliffs, N.J.: Prentice-Hall, Inc., 1950), pp. 287–93; or F. A. Laws, *Electrical Measurements* (New York, McGraw-Hill Book Co., Inc., 1938), pp. 356–75.

is rolled into a tight cylinder in order that the final capacitor shall occupy less space and be a more convenient shape for installation in equipment.

When high voltage is to be used, the plates in Fig. 12–1–1 are rigid sheets of metal supported by rigid side bars W_1 and W_2. The whole assembly is immersed in a tank of dielectric oil and the tank is sealed. As mentioned before, a fluid dielectric heals itself after dielectric breakdown, and thus the capacitor is not ruined. This explains the virtue of using a fluid dielectric when high voltage is employed.

Carefully selected mica is used as the dielectric for the high quality standard capacitors which you will use from time to time in the laboratory. Such a capacitor is firmly clamped inside its housing so that the distance between plates will not change appreciably as the charge on the capacitor (and thus the force between plates) is changed.

The variable air capacitor is used extensively when a continuously variable capacitor of relatively low capacitance is needed. The tuning capacitor of a radio receiver is this type, and you will also encounter this type of capacitor in the laboratory, where it is used as a variable calibrated capacitor. The construction may be visualized in Fig. 12–1–1. Imagine that the plates are rigid sheets of metal and that the dielectric between the plates is air. Further imagine that W_1 is a shaft, mounted in bearings, and that the odd numbered plates are firmly attached to it. When W_1 is rotated, the odd numbered plates rotate with it and the effective area of each plate is changed. Thus, the capacitance of the capacitor is changed.

12–2 SPHERICAL AND CYLINDRICAL CAPACITORS

1. SPHERICAL CAPACITORS. In (10–12–5) we showed that the potential difference, $V_1 - V_2$, between two concentric metal spheres with empty space between the spheres is given by

$$V_1 - V_2 = q(1/r_1 - 1/r_2)/4\pi\varepsilon_0 \qquad (10\text{--}12\text{--}5)$$

where q is the charge on the inner sphere (there is an equal and opposite induced charge on the inner surface of the outer sphere), and r_1 is the radius of the inner sphere, while r_2 is the inner radius of the outer sphere.

Hence, using (12–1–1), we have for the capacitance of a spherical capacitor with empty space between the spheres

$$C_0 = q/(V_1 - V_2) = 4\pi\varepsilon_0 r_1 r_2/(r_2 - r_1) \qquad (12\text{--}2\text{--}1)$$

The subscript zero on C indicates that there is empty space between the spheres.

In Problem 11–11 you considered the same concentric spheres with a class A dielectric, whose permittivity is ε, filling the space between the spheres and showed that the electric field intensity in the dielectric is given by

$$E = q/4\pi\varepsilon r^2 \qquad (12\text{--}2\text{--}2)$$

By reference to the derivation of (10–12–5), we see that the argument is the same as it was for empty space between the spheres, the only difference being that ε now appears in place of ε_0. Hence, the potential difference between the two spheres is given by a formula like (10–12–5) but with ε appearing in place of ε_0.

$$V_1 - V_2 = q(1/r_1 - 1/r_2)/4\pi\varepsilon \qquad (12\text{–}2\text{–}3)$$

Thus by the use of (12–1–1) we may compute the capacitance of a spherical capacitor which has a class A dielectric filling the space between the spheres as

$$C = 4\pi\varepsilon r_1 r_2/(r_2 - r_1) \qquad (12\text{–}2\text{–}4)$$

Dividing (12–2–4) by (12–2–1), we obtain (12–1–5) again.

The spherical capacitor has often been used in the past as a standard capacitor because its capacitance can be accurately computed from its dimensions if it is made with great care and if correction is made for the supports which hold the inner sphere and the wire lead to the inner sphere. As an example, Rowland in 1879 constructed such a spherical capacitor and estimated that the calculated capacitance was correct to about 2 parts in 100,000. With the capacitance of such a standard capacitor known, we may measure the capacitance of other unknown capacitors by a comparison method such as the capacitance bridge discussed in Sec. 8–3.

2. CYLINDRICAL CAPACITOR. In Sec. 9–10 we derived the formula

$$E = b/2\pi\varepsilon_0 r \qquad (9\text{–}10\text{–}4)$$

for the electric field intensity E between two concentric conducting cylinders, and in Sec. 10–6 we derived the formula

$$V_1 - V_2 = (b/2\pi\varepsilon_0) \ln (r_2/r_1) \qquad (10\text{–}6\text{–}2)$$

for the potential difference, $V_1 - V_2$, between the cylinders. In both these formulas b is the charge per unit length on the inner cylinder (there is an equal and opposite induced charge on the inner surface of the outer cylinder), r_1 is the radius of the inner cylinder, and r_2 is the inner radius of the outer cylinder. In (9–10–4), r is the radial distance from their common axis and r must lie in the range $r_1 \leqq r \leqq r_2$. Also the length, l, of either cylinder must be large compared to $r_2 - r_1$ in order for (9–10–4) and (10–6–2) to be good approximations.

Let q represent the total charge on the inner cylinder, and there is an equal induced charge on the inner surface of the outer cylinder. Then $b = q/l$ and we may write

$$V_1 - V_2 = (q/2\pi\varepsilon_0 l) \ln (r_2/r_1) \qquad (12\text{–}2\text{–}5)$$

Using (12–1–1) and (12–2–5), we obtain the formula for the capacitance, C_0, of a cylindrical capacitor which has empty space between its plates, i.e.,

$$C_0 = 2\pi\varepsilon_0 l/\ln (r_2/r_1) \qquad (12\text{–}2\text{–}6)$$

In Problem 12–15 you are asked to solve the same problem as above except that this time the space between the cylinders is *filled* with a class A dielectric whose permittivity is ε. When you solve this problem you will obtain for the electric field intensity in the dielectric, in place of (9–10–4),

$$E = b/2\pi\varepsilon r \qquad (12\text{–}2\text{–}7)$$

Next you will obtain for the potential difference between the cylinders, in place of (10–6–2),

$$V_1 - V_2 = (b/2\pi\varepsilon) \ln (r_2/r_1) \qquad (12\text{–}2\text{–}8)$$

Then finally you will obtain for the capacitance C,

$$C = 2\pi\varepsilon l/\ln (r_2/r_1) \qquad (12\text{–}2\text{–}9)$$

Again, by dividing (12–2–9) by (12–2–6) we get the now familiar formula (12–1–5). Equation (12–1–5) states a general proposition which we shall now put into words: *The ratio of the capacitance of a capacitor with a material dielectric filling the space between its plates to the capacitance of the same capacitor with empty space between its plates is equal to the relative dielectric constant of the material dielectric.* This ratio is sometimes called *specific inductive capacity* and, as mentioned earlier, you will often find relative dielectric constant given in tables under the heading of specific inductive capacity.

12–3 THE GUARD RING ON A CAPACITOR AND MEASUREMENT OF CAPACITANCE

1. PARALLEL PLATE CAPACITOR WITH GUARD RING. We have talked several times about the geometrical requirements which, when satisfied, permit us to neglect fringing of lines of force and still have a good approximation when using a parallel plate capacitor. Now we wish to consider an experimental arrangement and procedure such that the error due to fringing will be reduced almost to zero. The experiment which we are about to discuss will also permit us to measure the capacitances of unknown capacitors.

The experimental apparatus involves a *guard ring* which surrounds the edge of one plate of a parallel plate capacitor as shown in Fig. 12–3–1. The guard ring is shown as GG in both cross section views (a) and (c) and in the top view (b), where P_1 and P_2 are the plates of the capacitor. The guard ring surrounds P_1, is in the same plane as P_1, and is insulated from P_1 in the construction of the capacitor. The whole assembly is surrounded by a grounded wire mesh (not shown) which serves as an electrostatic shield. The air gap between G and P_1 is just large enough for insulation purposes, and the width of the gap is small compared with the distance d between the plates. Distance d, in turn, is small compared with the linear dimensions of the plates.

In Fig. 12–3–1 (a) and (c), BG represents a ballistic galvanometer. We shall see later, in Sec. 13–6, that a ballistic galvanometer gives a maximum scale deflection, on its first throw, which is proportional to the quantity of charge that flows through it provided that the flow is completed in a time which is short compared with the period of the galvanometer.

When the apparatus is properly used, we may charge the capacitor with a definite quantity of electricity q which corresponds with a calculated capacitance C and a known potential difference V. Then with C and V known, we may calculate q from $q = CV$. Now we may undertake the experiment which will permit us to know C and use the known charge q for a useful measurement. The procedure is as follows.

1. In Fig. 12–3–1 (a), close switch S_1 so that P_2 is grounded and thus all parts of the capacitor are at zero potential at the outset. Open S_1.

2. Connect the battery $\mathscr{E}$ and switch S_2 as shown in Fig. 12-3-1 (c), but leave S_2 open for the present. The emf $\mathscr{E}$ of the battery must be known for this experiment, and we shall learn in Sec. 12-7 how we may make an absolute measurement of $\mathscr{E}$, i.e., how we may measure $\mathscr{E}$ from length and weight measurements without using previously calibrated electric meters.

3. Close S_2 and record the maximum deflection of the first throw of the ballistic galvanometer BG. The charge which flows through BG is the charge q that accumulates on P_1 during the charging process, but does not include the charge that flows onto the guard ring GG. Since P_1 and GG are at the

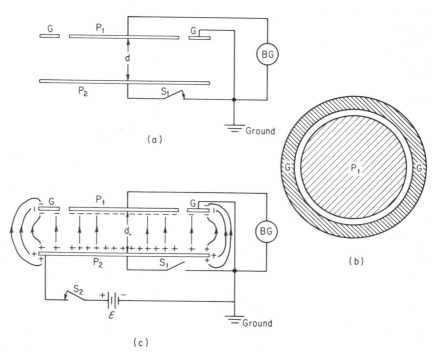

Figure 12-3-1. Parallel plate capacitor P_1, P_2 with guard ring GG. (a) Cross section of capacitor with GG and P_2 hooked directly to ground and P_1 hooked to ground through a ballistic galvanometer BG. (b) Top view showing plate P_1 surrounded by the guard ring GG. (c) Cross section of the capacitor after it has been charged from the battery $\mathscr{E}$.

same potential (ground potential) both before and after the charging process, any capacitance between P_1 and GG does not influence the charge which is located on P_1 after the completion of the charging process.

Notice in Fig. 12-3-1 (c) that the major part of the fringing of lines of force occurs at the outside edge of GG and is not associated with the charge q which flowed through BG onto P_1. The charge q is given by $q = C\mathscr{E}$, where $\mathscr{E}$ is the known emf of the battery and C is the capacitance of the part of the capacitor whose charge flowed through BG. Thus, C is the capacitance between P_1 and P_2 and is given by an equation of the form of (12-1-4), the formula for an ideal parallel plate capacitor, if A is suitably chosen. It is found empirically that, if the air gap is small compared with the diameter of P_1 and small compared with d, the error due to the small amount of fringing at the air gap may be corrected fairly well by taking A to be the area of P_1 plus half the area of the air gap.

We can measure A and d with fair precision and, with air between the plates, we may consider that $\varepsilon = \varepsilon_0$ within the error of measuring A and d. Thus, C and $\mathscr{E}$ are known, and q may be computed from $q = C\mathscr{E}$ as stated above. The recorded deflection of the ballistic galvanometer, and the computed value of q, give one calibration point for the ballistic galvanometer. (See Sec. 13–6 for the correction made necessary because of the damping of the galvanometer.)

4. Repeat the above experiment, using a battery with a larger known emf and secure another calibration point for the ballistic galvanometer. Continue the repetition of the experiment with batteries of various known emf's until the ballistic galvanometer has been calibrated over the entire length of its scale.

5. As a result of the above experiment we have a calibrated ballistic galvanometer. Thus, for any future deflection of the galvanometer, we know the magnitude of the charge which caused the deflection.

Now replace the known capacitor and its guard ring in the circuit of Fig. 12–3–1 with a new capacitor whose capacitance C_x is unknown. Charge C_x from the battery of known emf $\mathscr{E}$ by closing switch S_2 and note the maximum deflection of the first throw of the ballistic galvanometer. Let q_x represent the charge which the battery puts on the unknown capacitor. From the deflection and the calibration data, q_x is measured, and the capacitance of the unknown capacitor may be computed from $C_x = q_x/\mathscr{E}$.

In conclusion, by the use of the guard ring we secure a parallel plate capacitor whose capacitance we may compute fairly accurately from measurements of lengths. Thus, we have an absolute determination of the capacitance of the capacitor, i.e., we determined its capacitance without comparison with a known capacitance and without use of previously calibrated electric meters. As mentioned previously, in Sec. 12–7 we shall learn how to make absolute measurements of the emf's of batteries. By use of the known capacitance of the parallel plate capacitor and the batteries whose emf's had been measured, we calibrated a ballistic galvanometer. In turn the calibrated ballistic galvanometer and the batteries of known emf's were used to measure the capacitances of unknown capacitors. Thus we obtained an absolute measurement of the capacitances of unknown capacitors. Contrast this with the capacitance bridge method discussed in Sec. 8–3, which gives the capacitance of an unknown capacitor in terms of the capacitance of a known capacitor and the resistances of known resistors.

2. CYLINDRICAL CAPACITOR WITH GUARD RING. In a manner similar to the above, a guard ring may be placed on each end of a cylindrical capacitor and the cylindrical capacitor used as a standard whose capacitance is given by (12–2–9). The technique of use is the same as it is for the parallel plate capacitor with a guard ring except that there are two guard rings which must be connected electrically.

12–4 CAPACITORS IN PARALLEL AND IN SERIES

We wish to compute the equivalent capacitance of a group of capacitors which may be connected either in series or in parallel. By equivalent capacitance we mean the capacitance of a single capacitor which could be substituted for the group and have the same charge for the same applied potential difference.

1. CAPACITORS IN PARALLEL. Figure 12–4–1 shows three capacitors in parallel

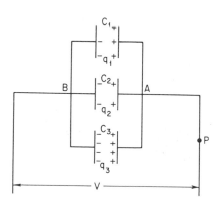

Figure 12–4–1. Three capacitors in parallel.

with a potential difference V applied across the parallel combination. We wish to show that the three capacitors could be replaced by a single capacitor of equivalent capacitance C, using the above definition of equivalent capacitance. Further, we wish to compute C in terms of the individual capacitances C_1, C_2, and C_3.

Since the potential difference between two points is the same regardless of the path followed between the two points, each capacitor has the potential difference V across its plates. Let q_1, q_2, and q_3 represent the charges on the three capacitors, respectively. Then $q_1 = C_1V$, $q_2 = C_2V$, and $q_3 = C_3V$.

The total charge Q, which passed a point such as P, in the charging process is equal to the sum of the charges which accumulated on the capacitors. Hence, $Q = q_1 + q_2 + q_3 = C_1V + C_2V + C_3V$ or $Q = V(C_1 + C_2 + C_3)$. Thus, a single capacitor whose capacitance is

$$C = C_1 + C_2 + C_3 \qquad (12\text{–}4\text{–}1)$$

would acquire the same charge Q if the same potential difference V were applied across its plates. *The equivalent capacitance of several capacitors in parallel is equal to the sum of their separate capacitances.*

2. CAPACITORS IN SERIES. Figure 12–4–2 shows three capacitors in series with a voltage V applied to the series combination. Since this is a series circuit, the same total charge passed all points in the circuit while the capacitors were being charged, so each capacitor has the same charge q. (Answer Problem 12–20 at this point.)

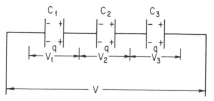

Figure 12–4–2. Three capacitors in series.

Also, since this is a series d-c case, the applied voltage equals the sum of the potential differences across the separate parts, so $V = V_1 + V_2 + V_3$. But $V_1 = q/C_1$, $V_2 = q/C_2$, and $V_3 = q/C_3$,

so

$$V = q(1/C_1 + 1/C_2 + 1/C_3) \qquad (12\text{–}4\text{–}2)$$

But, in general, $C = q/V$. Hence, if we were to replace the three capacitors in series by a single capacitor whose capacitance C is given by

$$1/C = 1/C_1 + 1/C_2 + 1/C_3 \qquad (12\text{–}4\text{–}3)$$

this single capacitor would acquire the same charge q for the same potential difference V between its plates, so it has the capacitance that is equivalent to the three capacitors in series. Hence, *for capacitors in series, the reciprocal of the equivalent capacitance is equal to the sum of the reciprocals of the capacitances of the separate capacitors.*

12–5 ENERGY DENSITY IN AN ELECTRIC FIELD

In Sec. 4–5 we derived the formula

$$W_C = \tfrac{1}{2}Vq = CV^2/2 = q^2/2C \qquad (12\text{–}5\text{–}1)$$

for the energy of a charged capacitor where C is its capacitance, V is the potential difference between its plates, and q is the charge on the capacitor. We may look upon this potential energy as being associated with the charges only, i.e., in the charging process, charges were forced onto the plates of the capacitor against the repulsion of the charges that were already present, and a state of stress was established which represents potential energy. The capacitor can do work when it discharges, and thus loses this potential energy because the repulsive forces will do work in removing the charges from the plates.

From another point of view we may say that the energy is contained in the electric field which is present between the plates of the capacitor. Work was required to establish the electric field, and the electric field will do an equal amount of work when it is permitted to return to zero intensity. From this point of view the charges established the field, but the field contains the energy.

These two points of view run all through electrical theory. However, in some parts we consider only the charges and their behavior as we did in most of the circuit analysis of the first eight chapters. There we gave minimum consideration to the fields produced by the charges. In other parts of the subject we lay more emphasis on the fields and consider the charges, somewhat incidentally, as the sources of the fields. But the two points of view are simply different aspects of the same physical situation.

Now, to return to the charged capacitor, we may take the field point of view and consider that all the capacitor's potential energy is associated with the electric field between the plates. Then we may compute the energy per unit volume in the electric field. The energy per unit volume in the electric field is called the *energy density* of the field. Let us consider a parallel plate capacitor, because it has a uniform electric field between its plates and thus the computation of energy density is easy. We shall consider that a class A dielectric fills the space between the plates. As before, let A represent the area of either plate and d represent the distance between the plates. Neglecting fringing, the volume occupied by the field is Ad. The energy of the charged capacitor is $\tfrac{1}{2}Vq$, so energy density $= Vq/2Ad$. But $q/A = \sigma = D$, and $V/d = E$, so

$$\text{energy density} = \tfrac{1}{2}DE \qquad (12\text{–}5\text{–}2)$$

But $D = \varepsilon E$, so we may write (12–5–2) in either of the two equivalent forms:

$$\text{energy density} = \tfrac{1}{2}\varepsilon E^2 = D^2/2\varepsilon \qquad (12\text{–}5\text{–}3)$$

In the mks system of units, energy density has the units joules/m³, as you can show by substitution of units into any one of the equivalent forms.

Although we have derived the formulas for energy density in the special case of a uniform field, they may be used in a nonuniform field. In a nonuniform field the formulas (12–5–2) or (12–5–3) give the energy density in a small region where E and D are the values, in that small region, of electric field intensity and displacement, respectively. Thus the value of energy density will vary from place to place in a nonuniform field. (Solve Problems 12–33 and 12–34.)

12–6 FORCE BETWEEN THE PLATES OF A PARALLEL PLATE CAPACITOR

1. EMPTY SPACE BETWEEN THE PLATES. We wish to compute the force which one plate of a parallel plate capacitor exerts on the other plate under conditions such that the effect of fringing of lines of force may be neglected. This signifies that we wish to compute the force on all the charges on one plate due to all the charges on the other plate. We shall employ Coulomb's law and the principle of superposition for this calculation.

You performed the first part of this calculation in Problem 9–38 (refer to Fig. 9–P–4) when you showed that the electric field intensity between the plates of a parallel plate capacitor is given by $E = \sigma/\varepsilon_0$ and that half of the magnitude of E is due to the charge on each of the plates. Let f represent the force per unit charge on an infinitesimal test charge q' at 0 of Fig. 9–P–4 due to all the charges on the upper plate of the capacitor. Then $f = \sigma/2\varepsilon_0$ from your proof in Problem 9–38.

Now consider again that q' (in Fig. 9–P–4) is at O and then that q' moves closer and closer to the positively charged plate. The force on q' remains constant until q' merges with the positive charges on the lower plate. When q' merges with these positive charges on the lower plate, they exert forces on q' parallel to the plate only, and since the positive charges surround q' symmetrically, their forces on q' will cancel in pairs. Again this is not true for points near the edge of the plate. Thus, the only force on q' that remains is the force due to the negative charges on the upper plate and is given by $f' = \sigma q'/2\varepsilon_0$. Hence, any charge on the lower plate experiences a force equal to $\sigma/2\varepsilon_0$ times the magnitude of the charge. Let q represent the total charge on the lower plate and F represent the total force on q and we have

$$F = \sigma q/2\varepsilon_0 \qquad (12\text{–}6\text{–}1)$$

Let A represent the area of either plate and, remembering that the charge on the upper plate equals the charge on the lower plate, we have $\sigma = q/A$, or (neglecting fringing)

$$F = q^2/2\varepsilon_0 A \qquad (12\text{–}6\text{–}2)$$

for the force on either plate due to all the charges on the other plate.

2. A FLUID DIELECTRIC BETWEEN THE PLATES. Next, we wish to solve the same problem when there is a gas or liquid dielectric between the plates of the parallel plate capacitor and in all the space around the capacitor. If we were to solve it by the method employed in Problem 9–38, we would have to take complete account of all forces which arise due to the polarization charge induced in the dielectric. However, we may avoid this difficult calculation by analysis of the problem from an energy point of view.

Charge the capacitor from a battery, and then disconnect and insulate it so that the charge q on the capacitor remains constant. Let y represent the distance between the plates, as we did in Fig. 10–5–1 and as shown in Fig. 9–P–4 (a).

Exert a force F_1 on the upper plate just sufficient to pull the upper plate away from the lower plate against the electric forces and without acceleration. Let the force F_1 move the upper plate an infinitesimal distance dy, and the element of work done against the electric forces is

$$dW = F_1 \, dy \qquad (12\text{–}6\text{–}3)$$

We assume that the fluid dielectric flows in from outside to fill the additional infinitesimal volume, and further that the infinitesimal increase in the separation of the plates does not increase fringing appreciably.

The total energy W in the field before the upper plate was moved is the energy density times the volume of the field, or using (12–5–3),

$$W = D^2 Ay/2\varepsilon \qquad (12\text{–}6\text{–}4)$$

Since the charge on the capacitor is kept constant, the charge density on its plates is constant and thus D is constant during the infinitesimal motion of the upper plate. Hence we may differentiate (12–6–4), consider D as constant, and obtain the change in potential energy when y is changed by dy, or

$$dW = D^2 A \, dy/2\varepsilon \qquad (12\text{–}6\text{–}5)$$

Equate this value of dW in (12–6–5) to the one in (12–6–3), and we have

$$F_1 = D^2 A/2\varepsilon \qquad (12\text{–}6\text{–}6)$$

But $D = \sigma = q/A$, so

$$F_1 = q^2/2\varepsilon A = q^2/2\varepsilon_r\varepsilon_0 A \qquad (12\text{–}6\text{–}7)$$

By comparison of (12–6–2) and (12–6–7), we see that the force that one plate exerts on the other has been reduced by the factor $1/\varepsilon_r$, due to the presence of the material dielectric. The direct force which the conduction charges on one plate exert on the conduction charges on the other plate is the same when there is a dielectric between the plates as it is when there is empty space between them. Thus, (12–6–2) gives this force in either case. However, with the material dielectric* present there is, in addition, the direct force between

---

* In general, mechanical forces of electrical origin arise in the dielectric because of the elastic deformation of the dielectric due to the electric field. These mechanical forces are said to be due to electrostriction of the dielectric. It is by no means easy to deal with electrostrictive force (see J. A. Stratton, *Electromagnetic Theory* (New York: McGraw-Hill Book Co., Inc., 1941), pp. 149–53, but our energy argument takes them into account for the very simple and special case considered here.

the polarization charge and the conduction charge, and the polarization charges reduce the magnitude of the field between the plates. In the derivation above of (12–6–7) for the very special case of a parallel plate capacitor immersed in a fluid dielectric, and under conditions where fringing may be neglected, we avoided detailed consideration of these individual forces by the use of an energy argument.

Note that the presence of the fluid dielectric reduced the force between the plates by a factor $1/\varepsilon_r$. Do not, however, interpret the result as a general one, for the case is a very special one.

In (12–6–7), F_1 is the force which the supports of the capacitor plates must exert on either plate, against the force of the electric field. Thus, F_1 is the additional force which must be exerted on either plate when the capacitor is charged. We shall see in the next section that the formula for F_1 is useful as the basic theory of an electrostatic voltmeter, called the absolute electrometer, which measures F_1 directly.

12–7 ELECTROMETERS AS ELECTROSTATIC VOLTMETERS

1. THE ABSOLUTE ELECTROMETER. The absolute electrometer is the one referred to in the last sentence of the previous section. As stated there, it measures

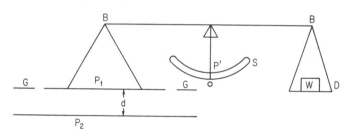

Figure 12–7–1. Absolute electrometer.

directly the force between the plates of a parallel plate capacitor, and we shall see that this measurement permits calculation of the potential difference between the plates in terms of other directly measurable quantities. The word "absolute" in the name of this instrument arises because it may be calibrated without reference to other calibrated electric meters.

Figure 12–7–1 shows schematically the construction of the instrument. There P_1 and P_2 are the plates of the parallel plate capacitor, and GG is the guard ring which surrounds the plate P_1. Plate P_1 is suspended from the beam BB of a precision equal-arm balance that is used to measure the force on P_1 due to P_2. Electrical contact with P_1 is established through the frame of the balance. Plate P_2 is carefully insulated from all parts of the balance, and electrical contact with P_2 is achieved through an insulated connecting wire.

During the measurement of the force on P_1, the guard ring is kept at the same potential as P_1, so the air gap between G and P_1 need be only large enough to permit mechanical clearance. Thus, the fringing of lines of force due to this gap is all but negligible, and we shall make an empirical correction which will reduce the error still more. The only appreciable fringing that exists is at the outside edge of the guard ring. The force measured by the balance does not include the force which P_2 exerts on the guard ring. Hence, the fringing does not affect the measurement, and the conditions imposed on the derivation of (12–6–7) are well satisfied by the experimental conditions. In (12–6–7), q is the charge on P_1, A is the area of P_1, and F_1 is the additional weight which must be placed on the right pan of the balance in order to maintain equilibrium when the charge q is placed on P_1. The whole instrument is electrostatically shielded so that electric fields from outside will not influence the behavior of the balance. Stops are provided (not shown in figure) which prevent P_1 from moving more than a very short distance out of the plane of the guard ring. Equilibrium of the balance is established with P_1 in the plane of the guard ring as judged by the position of the pointer P' on the scale S. Plate P_2 is mounted on a micrometer screw which permits the distance d between the plates to be adjusted and also reads d directly for any given setting. The fluid dielectric is the air which fills the space between the capacitor plates as well as the region surrounding the capacitor.

In Sec. 12–3 we anticipated that in the present section we would learn how to make absolute measurements of the emf's of batteries. We wanted these batteries with measured emf's for use in the experiment of Sec. 12–3, where we made absolute measurements of the capacitances of unknown capacitors. Thus, let us select a battery which is good enough so that its emf will remain constant while we perform subsequent experiments immediately following the present one, and learn how to measure its emf with the absolute electrometer.

The procedure for measuring the emf of this battery is as follows.

1. Place proper weights on pan D of the balance so that P_1 is in equilibrium in the plane of GG when there is no charge on the capacitor.

2. Add a weight W' to the pan D.

3. Connect the battery terminals, one to P_2 and one to P_1 and G through the frame of the balance. Then the potential difference between P_1 and P_2 is $\mathscr{E}$.

4. By means of the micrometer screw which supports P_2, adjust d to a value such that the balance is again in equilibrium with P_1 in the plane of GG. This is a little tricky, because when P_1 starts to move down, the capacitance of the capacitor increases, more charge flows from the battery onto the capacitor, and the force between the plates increases. Thus, the balance will not oscillate about its equilibrium position as it does in ordinary weighing. It is best to start with d larger than the desired final value and raise P_2 very slowly to the point where P_1 first starts to move out of the plane of GG. This may be judged by the pointer on the scale. Record the value of d from the micrometer screw.

5. Disconnect the battery, measure the diameter of P_1, and compute its area. Add to the area of P_1 one-half the area of the ring gap between P_1 and GG, and call this total area A. The addition of half the area of the annular air gap is the empirical correction which we mentioned earlier. Let W' be the force between P_1 and P_2, and $W' = F_1$ in (12–6–7). Let C represent the

capacitance of the parallel plate capacitor made up of P_1 and P_2 but not including the guard ring. Then $q = C\mathscr{E}$, so (12–6–7) becomes for this case

$$W' = C^2\mathscr{E}^2/\varepsilon_r 2\varepsilon_0 A \tag{12–7–1}$$

Use C for a parallel plate capacitor from (12–1–4) and solve for $\mathscr{E}$ to obtain

$$\mathscr{E} = d\sqrt{2W'/\varepsilon_r\varepsilon_0 A} \tag{12–7–2}$$

In the use of (12–7–2) remember that W' is a force and thus, in the mks system, must be expressed in newtons. Sets of weights for use with analytical balances are usually calibrated in grams, however.

Of course, d must be expressed in meters and A in meters^2 in this system. The accurate determination* of the value of ε_0 in the mks system involves an accurate measurement of the velocity of light in empty space, which can be done by mechanical means without the use of calibrated electric instruments. If the preceding absolute electrometer experiment were performed in empty space, where ε_r is unity, we should have an absolute measurement of the emf of the battery, because d, W', and A are directly measured without use of calibrated electric meters. As previously pointed out, it is for this reason that the word "absolute" appears in the name of this type of electrometer. Actually, ε_r for air may be considered unity within the usual accuracy of measurement of d, W', and A, and the instrument may be considered "absolute" when the measurement is made in air.

After we have measured the emf of this battery, we repeat the experiment for several more batteries and thus have the supply of batteries with known emf's needed for the experiment in Sec. 12–3.

2. THE ELECTROSCOPE AS AN ELECTROSTATIC VOLTMETER. The simple gold leaf electroscope, described in Sec. 9–1 and illustrated in Fig. 9–1–2 (b), may be used as an electrostatic voltmeter. When it is used for this purpose, it must be equipped with a scale which permits quantitative measurement of the deflection of the leaf. An example of such a scale is shown in Fig. 9–2–1.

We have seen in Sec. 9–2 that the magnitude of the deflection of the leaf depends on the magnitude of the charge on the electroscope. We used the electroscope previously as an instrument for comparing the magnitudes of charges. However, if the electroscope is shielded in such a way that its capacitance remains constant, we may treat it as a capacitor of constant capacitance. For such a capacitor, q is directly proportional to the potential difference V between its plates (from the equation $q = CV$) and, thus, the charge on the electroscope is directly proportional to the potential difference between the knob and the case of the electroscope. This argument justifies

---

* In electromagnetic theory it is shown that

$$\varepsilon_0 = \cfrac{1}{4\pi \times 10^{-7}\cfrac{\text{kg meter}}{\text{coulomb}^2}}\cfrac{1}{c^2}$$

where c is the velocity of light in free space, and has the value 2.99773×10^8 m/sec; it is one of the accurately known constants of nature.

the above statement that the electroscope may be used as an electrostatic voltmeter.

The above does not say, however, that there is a simple relationship between V and the deflection of the leaf. In fact, the geometry of the electroscope is sufficiently complicated so that no attempt is made to derive a formula relating V to the deflection of the leaf. Instead, the electroscope must be calibrated against known potential differences and then it may be used to measure unknown potential differences.

You will encounter many modifications* of the electroscope, or electrometers as they are often called, each one adapted to a particular requirement in a special type of measurement. However, the fundamental principles are the same and in each case the electroscope is calibrated against known potential differences.

3. ADVANTAGES OF AN ELECTROSTATIC VOLTMETER. An electrostatic voltmeter does not draw current from the steady d-c circuit to which it is connected except during the short time when the capacitance of the instrument is being charged. This behavior gives the electrostatic voltmeter a distinct advantage over an ordinary voltmeter in those situations where a continuing flow of current would disturb or destroy the potential difference which is being measured. Thus an electrostatic voltmeter may be calibrated against an ordinary d-c voltmeter under conditions where flow of current is unimportant, and then the calibrated electrostatic voltmeter may be used under conditions where the steady flow of current must be avoided.

Many electrostatic voltmeters may be used to measure alternating as well as direct voltages. This is true in those cases where the direction of force or torque on the moving part remains the same when the signs of the charges are reversed. We can see that this is true in the absolute electrometer, and various types of electroscopes.

In contrast with the situation on direct current, an electrostatic voltmeter on alternating current does draw some current throughout the a-c cycle because of the capacitance of the instrument. At power frequencies, however, this current is usually negligibly small and does not seriously disturb the potential difference that is being measured.

PROBLEMS

Treat all dielectrics as class A.

12–1 A metal sphere of 98.6 cm radius is so mounted that it may be considered isolated and perfectly insulated. Initially it is grounded and then the ground connection broken. A 20,000 v d-c source has its negative terminal connected to ground and, at an instant called $t = 0$, its positive terminal is connected to the metal sphere through a resistor of 5.35×10^{12} ohms. What is the charge on the sphere 10.6 min. after the start of the charging process? [*Ans:* 1.44×10^{-6} coulomb.]

12–2 The sphere in Problem 12–1 is left connected to the charging source for a very long time and then disconnected and insulated. Next it is connected,

* See for example, G. P. Harnwell, *Principles of Electricity and Electromagnetism* (New York: McGraw-Hill Book Co., Inc., 1949), pp. 53–58.

by means of a long, fine wire, to a sphere of radius 24.0 cm, similarly isolated and insulated. (a) The term *very long time* can have meaning only when compared to some reference length of time. In this problem, what is the reference length of time in terms of which "very long time" has meaning? (b) Assuming that no charge remains on the connecting wire, what is the charge on each sphere after the redistribution is complete? [*Ans:* 177×10^{-8} coulomb and 43.0×10^{-8} coulomb.]

12-3 A sphere of 12.0 cm radius rests on a tall slender support in the air over the lecture table. The support may be considered a perfect insulator. The sphere is given a charge of 6.00×10^{-9} coulomb. (a) What is the capacitance of the sphere? [*Ans:* 13.3×10^{-12} farad.] (b) Will the sphere retain the charge?

12-4 (a) What is the maximum charge that the sphere in Problem 12–3 can retain? (b) What is the potential of the sphere when it has this charge? [*Ans:* 3.6×10^5 v.] (c) What energy has the sphere due to this charge? [*Ans:* 0.86 joule.]

12-5 A metal sphere of radius r_1 has a positive charge q and is situated in a class A fluid dielectric which fills all space except that occupied by the metal sphere. The permittivity of the dielectric is ε. (a) Use Gauss's theorem in terms of D and show that $E = q/4\pi\varepsilon r^2$ for $r \geqq r_1$. (b) Prove that the potential of the sphere is given by $V = q/4\pi\varepsilon r_1$. (c) Derive the formula for the capacitance of this sphere.

12-6 A metal sphere of 12.0 cm radius is suspended by a fine silk thread in the center of a very large tank of transformer oil whose relative dielectric constant is 2.40. (a) What is the capacitance of the sphere? (b) If the sphere is given a charge of 10^{-7} coulomb, what is its energy due to the charge? [*Ans:* 157×10^{-6} joule.] (c) What is the potential of the sphere? [*Ans:* 3.13×10^3 v.]

12-7 A parallel plate capacitor with many plates has its plates separated by a distance of 3.00 mm and each plate has an effective area of 3.00 m². With air between the plates, the capacitor is charged to a potential difference of 2500 v and then insulated from its surroundings. Without any loss of charge, the capacitor is immersed in a liquid dielectric and the potential difference between the plates becomes 500 v. What is the relative dielectric constant of the liquid?

12-8 Each of the two plates of a special experimental parallel plate capacitor is 2.00 by 2.00 m and the plates are 1.00 cm apart. With empty space between the plates, the capacitor is charged to a potential difference of 5000 v and is then insulated from its surroundings. A flat sheet of dielectric 2.00 by 2.00 m and 0.500 cm thick is now inserted between the plates and held so that its faces are parallel with the plates of the capacitor. After the dielectric is in place the potential difference between the plates is 3500 v. What is the relative dielectric constant of the dielectric? [*Ans:* 2.5.]

12-9 In a certain experimental measurement a parallel plate capacitor with air as the dielectric is used. This capacitor has a capacitance of 9.15×10^{-8} farad when the distance between its plates is 0.0151 mm. An initial calculation concerning the experiment predicts that the event being studied will put a charge of $Q = 50.0 \times 10^{-12}$ coulomb on the capacitor. This will produce a potential difference across the plates which is less than the minimum of 5.50×10^{-2} volts, which can be measured with satisfactory accuracy on the most sensitive electrostatic voltmeter at hand.

The charge Q is put on the capacitor by the event being studied. Next the capacitor is insulated from its surroundings and then, by use of a micrometer screw, its plates are pulled apart enough so that the potential difference across its plates can be measured with sufficient accuracy with the electrostatic voltmeter at hand, provided Q is no smaller than the initially predicted value. Assuming that fringing of electric lines of force may be neglected, what is the least value that the new separation between the plates can have? [*Ans:* 1.52 mm.]

12–10 One plate of a parallel plate capacitor, of area A, is fixed and the other plate, of equal area, is connected to a prong of an electrically driven tuning fork and thus vibrates in simple harmonic motion with a frequency f. The equilibrium distance between the plates (when the fork is at rest) is d_0 and the amplitude of the motion of the vibrating plate is y_0 where $y_0 < d_0$. The dielectric between the plates is air. The capacitor has a constant charge Q.

Write an equation giving the instantaneous potential difference v across the plates as a function of time. [*Ans:* $v = Q(d_0 - y_0 \sin 2\pi ft)/A\varepsilon_0$.]

12–11 Each of the two plates of the special experimental parallel plate capacitor of Problem 12–8 has an area 4.00 m², and the plates are 1.00 cm apart. With empty space between the plates, the capacitor is charged to a potential difference of 5000 v and then insulated from its surroundings. Without any loss of charge from the capacitor, two flat sheets of class A dielectric are inserted between the plates and completely fill the space. One dielectric sheet is 4.00 mm thick and has a relative dielectric constant of 5.00, and the other dielectric sheet is 6.00 mm thick and its relative dielectric constant is 2.00. (a) What is the potential difference between the capacitor plates after the two dielectric sheets are inserted? [*Ans:* 1900 v.] (b) What is the capacitance of the capacitor after the dielectric sheets are inserted? By what factor has the capacitance been increased due to the two sheets? [*Ans:* 0.932×10^{-8} farad.]

12–12 Eleven flat sheets of aluminium foil, each 50.0 by 50.0 cm, are stacked with paraffin impregnated paper interleafed between each two aluminum foil sheets. One wire is connected to alternate sheets of foil, and a second wire is connected to the remaining alternate sheets of foil (see Fig. 12–1–1). The paraffin impregnated paper has a relative dielectric constant of 2.50 and is 0.200 mm thick. (a) What is the capacitance of the capacitor? [*Ans:* 27.6×10^{-8} farad.] (b) If the capacitor is charged to a potential difference of 500 v, will the dielectric strength of 11,000 kv/m be exceeded? [*Ans:* No.] (c) What is the surface density of polarization charge on each face of each sheet of paraffin paper? [*Ans:* 33×10^{-6} coulomb/m².]

12–13 The air is pumped out of the space between the spheres of a spherical capacitor and then the spheres are charged to a potential difference of 1000.000 v. At this point, the spheres are disconnected from the source and insulated. Next dry air is admitted to the space between the spheres, and when the air reaches atmospheric pressure the potential difference between the spheres is found to be 999.410 v. What is the relative dielectric constant of dry air?

12–14 Two concentric spheres have radii of 10.00 cm and 12.00 cm, respectively. With air in the space between the spheres the capacitor is charged to a potential difference of 1600 v and then insulated. Next, without any loss of charge, a dielectric oil is poured into the space between the spheres until the space is full. The potential difference between the spheres is now found to be 400 v. (a) What is the susceptibility of the oil? (b) What is the surface density of free charge on the inner sphere? on the outer sphere? [*Ans:* $\sigma_{inner} = 85.1 \times 10^{-8}$ coulomb/m^2; $\sigma_{outer} = 59.1 \times 10^{-8}$ coulomb/m^2.] (c) When the oil fills the space between the plates, what is the surface density of polarization charge at the inner sphere? at the outer sphere? [*Ans:* $\sigma_{P\,inner} = 63.8 \times 10^{-8}$ coulomb/m^2; $\sigma_{P\,outer} = 44.3 \times 10^{-8}$ coulomb/m^2.] (d) What is the energy of the capacitor before the oil is added? After the oil is added? No charge escaped from the capacitor when the oil was added, so how do you explain the fact that these two answers are not the same? [*Ans:* before, 8.54×10^{-5} joule; after, 2.13×10^{-5} joule.]

12–15 Refer to Sec. 12–2, the dicussion of the cylindrical capacitor. Consider two coaxial metal cylinders with a class A dielectric filling the space between the cylinders. The permittivity of the dielectric is ε. The inner cylinder has a radius r_1 and the outer cylinder has a radius r_2. The length, l, of the two cylinders is the same, and l is large compared with their radial separation so fringing of lines of force may be neglected. (a) Apply Gauss's theorem in terms of D and obtain the formula in (12–2–7) for the electric field intensity in the dielectric between the cylinders. (b) Using (12–2–7) and (10–2–2) prove that the potential difference between the cylinders is given by (12–2–8). (c) Show that the capacitance of this capacitor is given by (12–2–9).

12–16 A certain telephone cable has many wires packed together in its core, but the many wires are equivalent to a single wire with a radius of 5.00 $\times 10^{-3}$ m. The outside of the cable is a round sheath of inner radius 3.00×10^{-2} m, and the space between the central wires and the sheath is filled with gutta percha whose relative dielectric constant is 4.10. What is the capacitance of 10 miles of this cable? [*Ans:* 2.05 μf.]

12–17 A cylindrical capacitor has a straight copper rod 1.00 cm in radius for the center cylinder. Soft rubber, whose relative dielectric constant is 2.50, is molded on the copper rod to a thickness of 1.00 cm so that the rubber makes a cylinder of 1.00 cm inner radius and 2.00 cm outer radius concentric with the wire. Outside the rubber is a concentric cylinder of gutta percha ($\varepsilon_r = 4.10$) of inner radius 2.00 cm and outer radius 5.00 cm. A lead sheath of 5.00 cm inner radius encases the gutta percha. The capacitor is 10.00 m long. A positive conduction charge of 5.00×10^{-6} coulomb is placed on the central wire. (a) What is the magnitude of D in the rubber at the surface of the copper rod? [*Ans:* 7.97×10^{-6} coulomb/m^2.] (b) What is the magnitude of D at the interface between the rubber and the gutta percha? [*Ans:* 3.98×10^{-6} coulomb/m^2.] (c) What is the magnitude of D at the inner surface of the lead sheath? (d) What is the potential difference between the central wire and the interface between the rubber and gutta percha? Between this interface and the lead sheath? Between the central wire and the lead sheath? [*Ans:* $V_R = 2500$ v; $V_{GP} = 2000$ v; $V = 4500$ v.] (e) What is the capacitance of the capacitor? [*Ans:* 1.11×10^{-9}

farad.] (f) At the interface between the two dielectrics, what is the surface density of polarization charge on the surface of the rubber? On the surface of the gutta percha? [*Ans:* $\sigma_{P,R} = 2.38 \times 10^{-6}$ coulomb/m²; $\sigma_{P,GP} = -3 \times 10^{-6}$ coulomb/m².]

12-18 Consider Problem 10–22, which concerns two long straight parallel wires with equal and opposite uniformly distributed charges. (a) Adapt the result to show that the potential difference between the two wires is given by

$$V_A - V_B = (b/2\pi\varepsilon_0) \ln [(l - r_1)^2/r_1^2]$$

(b) Derive the approximate formula $C = 0.0194/\log_{10} (l/r_1)$ microfarads/mile which is frequently used in engineering for the distributed capacitance of a 2-wire line when the distance between the wires is *very large* compared with the radii of the wires.

12-19 A certain 150,000 v 2-wire transmission line has its wires spaced 6.00 ft on centers and each wire has a radius of 0.200 in. (Refer to Problem 12–18.) (a) What is the wire-to-wire capacitance (i.e., neglect capacitance to ground and to towers) of 50 miles of this line? (b) What energy is required just to charge the wires to a potential difference of 150,000 v. [*Ans:* 4.28×10^3 joules.] (c) Will the electric field intensity in the air just outside either wire exceed the dielectric strength of the air?

12-20 Referring to Fig. 12–4–2, explain the statement, "Since this is a series circuit, the same total charge passed all points in the circuit while the capacitors were being charged, so each capacitor has the same charge q." Explain it first in terms of Kirchhoff's first law for circuits and then in terms of induced and inducing charges in each capacitor.

12-21 A common type of calibrated variable capacitor bank that you may use in the laboratory is shown schematically in Fig. 12 P–1. The shaded areas are metal bars, and T_1 and T_2 are terminals which are used for connection to a circuit. The individual capacitors in the bank are housed in a box and are connected between the metal cross bars as shown schematically in the figure. The capacitance of each one, in microfarads, is stamped on the side bar adjacent to the capacitor.

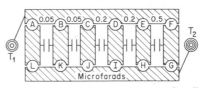

Figure 12–P–1. Common type of calibrated capacitor.

The lettered circles are tapered holes at the joints between metal bars into which tapered metal plugs may be inserted in order to connect the metal cross bars to the metal side bars and thus to T_1 and T_2. What is the capacitance between T_1 and T_2 if plugs are inserted into holes: (a) F and H? (b) F, H, D, and J? (c) F, H, D, J, B, and L? [*Ans:* 1.00 μf.] (d) F, H, and C? [*Ans:* 0.600 μf.] (e) F and L? [*Ans:* 0.0192μf.] (f) A, K, and D? [*Ans:* 0.0900 μf.] (g) A and L?

12-22 Refer to the calibrated capacitor described in Problem 12–21 and shown in Fig. 12–P–1. In which holes should plugs be placed in order to secure a capacitance between T_1 and T_2 of: (a) 0.15 μf? (b) 0.0812 μf? (c) 0.300 μf?

12-23 Three capacitors whose capacitances are 0.300 μf, 0.500 μf, and 0.700 μf are connected in series, and the combination is connected across a d-c generator. An electrostatic voltmeter connected across the 0.300 μf capacitor reads 25.0 v. (a) What is the emf of the generator? [*Ans:* 50.7 v.] (b) What is the energy stored in all three capacitors? [*Ans:* 190 × 10^{-6} joule.]

12–24 Three capacitors, whose capacitances are 2.00 μf, 4.00 μf, and 6.00 μf, respectively, are charged in parallel from a 500 v battery. They are then disconnected without any loss of charge and reconnected in series with the 4.00 μf capacitor in the middle between the 2.00 μf and 6.00 μf capacitors and with the negative plate of the 2.00 μf connected to the positive plate of the 4.00 μf and with the negative plate of the 4.00 μf connected to the positive plate of the 6.00 μf. Finally the positive plate of the 2.00 μf is connected to the negative plate of the 6.00 μf. After the final connection has been made: (a) What is the charge on each capacitor? [*Ans:* $q_2 = -6.37 \times 10^{-4}$ coulomb; $q_4 = 3.63 \times 10^{-4}$ coulomb; $q_6 = 13.63 \times 10^{-4}$ coulomb.] (b) What is the potential difference across each capacitor? [*Ans:* $V_2 = -318$ v; $V_4 = 91.0$ v; $V_6 = 227$ v.]

12–25 A variable air capacitor used in the laboratory for a capacitance bridge has a capacitance of 50.0 μμf when its pointer is at zero on the scale, and a capacitance of 6000 μμf when its pointer is at 100 on the scale. You charge the capacitor from a 100 v battery when the pointer is at 100 on the scale and then disconnect it from the battery without loss of charge. How much work must you do against electric forces in order to turn the pointer to zero on the scale?

12–26 A certain absolute electrometer (see Fig. 12–7–1) which is used in an electrical measurements laboratory has a movable plate P_1 of diameter 10.16 cm, and weight 32.895 g. The inside diameter of the guard ring, which surrounds P_1, is 10.26 cm. When a selected battery, whose emf is to be measured, is connected between P_1 and P_2 and an additional weight of 0.0900 g is placed on pan D, it is found that equilibrium is established again when the separation between P_1 and P_2 is 0.247 cm. What is the emf of the battery? [*Ans:* 385 v.]

12–27 A calibrated electrostatic voltmeter is connected to a battery and reads 500 v. It is then disconnected from the battery without any loss of charge. A capacitor whose capacitance is 6.00 μμf, and which is initially discharged, is now connected across the terminals of the electrostatic voltmeter, again without any loss of charge to a third body. The voltmeter now reads 325 v. (a) What is the capacitance of the electrostatic voltmeter? [*Ans:* 11.1 μμf.] (b) What was the initial charge on the electrostatic voltmeter? The final charge on the electrostatic voltmeter?

12–28 Refer to Problem 11–10 and consider that one metal plate and the slab of glass form one parallel plate capacitor and that the slab of rubber and the other metal plate form a second parallel plate capacitor. Look upon these two parallel plate capacitors as being in series. Using this point of view, compute the capacitance of each capacitor separately and then the equivalent capacitance of the two in series. Check your result against the answer given for Problem 11–10 part (d).

12–29 Refer to Problem 12–17 and consider that the lead sheath and the gutta percha make one cylindrical capacitor and that the soft rubber and the central copper rod make a second cylindrical capacitor. Look upon these two cylindrical capacitors as being in series. Using this point of view, compute the capacitance of each capacitor separately and then the equivalent capacitance of the two in series. Check your result against the answer given in Problem 12–17 part (e).

In some of the early problems in this chapter (see Problems 12–7, 12–8, 12–13, 12–14) we tacitly assumed that the potential difference between the plates of an insulated capacitor can be measured without loss of charge from the capacitor. This in turn assumed that the electrostatic voltmeter had a capacitance which was very small compared with the capacitance of the capacitor being measured. Let us now consider some problems where this assumption cannot be made.

12–30 A capacitor with a capacitance of 205 $\mu\mu f$ is charged from a battery and then insulated. A calibrated electrostatic voltmeter, whose capacitance is 55.0 $\mu\mu f$, is now connected across the capacitor and reads 500 v. (a) What was the potential difference across the capacitor before the electrostatic voltmeter was connected? [*Ans:* 634 v.] (b) What is the magnitude of the charge that moved from the capacitor onto the electrostatic voltmeter? What charge remains on the capacitor? (c) What was the potential energy of the charged capacitor before the voltmeter was attached? What is the potential energy of the capacitor and the voltmeter after they are connected? What became of the difference between these two energies? [*Ans:* 41.2 × 10⁻⁶ joule; 32.5 × 10⁻⁶ joule.]

12–31 A parallel plate air capacitor whose capacitance is 200 $\mu\mu f$ has its terminals connected to the terminals of an electrostatic voltmeter whose capacitance is 11.0 $\mu\mu f$. The combination is charged from a battery and then the battery is disconnected. After the battery is disconnected the electrostatic voltmeter reads 500 v. Next, without loss of any charge, a slab of dielectric is inserted between the plates of the parallel plate capacitor and fills this space. After the slab of dielectric is inserted the voltmeter reads 229 v. (a) What is the relative dielectric constant of the dielectric? [*Ans:* 2.25.] (b) Was there any net transfer of charge while the dielectric was being inserted? If so, in which direction (from the capacitor to the voltmeter or from the voltmeter to the capacitor) and how much?

12–32 An electrostatic voltmeter whose capacitance is 200 $\mu\mu f$ is connected across a charged capacitor whose capacitance C_1 is unknown, and after the connection the voltmeter reads 200 v. Next an uncharged capacitor whose capacitance is 1000 $\mu\mu f$ is connected in parallel with the above combination and the voltmeter reads 50.0 v. All connections are made in such a way that no charge escapes to outside bodies. What is the value of C_1? [*Ans:* $C_1 = 133 \ \mu\mu f$.]

12–33 A metal sphere of radius r_1 has a positive charge q and is situated in a class A fluid dielectric which fills all space except that occupied by the metal sphere. The permittivity of the dielectric is ε. (a) From Problem 12–5 the electric field for points outside the sphere is given by $E = q/4\pi\varepsilon r^2$. Use (12–5–3) for the energy density in an electric field and compute the energy in a spherical shell of radius r and thickness dr. Then compute the total energy in the field of the metal sphere by summing for all such shells from $r = r_1$ to $r = \infty$. [*Ans:* $W = q^2/8\pi\varepsilon r_1$.] (b) Check this answer by considering the charged sphere as a capacitor and use the formula for the energy of a charged capacitor.

12-34 Consider the energy density in the electric field of the cylindrical capacitor described in Problem 12–15 and Sec. 12–2. (a) Use $E = b/2\pi\varepsilon r$ and the energy density formula (12–5–3) to compute the energy in a cylindrical shell of unit length (parallel to the metal cylinders), of radius r and of thickness dr in the field between the two charged metal cylinders. Next compute the total energy in the field between the charged cylinders for unit length of the cylinders by summing from $r = r_1$ to $r = r_2$. [*Ans:* $W = (b^2/4\pi\varepsilon) \ln (r_2/r_1)$.] (b) Check this answer by computing the energy of this charged capacitor by use of (12–2–9) and (12–5–1).

MAGNETIC FORCE

ON MOVING

CHARGES

13–1 FORCE ON A CURRENT-CARRYING CONDUCTOR IN A MAGNETIC FIELD

In Secs. 3–1 through 3–3 we introduced the concept of a magnetic field, and you are urged to review these sections as an introduction to the present chapter. In Chapter III we set forth the fundamental theory of the force that a magnetic field exerts on a moving charge, so this chapter is primarily a collection of some of the special problems in which this magnetic force is important. In this collection of special problems we shall discuss several instruments of considerable usefulness in physics and engineering.

1. VECTOR PRODUCT OR CROSS PRODUCT OF TWO VECTORS. Another notation of vector analysis is useful to us in the discussion of the magnetic force on moving charges. This has to do with the vector product of two vectors, as contrasted with the scalar product of two vectors, which we introduced earlier. The vector product of two vectors A and B is defined as a vector C whose magnitude is given by

$$C = AB \sin \theta \qquad (13–1–1)$$

where θ (less than 180°) is the angle between A and B. Also, by definition, the direction of C is perpendicular to the plane of A and B and in the sense given by the right-hand rule. To apply the right-hand rule for the vector product, curl all four fingers of the right hand and extend the thumb as you would if you were determining the sense of the magnetic field about a straight wire which is carrying a current. Then, if A is stated first in the vector product, point the fingers in the direction which will turn A into B through the angle (less than 180°) between them, and the thumb will point in the direction of the vector product C. You will recall that this is the same rule used to construct a right-hand Cartesian coordinate system, i.e., using the right hand, point the fingers to turn the positive X-axis into the positive Y-axis and the thumb points along the positive Z-axis. We have used right-hand Cartesian coordinate systems exclusively.

The vector product is written with a cross between the two vectors being multiplied and thus the vector product is often called the cross product.

Hence, we express the fact that C is the vector product of A and B by the equation

$$C = A \times B \qquad (13\text{–}1\text{–}2)$$

Equation (13–1–1) gives the magnitude of C, and Fig. 13–1–1 illustrates the rule for determining the direction of C.

If you apply the rule for the direction of the vector product to $B \times A$ in Fig. 13–1–1 you observe that the resultant points downward on the page. This yields the result that

$$B \times A = -A \times B \qquad (13\text{–}1\text{–}3)$$

and you observe that the vector product does not obey the commutative law of algebra. Also from (13–1–1), since the $\sin 0 = 0$, we have the fact that the vector product of a vector with itself is zero, or

$$A \times A = 0 \qquad (13\text{–}1\text{–}4)$$

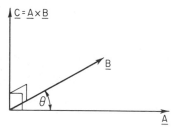

From (13–1–1) through (13–1–4) we get the following relationship between the unit vectors (see Fig. 9–6–1) of the Cartesian coordinate system:

Figure 13–1–1. Illustration of the rule for determining the direction of C in the vector product $C = A \times B$. Point the fingers of the right hand in a direction to rotate A into B, through an angle less than 180°, and the thumb will point in the direction of C.

$$
\begin{aligned}
i \times i &= j \times j = k \times k = 0 \\
i \times j &= -(j \times i) = k \\
j \times k &= -(k \times j) = i \\
k \times i &= -(i \times k) = j
\end{aligned}
\qquad (13\text{–}1\text{–}5)
$$

Next we need to express C in terms of the components of A and B when $C = A \times B$. To do this, first write A and B in terms of their components as we did in (9–6–9)

$$
\begin{aligned}
A &= iA_x + jA_y + kA_z \\
B &= iB_x + jB_y + kB_z
\end{aligned}
\qquad (13\text{–}1\text{–}6)
$$

and then form the cross product

$$A \times B = (iA_x + jA_y + kA_z) \times (iB_x + jB_y + kB_z) \qquad (13\text{–}1\text{–}7)$$

Solve Problem 13–1 and show that this becomes

$$A \times B = i(A_yB_z - A_zB_y) + j(A_zB_x - A_xB_z) + k(A_xB_y - A_yB_x) \qquad (13\text{–}1\text{–}8)$$

Thus C is a vector whose x, y, and z components are $A_yB_z - A_zB_y$, $A_zB_x - A_xB_z$, and $A_xB_y - A_yB_x$ respectively.

The usefulness of the vector product notation can be illustrated by the formulas for the magnetic forces on moving charges, which we discussed in Chapter III. Comparison of (3–2–1) and (13–1–1) followed by comparison of Fig. 3–2–3 and Fig. 13–1–1 shows that we may express the force F which a magnetic field of flux density B exerts on a charge q moving in the field with a velocity v as

$$F = qv \times B \qquad (13\text{–}1\text{–}9)$$

Figure 13–1–2 is Fig. 3–2–3 redrawn and applies to the same physical situation. You will observe that the vector product of (13–1–9) gives both the magnitude and the direction of the magnetic force on q. The vector product gives the same direction for F as does Fleming's left-hand rule, and thus this rule is incorporated in the vector product and the full information about F is contained in (13–1–9). Further, (13–1–9) takes full account of the situation if q is negative because, in this case, a negative number would be substituted for q (for example, $F = -5 \times 10^{-10}$ coulomb $v \times B$), F would be negative, and thus F would be oppositely directed to the F for a positive charge moving with the same velocity in the same direction.

2. STRAIGHT WIRE CARRYING CURRENT PERPENDICULAR TO A UNIFORM MAGNETIC FIELD. Now, let us consider a straight wire which has its length l perpendicular to a uniform magnetic field of flux density B. The wire has a steady direct current I flowing in it and we wish to find the force that the magnetic field exerts on the current in the wire. (Of course the magnetic field of flux density B in which the wire is situated is *not* due to the current in the wire but rather to other currents elsewhere, since the magnetic field of the current in the wire does not exert a net force on itself.) With the problem that we have proposed, the moving charges in the wire have a velocity v perpendicular to B.

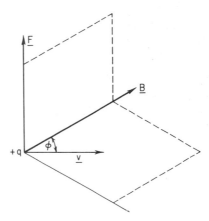

Figure 13–1–2. The magnetic force F on a positive charge q moving with a velocity v in a magnetic field of flux density B is given by the vector product $F = qv \times B$.

Let f represent the magnetic force that acts on each moving charge q in the wire. In our present problem ϕ is 90°, so we have from (13–1–9)

$$f = vqB \qquad (13\text{–}1\text{–}10)$$

Figure 13–1–3 pictures the situation that we are considering, where each dot represents a magnetic flux line directed perpendicular to the paper and out of the paper.

We know that the current is due to a maintained electric field in the wire which causes free electrons to drift in the wire in a direction opposite to E. However, in our circuit analysis in the first eight chapters, we pointed out that the direction of the current I is the direction in which positive charges would move, as it must be if we continue to use $i = +dq/dt$ and continue to call the charge on the electron negative. A positive charge q moving with a velocity v in a magnetic field experiences the same force in the same direction as does a negative charge of the same magnitude moving with the velocity $-v$ at the same place in the field. Thus, we obtain the same result for the force on the wire whether we use the actual motion of the electrons or the fictitious motion of the positive charges and consider that the electrons remain at rest.

In the case pictured in Fig. 13–1–3, the motion of positive charges would be from left to right, and this is the direction of the current I. Let n represent the number of moving positive charges per unit volume of the wire; each charge has a magnitude q and each has a velocity v directed from left to right. Let A represent the area of cross section of the wire, so nA is the number of moving charges per unit length and nAl is the total number of moving charges in the length l of the wire. Due to the magnetic field, each of these charges experiences a force given by (13–1–10), and all the forces, on all the moving charges in the length l, are parallel. In fact, by Fleming's left-hand rule or the cross product of (13–1–9),

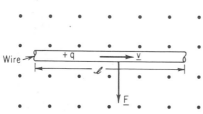

Figure 13–1–3. Magnetic force on a straight wire which is carrying a current perpendicular to a uniform magnetic field.

all these forces are directed toward the bottom of the page in Fig. 13–1–3. Hence, the total force F on all the moving charges in the length l is

$$F = nAlvqB \qquad (13\text{--}1\text{--}11)$$

But the current is defined as the total charge which passes any cross section of the wire in unit time, so

$$I = nAqv \qquad (13\text{--}1\text{--}12)$$

Hence, by substitution, we have

$$F = lIB \qquad (13\text{--}1\text{--}13)$$

Since the magnetic field exerts this force on the moving charges and the moving charges in turn exert this force on the wire, we usually say that the magnetic field exerts the force on the wire.

3. Straight wire at an angle ϕ with respect to a uniform magnetic field. Since the current is flowing at an angle ϕ with respect to B, we have the situation pictured

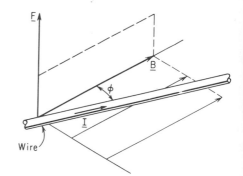

Figure 13–1–4. Magnetic force on a straight wire which is carrying a current I at an angle ϕ with respect to B.

in Fig. 13–1–4. In this case we must use (13–1–9) instead of (13–1–10) in the above derivation, and the result is

$$F = l\,I \times B \qquad (13\text{--}1\text{--}14)$$

for the force on a length l of the wire. The direction of F is shown in Fig. 13–1–4, and you can check it by use of Fleming's left-hand rule.

4. GENERAL CASE. If the wire is not straight and if the magnetic field is not uniform, we can express the element of force dF on an element of length dl of the wire. We consider that the wire is straight for the length dl and that the magnetic field is uniform over this infinitesimal length. Let ϕ be the angle between the direction of the current in the length dl and the direction of B at dl. Then

$$dF = dl\, I \times B \qquad (13\text{–}1\text{–}15)$$

with a magnitude $dF = dl\, IB \sin \phi$. If we wish to secure the force on a finite length l of the wire, we must obtain the vector sum of all the dF's for all the dl's along the length l. In general of course, both B and $\sin \phi$ will be functions of position along l, and these functional relationships must be known in a particular problem before the vector sum can be obtained.

The magnetic force on the current in one part of a circuit can be due, of course, to the B field set up by the current in another part of the same circuit. For example, an inductor wound in the form of a solenoid [see Fig. 14–7–1 (a) for a solenoid shown in cross section] experiences magnetic forces which tend to contract it along its length and expand it in diameter, as you can quickly show by application of the discussion above. For small currents and magnetic fields, these forces are of little importance. But for the big currents and magnetic fields now being used in some researches,* these forces can cause rupture of the strongest circuits with explosive violence.

5. HALL EFFECT. Figure 13–1–5 shows a flat ribbon conductor carrying a current I at right angles to a magnetic field of flux density B. In both (a) and (b) the current is directed in the negative Z direction. Because charges are in motion when there is a current, each charge experiences the magnetic force given by (13–1–9) and, as shown in Fig. 13–1–5, a transverse electric field is produced and a potential difference is developed between the right and left sides of the ribbon. The phenomenon described is known as the *Hall Effect* and, as shown in Fig. 13–1–5, the sign of the Hall voltage V_H reverses with the sign of the charge carrier for fixed directions of the current and magnetic field. The Hall voltage is directly measurable with a potentiometer. As explained in Sec. 1–4 (review that discussion and see the references given there for greater detail) the Hall Effect is used to determine whether the charge carriers are positive or negative, since other properties of a current fail to distinguish. Figure 13–1–5 (b) shows the situation for metals where the current is due to electron motion. It also shows the situation for the n-type semiconductors where electron flow dominates in the conduction process. Figure 13–1–5 (a) shows the situation for a p-type semiconductor and, in fact, suggests the experiment which lets one know that the conduction is due to motion of positive charge carriers and thus that the material is p-type.

The magnetic force causes the moving charge carriers to deflect and thus to accumulate on the right side of the conductor, until the reverse electric field E due to the charge separation exerts an equal and opposite force on each

* See for example: "Production and Use of High Transient Magnetic Fields" by Furth, Levine, and Waniek, *Rev. Sci. Inst.* **27**, pp. 195–203, April 1956 and **28**, pp. 949–958, Nov., 1957; and "Strong Magnetic Fields," *Sci. Am.* **198**, pp. 28–33, Feb., 1958, by the same authors.

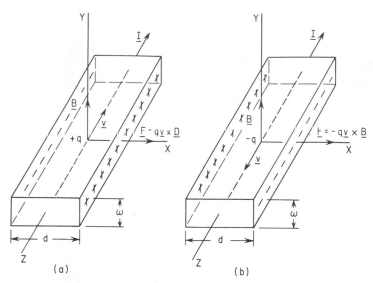

Figure 13–1–5. Hall voltage between right and left faces of a conductor due to a current I flowing in the negative Z-direction with B in the positive Y-direction. (a) Current is due to flow of positive charges in the direction of I. (b) Current is due to flow of negative charges in a direction opposite to that of I.

charge. Since v is perpendicular to B, $v \times B$ has the magnitude vB. Thus at equilibrium, $qE = qvB$, or $E = vB$. Multiply and divide the right side by nq (n is the number of moving charge carriers per unit volume and q is the charge on each) to obtain $E = vBnq/nq$. Let j_c represent the conduction current density, i.e., the current through unit area of cross section of the conductor, and $j_c = vnq$. Then

$$E = j_c B/nq \qquad (13\text{–}1\text{–}16)$$

The Hall coefficient R_H is defined as $R_H = 1/nq$, so

$$E = R_H j_c B \qquad (13\text{–}1\text{–}17)$$

If we consider that the geometry and current flow conditions result in a uniform E, we can express E in terms of the Hall voltage V_H as $E = V_H/d$. Thus $V_H/d = R_H j_c B$ and, since $j_c = I/wd$,

$$R_H = V_H w/IB \qquad (13\text{–}1\text{–}18)$$

All terms on the right of (13–1–18) can be determined directly by experiment. Hence R_H, and thus nq, can be directly determined experimentally. As an indication of order of magnitude, R_H for copper has the value of -5.5×10^{-11} vm³/amp w.

13–2 TORQUE ON A PLANE RECTANGULAR COIL IN A UNIFORM MAGNETIC FIELD

We wish to compute the torque that will act on a rectangular coil of wire when a current I is flowing through the wires of the coil and the coil is situated in a uniform magnetic field of flux density B. There are N turns of wire on the coil and these turns are closely spaced so that all of the coil is very nearly in a plane.

Figure 13–2–1 (a) shows the face of the coil and Fig. 13–2–1 (b) shows the coil in cross section. The length of the coil is l and the width is w. In Fig. 13–2–1 (a), the sides GJ and KM carry the current parallel to the magnetic flux lines and thus experience no force. In Fig. 13–2–1 (b), where the coil has been turned so that GJ and KM are no longer parallel with the magnetic flux lines, GJ experiences a force directed out of the page and KM experiences a force down into the page. Neither of these forces contributes to the torque about any axis because they have the same line of action. They simply tend to stretch the frame on which the coil is wound.

Sides KG and JM, however, experience forces which produce a torque

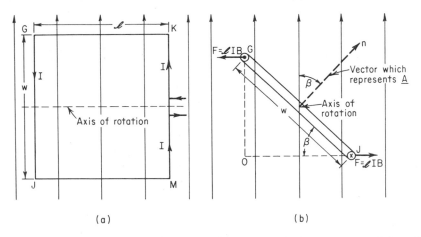

(a)   (b)

Figure 13–2–1. Plane rectangular coil in a uniform magnetic field. (a) Face of the coil when it is parallel with the magnetic flux lines. (b) Cross section of the coil when it is turned so that the normal n to its face makes an angle β with the magnetic flux lines. Current is flowing out of the page at G (as shown by the dot in the circle) and into the page at J (as shown by the cross in the circle).

about the axis of rotation and thus tend to rotate the coil. It is the torque produced by the forces on these two sides that interests us. In Fig. 13–2–1 (b) the forces on these two sides are shown by the two equal and oppositely directed arrows F and F when the normal n to the face of the coil makes an angle β with the magnetic flux lines. The force on each wire of the coil has a magnitude given by $F = lIB$, and the two forces constitute a couple, since a couple is defined as two equal and oppositely directed forces acting on the same body. You will recall from mechanics that the torque produced by a couple is equal to the product of one force and the perpendicular distance between the lines of action of the two forces. Also you will recall that the torque of a couple is the same, regardless of the axis of rotation selected. Thus the torque τ on one turn of the coil is F times GO, or $\tau = lIBw \sin \beta$. But $lw = A$, where A is the area of the face of the coil, so $\tau = IAB \sin \beta$. This is the torque on a single turn of wire on the coil, but there are N turns, all situated alike and all in series, so that each carries the current I. Hence the total torque on the coil is

$$\tau = NIAB \sin \beta \qquad (13\text{–}2\text{–}1)$$

Torque is often represented as a vector, and Fig. 13–2–2 shows the convention for this vector representation. In the figure, the magnitude of the torque which F produces around the Z-axis is equal to the component of F which is perpendicular to r times r, or $\tau_1 = rF \sin \theta$. This equation has the same form as the magnitude of a vector product. The convention for the direction of τ_1 is: curl the fingers of the right hand in the direction of the rotation that the torque tends to produce, and the thumb points in the direction of the vector that represents the torque. The direction of τ_1 as determined by this convention is shown in Fig. 13–2–2, and τ_1 is represented by the vector product

$$\boldsymbol{\tau}_1 = \boldsymbol{r} \times \boldsymbol{F} \qquad (13\text{–}2\text{–}2)$$

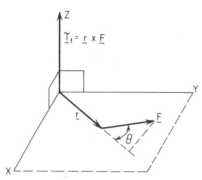

Figure 13–2–2. Convention for representing a torque as a vector.

where r is directed outward from the axis of rotation to the point of application of the force. A torque is uniquely determined by its magnitude and direction, as given above, so the vector representation gives a complete description of the torque.

As pointed out in Sec. 9–7, an area A may be represented as a vector by letting the length of the vector represent the magnitude of A and the direction of the vector be along the normal to A.

When a current flows around the periphery of the area, the direction along the normal that is to be used is selected as follows: curl the fingers of the right hand around the periphery of the area in the direction of the flow of current and the thumb will point in the direction of the vector which represents A.*

We see in Fig. 13–2–1 (b) that the arrow on n is in the correct direction for the vector which is to represent the area A of the face of the coil when the current is flowing around the wires of the coil in the direction indicated by the dot at G and the cross at J. Using the above described means of representing torque τ and area A as vectors, (13–2–1) may be written as the vector product

$$\boldsymbol{\tau} = NI\boldsymbol{A} \times \boldsymbol{B} \qquad (13\text{–}2\text{–}3)$$

---

* You will recall from elementary physics (we shall have more to say on this point in the next chapter) that the direction of the magnetic field produced along the axis of a plane coil, by a current flowing in the wires of the coil, is obtained in exactly the same way that we have just used to obtain the direction of the vector to represent the area A of the face of the coil. Hence, when a current flows around the periphery of an area A, the direction of the vector which represents A is the direction (along the axis) of the magnetic field produced by the current.

To check this equation in Fig. 13–2–1 (b), note that both the vector $\boldsymbol{\tau}$ and the vector for $A \times B$ are perpendicular to the paper and directed out of the paper, and that the magnitude of $\boldsymbol{\tau}$ as given by (13–2–3) is the same as that given by (13–2–1).

Note that the torque on the coil is maximum when β is 90°, i.e., when the plane of the coil is parallel with the magnetic flux lines. Also the torque on the coil is zero when β is zero, i.e., when the plane of the coil is perpendicular to the magnetic flux lines. Further, the direction of the torque on the coil is such as to turn the coil to a position where the magnetic flux lines due to its own current are parallel with the magnetic flux of the field in which the coil is placed. Regardless of the geometry of the coil, the above statement is true, i.e., the torque on the coil is always in such a direction as to turn the coil to a position where the magnetic flux lines due to the current in the coil are parallel with the magnetic flux lines of the field in which the coil is placed.

13–3 TORQUE ON A PLANE COIL OF ANY SHAPE PERIPHERY IN A UNIFORM MAGNETIC FIELD

In Sec. 13–2 we arrived at (13–2–3) for the torque on a plane rectangular coil carrying current in a uniform magnetic field, and in Problem 13–9 you are

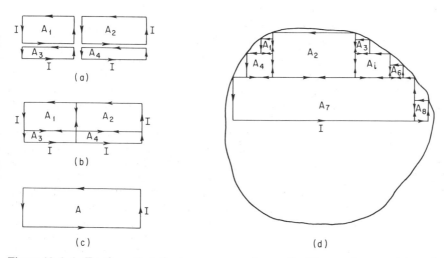

Figure 13–3–1. To show that the torque on a plane coil with any shape periphery is given by $\tau = NIAB \sin \beta$.

asked to show that this same formula applies to a plane circular coil under the same circumstances.

Now let us show that the torque on a plane coil with any shape periphery is given by (13–2–3). To see how the proof goes, first consider the four rectangular single-turn coils shown in Fig. 13–3–1 (a) and consider that they are in a uniform magnetic field which makes an angle β with the axis of each coil and that each coil has the same current I flowing in its wires. Further consider that the coils are fastened together mechanically. Again, the torque on each coil is a couple, and the torque produced by a couple is independent of the axis of rotation selected. Thus we may compute the torque without indicating the axis of rotation. The total torque on the system is the sum of the separate torques on the coils. Thus from (13–2–1) $\tau = IB \sin \beta \sum_{i=1}^{4} A_i$. But this formula is the same as if the four rectangles were in contact on their adjacent sides, as shown in Fig. 13–3–1 (b), and we were to recognize that the currents cancel everywhere except on the combined periphery of the four rectangles. In other words, the torque is the same as if we used the single coil shown in Fig. 13–3–1 (c), where the area of this coil is given by $A = \sum_{i=1}^{4} A_i$.

Now consider the single turn coil of Fig. 13–3–1 (d), which has any shape periphery. Divide its area into n rectangular coils, a few of which are shown, and consider that the same current I flows around the periphery of each rectangle. The total torque is $\tau = IB \sin \beta \sum_{i=1}^{n} A_i$, and again we may consider that the current cancels in all overlapping sides of rectangles, and is equivalent to a current I flowing around the periphery of all of the rectangles combined. We may continue to add rectangles until the periphery of all the rectangles combined approximates the periphery of the coil as closely as desired. At this stage the area A of the face of the coil is given by $A = \sum_{i=1}^{n} A_i$, so $\tau = IAB \sin \beta$ and if there are N turns the torque will have N times the magnitude. Thus (13–2–1), or the equivalent in terms of the vector product in (13–2–3), gives the torque on a plane coil of any shape periphery in a uniform magnetic field.

13–4 THE D'ARSONVAL GALVANOMETER FOR DIRECT CURRENT

A galvanometer is a device for detecting and measuring small currents. We have seen that a coil of wire experiences a torque when it is carrying a current and is situated in a magnetic field. Moving coil galvanometers, of which the D'Arsonval is one type, use the torque on the coil as a measure of the current flowing in the wires of the coil.

In the D'Arsonval type of galvanometer, a permanent magnet supplies the magnetic field in which the coil is located; thus the magnitude and direction of B is constant. As you can see from Fig. 13–2–1, the direction of the torque on the coil reverses if the direction of the current is reversed. Hence, the D'Arsonval type of galvanometer is not suitable for a-c measurements. Also, the moment of inertia of the moving coil is usually fairly large, and the coil will not respond to rapidly fluctuating direct currents. Thus, the D'Arsonval type of galvanometer and the ammeters and voltmeters that stem from it are chiefly useful for steady direct currents, and we shall assume that a steady direct current is flowing through the coil of the galvanometer in the discussion which follows in this section and in Sec. 13–5.

1. UNIFORM MAGNETIC FIELD. We have seen that a plane coil of wire in a uniform magnetic field experiences a torque given by (13–2–3), and from this equation $\tau = NIAB \sin \beta$. Here N, A, and B are constants, so τ is a function both of the current I and the angle β which the normal to the face of the coil makes with the direction of B. The coil is free to move, and β changes as I increases, so the torque is not a linear function of the current when the coil is situated in a uniform magnetic field. Thus, this type of galvanometer is not a

linear instrument. This difficulty is overcome to a large extent by having the coil situated in a radial magnetic field. We shall consider the radial field D'Arsonval galvanometer in some detail.

2. RADIAL MAGNETIC FIELD. The approximately radial magnetic field is obtained, as shown in Fig. 13–4–1 (c), by the use of a permanent horseshoe magnet whose pole faces, N and S, are cylindrically concave. An enlarged section at the pole faces is shown in Fig. 13–4–1 (a). Concentric with the pole faces, and enclosed by them, is a soft iron cylinder. As shown by the magnetic flux lines drawn in the top view in Fig. 13–4–1 (a), this configuration produces a magnetic field whose flux lines (for a limited distance on either side of the line OO') are along extensions of the radii of the soft iron cylinder in the air gap between the soft iron cylinder and the pole faces.

A rectangular coil of wire is suspended so that its sides are in the air gap

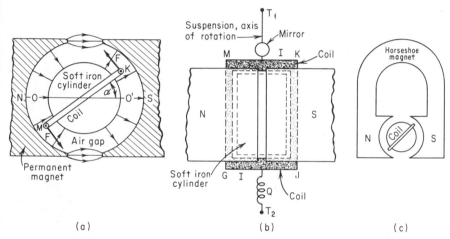

(a)   (b)   (c)

Figure 13–4–1. Radial field D'Arsonval galvanometer; (a) and (c) top views, (b) front view.

and parallel with the common axis of the two cylinders. The suspension is usually a fine wire of gold or phosphor bronze or a flat strip of either. The coil is shown as $MKJG$ in the front view of Fig. 13–4–1 (b) and the suspension is labeled. The top of the coil is shown in Fig. 13–4–1 (a) by MK; current is flowing out of the page at K as shown by the dot in the circle, and into the page at M as shown by the cross in the circle. One electrical connection with the coil is made via the terminal T_1 and the suspension. The other electrical connection is obtained through the terminal T_2 and the very loosely wound helix Q, which exerts little or no torque on the coil as it turns. When the instrument is properly leveled, the sides of the coil hang symmetrically in the air gap, and the coil's axis of rotation is along the axis of the soft iron cylinder.

When no current is flowing through the coil, the suspension is adjusted so that the plane of the coil is along the line OO' of Fig. 13–4–1 (a). When a current is sent through the coil in the direction indicated in the figure, the magnetic forces on the sides *MG* and *KJ* will be as shown by *F* and *F* in Fig. 13–4–1 (a). The coil then rotates out of its zero position (which is along *OO'*). The figure shows the coil after it has rotated an angle α from its equilibrium position. Note that, in the region where the magnetic field is radial, the magnetic forces on the sides of the coil remain perpendicular to the face of the coil, as the coil turns, and thus (13–2–1) becomes

$$\tau = NIAB \qquad (13\text{–}4\text{–}1)$$

Thus τ is independent of the angle α. Care is taken in the construction of the instrument to have *B* as nearly constant as possible over the arc on which the sides of the coil swing. Hence, τ is linearly proportional to the current *I*, since the number *N* of turns of wire on the coil and the area *A* of the face of the coil are constant. The ends *MK* and *GJ* of the coil carry current very nearly parallel to the magnetic flux lines. Hence, the torque on the ends is usually negligible.

Under the action of the magnetic torque, the coil will turn until the restoring torque of the suspension is equal to the magnetic torque. It will come to rest in this position after some oscillation. Let us say that the coil has turned through the angle α to reach its new equilibrium position.

The behavior of the suspension obeys Hooke's law, if the elastic limit is not exceeded, so the restoring torque of the suspension is linearly proportional to the angle of twist of the suspension. Let *k* represent the torsion constant of the suspension, i.e., *k* is the torque required to twist the suspension through 1 radian. Hence, at equilibrium the restoring torque τ_s of the suspension is given by

$$\tau_s = k\alpha \qquad (13\text{–}4\text{–}2)$$

At equilibrium $\tau_s = \tau$, so $k\alpha = NIAB$, or

$$I = k\alpha/NAB \qquad (13\text{–}4\text{–}3)$$

Hence, α is a linear function of *I*, and the galvanometer is a linear one if *B* is constant and radial. Since *B* is never strictly constant over the arc covered by the coil in its swing, the galvanometer is never strictly linear.

Here α is measured by the use of a beam of light reflected from the mirror which is attached to the coil [see Fig. 13–4–1 (b)]. Usually a lamp, with a lens, furnishes a parallel beam of light and there is a fine thread across the beam. The beam is incident on the mirror through a second lens which is attached to the frame of the galvanometer. The mirror reflects the beam back through this second lens and the lens focuses an image of the fine thread on a ground-glass ruled scale, where the position of the image can be read. Since the angle of incidence at the mirror equals the angle of reflection, the beam of light swings through twice the angle α.

The scale should be an arc of a circle whose center of curvature is at the mirror of the galvanometer, in order to maintain linearity between α and the deflections read on the scale. However, the galvanometer must be calibrated, since *k* and *B* in (13–4–3) cannot be measured with sufficient accuracy to permit calculation of *I* from measured values of α. This calibration is made by sending known currents through the galvanometer and recording the deflections produced. Hence, the galvanometer can be calibrated with a straight scale and then used with the same scale for the measurement of unknown currents. The scale distance must be kept constant after the galvanometer and scale have been calibrated. A good galvanometer of the D'Arsonval type commonly has a sensitivity of the order of 10^{-10} amp for a 1 mm deflection at a scale distance of 1 m.

The zero reading (scale position when the current is zero) of a high-sensitivity galvanometer will change with time due to temperature changes and elastic fatigue of the suspension. Hence, the zero reading must be taken just prior to each unknown current measurement.

3. DAMPING OF THE GALVANOMETER. If the current through the galvanometer is reduced to zero by opening a switch in the circuit to which the galvanometer is connected, the restoring torque of the suspension returns the galvanometer coil to its zero current position [along the line OO' of Fig. 13–4–1 (a)]. However, the potential energy of the twisted suspension is converted into kinetic energy of the moving coil, and only a little of this kinetic energy is converted into heat due to the viscous friction of the air through which the coil turns. Thus, if there is no damping of the coil system other than that due to the air, the coil will swing beyond its zero position and will oscillate back and forth until the mechanical energy is all dissipated as heat in the air. Hence, some additional damping is required in order that too much time shall not be consumed in a series of current measurements.

Some galvanometers secure the additional damping by means of a copper ring which is fastened to the coil frame and turns with the coil but is electrically insulated from the coil. When the ring turns in the magnetic field of the permanent magnet, the number of magnetic flux linkages with the ring changes and an emf is induced in the ring. Since the ring forms a complete circuit, the emf causes a current to flow in the ring. By Lenz's law, this current is in such a direction as to oppose (by the torque that the magnet exerts on it) the motion of the ring. The energy of motion of the coil is converted into heat due to the current flowing through the resistance of the ring. If the ring is properly selected with regard to area and resistance, the coil will return to its zero position in minimum time without overshooting. The coil is said to be *critically damped* when this condition is satisfied. Similarly, when the current is first turned on and the coil deflects from its zero position it will overshoot its final equilibrium position and oscillate about this equilibrium position if the only damping is air friction. However, the damping ring described above will also prevent oscillation in this case and will, if properly selected, permit a reading in a minimum time.

Such a ring increases the moment of inertia of the moving coil system and thus increases the period, i.e., the time for the coil to make one complete oscillation. Hence, a short-period galvanometer cannot have a damping ring of this sort. When the coil of the galvanometer turns in the magnetic field of the permanent magnet, it has an emf induced in it just as the ring did. When the current through the galvanometer is first turned on and the coil starts to turn, this induced emf is in the opposite direction to the current and thus opposes the rise of the current. It can be shown* that if the resistance of the circuit has just the right value for the particular galvanometer, the coil of the galvanometer will reach its deflection in minimum time without overshooting. The value of the circuit resistance that is just right for this purpose is called the *critical damping resistance* and is usually marked on a tag, attached to the galvanometer, as the *CDRX* (critical damping resistance external) resistance.

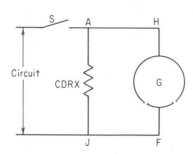

Figure 13–4–2. Critical damping resistance shunted across the terminals of a D'Arsonval galvanometer.

In a circuit whose resistance is high compared with the *CDRX* of the galvanometer being used, the galvanometer is usually shunted by the *CDRX* resistance, as shown in Fig. 13–4–2. When the switch *S* is opened, the resistance *CDRX* is still connected to the galvanometer terminals, the emf induced in the rotating coil causes a current to flow around the loop *HAJFGH*, and the galvanometer is still critically damped.

If the circuit is of low resistance, a galvanometer which requires a low critical damping resistance must be selected.

13–5 DIRECT CURRENT AMMETERS AND VOLTMETERS

Practically all d-c ammeters and voltmeters use the principle of the D'Arsonval galvanometer, except that the suspension is eliminated and the coil is mounted on a staff whose cone-shaped pivots turn in jeweled bearings [see Fig. 13–5–1 (a)]. This type of construction makes the instrument portable and eliminates the need for leveling. Also, with the delicate suspension eliminated, the instrument is more rugged. Two hairsprings furnish the restoring torque and also serve as the current leads for the coil of the instrument, being electrically connected to the terminals T_1 and T_2 of the meter for this purpose. A thin aluminum pointer is fastened to the coil and moves over the scale as the coil turns. The frame, on which the wires of the coil are wound, is made of thin aluminum and thus furnishes the required damping in the same way that we discussed for the copper ring which is sometimes used on a galvanometer coil.

Figure 13–5–1 (b) shows a top view of the meter with the coil in place in the radial field of the permanent magnet. In a meter which has its zero scale position at the left end of the scale, the hairsprings are adjusted so that the zero position of the coil is displaced counterclockwise from the $O'O''$ line, which is the zero position in the galvanometer. Such a meter is designed to deflect its pointer only in the clockwise direction from zero and thus the current must flow through its coil only in the direction shown in Fig. 13–5–1 (b). This arrangement makes it possible for the coil to rotate through a large total angle (90° to 100° in most instruments) and still remain in the region where the magnetic field is essentially radial. Thus, the scale may be long and still be linear over its entire length.

* After studying Sec. 13–6, solve Problems 13–15 and 13–16.

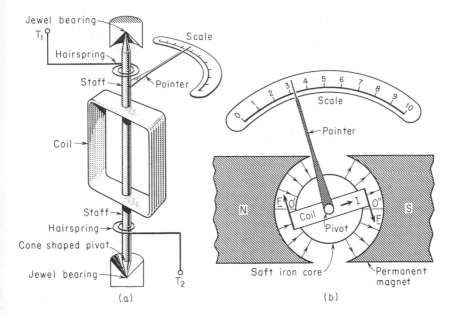

Figure 13–5–1. Pivoted coil D'Arsonval type of construction used for d-c ammeters and voltmeters. (a) Coil removed from magnetic field. (b) Top view with coil in place in magnetic field.

The frictional torque of the jewel bearings is larger than that of the suspension of the galvanometer. Since the restoring torque of the hairsprings must be considerably larger than the frictional torque in the bearings, a pivoted coil meter cannot be as sensitive as the suspension type galvanometer. A current of the order of 10^{-6} amp is about as small as a meter of this type will measure, and most such meters require a current which is from 10 to 1000 times as large for a readable deflection of the pointer.

In Sec. 2–2 we discussed multipliers for d-c voltmeters and shunts for d-c ammeters. The pivoted coil instrument* described here is the low-sensitivity galvanometer referred to there (e.g. see the galvanometer in Figs. 2–2–1 and 2–2–2). Thus, we have previously shown how to convert such a galvanometer into an ammeter of any selected range by the use of a suitable shunt and how to convert it into a voltmeter of any selected range by the use of a suitable series resistance.

13–6 BALLISTIC GALVANOMETER

We wish to consider a galvanometer with the D'Arsonval type of construction, which may be used to measure the total quantity of charge Q which flows through its coil. Here $Q = \int i \, dt$, and the galvanometer is to measure Q instead of i.

---

* See Secs. 20–5, 20–6, and 20–7 for descriptions of some a-c voltmeters and ammeters.

1. UNDAMPED BALLISTIC GALVANOMETER. We shall show that the maximum deflection of the first swing, of an undamped D'Arsonval galvanometer, is proportional to the quantity of charge which passes through its coil, provided that the flow of charge is completed in a time which is short compared with the period of the galvanometer. Since this restriction on the time of flow appears, the ballistic galvanometer is usually designed so that its moving coil system has a large moment of inertia, compared with a current galvanometer, and thus a longer period (20 to 30 sec) than a current galvanometer (1 to 10 sec). However, any D'Arsonval galvanometer will serve as a ballistic galvanometer.

In anticipation of this discussion, we used a ballistic galvanometer in Sec. 12–3 to measure the charge that flows from a capacitor when the capacitor discharges through the ballistic galvanometer. We saw there that we could calibrate a ballistic galvanometer by the use of capacitors of known capacitances and sources of known emf's and then use the same sources and the calibrated ballistic galvanometer to measure the capacitances of unknown capacitors.

Now we wish to prove the premise on which we based our previous use of the ballistic galvanometer. We may think of the situation in which a capacitor discharges through the galvanometer so that a large current of short duration flows through its coil. However, any situation which produces a large current of sufficiently short duration would be equally suitable.

Let τ represent the instantaneous unbalanced torque which acts on the coil of the D'Arsonval galvanometer in Sec. 13–4. Thus τ is equal to the torque which the magnetic field of the permanent magnet exerts on the current in the coil at a particular instant, minus the restoring torque of the suspension at that instant and minus the damping torque τ_f due to friction. Let i represent the instantaneous current flowing in the coil, and from (13–4–1) and (13–4–2) we may write

$$\tau = NiAB - k\alpha - \tau_f \qquad (13\text{–}6\text{–}1)$$

where α is the angular deflection of the coil from its equilibrium position at the instant under consideration, and N, A, B, and k are as defined in Sec. 13–4. We are considering an undamped galvanometer, so $\tau_f = 0$.

We are assuming that the time during which the current flows is very small compared with the period of the galvanometer. So, during the time that the current flows, the angle α through which the coil turns is negligibly small, and we may neglect the $k\alpha$ term. This is why all the charge which is to be measured must flow through the galvanometer in a time which is short compared with the period of the galvanometer if this theory is to be applied. Hence, in this case,

$$\tau = NiAB \qquad (13\text{–}6\text{–}2)$$

By Newton's second law of motion as applied to rotation, the unbalanced torque acting on a body is equal to the moment of inertia of the body, times the angular acceleration of the body. Let ω represent the instantaneous angular velocity of the coil and J represent the moment of inertia of the moving coil system, and we may write the law as $\tau = J\,d\omega/dt$, or $NiAB = J\,d\omega/dt$.

Hence, $$NABi\,dt = J\,d\omega \qquad (13\text{–}6\text{–}3)$$

Let ω_f represent the angular velocity of the coil at the time t_0 when the unbalanced torque becomes zero (i.e., when the discharge through the coil has just ended). Let $t = 0$ be the instant when the switch was closed to start the discharge through the galvanometer, and at $t = 0$, $\omega = 0$. Integrate (13–6–3) over the time of the discharge, and we may write

$$NAB \int_0^{t_0} i \, dt = J \int_0^{\omega_f} d\omega \qquad (13\text{–}6\text{–}4)$$

But $\int_0^{t_0} i \, dt$ equals the total charge Q that went through the galvanometer coil regardless of the form of the functional relationship between i and t. Hence, (13–6–4) becomes $NABQ = J\omega_f$, or

$$\omega_f = NABQ/J \qquad (13\text{–}6\text{–}5)$$

Equation (13–6–5) tells us that the angular velocity, which the coil acquired from the sudden passage of Q through the coil, is directly proportional to Q, since N, A, B, and J are all constants for a given galvanometer.

Since the coil has an angular velocity ω_f, it has an angular kinetic energy KE given by $KE = \frac{1}{2}J\omega_f^2$, or, using (13–6–5),

$$KE = N^2 A^2 B^2 Q^2 / 2J \qquad (13\text{–}6\text{–}6)$$

Since there is no damping, the coil will swing out, with diminishing angular velocity, to the angle where all this KE is converted into potential energy, PE, of the twisted suspension. The potential energy of the twisted suspension is the work required to give the suspension this twist. In angular motion, the element of work is the torque which acts times the element of angle through which it acts. Hence if we let α_m represent the maximum angle through which the coil swings (and thus the maximum angle of twist of the suspension) we have, using (13–4–2),

$$PE = \int_0^{\alpha_m} k\alpha \, d\alpha = \frac{1}{2}k\alpha_m^2 \qquad (13\text{–}6\text{–}7)$$

where, as before, k is the torsion constant of the suspension. Thus using (13–6–6) and (13–6–7), we have

$$Q = \alpha_m \sqrt{kJ}/NAB \qquad (13\text{–}6\text{–}8)$$

This is the result that we desired for, since k, J, N, A, and B are all constants for a given galvanometer, the maximum angle of the swing of the galvanometer coil is directly proportional to the charge that flows through the coil, provided that the flow is completed in a time that is short compared with the period of the galvanometer, and provided that there is no damping of the galvanometer.

2. BALLISTIC GALVANOMETER WITH SMALL DAMPING. We have derived the result in (13–6–8) on the assumption that there is no damping of the galvanometer. However, there is always some damping both as a result of air friction and of the emf induced in the wires of the moving coil. Let us see how this induced emf causes damping in our example where a capacitor discharges

through the ballistic galvanometer. We have seen that the discharge must be completed before the coil has moved through an appreciable angle. But, as the coil continues its motion through the magnetic field of the permanent magnet, the induced emf will cause a current to flow. This partially recharges the capacitor, followed by discharge of the capacitor as the velocity of the coil decreases to zero at the end of its swing outward. Thus, a current passes through the resistance of the galvanometer and the wires connecting it to the capacitor, and energy is changed into heat. The energy to produce this heat, and the heat resulting from air friction, come from the kinetic energy of the moving coil. Hence, not all the kinetic energy of (13–6–6) goes into potential energy of the twisted suspension as we assumed in the derivation of (13–6–8). This damping in turn means that α_m is not so large as it would have been if there had been no damping. If the circuit connected to the ballistic galvano- meter is a completely conducting circuit, instead of a circuit with a capacitor in series, the induced current may be large (for a low resistance circuit) and the damping may be large. It will be shown that the initial throw of the ballistic galvanometer is still proportional to the charge which flows through its coil, again with the same provision that the flow of charge is completed in a time which is short compared with the period of the galvanometer. However, the constant of proportionality is a different one than for the case of no damping. In fact, since the constant of proportionality depends on the resistance of the circuit, the constant of proportionality will in general be different for each different circuit connected to the galvanometer. Thus, a galvanometer cannot be calibrated in one circuit and used for measurement in another circuit, unless the circuits have identical resistances or a correction is made in each for the damping.

In some experiments it is possible to have the same galvanometer circuit during calibration and subsequent measurements of unknown quantities of charge. In such cases no correction due to damping is necessary. However, we wish to consider the case where the galvanometer is calibrated in one circuit and then used in another and see how corrections may be made.

Let us assume that the damping is small but not small enough so that it can be neglected. In this case, Newton's second law for rotational motion gives

$$NABi - k\alpha - b\,d\alpha/dt = J\,d\omega/dt \tag{13–6–9}$$

where $b\,d\alpha/dt$ is the total damping torque, including frictional and electro- magnetic damping and, by writing it this way, we are assuming that the damping is proportional to the angular velocity of the coil. Since the damping is small, this is a good approximation. The $k\alpha$ term is, of course, the restoring torque of the suspension. We may write (13–6–9) as

$$NABi\,dt - k\alpha\,dt - b\,d\alpha = J\,d\omega \tag{13–6–10}$$

which corresponds to (13–6–3) in the case of no damping. Now integrate as we did in (13–6–4):

$$NAB \int_0^{t_0} i\,dt - k \int_0^{t_0} \alpha\,dt - b \int_0^\alpha d\alpha = J \int_0^{\omega_f} d\omega$$

$$NABQ - k \int_0^{t_0} \alpha\,dt - b\alpha = J\omega_f \tag{13–6–11}$$

Again in this case, α is still negligibly small at t_0 when the current flow ceases. Thus we may put $\alpha = 0$ in the last two terms and have

$$\omega_f = NABQ/J \qquad (13\text{–}6\text{–}12)$$

Thus again, as in (13–6–5) for the undamped ballistic galvanometer, the angular velocity of the moving coil system at the end of the impulse is proportional to Q, provided the charge flows through the coil in a time which is short compared to the period of the galvanometer.

Now we must consider the motion of the coil after the current has completed its flow and is zero. For all times after the current flow ceases, (13–6–9) becomes

$$J\,d^2\alpha/dt^2 + b\,d\alpha/dt + k\alpha = 0 \qquad (13\text{–}6\text{–}13)$$

where $d\omega/dt$ has been replaced by its equivalent $d^2\alpha/dt^2$. Our boundary conditions are $\alpha = 0$ and $d\alpha/dt = \omega_f$ at $t = 0$, since $t = 0$ is now the instant represented by $t = t_0$ in the argument above. Using the value of ω_f from (13–6–12), $d\alpha/dt = NABQ/J$ at $t = 0$.

Comparison of (13–6–13) with (6–2–2) shows that the differential equations are the same if we let J replace L, α replace i, b replace R, and k replace $1/C$. Thus we may write the solution of (13–6–13) at once from inspection of the solution of (6–2–2). Also the boundary conditions are the same, namely, at $t = 0$, $i = \alpha = 0$ and $di/dt = \mathscr{E}/L$ in the circuit problem and $d\alpha/dt = NABQ/J$ in the galvanometer problem. Thus $NABQ/J$ replaces $\mathscr{E}/L$. Since the galvanometer has small damping, it is the oscillatory electrical case which interests us. Hence from (6–2–24) we may write the answer as

$$\alpha = (NABQ/\eta J)e^{-bt/2J}\sin \eta t \qquad (13\text{–}6\text{–}14)$$

where, in this problem,

$$\eta = \sqrt{k/J - (b/2J)^2} \qquad (13\text{–}6\text{–}15)$$

In (13–6–14) η appears as the angular natural frequency of oscillation of the galvanometer; thus $\eta = 2\pi f_0 = 2\pi/T_0$ where f_0 is its frequency in cycles per second and T_0 is its period in seconds.

Let

$$\alpha_m = NABQ/\eta J, \quad \text{and} \quad a = b/2J \qquad (13\text{–}6\text{–}16)$$

and (13–6–14) can be written as

$$\alpha = \alpha_m e^{-at}\sin (2\pi/T_0)t \qquad (13\text{–}6\text{–}17)$$

In (13–6–17) α_m is the maximum angular deflection that the galvanometer would attain if there were no damping and thus is the same α_m used previously in (13–6–8). Also, we see from (13–6–16) that α_m is again directly proportional to the charge Q which flows through the coil of the galvanometer. Thus it is α_m that we wish to calculate. Equation (13–6–17) is that of a damped harmonic motion, and is illustrated graphically in Fig. 13–6–1, where α is plotted as ordinate against the argument $2\pi t/T_0$, of the sine function as abscissa. The damped sine curve lies between the two exponential curves and, if the damping is small as we have assumed, is tangent to the upper one at about $\pi/2$, the lower one at about $3\pi/2$, the upper one again at about $5\pi/2$, etc. Thus $\pi/2$ corresponds in time to a quarter period $T_0/4$ of the galvanometer, which in turn is the instant when the galvanometer coil reaches its first maximum deflection α_1 (see Fig. 13–6–1). Hence, at $t = T_0/4$, $\alpha = \alpha_1$, and for this instant we may write (13–6–17) as

$$\alpha_1 = \alpha_m e^{-aT_0/4} \sin (2\pi T_0/4T_0) = \alpha_m e^{-aT_0/4} \qquad (13–6–18)$$

Similarly, at the instant $t = 5T_0/4$, the galvanometer has reached its second

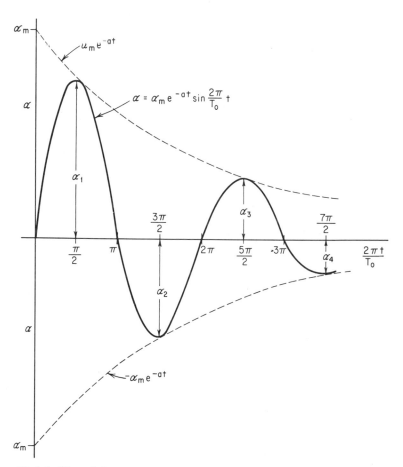

Figure 13–6–1. Plot of (13–6–17) as the equation of motion for the coil of a damped ballistic galvanometer.

maximum deflection, α_3, in the same direction as α_1, and $\alpha = \alpha_3$ at this instant. Hence, for this instant we may write (13–6–17) as

$$\alpha_3 = \alpha_m e^{-5aT_0/4} \qquad (13–6–19)$$

Take the ratio of (13–6–18) and (13–6–19) and we have

$$\alpha_1/\alpha_3 = e^{aT_0}, \quad \text{or} \quad \ln (\alpha_1/\alpha_3) = aT_0 \qquad (13–6–20)$$

Now define a new quantity called *logarithmic decrement** and represent it by the symbol λ, where λ is defined by

$$\lambda = \ln (\alpha_1/\alpha_3) \qquad (13\text{–}6\text{–}21)$$

Note carefully that this equation defines λ as the natural logarithm of the ratio of two successive maximum deflections on the *same* side of the galvanometer zero. We determine λ experimentally for a given galvanometer in a given circuit by reading the scale deflections which correspond to α_1 and α_3, calculate the ratio of the scale deflections, and obtain the natural logarithm of the ratio from a logarithm table.† Since any deflection could be the first, λ may be computed from the natural logarithm of the ratio of any two successive deflections on the same side of the galvanometer zero. From (13–6–20) and (13–6–21),

$$\lambda = aT_0 \qquad (13\text{–}6\text{–}22)$$

The object of this discussion has been to secure a formula for the computation of α_m from the measured values of α_1. Now we may achieve this objective. From (13–6–18) and (13–6–22),

$$\alpha_m = \alpha_1 e^{\lambda/4} \qquad (13\text{–}6\text{–}23)$$

Thus, with λ measured as outlined above and α_1 known, we may compute α_m. However, we may simplify this equation since $e^{\lambda/4}$ is given by the series

$$e^{\lambda/4} = 1 + \lambda/4 + (\lambda/4)^2/2! + (\lambda/4)^3/3! + (\lambda/4)^4/4! + \cdots \qquad (13\text{–}6\text{–}24)$$

We have assumed small damping, so $\lambda/4$ is small compared with unity. Thus, we may neglect terms containing λ^2 and higher in the series, and, to a sufficiently good approximation, $e^{\lambda/4} = 1 + \lambda/4$, so (13–6–23) then becomes

$$\alpha_m = \alpha_1(1 + \lambda/4) \qquad (13\text{–}6\text{–}25)$$

which is a very convenient formula for computation of α_m from α_1.

In making measurements‡ with a ballistic galvanometer, either for

---

* Frequently you will find logarithmic decrement defined by the equation $\lambda = \ln (\alpha_1/\alpha_2)$, i.e., the natural logarithm of the ratio of successive swings on the *opposite* sides of the galvanometer zero (see Fig. 13–6–1). However, many galvanometers are not symmetrical in their behavior on opposite sides of the zero, especially if they are not leveled with extreme care, so we shall take all readings on the same side of the zero. See Sec. 7–5 for discussion of logarithmic decrement in an oscillating circuit.

† When the damping is small, as we have assumed, the measured α_1/α_3 will be very nearly unity, and a large experimental error may be involved for a single measurement of α_1 and α_3. Hence the experimental determination should be repeated several times and an average value of $\ln (\alpha_1/\alpha_3)$ obtained. This may be accomplished with a single initial swing of the galvanometer, since all maximum values of the successive deflections on the same side of zero may be recorded and then the natural logarithm, of the ratio of each two successive deflections, computed.

An easy method of averaging is illustrated by the following example. Let α_1, α_3, α_5, and α_7 represent successive maximum values of deflections on the same side of zero. Then the average value of λ from these readings is λ_{av}, where

$$\lambda_{av} = [\ln (\alpha_1/\alpha_3) + \ln (\alpha_3/\alpha_5) + \ln (\alpha_5/\alpha_7)]/3 = [\ln (\alpha_1/\alpha_7)]/3$$

‡ See Sec. 20–3 for the use of a ballistic galvanometer to explore a magnetic field and Sec. 20–4 for the fluxmeter which is closely related.

calibration or measurement of an unknown, λ must be determined and α_m computed for each reading unless the calibration and measurement circuits are the same.

13–7 MAGNETIC MOMENT OF A PLANE LOOP OF CURRENT

A current flowing in a coil of wire produces a magnetic field, and because of this magnetic field the coil is said to have a magnetic moment. In this section we wish to give a precise definition to the term magnetic moment. The concept of magnetic moment will be useful when we consider the magnetic properties of matter.

It is the current which produces the magnetic field; the wires of the coil are

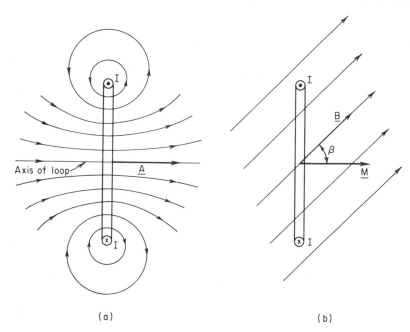

(a)   (b)

Figure 13–7–1. (a) Magnetic flux lines of a circular loop of current. (b) The same loop of current located in the uniform magnetic field due to other currents elsewhere.

simply conducting paths in which the current flows. A flow of charges around a loop under any circumstance would produce the same result, and thus the more general term "loop of current" is usually used. We shall confine our discussion to a plane loop of current. Figure 13–7–1 (a) shows a circular loop of current in cross section and some of the magnetic flux lines due to the current. Each magnetic flux line is a closed line even though only a short section of most lines has been drawn. Also, the field is three-dimensional and may be visualized in three dimensions, since the map of the flux lines in any plane containing the axis of the loop would look the same as this figure. In Fig. 13–7–1 (a) the vector A, which represents the area of the face of the loop, has been drawn in the direction required by the direction of I.

In Sec. 13–2 and Sec. 13–3 we considered such a plane loop of current as this, located in the uniform magnetic field due to other currents elsewhere. If the area A of the face of the coil is small, we may consider that any field is uniform over A. In Fig. 13–7–1 (b) the loop of current has been redrawn and the uniform magnetic field due to the "other currents elsewhere" has been indicated by parallel magnetic flux lines. The magnetic flux lines due to the current in the loop have been omitted in this figure. Let B represent the uniform magnetic flux density of the field in which the current loop is located, and the vector for B has been drawn in Fig. 13–7–1 (b). Note carefully that B in this discussion refers to the magnetic flux density of the field in which the current loop is located, *not* to the magnetic flux density of the current in the loop. From (13–2–3) we know that the torque on a single turn of this current loop is

$$\tau = IA \times B \qquad (13\text{–}2\text{–}3)$$

and τ is directed up out of the page in Fig. 13–7–1 (b), where β is the angle between A and B.

The *magnetic moment* of this loop of current is represented by M and is defined* by the equation

$$M = IA \qquad (13\text{–}7\text{–}1)$$

If there are N turns of wire on the loop, $M = NIA$ is usually used as the definition of M.

From the definition of M in (13–7–1), M is a vector quantity whose direction is that of the vector which represents A. Hence, from the convention adopted in Sec. 13–2 for the direction of A, the vector which represents M is along the axis of the loop and in the sense given by the direction of the thumb of the right hand when the fingers curl around the loop pointed in the direction of the current. The direction of M is shown in Fig. 13–7–1 (b) but not to the same scale as the vector for A in Fig. 13–7–1 (a).

From (13–7–1) $IA = M$, so (13–2–3) becomes

$$\tau = M \times B \qquad (13\text{–}7\text{–}2)$$

and τ, of course, has the same direction up out of the page in Fig. 13–7–1 (b) as it had before. The magnitude of τ is

$$\tau = MB \sin \beta \qquad (13\text{–}7\text{–}3)$$

If M is perpendicular to B, $\beta = 90°$ and (13–7–3) yields

$$M = \tau/B \qquad (13\text{–}7\text{–}4)$$

From (13–7–4) we see that the *magnetic moment of a loop of current is equal in magnitude to the torque* (or moment of force) *that the loop experiences if its axis is perpendicular to a magnetic field of unit magnetic flux density.* This

---

* Some authors, when using the mks system of units, define M by $M = \mu_0 IA$, and thus μ_0 is included in the definition. This definition is known as the *Kennelly proposal*, whereas the one that we are using in (13–7–1) is known as the *Sommerfeld proposal*. Thus, you need to note each author's definition of the magnetic moment of a loop of current (as well as the system of units used) when reading various texts.

statement with regard to M suggests the reason for calling M the magnetic moment of the coil.

From (13–7–1) the units of M are ampere meters^2.

Since we have shown in Sec. 13–3 that the torque formula (13–2–3) is valid for a plane coil with any shape of periphery, the discussion here is valid for a plane current loop with any shape of periphery.

Note again, for emphasis, that the direction of the torque on the loop of current is such as to turn it to a position where its magnetic field would be parallel to, and in the same direction as, the magnetic field in which it is located. If the loop is free to do so, it will turn to this position, and its magnetic field will strengthen the magnetic field in which it is located.

13-8 THE DIRECT CURRENT MOTOR

A motor is a machine whose purpose is the conversion of electrical energy into mechanical energy. Here we shall consider only the basic principles of the d-c motor as another illustration of the magnetic force on moving charges.

1. A SIMPLE MOTOR. Consider again the D'Arsonval galvanometer discussed in Sec. 13–4 and pictured in Fig. 13–4–1. Essentially the same sketch is drawn for the motor in Fig. 13–8–1 (a), where the dot in the circle at K shows that

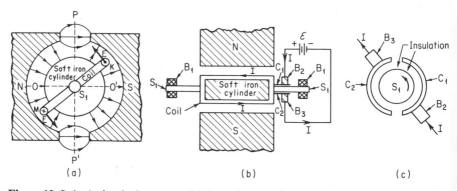

Figure 13–8–1. A simple d-c motor. (a) End view looking along the shaft S_1. (b) Cross section of motor to a smaller scale than (a). (c) End view of shaft S_1 showing commutator segments C_1 and C_2 and brushes B_2 and B_3 to a larger scale than (a).

the current is flowing up out of the page on the K side of the coil, and the cross in the circle at M shows that the current is flowing down into the page on the M side of the coil. By Fleming's left-hand rule (which in Sec. 3–2 we called the motor rule), the coil in the position shown in Fig. 13–8–1 (a) experiences a counterclockwise torque and will continue to experience a torque in this direction until its plane is in the PP' plane. When the plane of the coil is in the PP' plane, the forces F and F are parallel to the plane of the coil and simply tend to stretch the coil frame, but produce no turning torque. The coil will turn to the PP' plane, and its momentum will carry it beyond to a position where it experiences a clockwise torque returning it to the PP' plane. Thus, the PP' plane will be the equilibrium position of the coil if we make no further provisions.

Suppose, however, that just before the coil reaches the PP' plane a reversing switch in the coil circuit is thrown and thus the direction of the current in the coil is reversed. The momentum of the coil will carry it beyond the PP' plane to a position where the torque is again counterclockwise with the current in the new direction. Hence, the coil can be made to rotate continuously in a counterclockwise direction if the current in the coil is reversed each time that the coil passes the PP' plane. A device which automatically reverses the current in the coil at just the right time is called a *commutator*.

We may make the above machine into a simple motor as shown in Fig. 13–8–1 (b), which is a cross section through the motor with the N and S poles rotated 90° from their position in (a), and is drawn to a smaller scale than (a). In Fig. 13–8–1 (b) the coil is mounted on a shaft S_1 and is free to rotate in the bearings B_1 and B_1. Frictional torques, of course, oppose the rotation. An external battery, whose emf is $\mathscr{E}$, is sending a current I through the coil. The contact with the coil is through the brushes B_2 and B_3 to the commutator segments C_1 and C_2. The brushes are mounted on the motor frame and thus remain at rest, while the commutator segments are mounted on the shaft, insulated from it, and rotate with the coil and shaft. Figure 13–8–1 (c) shows an end view of the shaft S_1, the commutator segments C_1 and C_2, and the brushes B_2 and B_3. As the coil, shaft, and commutator segments rotate, while the brushes remain at rest, the splits in the commutator segments pass under the brushes each time that the plane of the coil passes the plane PP' in Fig. 13–8–1 (a), and thus the current in the coil is automatically reversed at the correct time. The torque on the coil remains constant at the value $\tau = NIAB$ while the coil is in the radial part of the magnetic field, and reduces to zero as the coil approaches the PP' plane.

Since the coil is rotating in a magnetic field, the number of magnetic flux linkages with the coil is changing, and an emf is induced in the coil. By Lenz's law this emf is in such a direction as to oppose the motion and thus is in the opposite direction to that of the current I. This emf induced in the motor is called the back emf of the motor, and in Chapter II you have solved numerous problems that involve the back emf of a motor. Also in Chapter II, we considered the conversion of electrical energy into other forms of energy (exclusive of heat) when a current flows against an emf, and we included the conversion of electrical energy into mechanical energy in a motor.

2. A MORE PRACTICAL MOTOR. The motor just described can develop only a small torque, because a permanent magnet with large area of pole faces produces a relatively small magnetic flux density B. Further, the number of turns of wire that can be wound on a plane coil is very limited unless the wire has a small area of cross section. A wire with a small area of cross section will become overheated unless the current I is kept small. The above motor also has the disadvantage that the torque becomes zero twice during each revolution of the coil, and thus the motor produces a fluctuating torque. Further, this simple motor has a "dead center," since it could not start itself again if it were to stop with the plane of the coil in the PP' plane. Hence, let us

consider a more practical d-c motor. The basis principle of operation is, however, the same for all d-c motors.

Figure 13–8–2 (a) shows in cross section the motor that we shall discuss. The coil is made a part of the soft iron cylinder by embedding the wires (indicated as W's) in slots in the cylinder but electrically insulated from the cylinder. Thus, the soft iron cylinder rotates with the wires and the whole rotating assembly is called the armature. The shaft is an integral part of the armature and is perpendicular to the page, in Fig. 13–8–2, with the bearings in front and behind the page. Since the soft iron cylinder is made of a conducting material and is rotating in a magnetic field, it has emf's induced in it

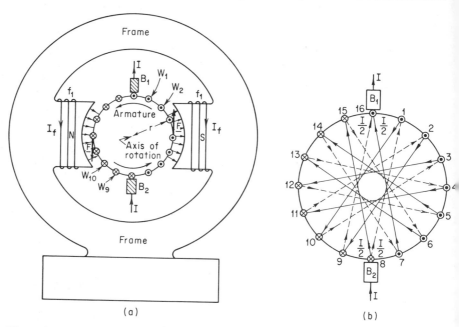

Figure 13–8–2. A d-c motor. (a) Cross section of motor. (b) Armature alone, in cross section and to a larger scale, showing schematically the winding and method of connection. (See Fig. 15–5–2 where the commutator has been added to this type of drum winding.)

which cause circulating currents (called eddy currents) to flow in the cylinder itself. To minimize energy loss due to the eddy currents, the cylinder is built up of thin laminations of soft iron (see Sec. 15–4 for details) which are insulated from each other.

In order to have a greater magnetic flux density, B, than a permanent magnet can produce, wires are wound on the pole pieces N and S, and thus the magnetic field for this motor is produced by an electromagnet. Figure 13–8–2 (a) shows, as f_1 and f_1, a few of these turns of wire which make up the field windings, and indicates as I_f the current that flows through the wires of the field windings. The direction of I_f shown is the one required to produce magnetic flux lines in the direction shown across the air gap between the pole faces and the armature.

The soft steel frame of the motor, the armature, and the air gaps make up the magnetic circuit (see Sec. 17–9). The air gap between the armature and the pole pieces is kept at a minimum for reasons which we shall discuss when we consider the magnetic circuit. For the moment it is sufficient to say that this arrangement gives a large magnetic flux density at the wires which are embedded in the armature.

In Fig. 13–8–2 (b), the same cross section of the armature is redrawn to a larger scale, and the wires embedded in the face of the armature are numbered 1 through 16. These wires are uniformly spaced around the cylindrical periphery of the armature, and the figure shows only a few of them. The lines drawn across the circular cross section of the armature in Fig. 13–8–2 (b) indicate the connections, at either end of the armature, between the numbered wires. The solid lines indicate wires on the end of the armature toward you in the picture, and the dotted lines indicate wires on the far end of the armature below the page. Note first that the winding on the armature is continuous. To see this, start at wire 1 and follow the winding in the direction 1, 10, 3, 12, 5, 14, and so on, back to the starting point at 1. Next notice that the current I that enters brush B_2 divides at wire 8. Half goes down wire 8 across the back of the armature, up wire 1, across to wire 10, down wire 10 and so on until it goes out brush B_1. The other half of the current that enters brush B_2 goes directly across the front end to wire 15, down wire 15, across the back to wire 6, up wire 6, across to wire 13 and so on until it also goes out brush B_1. Thus, there are two paths, of equal resistance, in parallel on the armature. The winding drawn here is called a drum winding, and we have shown the simple drum winding for a two-pole motor. This type of winding is only one of many which may be used. As the armature rotates, whatever its position may be, the current flows up out of the page in all wires on the right side of the armature and down into the page in all wires on the left side of the armature.

The figure is drawn as if the brushes B_1 and B_2 made contact with the wires on the face of the armature. Actually, a commutator with many segments is mounted on the shaft, electrical connection is made from the wires on the armature to the various segments, and the brushes rub on the commutator. The electric circuit, however, is the same as that shown in Fig. 13–8–2.

The length of each wire perpendicular to the page, i.e., down the length of the armature, is called a face conductor. [The face conductors are the numbered conductors in Fig. 13–8–2 (b).] The face conductors are the only parts of the winding on which a force, due to the magnetic field, is exerted. The wires that make the connections across the ends of the armature experience little or no force due to the magnetic field, and are called end connections (or sometimes, dead conductors). As shown in the Fig. 13–8–2 (a), not all the face conductors are in the magnetic field at any given moment, and those that are in the field are called the *active face conductors.*

Each active face conductor experiences a magnetic force which, from (13–1–13), is $F = lIB/2$ where l is the active length, B is the magnetic flux density at the conductor, and $I/2$ is the current flowing in the conductor. [I is the total armature current.] In the simple theory presented here, we shall assume that the magnetic flux lines are radial in the active region of the magnetic field (i.e., under the pole faces) and that B is zero outside this region. The force F on each active conductor is perpendicular to the radius r of the armature, so the armature experiences a torque

$$\tau = \tfrac{1}{2}rIlB \tag{13–8–1}$$

due to each active conductor. Let N represent the number of active conductors (counting the conductors on both sides of the armature) and the total torque on the armature is

$$\tau = \tfrac{1}{2}NrIlB \tag{13 8 2}$$

As the armature rotates, the number N of active conductors under the pole faces is essentially constant, since the conductors are uniformly and closely spaced around the periphery of the armature. Hence, with steady direct current, the motor produces a nearly constant torque as contrasted with the fluctuating torque of the simple motor.

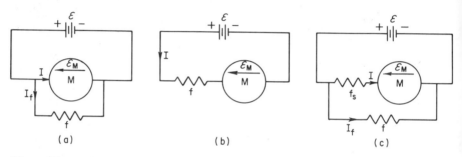

Figure 13–8–3. Three types of connection of the field coils f of a d-c motor relative to the armature M. (a) Shunt. (b) Series. (c) Compound. In each figure the back emf of the motor is designated as $\mathscr{E}_M$.

In general, the same source that supplies the armature current I also supplies the field current I_f. There are three commonly used types of connection of the field coils relative to the armature, and these are shown in Fig. 13–8–3. For a steady direct current flowing through the field coils, these coils behave like a pure resistance because there is no emf of self-induction. Hence, the field coils have been represented as resistors in the figure.

For further details concerning d-c motors you should consult an engineering text* which deals with d-c machinery. We have described only the basic principles.

13–9 PATH OF A CHARGED PARTICLE MOVING WITH CONSTANT SPEED IN A UNIFORM MAGNETIC FIELD

So far in this chapter we have been discussing the magnetic forces on charges which are moving in a conductor, and thus the charges are forced to follow the conductor. In other words, the path of the charges is the path of the conductor.

* For example, C. L. Dawes, *Electrical Engineering, Vol. I, Direct Currents* (New York: McGraw-Hill Book Co., Inc., 1937), pp. 476–526.

Now we wish to consider a case where charged particles are moving through a magnetic field in empty space and thus the paths of the particles are determined by the magnetic field, not by constraints due to a conductor. For this purpose let us imagine that we have an airtight container, say a large glass bulb, and that we have pumped out as much of the air as possible. There will be some residual air molecules but we shall talk only about those charged particles which do not collide with air molecules. We are thinking in terms of charged particles of atomic dimensions, such as protons (hydrogen nuclei) or alpha particles (helium nuclei) or electrons, whose mean free paths are long in the residual gas in our container.

These particles, of atomic dimensions, fall under the action of the force of gravity as does any other body. However, we assume that the velocities of the particles are large in the direction that we indicate, and thus that the time required for the particle to travel over the path under discussion is too short for the fall of the particle to influence the discussion. Hence, in our discussion, we neglect entirely the force of gravity on the particle. It turns out in practice that, in most experiments where the results obtained here are needed, the velocities of the charged particles are high enough to meet the conditions of our assumption.

Now imagine that there is a uniform magnetic field of flux density B all through the region occupied by the container. Thus, any particle with a charge q moving with a velocity v in this region will experience a force, due to the magnetic field, given by (13–1–9). We have seen that (13–1–9) contains the correct magnitude and direction for either a positive or a negative charge moving at any angle with respect to the direction of B.

We shall assume that no electric field is present in the region, so the charge does not experience a force due to an electric field.

1. VELOCITY v PERPENDICULAR TO B. Let us consider an important special case in which the charged particle, of mass m, is moving with constant speed, and its velocity vector is perpendicular to the direction of B. In Fig. 13–9–1 (a) imagine that a particle with a positive charge q is at P at a particular moment and has a velocity v in the direction of the v vector. The magnetic field is perpendicular to the page and directed out of the page, as indicated by the square array of dots, which we interpret as tips of B vectors pointing out of the page. The magnitude of the magnetic force F on the particle is given by (13–1–10) as $F = qvB$ and is in the direction indicated by the F vector. (A negatively charged particle would, of course, experience a force in the opposite direction.) Since the force is perpendicular to the velocity, the acceleration is perpendicular to the velocity and does not alter the magnitude of the velocity, only its direction. As you learned in mechanics, a body that moves with constant speed but at all times experiences a force which is perpendicular to its velocity will move in a circle of such radius r that the central force furnishes the required centripetal force. Also, you learned in mechanics that the required centripetal force is given by

$$F_c = mv^2/r \qquad (13\text{–}9\text{–}1)$$

Hence, the charged particle will move in a circle of such radius r that the magnetic force, qvB, furnishes the required centripetal force, mv^2/r, so $qvB = mv^2/r$, or

$$r = mv/qB \qquad (13\text{-}9\text{-}2)$$

Thus, we conclude that the path followed by the charged particle is a circle whose radius is given by (13–9–2).

2. VELOCITY v AT AN ANGLE ϕ WITH RESPECT TO B. Next let us consider a slightly more general case in which the speed of the charged particle is still constant and the magnetic field is still uniform, but this time the direction of the velocity of the particle makes any angle ϕ with respect to the direction of the magnetic field. This case is pictured in Fig. 13–9–1 (b), where the magnetic flux lines and the velocity vector are drawn in the plane of the figure.

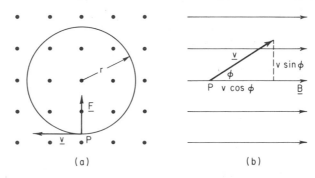

(a)   (b)

Figure 13–9–1. Path of a positively charged particle in a magnetic field. (a) Particle moving with constant speed perpendicular to a uniform magnetic field. (b) Same as (a) except that the direction of the velocity of the particle makes an angle ϕ with the direction of the magnetic field.

We may solve this problem most conveniently by dividing v into two components, one parallel to B and the other perpendicular to B. The component $v \sin \phi$, perpendicular to B, will cause the charged particle to move in a circle just as before, but now we must use $v \sin \phi$ in place of v. Hence, the radius of the circle, from (13–9–2), will be

$$r = (mv \sin \phi)/qB \qquad (13\text{-}9\text{-}3)$$

At the same time that the charged particle is going around this circle, it is also moving parallel to B with the constant velocity $v \cos \phi$. Hence, its path will be a helix. You may visualize this helical path by considering a coiled spring (such as a screen door spring) with its length parallel with the flux lines, and consider that the particle follows the path represented by the wire of the spring. If ϕ is small, so that $v \cos \phi$ is large, stretch the spring considerably, because the charged particle travels a considerable distance along a flux line while it makes one trip around a circle. If ϕ approaches 90°, so that $v \cos \phi$ is small, let the spring contract, because the particle travels only a short distance along a flux line while it makes one trip around a circle. If ϕ is 90°, we have the case treated earlier, and the particle goes around in the same circle all the time.

In the next sections we shall discuss a few applications of the theory developed here. These will apply to important scientific experiments.

13–10 THE RATIO OF CHARGE TO MASS FOR AN ELECTRON. BAINBRIDGE METHOD*

In (13–9–2) we expressed the radius of the circle traversed by a charged particle when it moves with constant speed v at right angles to a magnetic field of flux density B. This formula for the radius of the circle contains the mass m and charge q of the particle, and tells us that the ratio q/m could be computed after measuring r, v, and B, i.e., $q/m = v/rB$. The charge on an electron is usually represented by e so, for an electron, we may write

$$e/m = v/rB \qquad (13\text{–}10\text{–}1)$$

You will recall that the charge e can be measured by the Millikan Oil Drop Experiment. Thus, if we measure e/m we shall be able to compute the mass, m, of an electron. The mass of an electron is an important physical constant and not one that can be measured by the everyday weighing methods of determining mass.

Many methods, starting with Sir J. J. Thomson's in 1897, have used the theory of Sec. 13–9 as a basis for measuring e/m. We shall describe one that is interesting because of its experimental simplicity and elegance in the hands of students. The theory is much the same for all such experiments. As noted above, we need to know the velocity v of an electron when it traverses a circle of measurable radius r in a uniform magnetic field of known flux density B. In the experiment which we are about to describe, the uniform magnetic field is produced by a pair of Helmholtz coils (see Sec. 14–6), and the magnetic flux density at the center of such a pair of coils can be computed from the measured current flowing through

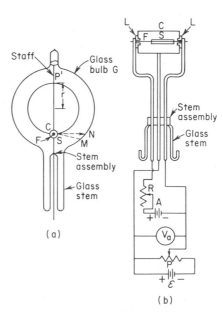

Figure 13–10–1. Tube for measuring e/m for an electron. (a) Cross section of tube. (b) Enlarged diagram of essential parts with control circuit attached.

the wires of the coils, the counted number of turns of wire on the coils, and the measured dimensions of the coils. Thus, we shall assume that we know B when it is needed in the following experiment. The value of B computed from the Helmholtz formula must be corrected for the B of the earth's magnetic field (see Problem 14–17).

Figure 13–10–1 (a) shows the experimental tube, which consists of an evacuated spherical glass bulb G with a metal cylinder C and tungsten filament

* For a description of an undergraduate laboratory experiment using this method see K. T. Bainbridge, "Specific Charge of the Electron," *Am. Phys. Teacher*, **6**, 35 (1938).

F mounted inside by means of a stem assembly. The stem assembly, cylinder, filament, and their supports are shown in Fig. 13–10–1 (b) to four times as large a scale. Here *L* and *L* are insulators between the filament *F* and the ends of the cylinder. Figure 13–10–1 (b) also shows the external circuit used to operate the tube. Some of these electrons from the heated filament *F* are aimed toward the slit *S* in the side of the cylinder and come out into the space outside the cylinder, where they travel with constant speed until they make collisions. It is these electrons that we use for our experiment.

Inside the tube is a drop of liquid mercury, so mercury vapor at low pressure is present all through the tube. When an electron with sufficient energy (10.4 electron volts or more) collides with a mercury vapor atom in the right kind of a collision, the atom is ionized. When an ionized mercury atom captures a stray electron, the atom radiates light. Some of the electrons in the beam that come out through the slit *S* make ionizing collisions with mercury atoms, and the light from the recombination that follows makes the path of the electrons visible. Thus, we "see" the path of the electrons by this secondary process of recombination, and it is the fact that the path of the electrons is visible that makes a striking experiment. The radius *r* of the electrons' path is obtained by sighting this visible circle against cross bars on the staff *CP*. The distance from *F* to each cross bar was measured before the tube was assembled.

So far we have the radius *r* of the circle and the magnetic flux density *B*. Thus, there remains a calculation of the speed *v* of the electrons. The electrons acquired their velocity by acceleration in the electric field between the filament and the cylinder. Using the method of calculation which you developed in Problem 10–10, the speed of the electrons is

$$v = \sqrt{2Ve/m} \,. \qquad (13\text{–}10\text{–}2)$$

where *V* is the potential difference between the filament and the cylinder. Substitute (13–10–2) into (13–10–1) and we have

$$e/m = 2V/B^2r^2 \qquad (13\text{–}10\text{–}3)$$

Thus, e/m may be computed, since all quantities on the right are now known.

The average value obtained from more precise experiments that the one described here is $e/m = 1.75890 \times 10^{11}$ coulomb/kg. Then with the charge on the electron known as $e = 1.60206 \times 10^{-19}$ coulomb, we obtain for the mass of the electron $m = 9.1083 \times 10^{-31}$ kg.

13–11 BASIC THEORY OF THE CYCLOTRON

When a high-speed positive ion collides with an atomic nucleus, a nuclear transmutation may result, i.e., the original nucleus may be changed into the nucleus of an atom of a different chemical element. The transmutation results because the bombarding ion has either added protons to the target nucleus or removed protons from the target nucleus. Other types of nuclear reactions as well are produced and studied in such bombardment experiments, and a great deal of information about nuclei has been obtained and is being obtained in this manner. In this section we wish to discuss the basic principles of one type of instrument, the cyclotron, which is used to accelerate positive ions to such a speed that they have the energy necessary to produce transmutations. Although the cyclotron is a large and complex instrument, its basic principles of operation are simple, and follow directly as applications of theory which we have developed.

Figure 13–11–1 shows a schematic diagram of the cyclotron with a vertical cross section shown in (a) and a horizontal cross section, viewed from above, shown in (b). The N and S poles of the large electromagnet are shown in Fig. 13–11–1 (a). To give an idea of size, the University of California cyclotron at Berkeley has pole pieces of 60 in. diameter. In the gap between the pole

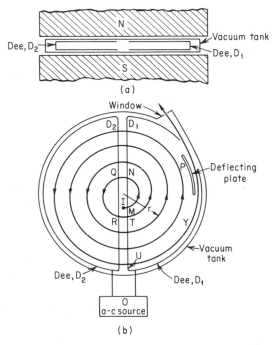

Figure 13–11–1. Schematic diagram of cyclotron. (a) Vertical cross section. (b) Horizontal cross section viewed from above. Magnetic flux is directed down into the page in (b).

faces is an airtight metal tank (called the vacuum tank in the figure), which is evacuated to a sufficiently low residual air pressure so that an ion moving within the tank has a long mean free path. Inside the tank is a pair of metal dees shown as D_1 and D_2 in the figure. The origin of the name dee is obvious from comparison of the shape of each one with the letter D. Note that each dee has an upper and lower face with empty space between its faces, and that the dees are mounted so that there is a gap between the straight sides of the two dees. The two dees are insulated electrically from each other.

The magnet pole faces are so shaped that there is a uniform magnetic field all through the region occupied by the dees. At I in Fig. 13–11–1 (b) is a source of the kind of positive ions desired in a particular experiment. It is usually a gas discharge tube and, if protons are desired, hydrogen gas is used; if alpha particles, helium gas is used; if deuterons, heavy hydrogen gas is used.

A potential difference is applied across the gap between the dees by means of the source O. Thus, there are electric lines of force across the gap from one dee to the other. However, in the space between the upper and lower faces of each dee there is no electric field, because the metal dees act as electric shields for this region.

Let us imagine that, at a particular moment, D_1 is negative with respect to D_2. Positive ions produced at I are attracted and accelerated toward D_1. Thus, the ions now have a velocity perpendicular to the magnetic field, and move in arcs of circles of increasing radii as long as they are being accelerated. At M the ions go into the space between the upper and lower faces of D_1 and thus are no longer accelerated by the electric field, so they travel with constant speed and traverse the semicircle MN. (In the figure the width of the gap between the dees is grossly exaggerated with respect to the diameter of the dees.) Now suppose that, while the ions are traversing the semicircle MN, the electric field between the dees is reversed, and that D_2 is now negative. The ions are again accelerated from N to Q and thus move in arcs of circles of increasing radii until they arrive at Q. Here they go into the space between the upper and lower faces of D_2 and have no acceleration due to the electric field. They now traverse the semicircle QR, but this semicircle is of larger radius than MN because the ions have a higher speed. While the ions are traversing the semicircle QR the potential difference between the dees is again reversed, and when the ions arrive at R, D_1 is negative and the ions are again accelerated across the gap and arrive at T. This process continues, and each time that the ions cross the gap they are accelerated, and each time that they travel in the space between the upper and lower faces of a dee they traverse a semicircle. Only a few of the semicircles are shown in Fig. 13–11–1 (b). Finally the ions reach the outer semicircle UY and travel into the space between the plate P and the outside back wall of D_1. Plate P is positively charged and deflects the ions just enough so they go through the hole in the back wall of D_1, through the window, and into the target chamber. Here some of them collide with atomic nuclei whose transmutations are being studied.

Now we must see how and why it is possible to achieve the operation described above. Let q represent the positive charge on an ion. If the ion is a proton or deuteron, q is positive but equal in magnitude to the electronic charge. If the ion is an alpha particle (helium nucleus), q is positive but has a magnitude twice that of the electronic charge. From (13–9–2) the radius r of any semicircle is given by $r = mv/qB$, where m is the mass of the ion, v is its speed, and B is the magnetic flux density. Hence,

$$v = rqB/m \tag{13–11–1}$$

Let t_s be the time required for the ion to traverse a semicircle, with the constant speed v, and we have $t_s = \pi r/v = \pi r m/rqB$, or

$$t_s = \pi m/qB \tag{13–11–2}$$

Equation (13–11–2) is fundamentally important for the cyclotron because r has canceled. Thus, the equation shows us that the time required for a given kind of ion to traverse any semicircle is the same as the time required for that ion to traverse any other semicircle. This is true if m and B are the same on all semicircles (q is a constant for a given kind of ion). The magnet is carefully designed to give a uniform magnetic field, so B is the same at all semicircles. We know from relativity theory that the mass of a body increases as the velocity of the body approaches that of light, and some of the laws that we have discussed are altered. But for velocities below about one-tenth of the velocity of light we may neglect these changes. This condition imposes a fundamental upper limit to the operation of the instrument as a simple cyclotron, and we shall have a little more to say later on this point. Thus, within the limits on velocity mentioned, all ions of a given kind on all semi-circles traverse a semicircle in the same length of time. Those that start on various semicircles at the same instant are ready to cross the gap simul-taneously and are all accelerated together. Hence, an a-c source O can be used to reverse the electric field across the gap at regular intervals spaced t_s apart. The a-c source is called an oscillator.

Let us next compute the frequency, f, that the oscillator must have in order to synchronize with the trips of the ions around the semicircles. Let T be the time for an ion to go completely around one trip, so $T = 2t_s$. Then $f = 1/T$, so

$$f = qB/2\pi m \qquad (13\text{–}11\text{–}3)$$

and the required frequency depends on the charge-to-mass ratio of the ions that are being accelerated and the magnetic flux density B in the gap between the pole faces of the magnet. The frequency for most cyclotrons is in the neighborhood of 10 megacycles/sec (10×10^6 cycles/sec), and the flux density is in the neighborhood of 1.5 webers/m^2.

Next let us compute the final energy acquired by an ion in the multiple accelerations across the gap between the dees. Equation (13–11–1) gives the velocity of an ion as it travels on any semicircle of radius r. Let r_M be the radius of the outermost semicircle [UY in Fig. 13–11–1 (b)], and from (13–11–1) the velocity v_M of the ion on this semicircle is

$$v_M = r_M qB/m \qquad (13\text{–}11\text{–}4)$$

Hence, the final kinetic energy of the ion is

$$KE = mv_M^2/2 = r_M^2 q^2 B^2/2m \qquad (13\text{–}11\text{–}5)$$

Using mks units, this energy will, of course, be in joules when computed from (13–11–5). As stated in Problem 10–16, the electron volt is defined as the energy acquired by an electron when it rises through a potential difference of 1 v. In that problem you showed that there is 1.60×10^{-19} joule/ev. The Mev (million electron volts) is probably the most commonly used energy unit in discussions of atomic and nuclear physics, so the energy of the ions from a cyclotron is usually expressed in Mev. From the above, there is 1.60×10^{-13} joule/Mev, and you can readily convert energy computed in joules to the equivalent energy in Mev.

As an example of the energies obtained with a cyclotron, the Pittsburgh cyclotron with a 47 in. pole diameter produces protons with an energy of 8 Mev, deuterons with 16 Mev, and alpha particles with 32 Mev.

SYNCHROCYCLOTRON. As pointed out earlier in this discussion, the relativity change of mass with velocity puts an upper limit on the energy that can be attained with simple cyclotron operation. From (13–11–3) we see that the frequency of the oscillator must be decreased as the mass of the ion increases in order to keep the reversal of the electric field at the gap in the dees in synchronism with the ions. For this purpose the larger cyclotrons (e.g., the Berkeley cyclotron with 184 in. pole diameter) are equipped with variable frequency oscillators. The oscillator selects a group of ions and gradually decreases its frequency as the ions go to larger and larger semicircles, always keeping in synchronism with the ions. By this means ions are accelerated to velocities where the change of mass with velocity is very appreciable. The Berkeley synchrocyclotron, for example, gets protons with an energy in the neighborhood of 350 Mev.

For a discussion of the many problems, in addition to basic theory, which must be solved for both the cyclotron and synchrocyclotron, a book* which discusses the instruments of nuclear physics should be consulted. The same book discusses many other instruments which employ the same basic theory. Some are designed for the acceleration of the ions to high velocities, others are designed for use in the measurement of the energies of particles produced in nuclear reactions. Still others are used to measure the relative masses of atoms.

PROBLEMS

13–1 Carry out the direct multiplication indicated in (13–1–7), use the relationships given in (13–1–5), and show that (13–1–8) results.

13–2 A proton has a velocity, in m/sec, given by $v = 5520i + 2170j + 3860k$ in a magnetic field whose flux density in wb/m² is given by $B = 0.864i - 0.539j + 0.223k$. Show that the vector expression for the magnetic force on the proton, in newtons, is $F = (4.10i + 3.36j - 7.76k) \times 10^{-16}$.

13–3 A charge q is travelling through a region where there is an electric field given, in newtons/coulomb, by the equation $E = 3.28i - 4.35j + 9.12k$. Superimposed on the electric field is a magnetic field whose flux density, in wb/m², is given by $B = 2.00i + 3.00j + 4.00k$. The velocity of the charge is $v = 1.00i + 3.00k$ in m/sec at the point where the above vector expressions give the values of E and B. Find the force on the charge at this point. [*Ans:* $F = q(-5.72i - 2.35j + 12.1k)$.]

13–4 (a) Find the magnitude and direction of the magnetic force on 10 m of wire suspended horizontally in a magnetic east-west direction at a place (in the northern hemisphere) where the earth's magnetic field has a flux density of 5.9×10^{-5} wb/m². At this place the earth's field is directed at a dip angle (angle with the horizontal) of 73°. The wire carries a current of 50 amp flowing west. Show, by substitution of units with numerical quantities, that the force comes out in newtons. [*Ans:* 0.030 newton directed southerly and 17° below the horizontal.] (b) The wire in the above problem is No. 7 American Wire Gauge, which according to the wire tables, weighs 63 lb

* For example D. Halliday, *Introductory Nuclear Physics*, 2d ed. (New York: John Wiley & Sons, Inc., 1955), pp. 283–310.

per 1000 ft. How does the magnetic force compare in magnitude with the weight of the wire? [*Ans:* Magnetic force is about 0.0030 of the weight.]

13-5 A straight wire on the face of the armature of a motor is 20 cm long and carries a current of 25 amp perpendicular to the magnetic field whose uniform flux density is 1.0 wb/m². (a) Find the magnetic force in pounds on the wire. [*Ans:* 1.1 lb.] (b) Find the work done by the magnetic force if the wire moves 10 cm parallel to the force.

13-6 The magnetic force on a certain section of a straight wire in a uniform magnetic field is given by the equation $F = 2.0$ meter **20** amp × **0.50** weber/meter² where $\phi = 60°$. Draw a possible figure that shows the physical situation described by this problem and label the force vector with its magnitude.

13-7 A plane coil has 50 turns of wire and is situated in a uniform magnetic field whose flux density is 0.350 wb/m². The area of the face of the coil is 0.0620 m², and a current of 12.0 amp flows in the wires of the coil. (a) What torque does the magnetic field exert on the coil when the torque is at its maximum? Show by substitution of units with the numerical quantities, that the answer for the torque comes out in meter newtons. [*Ans:* 13.0 meter newtons.] (b) You hold the coil from turning by grasping it at a distance of 5.00 cm from the axis of rotation. What is the minimum force, in pounds, that you must exert to hold the coil at rest? [*Ans:* 58.6 lb.]

13-8 Figure 13-P-1 (a) shows a lightweight wire stirrup which rests on metal supports S_1 and S_2, is free to rotate about the axis of rotation indicated,

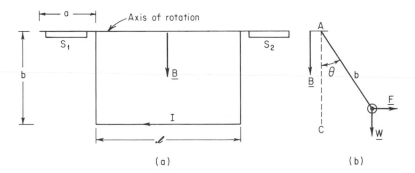

(a) (b)

Figure 13-P-1. Stirrup for measuring magnetic flux density.

and has the dimensions shown. A current I is sent through the stirrup from an external battery. The current flows in through S_2, goes around the stirrup and out through S_1. The stirrup is situated in a uniform magnetic field of flux density B and under the action of the magnetic force F, swings out to the position in cross section in Fig. 13-P-1 (b), where it is in equilibrium. (a) If ρ is the uniform mass per unit length of the wire of which the stirrup is made and g is the acceleration of gravity, prove that the magnetic flux density* B is given by $B = [\rho g(b + l) \tan \theta]/lI$. (b) In a measurement of

* Professor Edgar Everhart describes an interesting laboratory method of measuring B between the poles of a permanent magnet, using the scheme suggested by the theory of this problem. See "An Experiment for the Direct Measurement of Magnetostatic Fields," *Am. J. Phys.*, **19**, 474 (1951).

magnetic flux density by the method suggested here the following data are obtained: $\rho = 1.2 \times 10^{-2}$ kg/m, $b = 0.055$ m, $l = 0.043$ m, $\theta = 42°$, $I = 15$ amp. What is the value of B? Show, by substitution of units, that the answer comes out in wb/m². [*Ans:* 0.016 wb/m².]

13–9 Starting with (13–1–15) and Fig. 13–P–2, prove that the torque on a plane circular coil of wire with N turns, in a uniform magnetic field of flux density B is given by $\tau = NIA \times B$ where I is the current flowing in each turn of the coil and A is the area of the face of the coil. First, in Fig. 13–P–2 (a), show that $d\tau$ due to dF on the element dl of length of wire is $d\tau = dl\, IBr \sin^2 \phi$ and then sum for all such $d\tau$'s for all the dl's. Why can you

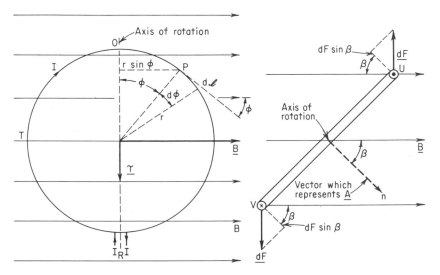

Figure 13–P–2. Circular coil of wire in a uniform magnetic field. (a) Normal n to the face of the coil is perpendicular to the flux lines. (b) Coil in cross section when the normal n is at an angle β to the flux lines.

use the scaler summation of integration when a vector sum is required? Next consider the more general case in Fig. 13–P–2 (b) and derive the required torque formula.

13–10 A certain radial magnetic field D'Arsonval galvanometer has a coil with 100 turns of wire and a face area of 3.00 cm². The magnetic flux density at the coil sides is 0.250 wb/m². The torsion constant of the 24 K gold strip suspension is 6.00×10^{-3} cm dyne/radian of twist for the 10.0 cm length of the suspension.

What current through the coil of the galvanometer will produce a scale deflection of 1.00 cm at a scale distance of 1.00 m? Substitute units with numerical quantities and show that a proper unit comes out for the answer. [*Ans:* 4.00×10^{-10} amp.]

13–11 The tag on a certain D'Arsonval current galvanometer shows its $CDRX$ to be 10,000 ohms. The galvanometer has a current sensitivity of 2.00×10^{-10} amp/mm deflection at a scale distance of 1.00 m, and is to be used in a circuit whose resistance is large compared with the $CDRX$. The length of the galvanometer scale is 50 cm. The galvanometer has a resistance of 500 ohms.

It is computed that the maximum current in the main circuit, during a series of measurements, will be approximately 10^{-5} amp. Explain quantitatively, with the aid of a circuit diagram, how the galvanometer may be critically damped for these measurements and at the same time the sensitivity of the galvanometer may be reduced so that a current in the main circuit of 10^{-5} amp will produce no more than full-scale deflection.

13–12 Figure 13–P–3 shows an *Ayrton* shunt which is often used to control the sensitivity of a galvanometer and at the same time provide the critical damping resistance. Here A, B, C, and D are metal posts mounted on the top of an insulating box with the resistors, R_{AB}, R_{BC}, and R_{CD}, enclosed in the box and connected electrically to the posts as shown; K is an insulating knob by means of which the metal arm F may be rotated into contact with

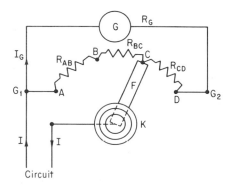

Figure 13–P–3. Ayrton shunt for critical damping and control of sensitivity of a galvanometer.

any one of the metal posts. Let R represent the total resistance of R_{AB}, R_{BC}, and R_{CD} in series. With F on any post, let R/n represent the resistance from A to the metal arm F via the resistors mounted in the box ($R/n = R_{AB} + R_{BC}$ as the picture is drawn) where n is any number greater than unity. Then the resistance from the metal arm F to D, via the resistors mounted in the box, is $R - R/n$. (a) Prove that $I_G = IR/n(R_G + R)$. (b) Each post [A, B, C, and D] of an Ayrton shunt is commonly marked to show the fraction of the line current I that passes through the galvanometer when the arm F is set on that post. A galvanometer requires a $CDRX$ of 20,000 ohms and its coil resistance is 200 ohms. Calculate the values of R_{AB}, R_{BC}, and R_{CD} such that post A may be marked 0, post B may be marked $\frac{1}{100}$, post C may be marked $\frac{1}{10}$, and post D may be marked 1, within an accuracy of 5%. [*Ans:* R_{AB} = 200 ohms, R_{BC} = 1800 ohms, R_{CD} = 18,000 ohms.]

13–13 (a) A standard 0.500 μf capacitor is discharged through a ballistic galvanometer and the following values are recorded for the successive maxima of the galvanometer deflections, in cm, on the same side of zero: $d_1 = 16.6$,

$d_3 = 13.7$, $d_5 = 11.1$, $d_7 = 9.1$, $d_9 = 7.5$. On a repetition of the above: $d_1 = 14.7$, $d_3 = 12.3$, $d_5 = 10.2$, $d_7 = 8.5$, $d_9 = 7.0$. What is the average value of the logarithmic decrement for the galvanometer with this capacitor across it terminals? The galvanometer has a curved scale, so the angular deflections (α's) are directly proportional to the scale deflections (d's). [*Ans:* 0.193.] (b) The following table shows the calibration data that are secured for the galvanometer by charging the 0.500 μf standard capacitor to the measured potential differences V listed in column 1 and then immediately discharging the capacitor through the ballistic galvanometer.

Table for Problem 13–13

Column 1	Column 2	Column 1	Column 2	Column 1	Column 2
V	d_1	V	d_1	V	d_1
volts	cm	volts	cm	volts	cm
1.50	19.5	1.00	13.0	0.50	6.4
1.40	18.1	0.90	11.5	0.40	5.1
1.30	16.9	0.80	10.3	0.30	3.8
1.20	15.5	0.70	8.9	0.20	2.5
1.10	14.2	0.60	7.6	0.10	1.3

The deflections in column 2 are the corresponding first maximum throws as recorded from the galvanometer scale readings. Calculate the charge Q in coulomb corresponding to each voltage in Column 1 and the d_m corresponding to each d_1 in Column 2. Plot the calibration curve for the galvanometer plotting Q as abscissa against d_m as ordinate. Is the galvanometer linear? What is its average sensitivity in coulombs/mm deflection? [*Ans:* 3.68×10^{-9} coulomb/mm.]

13–14 A capacitor of unknown capacitance is charged to a potential difference of 0.450 v and then immediately discharged through the ballistic galvanometer of Problem 13–13. The following maximum deflections in cm, all on the same side of the galvanometer zero as used in Problem 13–13, are recorded: $d_1 = 17.8$, $d_3 = 13.8$, $d_5 = 10.7$, $d_7 = 8.3$, $d_9 = 6.4$. (a) What is the average value of the logarithmic decrement of the galvanometer with the unknown capacitor across its terminals? [*Ans:* 0.255.] (b) What is the capacitance of the unknown capacitor? [*Ans:* 1.6 μf.]

13–15 In Fig. 13–P–4 the battery of constant emf $\mathscr{E}$ is sending current i through the galvanometer and a resistance R. The switch is closed at $t = 0$ and the current starts at zero and rises to the final value $I = \mathscr{E}/(R + R_g)$. The instantaneous back emf e_g of the galvanometer exists, because its coil turns in the magnetic field of its magnet. The self inductance of the galvanometer coil is represented by L_g and its resistance is represented by R_g. (a) Using Kirchhoff's second law, set up the electrical differential equation for this circuit. Next assume, as is usually done in galvanometer dynamics, that L_g is so negligibly small that the $L_g \, di/dt$ term can be neglected. (b) Guided by (13–6–9), set up the

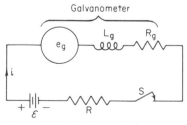

Figure 13–P–4. Rise of current in a galvanometer circuit.

differential equation for Newton's second law for rotational motion for the galvanometer coil system in this case. Combine this equation with the one in (a) and arrive at

$$J \, d^2\alpha/dt^2 + P \, d\alpha/dt + k\alpha = NABI \qquad (13\text{–}P\text{–}1)$$

where J, k, N, A, and B have the same meanings as in (13–6–9). Show what terms go to make up the constant P.

13–16 Using Kirchhoff's second law, set up the differential equation for the circuit in Fig. 13–P–5 in terms of the instantaneous charge q (*not* in terms of current) on the capacitor as a function of time after the switch S is closed. Compare this differential equation with the one in (13–P–1) for Problem 13–15 and note that they are identical in form with L replacing J, R replacing P, $1/C$ replacing k, and $\mathscr{E}$ replacing $NABI$ and that all these quantitites are constants in both equations. The variable q replaces the variable α, the variable t has the same meaning in both equations, and they have the same boundary conditions. The solution of Problem 6–13 is a solution of the differential equation for the circuit in Fig. 13–P–5 and thus is a solution of (13–P–1) of Problem 13–15. Hence from the answers printed for

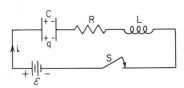

Figure 13–P–5. Charging a capacitor from a source of constant emf $\mathscr{E}$. Switch is closed at $t = 0$.

Problem 6–13 (without solving the differential equation for Fig. 13–P–5 again), write down the answers for (13–P–1) in the three cases of the overdamped, critically damped, and oscillatory galvanometer. Sketch rough curves showing the angular deflection α of the galvanometer as a function of time after S is closed in Fig. 13–P–4.

13–17 (a) The standard 0.500 µf capacitor of Problem 13–13 may be looked upon as an ideal capacitor, since it is found by measurement to have lost a negligible amount of its charge during 5 min after it is charged and insulated. Explain how such a measurement could be made. (b) An unknown resistance is connected across the terminals of the standard 0.500 µf capacitor of Problem 13–13 and left there for the remainder of the following experiment. A 1.50 v potential difference is connected across the parallel combination and shortly afterward disconnected. Immediately after the potential is disconnected the capacitor is discharged through the ballistic galvanometer of Problem 13–13 and the following scale readings in cm are obtained: $d_1 = 19.5$, $d_3 = 16.0$, $d_5 = 13.1$, $d_7 = 10.8$, $d_9 = 8.8$. Next the 1.50 v potential difference is again connected across the parallel combination, and when the potential difference is disconnected a stop watch is started. When the stop watch reads 20.0 sec. the capacitor is again discharged through the ballistic galvanometer, and the first throw of the galvanometer is a deflection of 12.9 cm. What is the resistance of the resistor which is connected across the terminals of the capacitor (see Sec. 4–4)? [*Ans:* 100 megohms.]

13–18 A simple d-c motor, such as the one shown schematically in Fig. 13–8–1, uses a permanent magnet whose magnetic flux density in the air gap is 0.10 wb/m². The area of the face of the coil is 50 cm², there are 25 turns of wire on the coil, and an average current of 5.0 amp flows through the coil. (a) What is the maximum torque on the coil? (b) Assuming that the average torque during each revolution is 90% of the maximum torque, compute the mechanical power developed by the motor, in watts and in horsepower, when the motor is turning at 1200 revolutions/min. Remember from mechanics that power is equal to torque times angular velocity. [*Ans:* 7.1 w.]

13–19 A motor like the one in Fig. 13–8–2 has 200 conductors on its armature and 60% are active. The length of each active conductor is 15.0 cm. The flux density under each pole face is 0.800 wb/m². The current flowing through each face conductor of the armature winding is 20.0 amp. (This means that the armature current I is 40.0 amp, because there are two identical paths in parallel.) The radius of the armature is 10.0 cm and the motor is turning at 1800 revolutions/min. (a) What mechanical power is developed by the motor? [*Ans:* 5440 w, or 7.25 hp.] (b) What is the back emf of the motor? Calculate in two ways (see Sec. 3–5 for one method). [*Ans:* 136 v.] (c) If the armature resistance is 0.325 ohm for each of the parallel paths through the armature, what must be the potential difference applied across the motor terminals?

13–20 You have a motor of the kind shown in Fig. 13–8–2, and it is shunt connected as shown in Fig. 13–8–3 (a). When in operation it rotates counterclockwise and you wish to have it rotate clockwise. Explain the changes that you must make in order to secure this reversal.

13–21 Same problem as 13–20 except that the motor is series connected as in Fig. 13–8–3 (b). Explain how to change the direction of rotation of the armature.

13–22 The kinetic energies of moving electrons are often measured by use of the theory of Sec. 13–9. Electrons emitted from the nuclei of radioactive atoms are called beta rays, and the term has been taken for general use, i.e., electrons in motion are often called beta rays regardless of the source from which they come. Hence many types of instruments which measure kinetic energies of moving electrons are called beta ray energy spectrometers. One type of beta ray energy spectrometer is shown schematically in Fig. 13–P–6. Here $AEGH$ is a flat airtight box which is evacuated. The source of electrons is at S, and electrons come out of this source in all directions. Those electrons which are moving in the correct direction go through the very narrow slit at D. The box is between the pole pieces of a large electromagnet, and there is a uniform magnetic field perpendicular to the page all through the box. All electrons with the same velocity travel on circles of the same radius, and those with different velocities travel on circles of different radii. The figure shows three circles, all of the same radius, for electrons of the same velocity which go through the slit D and strike the photographic plate at L, where they produce a developable image. The arc $C_L C_C C_R$ has its center at S and is an arc of the circle of centers for the electron paths shown. Point C_L is the center for the circle from S to L that just clears the left edge of the slit D. Point C_C is the center for the circle from S to L that goes through the center of D, and C_R is the center for the circle that just clears the right edge of D. It will be noted that the three circles from S to L focus approximately at L, and that S, C_C, and L lie on a diameter of the circle through the center of D; hence, the name "semi-

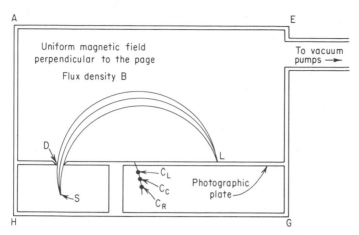

Figure 13–P–6. Semicircular focusing beta ray energy spectrometer.

circular focusing." (a) What is the direction of the magnetic field in Fig. 13–P–6? (b) Redraw Fig. 13–P–6 at least six times as large as it is in the text. Draw the three circles shown for electrons with the same velocity. Draw three more circles for electrons with a larger velocity. Repeat for electrons with a smaller velocity. (c) Tell how the radius of the circle described by the electrons can be measured experimentally after the photographic plate is developed and L is located. (d) Derive the formula $KE = B^2r^2e^2/2m$ for the kinetic energy, KE, of the electrons which traverse a semicircle of radius r. (This formula is good for electron velocities below about one-tenth the velocity of light, i.e., for electron velocities low enough so that the relativity changes in the laws of motion need not be taken into account.) (e) What is the KE of an electron which follows a semicircle of radius 10.0 cm when the magnetic flux density is 0.00114 wb/m²? Does the velocity of this electron exceed the restriction stated in part (d)? Substitute units with numerical quantities and show that the answer comes out in proper units. [*Ans:* 1.83×10^{-16} joule.]

13–23 What magnetic flux density would be required to make a proton follow a semicircle of 10.0 cm radius in the energy spectrometer described in Problem 13–22 if the proton had a velocity of 2.00×10^7 m/sec? [*Ans:* 2.10 wb/m².]

13–24 (a) Look at Fig. 13–9–1 (b) and consider that an electron at P is traveling in an evacuated container with a velocity v in the direction shown. The electron is to make one complete circle, of radius r, on its helical path in the same time that it travels a distance L parallel to the magnetic flux lines. Prove that $r = (L \tan \phi)/2\pi$ gives the relationship between r, L and ϕ in order that the above condition may be satisfied by the electron. (b) Using the above formula and (13–9–3), show that the kinetic energy of the electron is given by $KE = L^2e^2B^2/8\pi^2m \cos^2 \phi$ (if the velocity of the electron is not high enough so that relativity change of mass with velocity need be taken into account). Here e is the charge on the electron. The theory here is the basis for another important type of beta ray energy spectrometer. (c) What are the velocity and kinetic energy of an electron that makes one complete circle while it travels a distance of 1.0 m parallel to the magnetic flux lines? The magnetic flux density is 5.0×10^{-4} wb/m², and the velocity of the electron makes an angle of 30° with the direction of B. [*Ans: KE* $= 1.2 \times 10^{-16}$ joule.]

13-25 Using the experiment described in Sec. 13–10 for the measurement of e/m for electrons, the following data were obtained:

Table for Problem 13–25.

V_a volts	B weber/m² $\times 10^{-4}$	r cm	V_a volts	B weber/m² $\times 10^{-4}$	r cm
20.0	5.22	2.95	70.0	9.57	2.95
	4.32	3.49		8.19	3.49
	3.60	4.16		6.83	4.16
	2.89	5.06		5.60	5.06
30.0	6.30	2.95	90.0	10.85	2.95
	5.31	3.49		9.29	3.49
	4.45	4.16		7.84	4.16
	3.56	5.06		6.36	5.06
50.0	8.15	2.95	100.0	11.53	2.95
	6.87	3.49		9.88	3.49
	5.79	4.16		8.22	4.16
	4.71	5.06		6.75	5.06

The values of B that are given in the table are the corrected values, and the 10^{-4} at the head of the column means that each value in the column is to be multiplied by 10^{-4}.

Calculate the average value of e/m from these data and the percentage error with respect to the accepted value. [*Ans:* about 1% low.]

13-26 In a cyclotron, which has 80 cm usable diameter inside the dees, there is a uniform magnetic flux density of 1.6 wb/m². (a) What is the maximum velocity of a deuteron accelerated in this cyclotron? [*Ans:* 3.1×10^7 m/sec.] (b) How long a time is required for the deuteron to traverse the last semicircle? [*Ans:* 4.1×10^{-8} sec.] (c) What is the maximum kinetic energy, in Mev, acquired by the deuteron? [*Ans:* 9.81 Mev.] (d) If the potential difference across the gap in the dees was 150,000 v each time that the deuteron crossed the gap, how many semicircles did the deuteron traverse? [*Ans:* About 65.]

MAGNETIC FIELD

IN FREE SPACE

DUE TO CURRENTS

14–1 AMPERE'S LAW AND PERMEABILITY μ_0 OF FREE SPACE

As we have pointed out many times, whenever a current flows a magnetic field is always set up by the current. In this chapter we wish to secure more information about the relationship between the current and the magnetic field set up by the current.

Whenever a current flows there must be a complete circuit, and the magnetic flux density B at any point P in the neighborhood of the circuit, must be the B due to the current in all parts of the circuit. For calculation of B at P, it is desirable to divide the circuit into infinitesimal segments, each of length dl, and consider that the current in each segment makes a contribution dB to B at P. Since B is a vector quantity, we expect that we must use vector methods when we calculate the resultant B at P. Hence, for purposes of calculation, it is postulated that the resultant B at P is the vector sum of all the dB's due to the current flowing in all the dl's around the circuit. This postulate is often called the principle of superposition for magnetic fields.

Next we need a differential formula which tells us the magnitude and direction of each of the dB's at P. This differential formula must be in terms of the current I which is flowing in the element dl of circuit length, and in terms of the geometry. Such a formula cannot be established or tested directly by experiment, because it is impossible to have one element of circuit length only. However, Biot suggested a suitable formula, and Ampere worked out many of its implications. This formula is called by various names, including Biot's law, Ampere's law, Biot-Savart law, and Ampere's formula. *Ampere's law* is probably the most common name for the formula and we shall so refer to it. Remember, however, that it is an assumption and its validity must be established by testing the answer that it gives for a complete circuit. Ampere's law has been tested in this fashion many, many times and always found to give an answer that is in agreement with experiment.

In Fig. 14–1–1, imagine that CA is a piece of wire which is a part of an electric circuit located in empty space. We wish to know the element dB of magnetic flux density at P due to the current I flowing in the element dl of length of the wire. Here r is the distance from dl to P, and θ is the angle between dl and r. Ampere's law deals with both the magnitude and direction of dB at P and thus is divided into two parts.

The *first part of Ampere's law* deals with the magnitude of dB and says that dB is proportional to $I \, dl \, (\sin \theta)/r^2$. In the rationalized mks system of units, the constant of proportionality is written as $\mu_0/4\pi$, where μ_0 is called the *permeability of free space*. The term "free space" (or empty space) appears here because there is no material medium near the circuit. Thus, we may write the first part of Ampere's law in a rationalized system of units as

$$dB = \mu_0 I \, dl \, (\sin \theta)/4\pi r^2 \qquad (14\text{--}1\text{--}1)$$

Solving for μ_0 we have

$$\mu_0 = 4\pi r^2 \, dB/I \, dl \sin \theta \qquad (14\text{--}1\text{--}2)$$

and this is the defining equation for μ_0. Substitution of units into (14–1–2)

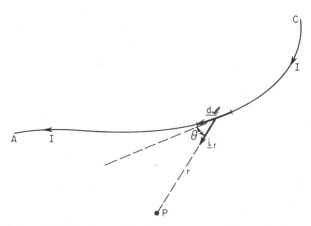

Figure 14–1–1. Illustration for statement of Ampere's law.

gives for the units of $\mu_0 = $ wb/amp m. Since the magnitudes and units of the quantities appearing on the right side of (14–1–2) have all been defined, the numerical value of μ_0 must be such that the forces between current bearing wires will agree with experiment. The exact value of μ_0 is

$$\mu_0 = 4\pi \times 10^{-7} \text{ weber/ampere meter} \qquad (14\text{--}1\text{--}3)$$

in the mks system of units.

The *second part of Ampere's law* deals with the direction of dB and says (see Fig. 14–1–1) that *dB at P has a direction perpendicular to the plane determined by dl and r and is in the sense given by the right-hand rule*. This right-hand rule is the one that you learned in elementary physics, and that we have used previously in Chapters VIII and XIII. It says: in imagination grasp the wire with the right hand, extend the thumb in the direction of the current and the fingers will encircle the wire in the direction of the magnetic flux lines. As an illustration of the use of the second part of Ampere's law, apply it to Fig. 14–1–1. The plane of the page is the plane determined by dl and r, so dB at P is perpendicular to the page and directed out of the page.

Let $\boldsymbol{dl}$ be a vector pointed in the direction of the current, which is flowing in dl, and let $\boldsymbol{i_r}$ be a unit vector pointed in the direction of increasing r, i.e., from dl toward P (see Fig. 14–1–1). Then we may incorporate both parts of Ampere's law in a single statement by the use of the vector product as

$$\boldsymbol{dB} = \mu_0 I \, \boldsymbol{dl} \times \boldsymbol{i_r}/4\pi r^2 \qquad (14\text{–}1\text{–}4)$$

As stated earlier, the total magnetic flux density $\boldsymbol{B}$ at P due to the entire circuit is the vector sum of all the $\boldsymbol{dB}$'s due to the current I flowing in all the $\boldsymbol{dl}$'s around the circuit.

14–2 MAGNETIC FIELD INTENSITY H

In electrostatics we found it convenient to introduce the displacement D, which was defined in such a way that D depends on the conduction charges. Similarly, in magnetic fields, it is convenient to introduce a quantity called *magnetic field intensity H*, which depends on the currents flowing in circuits without the constant μ_0 appearing in the formulas. We shall see that it will be necessary to generalize the definition of H when we deal with magnetic properties of materials in Chapters XVI and XVII.

The vector quantity H is introduced by means of an element of magnetic field intensity dH defined from (14–1–4) by

$$\boldsymbol{dH} = I \, \boldsymbol{dl} \times \boldsymbol{i_r}/4\pi r^2 \qquad (14\text{–}2\text{–}1)$$

and $\boldsymbol{dH}$ is a vector which is parallel to $\boldsymbol{dB}$. Thus in empty space, we have

$$\boldsymbol{dB} = \mu_0 \, \boldsymbol{dH} \qquad (14\text{–}2\text{–}2)$$

The magnetic field intensity $\boldsymbol{H}$ at P due to the current in the entire circuit is the vector sum of all the $\boldsymbol{dH}$'s due to current I flowing in all the $\boldsymbol{dl}$'s around the circuit. Since μ_0 is a constant, all the variables on the right side of (14–1–4) are contained in the expression for $\boldsymbol{dH}$. Hence, for a circuit of any shape located in empty space, $\boldsymbol{B}$ at P is related to $\boldsymbol{H}$ at P by the formula

$$\boldsymbol{B} = \mu_0 \boldsymbol{H} \qquad (14\text{–}2\text{–}3)$$

From (14–2–1) or (14–2–3) we see that the unit of H is given by amp/meter.

H is a vector-point function and it is convenient to represent it graphically by *magnetic lines of force.** The convention for drawing the magnetic lines of force is: *the lines of H shall be parallel to H at each point, and the number of magnetic lines of force drawn through an imaginary unit area perpendicular to H shall be numerically equal to the magnitude of H.*

Note that lines of B are magnetic *flux* lines, whereas lines of H are called magnetic lines of *force*. In empty space there are μ_0 times as many magnetic flux lines per unit area as there are magnetic lines of force per unit area for the same magnetic field. Since, from (14–1–3), μ_0 is a number much smaller than unity, there are many times more magnetic lines of force per unit area than there are magnetic flux lines per unit area.

* In Sec. 14–5, under "Basis of the Absolute Electromagnetic System of Units," we shall see the historical reason for calling lines of H lines of force.

Next we wish to consider several examples of circuits with simple geometries and use Ampere's law to compute for each the magnetic flux density B at selected points in empty space.

If there is a material medium around the wires of the circuit the magnetic flux density at a point in the neighborhood of the circuit is due to the magnetization of the medium as well as to the current in the circuit. We shall consider the magnetic properties of matter in Chapters XVI and XVII, so in this chapter we consider that there is empty space around the circuit. It develops, however, that only the ferromagnetic materials (iron, nickel, cobalt, gadolinium, and the ferromagnetic alloys) contribute appreciably to the magnetic flux density. Hence, for practical purposes, the circuits can be in air, and have any nonferromagnetic material nearby, and the result for magnetic flux density is essentially the same as for empty space. This is a convenient situation, since we may insulate our wires and support our circuits by the use of nonferromagnetic materials such as rubber, cambric, tape, mica, glass, wood, and all the usual materials for this purpose. Most materials are nonferromagnetic. However, we shall continue to talk about empty space because the formulas which we shall derive are strictly true only for empty space.

14–3 MAGNETIC FIELD OF A STRAIGHT CONDUCTOR

As the first example of the use of Ampere's law, let us consider a current I flowing in a straight wire and compute the magnetic flux density at a point P in the neighborhood of the wire. If the remainder of the circuit, of which the straight wire is a part, makes appreciable contribution to the magnetic flux density at P, we shall have to arrive at the total flux density at P by additional computations.

Figure 14–3–1 (a) shows the straight wire CA with a current I flowing in it and we wish to compute the magnetic flux density at P due to this much of the circuit only. Let dl be an infinitesimal length of the wire with its direction that of the current as shown. Then r is the distance from dl to P, and i_r is a unit vector directed along r from dl toward P. Angle θ is the angle between dl and i_r as required by Ampere's law. Equation (14–1–4) gives the dB at P due to I flowing in dl. All the dB's at P, due to all the dl's along the straight wire, are perpendicular to the page and directed into the page. Hence, the vector summation of the dB's becomes a scalar summation and we may use integration of the magnitude of dB to find the magnitude of the resultant B at P. Hence

$$B = (\mu_0 I/4\pi) \int dl \, (\sin \theta)/r^2 \qquad (14\text{–}3\text{–}1)$$

It is convenient to carry out this integration in terms of the angle ϕ of Fig. 14–3–1 (a), where ϕ is the complement of θ. Hence $\sin \theta = \cos \phi$. To express dl and r in terms of ϕ, use the relationship $l = r_1 \tan \phi$, so $dl = r_1 \, d\phi/\cos^2 \phi$ and $r = r_1/\cos \phi$. Then (14–3–1) becomes

$$B = (\mu_0 I/4\pi r_1) \int_{\alpha_1}^{\alpha_2} \cos \phi \, d\phi = (\mu_0 I/4\pi r_1) \left[\sin \phi \right]_{\alpha_1}^{\alpha_2}$$

Thus, $$B = \mu_0 I(\sin \alpha_2 - \sin \alpha_1)/4\pi r_1 \qquad (14\text{–}3\text{–}2)$$

and B is perpendicular to r_1 and directed into the page, i.e., in the sense given by the right-hand rule. For the particular location of P as shown in Fig. 14-3-1, α_1 is a negative angle, and the sine of a minus angle is minus the sine of the angle. If however, P were below C at a point such as P', α_1 would be a positive angle and $\sin \alpha_1$ would be positive. Similarly, if P were above A at a point such as P'', both α_1 and α_2 would be negative angles. As mentioned earlier, the contribution to the magnetic flux density at P due to the remainder of the circuit must be calculated separately and added vectorially to the B of (14-3-2) in order to obtain the total flux density at P.

If the straight wire is infinitely long and the remainder of the circuit is so

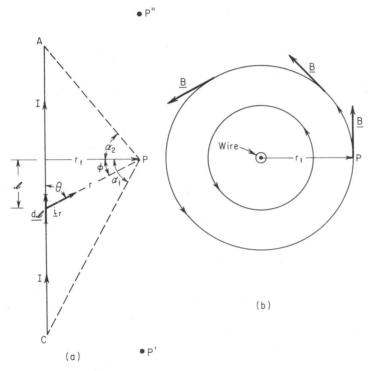

Figure 14-3-1. (a) Computation of the magnetic flux density B at point P due to a current I flowing in a straight wire. (b) Magnetic flux lines about the straight wire.

far away that it makes a negligible contribution to the flux density at P, we may compute the total magnetic flux density at P very simply. In this case $\alpha_2 = \pi/2$ and $\alpha_1 = -\pi/2$ and (14-3-2) becomes

$$B = \mu_0 I / 2\pi r_1 \qquad (14\text{-}3\text{-}3)$$

and, again, B is perpendicular to r_1 and directed into the page. If we write (14-3-3) in terms of the vector product and let i_r now be a unit vector along r_1 in Fig. 14-3-1 (a)

$$\boldsymbol{B} = \mu_0 \boldsymbol{I} \times \boldsymbol{i}_r / 2\pi r_1 \qquad (14\text{-}3\text{-}4)$$

the formula contains statements concerning both the magnitude and direction of B. Equation (14–3–3) is often called the *Biot* and *Savart* law because Biot and Savart discovered it experimentally before Ampere's law was known.

Since $B = \mu_0 H$ from (14–2–3), the magnitude of the magnetic field intensity H at P in Fig. 14–3–1 (a) can be obtained at once from (14–3–2) as

$$H = I(\sin \alpha_2 - \sin \alpha_1)/4\pi r_1 \qquad (14\text{–}3\text{–}5)$$

Also, from (14–3–4), the magnetic field intensity due to an infinitely long wire is

$$H = I \times i_r/2\pi r_1 \qquad (14\text{–}3\text{–}6)$$

Magnetic flux lines for a long straight wire. The requirement on a magnetic flux line is: at every point the line shall be tangent to B at that point. Let us pass an imaginary plane through the wire and through P and have the plane perpendicular to the wire as in Fig. 14–3–1 (b), where the current is flowing up out of the page. Since the B vector must lie in the plane of the page in Fig. 14–3–1 (b), and at every point must be perpendicular to r_1, the magnetic flux line through any point such as P must be a circle of radius r_1 (see also Problem 14–9). Hence, the magnetic flux lines are concentric circles about the wire, with the centers of the circles at the center of the wire. From (14–3–3) the magnetic flux density is inversely proportional to r_1, so the magnetic flux lines will be crowded close together near to the wire and the density of lines will decrease as r_1 increases.

Notice in Fig. 14–3–1 (b) that each magnetic flux line is a *closed* line without beginning or end. We have shown that each magnetic flux line is a closed line for the special case of a straight wire but it is true in general, i.e., *magnetic flux lines are always closed* lines* regardless of the geometry of the circuit. From this we conclude that the number of magnetic flux lines which cut in through any imaginary closed surface in a magnetic field is equal to the number that cut out through the surface, and the net number cutting outward through the surface is always zero. We may express this general proposition by the equation

$$\int_A B_n \, dA = 0 \qquad (14\text{–}3\text{–}7)$$

This situation is in marked contrast with that for electric lines of force which originate on positive charges and terminate on negative charges. Also

---

* As we have pointed out each time that we introduced lines to represent a field, the lines are imaginary and are simply used as a graphical aid to quantitative thinking. But this device, although used for more than a century, has a major weakness; namely, B has a definite magnitude and direction at every point in the neighborhood of a current, so that every point equally deserves to have a magnetic flux line going through it. However, we draw only a finite subset of this infinite bundle of lines and this does not give an exact picture of the magnetic flux. In particular, there are difficulties with the statement that the flux lines around a circuit are always closed. See J. Slepian, "Lines of Force in Electric and Magnetic Fields," *Am. J. Phys.* **19**, 87 (1951). The difficulties do not cause any trouble in applications of the construction of the kind we shall make in this book, but they are all the more reason why we must not ascribe physical reality to the lines which represent a field. The presentation we are using in this book is the traditional one.

the net number of electric lines of force which cut out through an imaginary closed surface is given by Gauss's theorem as

$$\int_A E_n \, dA = q/\varepsilon_0$$

and is zero only if zero net charge q is enclosed in the surface. The distinction between the electrostatic and magnetic phenomena in this respect arises because there are no magnetic "charges."

14-4 FORCE BETWEEN PARALLEL STRAIGHT WIRES; BASIS OF THE DEFINITION OF THE AMPERE

We wish to compute the magnetic force, between two very long parallel straight wires, due to the currents flowing in the two wires. Figure 14–4–1 (a) shows a section of the lengths of the two parallel wires with a current I_1

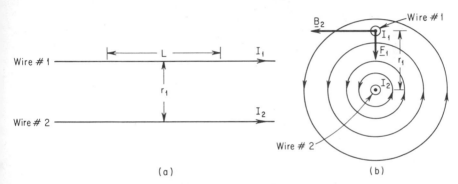

Figure 14–4–1. Magnetic force between parallel straight wires. (a) A section of the lengths of the two wires. (b) Cross section of the two wires with the currents flowing up out of the page and some of the magnetic flux lines due to the current in wire 2.

flowing in wire 1 and current I_2 in wire 2. As the figure is drawn, these currents are flowing in the same direction, and there is a distance r_1 between the centers of the wires. Let us compute the magnetic force on a length L of wire 1 due to the magnetic flux density which the current in wire 2 maintains at wire 1.

Figure 14–4–1 (b) shows the two wires in cross section and shows some of the magnetic flux lines due to I_2 (the flux lines due to I_1 have not been drawn). Since the magnetic flux density B_2 at wire 1 due to I_2 is directed toward the left in Fig. 14–4–1 (b) and I_1 is directed up out of the page, the force F_1 on wire 1 will be toward wire 2 as shown. Thus, currents flowing parallel to each other and in the same direction (like currents) attract each other by their magnetic force.

From (14–3–3) the magnitude of B_2 is given by $B_2 = \mu_0 I_2/2\pi r_1$. From (13–1–13) the magnetic force F_1, on a straight wire in a magnetic field whose flux density is the same in magnitude and direction all along the length L of the wire, is

$$F_1 = LI_1B_2 \tag{14-4-1}$$

Hence $$F_1 = \mu_0 I_1 I_2 L / 2\pi r_1 \tag{14-4-2}$$

An equal and opposite force acts on a length L of wire 2.

If the current in either wire were reversed so that the currents flow in opposite directions (unlike currents), the force on each wire would be reversed and the wires would repel each other.

In Sec. 1–4 we defined *the ampere in the mks system as that unvarying current that will produce a force of precisely* 2×10^{-7} *newton per meter of length of two infinitely long straight parallel wires in empty space when the same current* (of one ampere) *flows in both wires and the wires are one meter apart.* We pointed out there (see also Sec. 14–5) that a force of 2×10^{-7} newton was selected in order that the ampere so defined should agree with the ampere already in use when the mks system was adopted. Equation (14–4–2) is the basic equation for the above definition of the ampere.

In practice in standardizing laboratories, the force between currents flowing in coils (rather than in straight wires) is measured by a weighing process. An instrument for this purpose is called a current balance, and an accuracy of the order of 1 part in 10^5 is attained.

14-5 MAGNETIC FIELD OF A PLANE CIRCULAR COIL OF WIRE

As a second example of the use of Ampere's law, we wish to derive a formula for the magnetic flux density at any point on the axis of a plane circular coil of wire which has a current I flowing in the wires of the coil. Figure 14–5–1

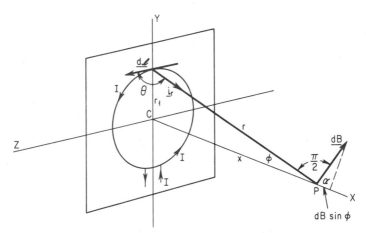

Figure 14–5–1. Magnetic field on the axis of a plane circular coil of wire carrying a current I.

shows the circular coil of radius r_1 in the YZ-plane of a Cartesian coordinate system with the center of the coil at the origin of coordinates. The axis of the coil is a line perpendicular to the plane of the coil and passing through the center of the coil so, in Fig. 14–5–1, the X-axis is the axis of the coil. Thus we wish a formula for B at any point P on the axis of the coil where the coordinate of P is x. We assume that the remainder of the circuit, of which the coil is a part, makes a negligible contribution to B at P.

Consider the element of length dl of the coil shown in the figure. The element dB of magnetic flux density at P due to I flowing in dl (where dl is directed in the direction of the current) is given by Ampere's law in (14–1–4), and is shown as dB in the figure. Element dB has been divided into two components, one along the axis of the coil and the other perpendicular to the axis of the coil.

Imagine another dB (call it dB_2) at P due to the current in a dl across the diameter of the circle from the one drawn. You will see that dB_2 has a component perpendicular to the axis of the coil which is equal and oppositely directed to the component shown for dB. Consider another pair of dl's on opposite ends of any diameter of the circle, and you can see that the components of the dB's at P, perpendicular to the axis will cancel. Thus, all components perpendicular to the axis for all the dB's will cancel in pairs, and the magnitude of B at P is the sum of the components parallel to the axis. Thus, the vector summation of the dB's reduces to a scalar summation of these parallel components and we may use integration for this scalar summation.

Equation (14–1–1) gives the magnitude of dB and the component of dB parallel to the axis is

$$dB \sin \phi = \mu_0 I \, dl \, (\sin \theta)(\sin \phi)/4\pi r^2 \qquad (14\text{–}5\text{–}1)$$

From Fig. 14–5–1, $\theta = \pi/2$ for all dl's around the circle, so $\sin \theta = 1$. As we have shown, the resultant B at P is the sum of the $dB \sin \phi$ components, so

$$B = (\mu_0/4\pi) \int I \sin \phi \, dl/r^2$$

where the integration is to be carried around the circle for a fixed position of P. As the integration is carried around the circle, I, $\sin \phi$, and r remain constant, and l goes from 0 to $2\pi r_1$, so

$$B = \mu_0 I \, (\sin \phi) 2\pi r_1/4\pi r^2 \qquad (14\text{–}5\text{–}2)$$

But $\sin \phi = r_1/\sqrt{r_1^2 + x^2}$ and (14–5–2) becomes, for N turns of wire on the coil,

$$B = N\mu_0 I r_1^2/2(r_1^2 + x^2)^{3/2} \qquad (14\text{–}5\text{–}3)$$

when the N turns of wire are in series on the coil and so closely spaced that we may consider that they all lie in the same plane.

Now consider the special case where the point P is at the center C of the coil in Fig. 14–5–1. Then $x = 0$ and B is given by

$$B = \mu_0 NI/2r_1 \qquad (14\text{–}5\text{–}4)$$

In both (14–5–3) and (14–5–4) the direction of B is along the axis of the coil and in the sense given by the right-hand rule.

From (14–2–3), $B = \mu_0 H$, so we may express the magnitude of the magnetic field intensity for any point on the axis of the coil as

$$H = NI r_1^2/2(r_1^2 + x^2)^{3/2} \qquad (14\text{–}5\text{–}5)$$

and for the center of the coil as

$$H = NI/2r_1 \qquad (14\text{–}5\text{–}6)$$

and H is parallel to B.

BASIS OF THE ABSOLUTE ELECTROMAGNETIC SYSTEM OF UNITS. The absolute electromagnetic system of units (emu) is the parent of the mks system in the sense that many of the units of the mks system were defined as multiples or submultiples of the corresponding emu units before the mks system was unified into a self-consistent system. The units so defined from emu were called *practical units*. The emu system is a very important one frequently encountered in both science and engineering. The emu system is not a rationalized system.

The basic definition of the emu system is the *unit magnet pole* (UP) *which is defined as a pole of such strength that it will repel a like pole* (like as to magnitude and kind) *at a distance of one cm in empty space with a force of one dyne*. We shall reserve our general discussion of magnets for Chapter XVII, but the concept of a unit magnet pole, as defined above, is simple enough.

Next the emu system defines the unit of magnetic field intensity H. First, a magnetic field is defined as a region where a magnet pole experiences a force. Then, by definition, *the magnetic field intensity at a point is the force that would be exerted on a unit north pole placed at the point*. It is from this definition that the usage arose whereby lines of H were called "lines of force." A magnetic field of unit magnetic field intensity is one in which a unit pole experiences a force of one dyne. Thus, the unit of H in this system is dyne/UP and this combination of units is called the oersted. Hence, 1 dyne/UP = 1 oersted.

The unit of current in the emu system is called the abampere and is defined by the use of (14–5–6). However, since the emu system is not rationalized (and the mks system is rationalized), it turns out that (14–5–6) must be multiplied* by the factor 4π in order to give the corresponding formula in the emu system. Thus, in the emu system (14–5–6) becomes

$$H = 2\pi NI/r_1 \tag{14–5–7}$$

From (14–5–7) *the abampere is defined as a steady current of such magnitude that, flowing in a single turn circular loop of wire of one cm radius, it produces a magnetic field of* 2π *oersteds at the center of the circle*, (i.e., a force of 2π dynes is exerted on a UP at the center of the circle). Conversion from magnetic field intensity expressed in oersteds to the equivalent magnetic field intensity expressed in amperes/meter can be made by using the factor given in Appendix A–3.

Also, conversion from current expressed in abamperes to the same current expressed in amperes can be made by using the fact that there are 10 amperes/abampere. In fact, the ampere was originally defined as exactly $\frac{1}{10}$ abampere and thus the magnitude of the ampere was established before the mks system was originated. This fact leads to the choice of the force of precisely 2×10^{-7} newton, which enters into the definition of the ampere in the mks system (as we stated it in Secs. 14–4 and 1–4) in order that the ampere in the mks system shall have the same magnitude as the ampere defined from the abampere. In

---

* This scheme must not be taken as a general rule for conversion of formulas from an unrationalized system into a rationalized system. See W. R. Smythe, *Static and Dynamic Electricity* (New York: McGraw-Hill Book Co., Inc., 1950), pp. 585–89, where tables are given for conversion of formulas in one system of units to the corresponding formulas in another system of units.

the emu system, the unit of magnetic flux density is the *gauss*. Conversion of magnetic flux density from one system to the other can be made by using the factor given in Appendix A–3.

14–6 MAGNETIC FIELD AT THE CENTER OF A PAIR OF HELMHOLTZ COILS

In Sec. 13–10 we used a pair of Helmholtz coils to produce a uniform magnetic field over a limited region. Now we wish to describe the coils and derive the formula by means of which the magnetic flux density may be computed.

As a step toward this goal, consider again the formula for the magnetic flux density on the axis of a plane circular coil as given in (14–5–3). Imagine that a curve which shows B as a function of x has been plotted (see curve 1 Fig. 14–6–1), and let us determine whether or not there is a place where the slope, dB/dx, is constant. If there is such a place, the second derivative of B with respect to x will be zero at that place. From (14–5–3), since μ_0, N, I, and r_1 are constant for changes in the position of P in Fig. 14–5–1,

$$d^2B/dx^2 = -\tfrac{3}{2}\mu_0 NIr_1^2[-5x^2(r_1^2 + x^2)^{-7/2} + (r_1^2 + x^2)^{-5/2}] \qquad (14\text{–}6\text{–}1)$$

Equate the right side of (14–6–1) to zero in order to find the place where d^2B/dx^2 is zero. The coefficient $\tfrac{3}{2}\mu_0 NIr_1^2$ cannot be zero unless the current is zero, and this is a trivial case that does not interest us. Hence, equate the terms in the bracket to zero and solve for x, obtaining

$$x = r_1/2 \qquad (14\text{–}6\text{–}2)$$

Hence, at a point on the axis at a distance $r_1/2$ from the plane of the coil the magnetic flux density is decreasing linearly as x increases.

The above fact suggests that we can obtain a uniform magnetic field by the use of a second plane circular coil identical with the first and carrying the same current. The second coil must be placed with its axis coinciding with the axis of the first (thus its plane is parallel with the plane of the first) and with a separation between the planes of the coils equal to the radius of each coil. The two coils must be connected electrically so that their magnetic fields are in the same direction along their common axis.

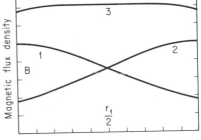

Figure 14–6–1. Magnitude of the magnetic flux density as a function of distance along the axis of a pair of Helmholtz coils. Curve 1, for the left-hand coil only; curve 2, for the right-hand coil only; curve 3, for both coils of the Helmholtz pair.

In Fig. 14–6–1 imagine that coil number 1 has its plane along the left edge of the graph and coil number 2 has its plane along the right edge of the graph. Curve 1 is a plot of the magnitude of the magnetic flux density, along the common axis, due to coil 1 alone [i.e., a plot of B as ordinate against x as abscissa for (14–5–3)]. Curve 2 is a similar plot for coil 2 where, of course,

x is zero at the right side of the plot and increases toward the left for curve 2. Since the two magnetic flux densities, on the axis, due to the two coils are both parallel to the axis and in the same direction, the resultant flux density is the arithmetic sum of the separate flux densities. The magnitude of the resultant magnetic flux density is plotted in curve 3 by addition of ordinates at each abscissa. From curve 3 you can see that, as you progress from left to right, the fall of curve 1 is compensated by the rise of curve 2 for an appreciable distance on either side of the center (which comes at $x = r_1/2$).

Such a pair of coils is known as Helmholtz coils, since Helmholtz first used this combination to produce a uniform magnetic field.

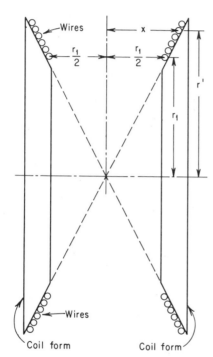

The resultant B at the mid-point of the axis of the two coils is twice the value of B in (14-5-3), with x set equal to $r_1/2$. Hence, B at this point is given by

$$B = 8\mu_0 NI/\sqrt{125}\, r_1 \quad (14\text{-}6\text{-}3)$$

Remember that N is the number of turns of wire on *each coil* of the pair, but B is the total field for the two coils. Moreover, from (14-2-3) $B = \mu_0 H$, so the magnetic field intensity at the center of the Helmholtz coils is given by

$$H = 8NI/\sqrt{125}\, r_1 \quad (14\text{-}6\text{-}4)$$

The derivation of (14-6-3) assumed that each coil is in a single plane and all turns have the same radius, or, failing this, that the distance between each turn of wire on one coil and the corresponding turn on the other coil is equal to the radius of that turn. If there are many turns of wire on each coil the turns cannot be confined to a plane and still have the same radius for all turns. Figure 14-6-2 suggests a coil form which satisfies the second possibility, namely, that the distance between each

Figure 14-6-2. One type of coil form for Helmholtz coils shown in cross section.

turn of wire on one coil and the corresponding turn on the other coil is equal to the radius of that turn.

Our discussion has been confined to the magnetic flux density on the common axis of the two coils. The problem of the magnetic flux density for off-axis positions is not simple.* But it is found that there is an appreciable region around the center point where the magnetic field is essentially uniform and for which (14-6-3) gives a very close approximation of the magnetic flux density. The larger the radius of the coils the larger the region for which this approximation is a good one.

* See H. Nazooka, "Magnetic Field of Circular Currents," *Phil. Mag.*, **41**, 377 (1921).

14–7 MAGNETIC FIELD OF A SOLENOID

A solenoid is a coil of wire wound on the surface of a cylinder as shown in cross section in Fig. 14–7–1 (a). We wish to derive a formula for the magnetic

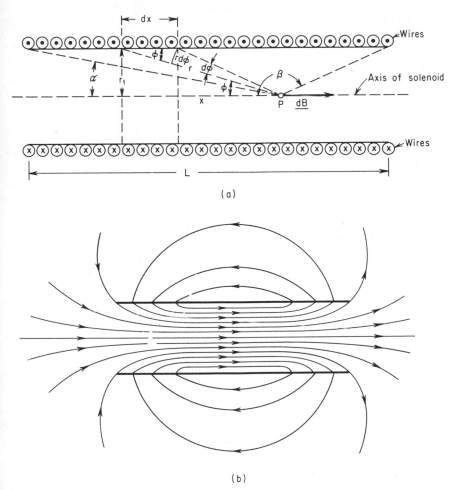

(a)

(b)

Figure 14–7–1. (a) A solenoid shown in cross section. Current is flowing out of the page in the wires on the upper surface (as shown by the dots in the circles which represent the wires in cross section) and into the page in the wires on the lower surface (as shown by the crosses in the circles which represent the wires in cross section). (b) An approximate map of the magnetic flux lines of a solenoid.

flux density on the axis of the solenoid due to the current flowing in the wires of the winding.

In the figure the wires are drawn much too large in cross section relative to the diameter of the cylinder; that is, there should be a great many turns whereas only a few are shown. On a properly wound solenoid the wires are very close together, being separated only by the thin layer of insulation on each wire. Thus, although the winding is a helix, each turn of wire may be considered to be a plane circular loop like the one shown in Fig. 14–5–1. Hence, we may use (14–5–2) for the magnetic flux density on the axis due to each turn of wire. For any point on the axis, such as P in Fig. 14–7–1 (a), the total magnetic flux density is the vector sum of the contributions due to all the turns of wire on the solenoid. All the magnetic flux densities at P, due to all the turns, will be parallel and in the same direction, so we may use integration to find the vector sum.

Let L represent the total length of the solenoid and N represent the total number of turns of wire on the solenoid, so that N/L represents the number of turns of wire per unit length. Let r_1 be the radius of the solenoid. Consider the element of length dx of the solenoid as shown in Fig. 14–7–1 (a). There are $(N/L)\,dx$ turns of wire on the length dx, and each turn contributes a flux density given by (14–5–2), so

$$dB = [\mu_0 I r_1 \,(\sin \phi)N/2r^2L]\, dx \qquad (14\text{–}7\text{–}1)$$

is the element of magnetic flux density at P due to the element of length dx of the solenoid, where, as before, ϕ represents the angle between the axis and a line drawn to dx from P. Thus, $d\phi$ represents the element of angle which dx subtends at P. In (14–7–1), of course, r is the distance from dx to P. Then from Fig. 14–7–1 (a), $r\,d\phi = dx \sin \phi$ and $\sin \phi = r_1/r$. Use these relationships to eliminate r, and (14–7–1) becomes

$$dB = (\mu_0 NI/2L) \sin \phi \, d\phi \qquad (14\text{–}7\text{–}2)$$

which has changed the variable from x to ϕ. Now we wish to add all the dB's at P due to all the dx's from the left end of the solenoid to the right end. This means that ϕ is to go from α to β in Fig. 14–7–1 (a). Hence, integrating from α to β

$$B = \mu_0 NI(\cos \alpha - \cos \beta)/2L \qquad (14\text{–}7\text{–}3)$$

and B is parallel to the axis of the solenoid. Equation (14–7–3) gives the magnetic flux density on the axis of the solenoid not only inside the solenoid but beyond the ends as well.

SPECIAL CASES

1. For P at the mid-point of the axis of the solenoid, $\cos \alpha = \frac{1}{2}L(r_1^2 + L^2/4)^{-1/2}$, $\cos \beta = -\frac{1}{2}L(r_1^2 + L^2/4)^{-1/2}$, and (14–7–3) becomes

$$B = \mu_0 NI/(4r_1^2 + L^2)^{1/2} \qquad (14\text{–}7\text{–}4)$$

2. If the solenoid is very long compared with its diameter and P is not near either end, β is almost $180°$ and α is almost zero, so (14–7–3) becomes

$$B = \mu_0 NI/L \qquad (14\text{–}7\text{–}5)$$

for the magnetic flux density on the axis of the solenoid. In this special case the magnetic flux density is found to be uniform (solve Problem 14–22) across the area of cross section of the solenoid, parallel to the axis of the solenoid, and equal to the magnitude given in (14–7–5). A solenoid built and used so that it satisfies the conditions of this special case is called a *standard solenoid*, and is frequently used for calibration purposes when a known flux density is needed. In (14–7–5) the number N of turns of wire can be counted, the length can be measured as accurately as needed, and the current can be determined with precision.

3. At the end of the solenoid, say the right end, $\beta = 90°$ and, if the solenoid is long compared with its diameter, α is almost equal to zero. Then

$$B = \mu_0 NI/2L \qquad (14\text{–}7\text{–}6)$$

Comparison of (14–7–5) and (14–7–6) shows that the flux density on the axis at the end of a long solenoid has only half as large a magnitude as it has farther inside the solenoid.

Figure 14–7–1 (b) shows an approximate map of the magnetic flux lines of a solenoid. The lines are found to be parallel to each other and parallel to the axis in the center section. Near the ends the lines diverge, and approximately half of the lines have cut through the sides of the solenoid before they reach the end; see (14–7–6). The flux lines are said to "leak" through the sides of the solenoid, and the phenomenon is called *flux leakage*.

Use of (14–2–3) and (14–7–3) shows that the magnetic field intensity H on the axis of a solenoid is

$$H = NI(\cos \alpha - \cos \beta)/2L \qquad (14\text{–}7\text{–}7)$$

and H is parallel to the axis of the solenoid, as is B.

14-8 AMPERE'S LINE INTEGRAL LAW FOR MAGNETIC FLUX DENSITY

We wish to derive the formula known as Ampere's line integral law, which is useful in various calculations. In particular we shall use it in the next section to derive the expression for the magnetic flux density due to current flowing in a toroidal winding.

In Sec. 14–3 we derived the formula in (14–3–3) for the magnetic flux density B at a distance r_1 from a long straight wire which carries a current I. Also, we saw that the magnetic flux lines are circles concentric with the wire. Figure 14–8–1 (a) shows the straight wire in cross section with the current flowing down into the page, and shows one of the magnetic flux lines. We wish to secure the value of the line integral $\int B \cos \theta \, ds$ around any closed path in the magnetic field of the straight wire, where ds is an element of path length and θ is the angle between B and ds. As a start toward this goal, consider the ds shown as an infinitesimal section of the magnetic flux line in Fig. 14–8–1 (a), where ds subtends the angle $d\phi$ at the wire. Since B is parallel to ds, $\theta = 0$ and $\cos \theta = 1$. Thus, from (14–3–3) and Fig. 14–8–1 (a), $B \cos \theta \, ds = \mu_0 I r_1 \, d\phi/2\pi r_1$,

or $\qquad\qquad\qquad B \cos \theta \, ds = \mu_0 I \, d\phi/2\pi \qquad (14\text{–}8\text{–}1)$

Now, as a special example, let us use (14–8–1) to determine the value of the line integral from D to G along the magnetic flux line in Fig. 14–8–1 (a).

$$\int_{(D)}^{(G)} B \cos \theta \, ds = (\mu_0 I/2\pi) \int_{(D)}^{(G)} d\phi$$

This changes from a line integral along the path to an integral in terms of the angle subtended at the wire by the path. Let us now substitute numerical limits for the symbolic limits on the right. At (D), $\phi = \phi_1$; at (G), $\phi = \phi_2$; so

$$\int_{(D)}^{(G)} B \cos\theta \, ds = \mu_0 I(\phi_2 - \phi_1)/2\pi \qquad (14\text{–}8\text{–}2)$$

We see from (14–8–2) that the value of the line integral is the same along all

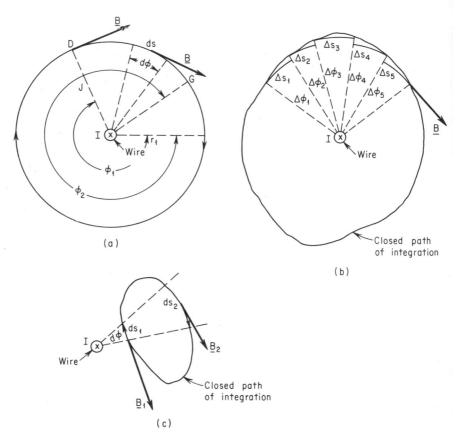

(a)

(b)

(c)

Figure 14–8–1. Figures for the derivation of Ampere's line integral law for magnetic flux density. The surface of the page enclosed in the paths of integration is called "surface bounded by the path of integration."

arcs of circles, with their centers at the wire, which subtend the same angle at the wire. Also we see that, for any path length such as DJ which subtends zero angle at the wire, the value of the line integral will be zero. Also, the line integral is zero along any path parallel with the wire because, along such a path, B is perpendicular to ds and $\cos\theta$ is zero. Thus, if the selected path goes out of the plane perpendicular to the wire, we may project the path into this plane and obtain the same result for the value of the line integral around the projected path as if we followed the actual path. Hence, in (14–8–1), $d\phi$ is the angle, in a plane perpendicular to the wire, which ds subtends at the wire.

Now, by the use of (14–8–1) let us evaluate the line integral around any imaginary closed path, such as the one shown in Fig. 14–8–1 (b). Approximate the path with arcs of circles [some of which are shown in Fig. 14–8–1 (b) as Δs_1 through Δs_5] and radial lines which connect the ends of the arcs. If the path goes out of the plane of the page, project it into the plane and follow the same procedure, using the projection of the path. By making the arc lengths infinitesimal, any path can be represented in this fashion. Then the integral of $B \cos \theta \, ds$ around the closed path is equal to $\mu_0 I/2\pi$, times the sum of the angles which the arc lengths subtend at the wire, since $\int B \cos \theta \, ds$ along any radial line is zero. Or we may say the same thing mathematically by using (14–8–1) and write

$$\oint B \cos \theta \, ds = (\mu_0 I/2\pi) \oint d\phi \qquad (14\text{–}8\text{–}3)$$

Since the path in Fig. 14–8–1 (b) encircles the wire, the sum of the angles which the arc lengths subtend at the wire is 2π radians, or $\oint d\phi = 2\pi$. Hence, (14–8–3) becomes

$$\oint B \cos \theta \, ds = \mu_0 I \qquad (14\text{–}8\text{–}4)$$

The same equation in vector notation is of course,

$$\oint \boldsymbol{B} \cdot \boldsymbol{ds} = \mu_0 I \qquad (14\text{–}8\text{–}5)$$

This formula requires that the direction of integration around the path shall be that given by the right-hand rule applied to the current. If the integration is in the opposite direction, the value of the integral will come out to have the negative sign, because $\cos \theta = -1$ in this case.

Next let us consider an imaginary closed path which does not encircle the wire, such as the path shown in Fig. 14–8–1 (c), and evaluate (14–8–3) around this path. For every $d\phi$ that is positive, such as the $d\phi$ for ds_2, there will be a $d\phi$ of equal magnitude which is negative, such as the $d\phi$ for ds_1. Hence, around this path $\oint d\phi = 0$, and (14–8–3) becomes

$$\oint B \cos \theta \, ds = 0 \qquad (14\text{–}8\text{–}6)$$

for a closed path that does not encircle the wire. (The fact that we use opposite signs at ds_2 and ds_1 can also be seen by observing that at ds_2, $\boldsymbol{B}_2$ is in the same direction as $\boldsymbol{ds}_2$; whereas at ds_1, $\boldsymbol{B}_1$ is in the opposite direction to $\boldsymbol{ds}_1$.)

We may let (14–8–4) or (14–8–5) represent both the situations in Fig. 14–8–1 (b) and (c) if we interpret I as the net current that cuts through the surface bounded by the path of integration. In Fig. 14–8–1 (b), I is the net current that cuts through this surface. If no current cuts through the surface bounded by the path of integration, (14–8–4) becomes (14–8–6), and this is the case in Fig. 14–8–1 (c).

Equation (14–8–4) is known as *Ampere's line integral law* for magnetic flux density in free space, and we may state it in words as: *the line integral of $\boldsymbol{B} \cdot \boldsymbol{ds}$ (i.e., $B \cos \theta \, ds$) around any imaginary closed path is equal to μ_0 times the net current that cuts through the surface bounded by the path.*

Although we have derived this law for the special case only of a long straight wire, it is valid for the magnetic field of any circuit shape in free space. An advanced text should be consulted for the general derivation.

14–9 MAGNETIC FIELD OF A TOROID

You may visualize a toroid by thinking of a very large doughnut with wire wound uniformly on the dough of the doughnut and the hole left open. A toroidal winding is shown in Fig. 14–9–1 and we wish to derive the formula for the magnetic flux density B at any point, such as P, inside the winding. The wires are wound as closely together as the thin insulation on each wire will permit, even though they are shown spaced out in the figure. In fact, we shall assume that the wires are in actual contact so that we need not consider any fine structure of the magnetic field due to the discrete wires. A well-made toroid is a very close approximation to the ideal that we are assuming. The toroid has N turns of wire wound on it.

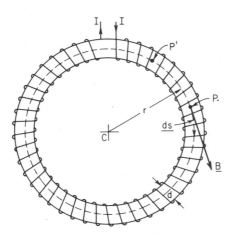

We are going to use Ampere's line integral law, as given in (14–8–4), for this calculation and wish to evaluate the line integral on the left of (14–8–4) around any circle inside the winding, such as the dotted circle in Fig. 14–9–1. For this purpose we must know B and $\cos\theta$ as functions of s. Let us get the functional relationship between B and s first. Let P and P' be any two points on the dotted circle. The wires of the winding have the same distribution and configuration with respect to P' that they have with respect to P. Thus, if we were to apply Ampere's law as given in (14–1–4) to compute B at P and P', we can see that we would get the same answer for the magnitude of B at both places. Hence, from symmetry, B has the same magnitude at all points on the circle, and B is independent of s.

Figure 14–9–1. A toroid with N closely spaced turns of wire on it. The dotted circle is the path of integration for the use of Ampere's line integral law and the surface of the page inside this circle is the surface bounded by the path of integration.

Next we need the functional relationship between $\cos\theta$ and s. We may think of the toroid as a solenoid which has been bent into a circle and its ends joined. We have seen, in special case 2 of Sec. 14–7, that inside a solenoid for points far removed from the ends, the flux lines are parallel to each other and parallel to the axis; see Fig. 14–7–1 (b). In a toroid there are no ends, so this condition applies at all points inside the windings. Further, the axis of the solenoid becomes a circle (like the dotted circle) which passes through the center of each turn of wire. Thus, the magnetic flux lines in the toroid are circles like the dotted circle drawn. Hence, our path of integration for the use of (14–8–4) is a flux line, and at every point B is parallel to ds, so $\cos\theta = 1$.

Hence, for this dotted circle path of integration, we may write the line integral of (14–8–4) as $B \oint ds$. On the right side of (14–8–4), I is the net current which cuts through the surface bounded by the path of integration. In Fig. 14–9–1, the surface of the page which is enclosed in the dotted circle is the surface bounded by the path of integration. N wires cut through this surface, each carrying a current I directed into the page so the net current cutting through the surface is NI. Hence (14–8–4) becomes, for this case,

$$B \oint ds = \mu_0 NI \qquad (14\text{–}9\text{–}1)$$

But the integral of ds around the circle is $2\pi r$, so (14–9–1) gives

$$B = \mu_0 NI/2\pi r \qquad (14\text{–}9\text{–}2)$$

Equation (14–9–2) is the desired formula, and tells us the magnetic flux density at any point inside of the winding. We notice that B is inversely proportional to r, so B is not uniform across a cross section of the winding.

Let d represent the radial distance across the cross section of the winding as shown in Fig. 14–9–1, and r_1 represent the value of r from C to the circle which passes through the center of each turn (i.e., r_1 is the radius of the circle that is the axis of the winding). If r_1 is very large compared with d we may consider that

$$B_{av} = \mu_0 NI/2\pi r_1 \qquad (14\text{–}9\text{–}3)$$

gives a good average of the magnitude of B across a cross section of the winding. Notice that (14–9–3) is the same as the solenoid formula (14–7–5) for points well inside a very long solenoid. $2\pi r_1$ in (14–9–3) corresponds in meaning to L in (14–7–5).

If we let Φ represent the total magnetic flux [see (3–3) and (3–4)] through a cross section of the winding and A represent the area of cross section,

$$\Phi = B_{av}A = \mu_0 NIA/2\pi r_1 \qquad (14\text{–}9\text{–}4)$$

In experiments where it is important to use (14–9–4) for the calculation of Φ, the toroid is constructed with r_1 very large compared with d. Then, in order to have a sufficiently large area A of cross section, the toroid may be made with a dimension, perpendicular to the page in Figure 14–9–1, which is several times as large as d.

The coil form on which the wires are wound should be empty space for this discussion but, as pointed out earlier, any nonferromagnetic material may be used, and (14–9–2) will give a very good approximation for the magnetic flux density. We shall use the toroid in our study of the magnetic properties of materials in Chapters XVI and XVII, and shall inquire more carefully there regarding the effect of the core material.

Using (14–2–3) and (14–9–2), the magnetic field intensity H inside the windings is given by

$$H = NI/2\pi r \qquad (14\text{–}9\text{–}5)$$

14–10 MAXWELL'S DISPLACEMENT CURRENT

We wish to present Maxwell's hypothesis that a changing electric displacement, D, produces a magnetic field.

Let us consider again the circuit of Fig. 4–2–1, which is redrawn in Fig. 14–10–1. In Sec. 4–3 we showed that the conduction current flowing in the wires of this circuit is

$$i = (\mathscr{E}/R)e^{-t/RC} \qquad (4\text{–}3\text{–}11)$$

where t is measured from the instant when the switch was closed. In order to simplify the discussion we shall consider that the capacitor in the circuit is an ideal parallel plate capacitor and, thus, that there is no fringing of the lines of force.

We wish to establish a relationship between the electric displacement D in the space between the plates of the capacitor and the current i which is flowing in the wires. Remember that i is the same, at any instant, in all metallic parts of the simple series circuit of Fig. 14–10–1.

Since q is the instantaneous charge on one plate of the capacitor and i is the instantaneous current in the wires, we have

$$i = dq/dt \qquad (14\text{–}10\text{–}1)$$

from (4–2–1). Let σ represent the instantaneous surface density of conduction charge on one plate of the capacitor and A represent the area of one plate, so $\sigma = q/A$. Then from (11–6–6), $D = \sigma$, so $D = q/A$

or $$q = DA \qquad (14\text{–}10\text{–}2)$$

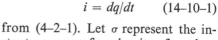

Figure 14–10–1. Capacitor C being charged from a source of constant emf.

Use (14–10–2) in (14–10–1) and we have

$$i = A\,dD/dt \qquad (14\text{–}10\text{–}3)$$

as you showed previously in the solution of Problem 11–7.

The fact that D is changing with time indicates that the state of affairs in the electric field between the capacitor plates is changing with time. Also, (14–10–3) reminds us that there is current in the wires only while D is changing, and that i is zero when the displacement is constant. Maxwell made the hypothesis that the changing state of affairs in the electric field is equivalent to the flow of a current in the sense that it produces a magnetic field, but only in this sense. This fictitious current, due to the changing electric displacement, Maxwell called a *displacement* current. If there is a class A dielectric in the space between the plates, there are no free electrons, and thus no conduction current flows through the capacitor. Hence, the magnetic field which Maxwell was talking about is produced by Maxwell's displacement current. Let us represent displacement current by i_D, and then from (14–10–3),

$$i_D = A\,dD/dt \qquad (14\text{–}10\text{–}4)$$

and Maxwell's displacement current in the dielectric between the plates of the capacitor is, at every instant, equal to the current in the wires at that instant. If you substitute units into (14–10–4), you find that $A\,dD/dt$ has the unit of current (ampere in the mks system).

This hypothesis is usually called *Maxwell's assumption* and, to repeat, *says that a displacement current produces a magnetic field just as a conduction current does.* This assumption makes Ampere's line integral law applicable all the way around a circuit with a capacitor in it as well as all the way around a fully conducting circuit. According to Maxwell's assumption, we should find a magnetic field in and about the capacitor, in the circuit of Fig. 14–10–1, which is due to the displacement current [of (14–10–4)] flowing through the dielectric of the capacitor. So far it has been impossible to make a quantitative check of the magnetic field produced by the capacitor only in this circuit because of the magnetic field produced by the conduction current in the remainder of the circuit. However, it is shown quantitatively in electro-magnetic theory that Maxwell's assumption is essential to the explanation of the propagation of electromagnetic waves as we know them in light and radio. Hence, the existence of electromagnetic waves is an indirect but impressive check on Maxwell's assumption. (Remember that displacement current is a current only in the sense that it produces a magnetic field. It has none of the other properties of a current.)

Let j_D represent the displacement current flowing through unit area of cross section of the dielectric; thus j_D is called the displacement current density. Since we are using a parallel plate capacitor, j_D is the displacement current per unit area of each plate. Hence, $j_D = i_D/A$, and (14–10–4) becomes

$$j_D = dD/dt \qquad (14\text{–}10\text{–}5)$$

Thus, Maxwell's displacement current density equals the time rate of change of electric displacement. In Fig. 14–10–1, the displacement current is flowing from the positive plate toward the negative plate and D is directed in the same direction. Hence, j_D and D are parallel, and we may write (14–10–5) as the vector equation

$$\boldsymbol{j_D} = d\boldsymbol{D}/dt \qquad (14\text{–}10\text{–}6)$$

Equation (14–10–6) turns out to be true in general, i.e., it is not limited to the case of a parallel plate capacitor where we derived it.

In (11–6–1) we defined D by the equation $D = \varepsilon_0 E + P$. If we use (11–6–1) in (14–10–5) we have

$$j_D = \varepsilon_0 \, dE/dt + dP/dt \qquad (14\text{–}10\text{–}7)$$

When P in a dielectric is changing, there is a shift of charges as the polarization of the individual molecules changes. We discussed this shift of charges in some detail in connection with Fig. 11–3–1, Sec. 11–3. We saw there that charge passes every cross section of a dielectric while the polarization is changing, even though the charges cannot leave the individual molecules and cannot go around the circuit. Thus, dP/dt can be looked upon as having a nature very much like that of a conduction current, since at any cross section of the dielectric there is a rate at which charge is passing across the cross section.

In (14–10–7) the term $\varepsilon_0 \, dE/dt$ does not represent any motion of charges however, but simply involves a time rate of change of electric field intensity. If there is empty space between the plates, there is nothing to polarize, and dP/dt is zero. In this case the displacement current is due entirely to the $\varepsilon_0 \, dE/dt$ term.

Maxwell's assumption is not limited to capacitors; it is a general one. That is, whatever the circumstances may be, a changing electric displacement produces a magnetic field (in and about the region where D is changing) as if a current density given by (14–10–7) were flowing in the region where change in D is occurring. Let us consider that the changes take place in free space where P is zero; then Maxwell's assumption says that *a changing electric field produces a magnetic field* as if a current density $j_D = \varepsilon_0 \, dE/dt$ were flowing.

But, on the other hand, a changing magnetic flux produces an electric field in and about the region where the magnetic flux is changing. This fact is the basis for Faraday's law (first stated in Sec. 3–5 and discussed further in Sec. 15–2), for the emf induced when the magnetic flux, through a circuit, changes. However, the electric field is set up by a changing magnetic flux whether or not there is a conducting circuit at hand in which an emf is induced. In Maxwell's assumption we have the complement of this effect.

As mentioned earlier, Maxwell's assumption makes Ampere's line integral law applicable in a dielectric where the displacement is changing. Let us see how to express Ampere's line integral law in such a case. From (14–8–5), $\oint B \cdot ds = \mu_0 I$ where I is the net current that cuts through the surface bounded by the path of integration for $B \cdot ds$, and the direction of ds, as we showed in Sec. 14–8, is that given by the right-hand rule applied to the current vector. Equation (14–8–5) applies strictly only in empty space, but is a good approximation in any nonferromagnetic material.* Now, from Maxwell's assumption, we are to look upon displacement current as equivalent to conduction current as far as the production of a magnetic field is concerned. In Fig. 14–10–2, imagine that there is a class A dielectric all

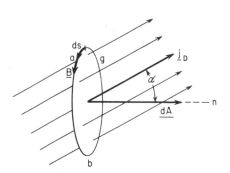

Figure 14–10–2. Increasing electric displacement D through an imaginary closed path *abg*.

through the region and that the electric field is changing in the dielectric. Let the parallel lines represent lines of D and imagine that D is increasing. With D increasing, j_D will be in the same direction as D, as shown by (14–10–6); conversely, if D were decreasing, j_D would be in the opposite direction to that of D, by the same equation. Let *abg* represent an imaginary closed path of integration for $B \cdot ds$, and let the vector marked j_D represent the displacement current density due to the rate of change of D. As drawn in the figure, j_D makes an angle α with the normal to the surface bounded by the path, *abg*, of integration. Then the net current I which cuts through the surface *abg* is given by

$$I = \int_A j_D \cos \alpha \, dA = \int_A j_D \cdot dA \qquad (14\text{–}10\text{–}8)$$

---

* In Sec. 16–2 we shall see how to apply this law inside a material medium including a ferromagnetic material.

where dA is an element of surface area of the surface abg and A is the area of this surface. We have chosen the direction of ds as that required by the statement immediately following (14–8–5), i.e., as that prescribed by the right-hand rule applied to the vector j_D shown in Fig. 14–10–2. Then dA is an infinitesimal vector normal to the area enclosed by the path and pointing in the direction given by the thumb of the right hand when the fingers encircle the path in the direction of ds.

Put (14–10–8) into (14–8–5) and we have

$$\oint \boldsymbol{B} \cdot \boldsymbol{ds} = \mu_0 \int_A \boldsymbol{j_D} \cdot \boldsymbol{dA} \qquad (14\text{–}10\text{–}9)$$

If we were to evaluate $\oint \boldsymbol{B} \cdot \boldsymbol{ds}$ in (14–10–9) in the opposite direction to that given above, this integral would change sign. On the other hand, dA, directed according to the right-hand rule applied to ds will likewise change sign, and (14–10–9) will still be correct. This liberty as to direction of progression around the path does not, however, extend to equations such as (14–8–5).

From (14–10–6) $j_D = dD/dt$, so (14–10–9) becomes

$$\oint \boldsymbol{B} \cdot \boldsymbol{ds} = \mu_0 \int_A \frac{dD}{dt} \cdot \boldsymbol{dA} \qquad (14\text{–}10\text{–}10)$$

Equation (14–10–10) is Ampere's line integral law applied to changing electric displacement, and says, just as before in Sec. 14–8, that the line integral of $\boldsymbol{B} \cdot \boldsymbol{ds}$ around any closed path is equal to μ_0 times the net current which cuts through the surface bounded by the path of integration. The only difference is that now the current is displacement current.

PROBLEMS

All currents are steady direct currents.

14–1 What is the magnetic flux density at the following distances from a very long straight wire which is carrying a current of 150 amp: (a) 5.00 cm, (b) 10.0 cm, (c) 20.0 cm? Include units with the numerical quantities and show that the answer comes out in proper units. [*Ans:* (a) 6.00×10^{-4} wb/m².]

14–2 Imagine that the very long straight wire of Problem 14–1 is the wire shown in Fig. 14–3–1 (a) except that α_1 and α_2 are very nearly 90° each. Also imagine a rectangle 20.0 by 50.0 cm drawn in the plane of the page with the long side of the rectangle parallel to the wire and 5.00 cm from the near side of the rectangle to the wire. What is the total number of magnetic flux lines through the rectangle? (Review Sec. 3–3.) [*Ans:* 2.41×10^{-5} wb.]

14–3 Brass ring 1 has a triangular cross section and encircles a very long straight wire concentrically as shown in Fig. 14–P–1. (Ignore brass ring 2 in this problem.) The wire is carrying a current I in the direction shown. Brass is a nonferromagnetic material. (a) Show that the total number of magnetic flux lines in the brass of the ring is

$$\Phi_1 = \frac{\mu_0 I h_1}{2\pi b}\left(b - d \ln\frac{d + b}{d}\right)$$

(b) If $d = 0.050$ m, $b = 0.20$ m, $h_1 = 0.50$ m, and $I = 150$ amp, find Φ. [*Ans:* 90×10^{-7} wb.]

14-4 Brass ring 2 has a triangular cross section and encircles a very long straight wire concentrically as shown in Fig. 14–P–1. (Ignore brass ring 1 in this problem.) Brass is a nonferromagnetic material. (a) Show that the total number of magnetic flux lines in the brass of the ring is

$$\Phi_2 = \frac{\mu_0 I h_1}{2\pi} \left(\ln \frac{b+d}{d} + \frac{d}{b} \ln \frac{b+d}{d} - 1 \right)$$

(b) If $d = 0.050$ m, $b = 0.20$ m, $h_1 = 0.50$ m, and $I = 150$ amp, find Φ. [*Ans:* 151×10^{-7} wb.]

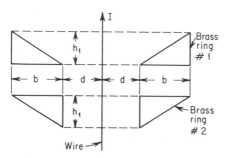

14-5 (a) Explain qualitatively why the answers for Problems 14–3 and 14–4 are not the same. (b) In Fig. 14–P–1 imagine that brass ring 2 is put above brass ring 1, and in contact with it, to form a ring of rectangular cross section. By direct integration, show that the total number of magnetic flux lines in the brass of the resulting ring, which has the rectangular cross section, is $\Phi = \mu_0 I h_1 \{\ln [(d + b)/d]\}/2\pi$ and then show that the same formula results from addition of Φ_1 given in Problem 14–3 part (a) and Φ_2 given in Problem 14–4 part (a).

Figure 14–P–1. Brass rings encircling a very long straight wire which is carrying a current I. The wire is along the axis of the rings.

14-6 Figure 14–P–2 shows a plane rectangular coil of wire with N turns in series and each carrying a current I. Point P is any point in the plane of the coil and enclosed in the periphery of the coil. (a) Use (14–3–2) to derive a

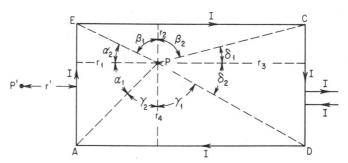

Figure 14–P–2. Plane rectangular coil of wire with N turns.

formula for the total magnetic flux density at P, assuming that the remainder of the circuit outside the rectangle makes a negligible contribution to B at P. What is the direction of the resultant B at P? (b) Use the formula derived in part (a) and compute the B at P with the following constants: $AE = 50.0$ cm, $EC = 100$ cm, $r_1 = 25.0$ cm, $r_2 = 10.0$ cm, $N = 100$ turns, $I = 10.0$ amp. [*Ans:* 28.4×10^{-4} wb/m².]

14-7 (a) If P is at the center of the plane rectangular coil of Problem 14-6, show that B at P is $B = 8\mu_0 NI\sqrt{w^2 + l^2}/4\pi wl$ where w is the width of the rectangle and l is its length. (b) Find the magnetic flux density at P if the coil has 50 turns, is carrying a current of 10.0 amp, is 40.0 cm long and 10.0 cm wide. [*Ans:* 41.2×10^{-4} wb/m^2.]

14-8 In Fig. 14-P-2 consider that the coil is a plane square coil with each side of length w. Point P' is outside the square at a distance r' from side AE and opposite the mid-point of AE as shown in the figure. Derive the formula for B at P'.

$$B = 2\mu_0 NI\,[\sqrt{w^2 + 4(r')^2}/r' - \sqrt{4(w + r')^2 + w^2}/(w + r')]/4\pi w$$

where B is directed perpendicular to the page and out of the page.

14-9 Refer to Fig. 14-3-1 and the discussion in Sec. 14-3 concerning the magnetic flux lines of a long straight wire. Consider that (14-3-3) is known for the magnitude of the magnetic flux density at a point P, and from Ampere's law that the direction of B is known to be perpendicular to the plane determined by the wire and the line drawn from the wire to P. Write (14-3-3) in Cartesian coordinates as $B = \mu_0 I/2\pi\sqrt{x^2 + y^2}$ where the XY-plane is the plane of the page in Fig. 14-3-1 (b) and the origin of coordinates is at the wire. Show that the x and y components of B are given by

$$B_x = -\mu_0 Iy/2\pi(x^2 + y^2) \quad \text{and} \quad B_y = \mu_0 Ix/2\pi(x^2 + y^2)$$

(If the current were flowing into the page in Fig. 14-3-1 (b), the minus sign would be on the value of B_y instead of B_x.) Using a method similar to the one used in example A Sec. 10-1, show that the equation of the magnetic flux lines in this special case is $x^2 + y^2 = 2C$, where C is the constant of integration. What is the shape of the curves for the magnetic flux lines as given by this equation?

14-10 Refer to the definition of the ampere as given in Sec. 14-4 and to (14-4-2). Substitute the magnitude and unit for each quantity in (14-4-2) as required by the definition of the ampere and show that the definition is satisfied by the equation both as to magnitude and units.

14-11 What is the force, in pounds per foot, between two long straight parallel wires each carrying a current of 125 amp if the wires are 10.0 cm apart? [*Ans:* 0.00214 lb/ft.]

14-12 A plane circular coil of wire with 500 turns in series has a mean radius of 6.00 cm and a current of 2.00 amp flowing in its wires. (a) What is the magnetic flux density at the center of the coil? [*Ans:* 0.0105 wb/m^2.] (b) What is the magnetic flux density in gauss, at a point on the axis of the coil 20.0 cm from the plane of the coil? [*Ans:* 2.5 gausses.]

14-13 Derive (14-5-4) for the magnetic flux density at the center of a plane circular coil of wire. Apply Ampere's law directly for P at the center of the circular coil in Fig. 14-5-1, i.e., do not follow the procedure in the text where P is first taken at a distance x on the axis of the coil and then x is reduced to zero.

14-14 (a) In Fig. 14-5-1 replace the circular coil in the YZ-plane by a square coil of N turns in the same YZ-plane and with the center of the coil at the origin of coordinates. The X-axis is the axis of the coil. Let w represent the length of each side of the square coil. Locate a point P on the X-axis at a distance x from the plane of the coil just as P is located in Fig. 14–5–1. Prove that the total magnetic flux density at P due to the current in the coil is

$$B = 16\mu_0 NIw^2/4\pi(w^2 + 4x^2) \sqrt{2w^2 + 4x^2}$$

(b) Prove that both the formula for B for a plane circular coil as given in (14–5–3) and the formula above for the square coil reduce to $B = \mu_0 NIA/2\pi x^3$ if x is very large compared with the linear dimensions of the coil. Here A is the area of the face of the coil.

14–15 (a) If the square coil of Problem 14–14 has 20 turns of wire, each carrying a current of 10 amp, what is the magnetic flux density on the axis of the coil 40 cm from the plane of the face of the coil? Each side of the coil has a length of 60 cm. [*Ans:* 9.8 × 10^{-5} wb/m^2.] (b) What is the magnetic field intensity, in oersteds, at the point P? [*Ans:* 0.98 oersted.]

14–16 Plot curves like those in Fig. 14–6–1. Draw curve 1 for the left coil only, curve 2 for the right coil only, and curve 3 the resultant for the two coils. Use the following data: Each coil has 72 turns of wire, a radius of 0.334 m, and a current of 4.92 amp. The current in the two coils is in the same direction, so their magnetic fields are parallel and in the same direction along their common axis. Space your plotted points not more than $0.1r_1$ apart.

Over what distance along the axis, on either side of the center point of the axis between the two coils, is the total magnetic flux density constant within about 0.9 per cent? Calculate this result from your graph. [*Ans:* about 0.1 m.]

14–17 The Helmholtz coils of Problem 14–16 were used for the experiment described in Sec. 13–10 to obtain the data in Problem 13–25. It was found that a current of 0.32 amp through the coils was required to straighten the electron beam. For a subsequent reading, a current of 6.25 amp was required to bend the electron beam in the desired circle. (a) What was the magnetic flux density of the earth's magnetic field at the place where the experiment was performed? [*Ans:* 0.62 × 10^{-4} wb/m^2.] (b) What was the net magnetic flux density at the center of the Helmholtz coils when the current of 6.25 amp was flowing through the wires of the coil? [*Ans:* 11.5 × 10^{-4} wb/m^2.]

14–18 Prove from Fig. 14–6–2 that the coil forms shown there satisfy the necessary requirement, namely, that the distance along the axis between each turn of wire on one coil and the corresponding turn on the other coil is equal to the radius of that turn.

14–19 A solenoid used in the laboratory is 1.00 m long, has a radius of 5.00 cm, and has 1000 turns of wire closely spaced. The current flowing in the wires is 8.00 amp. Compute the magnetic flux density on the axis of the solenoid at the following distances, in centimeters, from the center: 0, 10, 20, 30, 40, 45, 47, 48, 49, 50, 52, 53, 55, 60, 70, 80. Plot the magnetic flux density on the axis as ordinate against the distance along the axis as abscissa. Over how great a distance, on either side of the center, is the magnetic flux density on the axis constant within 1 per cent? [*Ans:* about 30 cm.]

14-20 (a) Consider again the square coil of Problem 14–14. Show that, for points on the axis of the coil for which x is very large compared with the dimensions of the coil, the magnetic flux density may be written as $B = \mu_0 M/2\pi x^3$, where M is the magnetic moment of the square coil. (b) Show that under the same conditions the magnetic flux density for the circular coil [see (14–5–3)] may be expressed by the same formula.

14-21 In Sec. 14–8, we derived Ampere's line integral law for magnetic flux density using the special case of the magnetic field about a current in a long straight wire, and then we simply stated that it could be shown to be true in general. In this problem, you are asked to derive the same law in another special case, namely that of a current I flowing in the plane circular coil of wire of N turns, discussed in Sec. 14–5 and shown in Fig. 14–5–1.

Pick, and describe, a suitable path of integration such that NI is the net current that cuts through the surface bounded by the path of integration. Tell how you know the magnitude and direction of B at every point on your chosen path (i.e., you picked the path so you would have this information, and you are now to tell how you have this required information at every point on your chosen path). Evaluate $\oint B \cdot ds$ for your chosen path and show, from your result, that you have derived Ampere's line integral law for magnetic flux density in this special case.

14-22 In Sec. 14–7, by the use of Ampere's law, we showed that B at a point P on the axis and near the center of an indefinitely long solenoid is given by $B = \mu_0 NI/L$ [see (14–7–5)] and that B is directed along the axis of the solenoid. Assume that off-axis magnetic flux lines in the vicinity of P, and inside the solenoid, are, as drawn in Fig. 14–7–1 (b), parallel with the axial magnetic flux line. (a) By the use of Ampere's line integral law, prove that B has the same magnitude at all points inside and across a cross section of the solenoid in the vicinity of P. To do this, select a path of integration and evaluate $\oint B \cdot ds$ around your selected path. Then, as required by Ampere's line integral law, equate this value to μ_0 times the net current that cuts through the surface bounded by your chosen path of integration. (b) Let P' be a point on a cross section of the solenoid through P, but just outside the solenoid. Show, by the use of Ampere's line integral law, that B must be zero at P' [a result that one might expect from the map in Fig. 14–7–1 (b) if it were drawn for an infinitely long solenoid].

14-23 (a) Draw in cross section, a straight copper (any nonferromagnetic metal will do) wire of radius R carrying a current I into the paper. Since the current is steady direct current the current density j_C (current per unit area of cross section) will be uniform across the cross section of the wire. Inside the circle which represents the wire, draw a dotted circle of any radius r and with the dotted circle concentric with the circle for the wire. Using this dotted circle as a path of integration apply Ampere's line integral law and prove that for points inside the wire the magnetic flux density is $B = \mu_0 Ir/2\pi R^2$ where $r \leq R$. (b) A long straight copper wire of radius 5.00 mm is carrying a current of 200 amp. Draw a graph showing the magnetic flux density as a function of distance from the center of the wire. Start the graph at the center of the wire and continue it to a point, at least six times the radius, outside the wire.

14-24 A coaxial transmission line contains a solid copper rod, which carries the current in one direction, surrounded by a concentric copper tube which carries the return current (in the opposite direction to that in the rod). The coaxial line is shown in cross section in Fig. 14–P–3. By the use of Ampere's line integral law (where needed) prove that the following formulas give the magnetic flux density in the regions indicated: (a) $B = \mu_0 Ir/2\pi R_1^2$, where $r \leq R_1$. (b) $B = \mu_0 I/2\pi r$, where $R_1 \leq r \leq R_2$. (c) $B = \mu_0 I[(R_3^2 - r^2)/(R_3^2 - R_2^2)]/2\pi r$, where $R_2 \leq r \leq R_3$. (d) $B = 0$, where $r > R_3$. Here r is the radial distance from the center of the central rod to the point where the value of B is being computed.

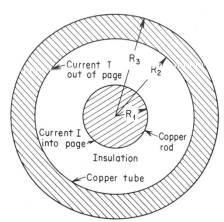

Figure 14–P–3. Coaxial line.

14-25 In the coaxial transmission line of Problem 14–24, $R_1 = 5.00$ mm, $R_2 = 1.00$ cm, $R_3 = 1.50$ cm, and $I = 200$ amp. Plot a curve showing the magnetic flux density as a function of the distance from the axis of the coaxial cable. Start the curve at the center of the cable and continue it to the point where $B = 0$.

14-26 A toroid, like the one in Fig. 14–9–1, is wound on a nonferromagnetic coil form whose inner radius is 10.0 cm and whose outer radius is 11.0 cm. (Both of these radii are in the plane of the page in Fig. 14–9–1.) The coil form is rectangular in cross section and its dimension, perpendicular to the page in Fig. 14–9–1, is 3.00 cm. There are 600 closely spaced turns of wire in the toroidal winding and the current flowing in the winding is 4.50 amp. (a) What is the value of B at $r = 10.1$ cm? At $r = 10.5$ cm? At $r = 10.9$ cm? (b) Find the total magnetic flux through a cross section of the winding, using (14–9–4). [*Ans:* 1.54×10^{-6} wb.] (c) By the use of integration find the total magnetic flux through a cross section of the winding. [*Ans:* 1.54×10^{-6} wb.]

14-27 A toroid is wound on a nonferromagnetic coil form whose inner radius is 4.00 cm and whose outer radius is 5.00 cm. The rest of the dimensions and conditions are as stated in Problem 14–26. Solve parts (b) and (c) for this toroid. What is the percentage error involved in the use of (14–9–4) in this case. [*Ans:* about 0.5 %.]

14-28 A toroid is wound on a nonferromagnetic coil form whose inner radius is 10.0 cm and whose outer radius is 16.0 cm. The rest of the dimensions and conditions are as stated in Problem 14–26. Solve parts (b) and (c) for this toroid. What is the percentage error involved in the use of (14–9–4) in this case? [*Ans:* about 2%.]

14-29 In an evacuated container, electrons are emitted from a point source P which is located on the axis and at the center of a very long solenoid which has a uniform magnetic flux density B. The situation can be visualized by imagining that the source is at point P in Fig. 13–9–1. As in this figure, let ϕ equal the angle between the axis of the solenoid and the vector for the velocity v of an electron. (Refer to Problem 13–24.) Electrons are emitted from P with all values of ϕ from 0 to 90°. Assuming that the electrons' velocities are all small compared to the velocity of light, prove that all electrons with the same axial component of velocity $v_a = v \cos \phi$ will come back to the same point on the axis of the solenoid regardless of their radial components of velocity $v_r = v \sin \phi$. What relationship does this result bear to the fundamentally important principle of operation of the cyclotron?

14–30 In a special application of the theory in Problem 14–29 all the electrons emitted from P have the same magnitude v of velocity. A circular diaphragm is placed to the right of P so that ϕ is restricted to values equal to or less than θ. What is the maximum value that θ can have if the electrons are to be focused within a 2.00 cm length along the axis at the place where they return to the axis? The average distance L_a from P to the middle of the "focal point" is 1.2500 m. [*Ans:* about 10° 13′.]

MORE ABOUT

INDUCED EMF'S

15–1 MOTIONAL INDUCED EMF*

In Sec. 3–4 we pictured the physical reason for the emf induced in a conductor, for example a copper wire, when the conductor moves with a velocity v, relative to the laboratory frame of reference, in a stationary magnetic field. The emf induced in such a case is called a "motional induced emf." You are urged to reread Sec. 3–4 as an introduction to our discussion, since we wish to enlarge on the concept of a motional induced emf.

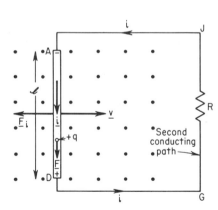

In Sec. 3–4 we pointed out that, as the conductor moves across the magnetic field of flux density B, each charge of magnitude q in the conductor experiences the magnetic force

$$F = qv \times B \qquad (15\text{--}1\text{--}1)$$

due to the velocity v of the conductor. Equation (15–1–1) is (3–2–1) rewritten in terms of the vector product, and thus is (13–1–9). Since the conductor's free electrons can move in the conductor under the action of this force, they do move, and electrons accumulate at the upper end A of the conductor in Fig. 3–4–1. This movement of the electrons leaves a deficiency of electrons, or a positive charge, at the lower end D. Figure 3–4–1 has been redrawn, with some additional features, as Fig. 15–1–1.

Figure 15–1–1. Conductor AD moving with a velocity v perpendicular to a magnetic field which is directed out of the page.

1. DERIVATION OF A FORMULA FOR MOTIONAL INDUCED EMF. Let us compute the emf induced in a conductor moving in a magnetic field. From (15–1–1),

* For a very helpful discussion of induced emf's see L. Page and N. I. Adams, Jr., "Some Common Misconceptions in the Theory of Electricity," *Am. Phys. Teacher*, **3**, 56 (1935).

$F/q = v \times B$, but the force per unit charge is the electric field intensity E which the motion of the conductor in the magnetic field establishes *in the conductor*. Thus,

$$E = v \times B \qquad (15\text{–}1\text{–}2)$$

which is (3–4–3). As defined in Sec. 1–4, the emf e of a source is the work per unit charge which the source could do in sending a charge completely around the circuit. Let e be the instantaneous emf of this source. E is the force per unit charge, so

$$e = \oint E \cdot dl = \oint E \cos \theta \, dl \qquad (15\text{–}1\text{–}3)$$

where dl is an element of length along the circuit in the direction of integration and θ is the angle between E and dl. Put (15–1–2) into (15–1–3) and we have

$$e = \oint (v \times B) \cdot dl \qquad (15\text{–}1\text{–}4)$$

which is the general formula for the motional induced emf and does not contain the special limitations imposed on the physical situation pictured in Fig. 15–1–1, since we did not employ any of these limitations in its derivation. Equation (15–1–4) cannot be evaluated in general, but rather can be evaluated only in a particular problem where the required functional relationships are known.

2. SPECIAL CASE. Let us now look further at the details of the special situation pictured in Fig. 15–1–1. As before, we shall talk as if the positive charges were the ones that are free to move in a metal, in order to agree with our usual convention for the sense of flow of current. The second conducting path from D to A is shown by $DGJA$, and this path is either outside the magnetic field or it is at rest. Due to the emf induced in AD, a current flows in the second path in the sense $DGJA$ and thence from A to D in the moving conductor. Let i represent the instantaneous magnitude of this current. In Sec. 13–1 we discussed the magnetic force on a straight conductor which carries a current i when the conductor is in a magnetic field of flux density B. We showed in (13–1–14) that the magnetic force on the conductor is given by

$$F_i = li \times B \qquad (15\text{–}1\text{–}5)$$

The subscript i appears on F_i to indicate that this magnetic force results from the fact that a current is flowing in the conductor as distinguished from F of (15–1–1) due to the motion of the wire. F_i is shown in Fig. 15–1–1 in the direction required by the cross product of (15–1–5). Note that F is the magnetic force on each charge of magnitude q, but F_i is the force on all such charges in the length l of the conductor.

Let us review the physical situation up to this point. An external agency causes the conductor AD to move with a velocity v toward the right in Fig. 15–1–1. Thus all the charges in the conductor are moving toward the right with a velocity v. Any charge q moving in a magnetic field with a velocity v experiences a magnetic force F given by the vector product of (15–1–1), and the force F on a positive charge q is shown as the vector labeled F in Fig. 15–1–1. Thus positive charge moves around the circuit in the direction $DGJAD$, and this motion of positive charges constitutes a current i. But when the current i flows in the conductor AD, the magnetic field exerts the force F_i of (15–1–5) on the conductor in the direction shown by the vector labeled F_i in Fig. 15–1–1. In other words, the positive charges in the conductor AD have two velocities (one due to the motion of the wire and the other due to the current), and experience the two magnetic forces F and F_i.

At this point we can see why the external agency must do work. In order for the external agency to move the conductor without acceleration toward the right, the external agency must exert a force equal and opposite to F_i. Thus the external agency must do mechanical work in moving the conductor against the magnetic force. In Sec. 3–4 we recognized, from the principle of conservation of energy, that mechanical work is required to move the conductor, because the current does work in the circuit through which it flows. From the above we can see the origin of the magnetic force against which the external agency must do this mechanical work.

Next let us evaluate (15–1–4) in this important special case pictured in Fig. 15–1–1. Here the conductor is straight and is moving perpendicular to the uniform magnetic field. In this case v and B are perpendicular to each other, so the magnitude of $v \times B$ is vB. Also dl is parallel to $v \times B$, so the magnitude of $(v \times B) \cdot dl$ is $vB \, dl$. Then (15–1–4) becomes

$$e = \oint vB \, dl \qquad\qquad (15–1–6)$$

In Fig. 15–1–1 we have shown the second conducting path $DGJA$ as located outside the magnetic field, so B is zero around the circuit except along the length l of AD. Equally well, we could have had the second conducting path in the magnetic field but at rest, and had the section AD sliding on contacts with the wires AJ and DG. In this case v would have been zero for all parts of the circuit except the length l of AD. In either case $\int vB \, dl$ is zero except along the length l, so (15–1–6) becomes

$$e = \int_0^l vB \, dl \qquad\qquad (15–1–7)$$

In this special case v and B are constant along l, so (15–1–7) becomes

$$e = vBl \qquad\qquad (15–1–8)$$

In this special case, B and l are both constants. If v is also constant with respect to time the induced emf is constant with respect to time. In the past we have represented a constant emf by $\mathscr{E}$, so with this further restriction, we may write

$$\mathscr{E} = vBl \qquad\qquad (15–1–9)$$

Solve Problem 15–1 at this point.

Equation (15–1–8) gives the emf induced in the moving straight conductor under the limitations of the special case set forth in Fig. 15–1–1. If l is not perpendicular to B, we must use the component of l which is perpendicular to B. Also, if v is not perpendicular to B, we must use the component of v which is perpendicular to B.

From (15–1–2), the direction of E is the direction of $v \times B$, so the sense of the induced emf e is the direction of $v \times B$. If $v \times B$ is not along the conductor, the sense of e is the sense of the component of $v \times B$ along the conductor. The sense of e predicted in this fashion is the same as that predicted by Lenz's law (which we discussed in Sec. 3–5) as you can see from the direction of F_i in Fig. 15–1–1. Often Lenz's law gives the easier method of deciding the sense of e in a particular problem.

3. DISCUSSION OF E IN (15–1–2). Notice that E of (15–1–2) is *not* an *electrostatic* electric field intensity for it is *not* due to a distribution of charges. We have shown in (10–2–3) that the line integral $\oint E_{stat} \cdot ds$ around any closed path is always zero and there is no exception in this case.

The E of (15–1–2) is due to the motion of the conductor in the magnetic field, and an external agency is doing work to move the conductor. Hence the external agency is feeding energy into the system, and a net amount of work is done by a charge in moving completely around the circuit.

Notice also that the E of (15–1–2) does not exist in the absence of moving charges, such as the charges of the conductor in Fig. 15–1–1, because it is the magnetic force on the charges moving with the wire which sets up the electric field intensity.

15–2 COMMENTS ON FARADAY'S LAW OF INDUCED EMF'S

In Sec. 3–5 we first stated Faraday's experimental law, which tells us that the emf induced in a fixed circuit (when the magnetic flux Φ through the circuit is changing) is proportional to the time rate of change of the magnetic flux. If there are N turns of wire in series on the circuit and all experience the same rate of change of flux, the total emf is N times that for a single turn. As we have seen, in the mks system the constant of proportionality is unity, and Faraday's law is expressed by the equation

$$e = -N \, d\Phi/dt \qquad (15\text{–}2\text{–}1)$$

where the minus sign results from Lenz's law and e is the instantaneous emf induced in the circuit.

We have used (15–2–1) many times in a wide variety of problems. However, it is useful to make some additional comments about it.

1. RELATIONSHIP TO MOTIONAL INDUCED EMF. We wish to show that the motional induced emf may also be computed from Faraday's law. We shall consider only the special case pictured in Fig. 15–1–1. In the figure, let dx represent the distance moved by the wire in a time dt. In the time dt, the total flux Φ which links the circuit in Fig. 15–1–1 decreases by the amount $d\Phi$ where $-d\Phi = B \, dA$. Put this into (15–2–1), use the facts that $N = 1$ and $dA = l \, dx$, and we have $e = Bl \, dx/dt$. But $v = dx/dt$, so $e = Blv$ which is (15–1–8).

It turns out that in general a motional induced emf may be computed from Faraday's law if a proper interpretation is put on $d\Phi/dt$. (This is not a new idea because you worked it out for yourself if you solved Problem 3–5.) Thus, a motional induced emf may be computed by the use of the methods of Sec. 15–1 or by the use of Faraday's law. However, if the magnetic flux through a stationary circuit changes, the induced emf may be computed only by the use of Faraday's law.

2. RELATIONSHIP BETWEEN THE ELECTRIC FIELD INTENSITY SET UP BY CHANGING
MAGNETIC FLUX AND THE RATE OF CHANGE OF THE FLUX. In Fig. 15–2–1, let
DJC represent a closed conducting circuit with magnetic flux lines threading
through it in the direction of the vector which represents *B*. In the figure *B*
makes an angle α with the normal *n* to the plane of the circuit. Let us assume
that the number of magnetic flux lines linking the circuit is decreasing and, by
Lenz's law, the sense of the induced emf must be that shown by the arrow
for *e*. As before, let *E* represent the electric field intensity which is due to the
changing magnetic flux. At each point
of the circuit in Fig. 15–2–1, the component of *E* which is parallel to the conducting path is in the same sense as *e*.
As stated before with (15–1–3), the
integration is to be taken around the
path in the sense of *e*. Using Faraday's
law, (15–1–3) becomes

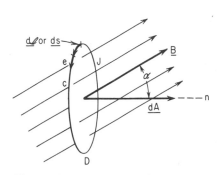

$$\oint E \cos \theta \, dl = -d\Phi/dt \quad (15\text{–}2\text{–}2)$$

From Fig. 15–2–1, the total magnetic
flux Φ linking the circuit is $\Phi = \int_A B$
$\cos \alpha \, dA$ where A is the area enclosed
in the circuit and dA is an element of
this area. The direction of *dA* is the
direction of the thumb of the right hand
when the fingers encircle the circuit in
the sense of *e*. This, in turn, determines

Figure 15–2–1. A decreasing magnetic
flux through a circuit. *B* is at an angle
α with respect to the normal to the plane
of the circuit.

the direction of the positive normal *n*, to the surface bounded by the circuit.
From the above equation for Φ we have

$$d\Phi/dt = (d/dt)\int_A B \cos \alpha \, dA = (d/dt)\int_A \boldsymbol{B}\cdot \boldsymbol{dA}$$

If we keep the wire loop *DJC* of Fig. 15–2–1 fixed so that the area which it
encloses does not change with time, we may differentiate under the integral,
and (15–2–2) becomes

$$\oint E \cos \theta \, dl = -\int_A [d(B \cos \alpha)/dt] \, dA \qquad (15\text{–}2\text{–}3)$$

Here *E* is due to changing magnetic flux and is not an electrostatic field
intensity. In this case, (15–2–3) tells us that the *line integral of E · dl around
any closed fixed path is equal to the negative of the time rate of change of the
magnetic flux through the surface bounded by the closed path.* This statement is
a different, but useful, way of expressing Faraday's law. In the term on the
right of (15–2–3), the time derivative of the product (*B* cos α) must be taken
because, in general, both the magnitude and direction of *B* will change with
time. It is understood also that only the time rate of change of (*B* cos α) is
involved. Hence, if *B* is a function of the coordinates (as it usually is) this
derivative must be the partial derivative with respect to time.

In contrast with the case of the motional induced emf, the electric field
intensity due to a changing magnetic flux exists whether the conducting circuit

is present or not, since its existence does not depend on the presence of moving charges. Of course, no current will flow unless the conducting circuit is present. We have been using dl to represent an element of length of a conductor, but have been using ds as an element of path length when expressing a line integral along an imaginary path. Consider DJC of Fig. 15-2-1 to be an imaginary closed path (not a conducting circuit), and we wish to express the line integral of $E \cdot ds$ around this closed path. As mentioned above, (15-2-3) is still valid, but now we replace dl by ds in order to indicate that we are using an imaginary path. Then (15-2-3) becomes,

$$\oint E \cdot ds = - \int_A (dB/dt) \cdot dA \qquad (15\text{-}2\text{-}4)$$

where now any rate of change of B, whether it be change of magnitude or direction or both, is accounted for in dB/dt.

We have shown from Gauss's theorem that electric lines of force begin and end only on charges. In the present situation there are not necessarily any charges in the region where B is changing. It follows that the electric lines of force due to changing B have no beginnings and no ends, so they form closed loops (see footnote near end of Sec. 14-3), and (15-2-4) shows that these loops must encircle the region where B is changing. If charges are present also, the total electric field intensity will be the vector sum of that due to the charges and that due to changing B.

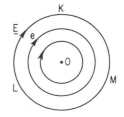

Figure 15-2-2. Electric lines of force due to changing magnetic flux.

As we have emphasized before, the $\oint E \cos \theta \, ds$ always equals zero for electrostatic lines of force which originate and terminate on charges. This situation is in contrast with (15-2-2) or (15-2-4) for electric lines of force due to changing magnetic flux. Electric lines of force due to changing magnetic flux are more nearly analogous to magnetic flux lines which encircle currents.

In order that we may be able to draw definite lines to illustrate the closed electric lines of force due to changing magnetic flux, let us consider a specific simple case. Consider that KLM in Fig. 15-2-2 is a wire loop fixed in the plane of the page, the wire being of uniform cross section. Imagine that above the page there is a plane circular coil of wire [like the one in Sec. 13-7, Fig. 13-7-1 (a)] with its plane parallel to the page and carrying current in such a direction that its magnetic flux lines are directed, in general, downward toward the page. Also the center of the coil is directly above O (the center of the wire loop) and, thus, the axis of the coil passes through the center of the wire loop. The magnetic flux lines from the current in the coil are symmetrical about the axis of the coil [like the illustration in Fig. 13-7-1 (a)]. Now, in Fig. 15-2-2, pull the coil away from the plane of the page, keep the axis of the coil through O, and keep the coil moving continuously away from the page. From the axial symmetry of the flux lines of the coil, the electric lines of force, established in the plane of the page by the changing magnetic flux, are circles with their centers at O. Some of these electric lines of force are drawn in

Fig. 15–2–2 with the sense of E shown by the arrowheads. The electrons in the wire loop experience a force due to E and, in this simple case, the force on the electrons is everywhere tangent to the loop and opposite to the sense of E. Thus, electrons move around the loop in the opposite sense to that of E, or current flows around the loop in the same sense as that of E. The left side of (15–2–4) is equal to the emf e induced in the wire loop, so e could be computed by evaluating the right side of (15–2–2). The emf, e, is in the same sense around the wire loop as is E. There is no single place in this wire loop circuit where one can point and say that the source of emf is there. The whole circuit is the source in this case.

Using this same example, we can point out the distinction between an emf and a potential difference; a distinction that we made and used in circuit analysis. As the electrons circulate around the wire loop KLM of Fig. 15–2–2, there is no place in the loop that has a net charge and thus there are no electrostatic lines of force from charges. The electric lines of force are entirely those due to changing magnetic flux. Scalar potential, which we discussed in detail in Chapter X, exists only when there are electric lines of force due to charges. Thus, there is no potential difference between any two points that you might select in the wire loop KLM, but there is an emf which is causing a current to flow. If we let i represent the instantaneous current flowing in the wire loop and R be the total resistance of the loop, then $e = \oint E \cdot ds = iR$ at every instant, but no potential difference exists between any two points in the loop. If, however, you were to cut a narrow gap at some point such as K, the flow of electrons would continue until enough electrons accumulated on the right side of the cut (with positive charges on the left side of the cut) so that the reverse electric field in the wire, due to the charges, would neutralize the E induced by changing magnetic flux, and then the flow of electrons would stop. In this case there is a potential difference across the gap which equals the induced emf if the gap is narrow so that we may neglect the emf induced in the gap.

15–3 BASIC THEORY OF THE BETATRON

The betatron, invented by D. W. Kerst* in 1941, is an instrument that accelerates electrons to high energies. Faraday's law is the basic principle of operation, and the betatron illustrates dramatically the fact that a changing magnetic flux produces an electric field even when there is no material conducting path present.

Electrons, for acceleration in a betatron, come from an electron gun which is part of an evacuated tube. The evacuated tube, with its electron gun, is located in a magnetic field, and the electrons are shot from the gun along a path which is perpendicular to the magnetic flux lines of this field. The magnetic field causes the electrons to travel in a circular orbit as we have seen in Sec. 13–9. While the electrons are traversing the orbit the magnetic

---

* D. W. Kerst, "The Acceleration of Electrons by Magnetic Induction," *Phys. Rev.*, **60**, 47 (1941); D. W. Kerst and R. Serber, "Electronic Orbits in the Induction Accelerator," *Phys. Rev.*, **60**, 53 (1941); D. W. Kerst, "The Betatron, Development and Application," *Am. Scientist*, **35**, 56 (1947).

flux through the orbit changes, producing an electric field tangent to the orbit. This electric field accelerates the electrons to higher and higher energies as the electrons make repeated trips around the orbit.

Figure 15–3–1 shows a schematic diagram of the apparatus. The vertical cross section in Fig. 15–3–1 (a) shows the pole pieces of the magnet which produces the changing magnetic field. An alternating current is sent through the wire windings (not shown) of the magnet, and the magnetic flux density between the pole faces changes as the current in the windings changes. We shall see that only the quarter cycle of the alternating current, during which the magnetic flux density between the pole faces is increasing, is effective in accelerating the electrons. The evacuated tube is in the form of a hollow toroid or doughnut shown in cross section as DD in Fig. 15–3–1 (a) and also as DD in the plane view of Fig. 15–3–1 (b). Here G is the electron gun which

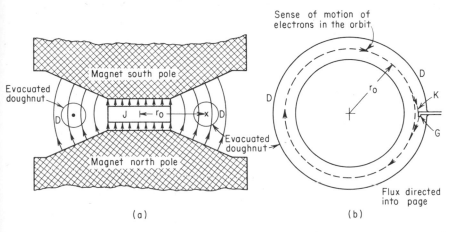

Figure 15–3–1. The betatron. (a) Vertical cross section showing magnet and evacuated doughnut DD. (b) Horizontal cross section showing electron orbit as dashed circle inside the evacuated doughnut. The arrows on the dashed circle give the sense of motion of the electrons.

shoots the electrons into their orbit; it is somewhat like the source of electrons in the e/m tube of Sec. 13–10, and consists of a heated cathode, which liberates the electrons, and a positively charged plate with a slit opening, which projects some of these electrons out of the gun in the desired direction. The circular orbit followed by the electrons in the magnetic field is shown as the dotted circle of radius r_0 in Fig. 15–3–1 (b). (Remember that we are dealing with negatively charged particles, so the magnetic force on each particle is oppositely directed to that on a positively charged particle traveling in the same direction.) The direction of motion of the electrons is shown by the arrows on the dotted circle in Fig. 15–3–1 (b). In Fig. 15–3–1 (a), the electrons are going into the page on the right side, as shown by the cross in the circle which represents the doughnut, and coming out of the page on the left side, as shown by the dot in the circle which represents the doughnut.

In order to keep the electrons inside the doughnut they must travel in an orbit of fixed radius which we shall call r_0. If the electrons deviate very much from this orbit they will hit the walls of the doughnut and be lost. At the same time that the electrons are going around the orbit, the total magnetic flux through the orbit increases. Of course, the magnetic flux density *at the orbit* increases as the total magnetic flux *through the orbit* increases, so the centripetal magnetic force on each electron increases. Now we wish to see what conditions must be satisfied in order to have a stable orbit (one of constant radius r_0) while the above mentioned changes are taking place. Let q be the charge and m the mass of each electron, and let B represent the instantaneous magnetic flux density *at the orbit*. Then, as we have seen in Sec. 13–9, the magnetic force Bqv must furnish the centripetal force mv^2/r_0 required to keep each electron on the circle of radius r_0. It is shown in relativity theory that this relationship is of the same form under conditions where relativity corrections must be made as it is for the conditions under which we derived it. From this relationship, $Bqv = mv^2/r_0$,

$$mv = Bqr_0 \qquad (15\text{–}3\text{–}1)$$

where mv is the momentum of the electron. In the betatron, the electrons very promptly acquire a velocity comparable with the velocity of light, so the mass of the electron cannot be considered to be constant. In fact the mass m of the electron becomes many times the rest mass m_0 before the acceleration is completed. This means that we must treat m, as well as v and B, as variables in our discussion. The charge q on the electron remains constant and the electron is to remain on the same circle, so r_0 is constant. Take the differential of both sides of (15–3–1)

$$d(mv) = qr_0 \, dB \qquad (15\text{–}3\text{–}2)$$

Equation (15–3–2) gives the change dB, in B at the orbit, which must accompany the change $d(mv)$ of the momentum of the electron in order that the electron shall stay on the orbit of radius r_0.

Let E represent the electric field intensity, at the orbit, which is set up by the changing magnetic flux. Then (15–2–2) applies, where Φ is the total magnetic flux which cuts through the face of the orbit. But E is everywhere tangent to the orbit and has the same magnitude at all points on the orbit because of the radial symmetry of the magnetic field. Hence (15–2–2) becomes

$$E \int_0^{2\pi r_0} ds = -d\Phi/dt, \quad \text{or} \quad E = -(1/2\pi r_0)(d\Phi/dt) \qquad (15\text{–}3\text{–}3)$$

The minus sign indicates the direction of E relative to the rate of change of the magnetic flux, and the apparatus arrangement is such that E will accelerate the electrons in the direction of motion shown in Fig. 15–3–1 (a) when the magnetic flux is in the direction shown and is increasing. Only during the part of the a-c cycle (for the current in the magnet windings) when the magnetic flux lines are in the direction shown and increasing will the electrons be accelerated in the proper direction, and this explains our earlier statement that only a quarter cycle of the alternating current is useful. Since, during this quarter cycle, the conditions are such as to satisfy the requirements of the minus sign in (15–3–3), we may use the absolute magnitude of the term on the right for this quarter cycle, and we have

$$E = (1/2\pi r_0)(d\Phi/dt) \qquad (15\text{–}3\text{–}4)$$

The unbalanced force F which this electric field exerts on each electron is tangent to the circle and has the magnitude Eq, so, from (15–3–4),

$$F = (q/2\pi r_0)(d\Phi/dt) \qquad (15\text{–}3\text{–}5)$$

By Newton's second law of motion, the unbalanced force F which acts on a body is equal to the rate of change of momentum which the unbalanced force produces, so Newton's second law is $F = d(mv)/dt$. In this case the derivative of the product (mv) with respect to time must be indicated, since both m and v are changing with time as the electron is accelerated.

Equate the values of F in (15–3–5) and in Newton's second law and obtain

$$d(mv) = q\, d\Phi/2\pi r_0 \qquad (15\text{–}3\text{–}6)$$

Equation (15–3–6) gives the change in momentum of the electron (due to Faraday's law) when the magnetic flux through the orbit changes by $d\Phi$. In order to have a stable orbit, the change in momentum of the electron as expressed in (15–3–2) must be the same as the change of momentum of the electron as expressed in (15–3–6), so equate these values of $d(mv)$, and solve for dB

$$dB = d\Phi/2\pi r_0^2 \qquad (15\text{–}3\text{–}7)$$

As before, B is the magnetic flux density at the orbit at any instant, and Φ is the total magnetic flux through the orbit at the same instant. At the instant when $B = 0$, Φ is also zero, so we may integrate (15–3–7) as

$$\int_0^B dB = (1/2\pi r_0^2)\int_0^\Phi d\Phi$$

to obtain the relationship between B and Φ at any subsequent instant. Thus, we have

$$B = \Phi/2\pi r_0^2 \qquad (15\text{–}3\text{–}8)$$

where πr_0^2 is the area of the face of the orbit. Let $\bar{B}$ represent the average magnetic flux density through the face of the orbit so defined that $\bar{B} = \Phi/\pi r_0^2$. Then we may write (15–3–8) as

$$B = \tfrac{1}{2}\bar{B} \qquad (15\text{–}3\text{–}9)$$

Equation (15–3–9) is the condition which must be satisfied in order to have a stable orbit, and says that the magnetic flux density at the orbit must have one-half as large a magnitude as the average magnetic flux density through the face of the orbit. Thus, at points inside the orbit, the magnetic flux density must be enough larger than the value at the orbit so that this condition will be satisfied. This condition is satisfied by careful shaping of the pole faces [much like that shown in Fig. 15–3–1 (a)] and by inserting the block J of material with a high permeability. Thus the magnetic flux density is large at the center of the magnet and becomes enough smaller at the doughnut so that the condition of (15–3–9) is satisfied.

In thinking about the preceding discussion of the betatron, be sure to notice the obvious, but important fact that the magnetic flux density B at the orbit guides the electrons around the orbit by the centripetal magnetic force that it exerts on each electron; the rate of change of total magnetic flux Φ

through the orbit produces the acceleration of the electrons; and B and Φ belong to the same magnetic field produced by the electromagnet. Equation (15–3–8) is the relationship between B and Φ such that the guiding done by B and the accelerating produced by $d\Phi/dt$ shall operate together and keep the electron on the same orbit of radius r_0 during its many trips around the orbit.

We have derived only the basic condition which must be satisfied in the betatron. There are numerous other important considerations for satisfactory operation and a detailed treatment* should be consulted for further information.

To give some concept of the magnitudes involved, one General Electric* betatron which produces electrons with 100 Mev energy has pole faces 76 in. in diameter and weighs 130 tons. Sixty cycle alternating current is used for the magnet, and the magnet takes 200 kw power at full load. The doughnut has 74 in. outside diameter, and the electron stable orbit diameter is 66 in. The maximum magnetic flux density at the orbit is 4000 gausses. Each electron makes 2.4×10^5 trips around the orbit and acquires, on the average, 420 ev of energy in each trip. Since the magnet is operated on alternating current, the iron core must be laminated (see Sec. 15–4) in order to minimize eddy current loss. The laminations for the General Electric magnet are 0.014 in. thick and are made of sheet steel with enameled surfaces.

So far we have seen how the electrons are accelerated during the proper quarter cycle of the current in the magnet windings. As the magnetic flux between the pole pieces reaches a maximum and starts to decrease, the induced electric field intensity at the orbit reverses, and the electrons, if they were still moving in the orbit, would be decelerated. Thus, the electrons must be removed from the orbit just as the electric flux density reaches its maximum value. This ejection of the electrons is accomplished by the use of orbit expanding coils (not shown in the figure), which are wound around the central part of the pole pieces. At just the right moment, a large current is sent through these coils in such a direction as to further increase the flux Φ through the orbit without increasing appreciably the flux density B at the orbit. From (15–3–8) we can see that, if Φ increases, but B remains essentially constant, r_0 must increase. Thus, the electrons move to an orbit of larger radius when the current is sent through the orbit expanding coils. As is shown by the dotted line at K in Fig. 15–3–1 (b), this orbit of larger radius is usually such that the electrons strike a metal target, on the back of the electron gun G, at a glancing angle. When high-speed electrons strike a metal target they produce x-rays, and the higher the energy of the electrons the more penetrating the x-rays. Since the electrons from the betatron have high energies (100 Mev per electron for the General Electric betatron cited) they produce x-rays which can penetrate through a greater depth of matter than those from ordinary x-ray tubes. The x-rays produced at G come out through the walls of the tube and are the final product of the betatron. In order to produce x-rays of comparable penetration with an x-ray tube of the usual design, a potential difference of 100 million volts would be required across

* W. F. Westendorp and E. E. Charlton, "A 100-Million Volt Induction Electron Accelerator," *J. App. Phys.*, **16**, 581 (1945). Also see reference to Kerst's articles at the beginning of this Sec.

the tube. This is completely unfeasible. The x-rays may be used for whatever purpose is desired such as nuclear transmutations, or x-ray analysis, or therapeutic treatment.

15–4 EDDY CURRENTS

As we have seen, whenever a conductor moves in a magnetic field or whenever the magnetic flux through a circuit changes, an emf is induced. If there is a complete circuit, the induced emf will cause a current to flow, and the magnitude of the current depends on the induced emf and the circuit constants. Thus, when a block of metal moves in a magnetic field, or the magnetic flux through the block of metal changes, an emf is induced in the block. The block itself offers a complete circuit in which the emf can cause currents to circulate. Such currents are called *eddy currents*.

We have talked briefly so far about two cases where eddy currents are troublesome and shall consider others later. The first case was that of the soft iron core of the d-c motor armature discussed in Sec. 13–8 and shown in Fig. 13–8–2. This soft iron core is necessary since it helps to produce the desired radial magnetic field. Also, it forms a part of the magnetic circuit (see Chapter XVII) which is designed to produce a larger magnetic flux density at the armature for a given field current, than could be obtained without the soft iron core. However, as the soft iron core rotates in the magnetic field of the pole pieces, emf's are induced in the iron, and the iron offers conducting paths in which the eddy currents circulate. The eddy currents flowing in the iron convert electrical energy into heat energy. This electrical energy is derived from the mechanical energy of rotation of the motor armature. Thus, in the armature core, an appreciable amount of the input electrical energy to the motor may be converted into heat energy, leaving less mechanical energy that the motor can expend in driving a machine. This energy loss is called *eddy current loss*, and it would be excessive if the core were a solid block of iron. In addition to the energy loss due to eddy currents, the magnetic fields produced by the eddy currents are usually undesirable, for they warp the magnetic field of the machine. Thus, in general, eddy currents must be minimized.

Nothing can be done to prevent the emf's from being induced in the iron as long as it rotates in the magnetic field of the pole pieces, and it must rotate or there will be no motor. However, the magnitudes of the eddy currents can be minimized by increasing the resistances of the circuits in which they flow. The resistances of the circuits are increased by building the iron core out of thin sheets, called *laminations*, of iron with one of the long dimensions of each sheet parallel with the flux lines and the thin dimension of the sheet perpendicular to the flux lines. The adjacent laminations are electrically insulated from each other either by a thin coat of shellac or varnish or by the oxide scale on the surfaces of the laminations. The induced emf is perpendicular to the magnetic flux lines, so the circuits offered to the eddy currents are those of the thin dimension of the lamination, and these are fairly high-resistance circuits.

The second case that we have considered, where eddy currents are troublesome, was that of the electromagnet of the betatron discussed in Sec. 15–3. In this case the alternating current in the magnet windings causes a changing flux in the iron of the magnet and, as we have seen, the changing flux is essential to the operation of the betatron. However, the changing flux causes eddy currents to flow in the iron of the magnet, and the power loss due to the eddy currents would be prohibitive if the iron were solid. Hence, the iron of the magnet is built up of laminations as we have described above. Let us consider this type of case in some more detail, since it is characteristic of all a-c machines which have ferromagnetic cores in their coils, and illustrates an eddy current discussion.

Figure 15–4–1 shows a block in the interior of a laminated core with six of the many laminations drawn. The magnetic flux is directed along one of the long dimensions of the laminations, as shown by the vector which represents B in the figure, and some typical eddy current paths are shown on the faces of the laminations. The direction indicated for the flow of current assumes that B is increasing at the instant of the picture.

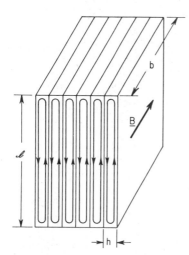

Since the current flowing in the winding is varying sinusoidally with time, let us assume that the magnetic flux density in the iron is also. This is a fair approximation of the variation of B with time, provided that the iron is not magnetized to saturation (see Chapter XVII), but it is an approximation. No satisfactory analytical expression can be written for the actual functional relationship between B in the iron and time, as we shall see when we discuss magnetic hysteresis in iron. However, we shall assume that

$$B = B_m \sin \omega t \qquad (15\text{–}4\text{–}1)$$

Figure 15–4–1. Lamination of a core to minimize power losses due to eddy currents. A section of a core showing several laminations and typical eddy current circuits. At the moment of the figure, B is increasing in magnitude in the direction shown by the vector which represents B.

gives a sufficiently good approximation, where B is the magnitude of the instantaneous magnetic flux density in the iron, B_m is the maximum value of B, and ω is the angular frequency of the sinusoidal current flowing in the wire winding of the magnet. When we use the term "iron" here, we mean any ferromagnetic material.

Figure 15–4–2 shows a cross section of a lamination of thickness h, which is the thin dimension of the lamination as shown in Fig. 15–4–1; h has been greatly magnified in Fig. 15–4–2, with less magnification for the length l. The changing magnetic flux will cause eddy currents to circulate in paths which go around the origin O symmetrically. Three possible current paths are shown as *acdfa*, *gjkmg*, and *nspqn*. Of course there will not be square corners on the paths but these paths should be fair approximations. Now let us look upon the shaded area between two of these current paths as an electric circuit so that we can calculate the emf induced in the circuit by the changing flux and can also calculate the resistance of the circuit. Notice that the ends of the circuit (*acjg* and *kdfm*) are wider than the sides, as they must be, since the lamination is long and thin.

Let Φ represent the instantaneous flux that cuts through the face of the shaded circuit and thus links the circuit. Let e represent the instantaneous emf induced in the circuit. Then by Faraday's law, $e = -d\Phi/dt$. But B is perpendicular to the face of the circuit and we shall assume that B is uniform over the face. This assumption introduces another approximation which we shall discuss later. The area of the face of the circuit is the area of the page enclosed by the shaded circuit, so the area is $4xy$. But from the similar triangles Ogw and Ouv we obtain $y = xl/h$, so the area is $4x^2l/h$. Hence, from (15–4–1) and Faraday's law,

$$
\begin{aligned}
e &= -(4x^2l/h)(dB/dt) \\
&= -4x^2lB_m\omega(\cos \omega t)/h \quad (15\text{–}4\text{–}2)
\end{aligned}
$$

We have expressed y in terms of x for later convenience in the derivation following (15–4–4).

Let ρ represent the electric resistivity* of the iron and L represent the total length of the circuit. Since the ends of the shaded circuit are very short compared with the sides, we shall assume that we can neglect the lengths of the ends. Thus, we shall represent the total length of the circuit as $L = 4y$. But $y = xl/h$, so $L = 4xl/h$. Consider a depth b into the iron [i.e., perpendicular to the page as shown in Fig. 15–4–1]. Let A represent the area of cross section of the sides of the shaded circuit for a depth b into the iron, and $A = b\,dx$. Then, if R represents the resistance of the shaded circuit for a depth b into the iron, and $R = \rho L/A$

$$
R = \rho 4xl/hb\,dx \quad (15\text{–}4\text{–}3)
$$

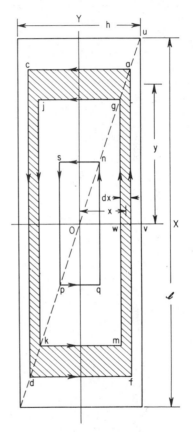

Figure 15–4–2. Cross section of one lamination very much magnified as to thickness h.

Notice that when we neglected the lengths of the ends of the circuit with respect to the lengths of the sides, we arranged it so that we neglected the resistances of the ends of the circuit with respect to the resistances of the sides. This is an even better approximation because the ends are much wider than the sides.

---

* You will recall from elementary physics that the resistivity of a conducting material is defined as the resistance between the faces of a cube which has unit length along each edge. The resistance R of a conductor of length L and area of cross section A is given by $R = \rho L/A$.

Let dp represent the instantaneous rate at which electrical energy is being converted into heat energy in the shaded circuit, and $dp = i^2R = e^2/R$. Use (15–4–2) and (15–4–3) and we have

$$dp = 4lB_m^2\omega^2b\,(\cos^2\omega t)x^3\,dx/\rho h \qquad (15\text{–}4\text{–}4)$$

Now we wish to add all such instantaneous powers for all such circuits across the whole lamination. This we can do by integrating with respect to x from $x = 0$ to $x = h/2$. Let p represent this instantaneous power for all such circuits for the whole cross section of the lamination and a depth b into the iron, and we have

$$p = (4l/\rho h)B_m^2\omega^2b\cos^2\omega t\int_0^{h/2} x^3\,dx = lh^3bB_m^2\omega^2(\cos^2\omega t)/16\rho \qquad (15\text{–}4\text{–}5)$$

Next let us compute the time average eddy current power loss P for half a cycle. (See Sec. 4–9, Problems II and III, where we first computed time average power). It will serve to compute the time average for half a cycle since all half cycles are alike. Thus $P = \int_0^{\pi/\omega} p\,dt/(\pi/\omega)$, and we obtain

$$P = lh^3bB_m^2\omega^2/32\rho \qquad (15\text{–}4\text{–}6)$$

Let v represent the volume of iron that we have considered and $v = lhb$. Also let f represent the frequency in cycles/sec of the alternating current in the winding of the magnet, and $\omega = 2\pi f$. Then (15–4–6) becomes

$$P = \pi^2B_m^2f^2vh^2/8\rho \qquad (15\text{–}4\text{–}7)$$

If, now, we let v represent the total volume of iron in the core of the a-c machine, (15–4–7) can be looked upon as the power loss due to eddy currents in the whole core. Experiments show that (15–4–7) gives very closely the correct type of functional relationship between P and B_m, f, v, and h, but that the constant term is not correct. Hence (15–4–7) is often written

$$P = K\pi^2B_m^2f^2vh^2/8\rho \qquad (15\text{–}4\text{–}8)$$

where K is a constant for the iron core of a given machine operating under given conditions. Here K may have a value approximately in the range from 1 to 2 for various machines. Let us enumerate the reasons why our derivation is approximate and thus does not take into account all the possibilities.

1. As pointed out, B is not a sinusoidal function of time and, therefore, our assumption regarding the functional relationship between B and t was an approximation at the outset.

2. The value of B is not uniform across a cross section of a lamination, because by Lenz's law the eddy currents produce magnetic flux in such a direction as to oppose the change of the magnetic flux inducing them. The magnetic flux set up by the eddy currents will be greatest near the center of a lamination and least at the outside edges. Hence, the net flux is least at the center and greatest at the edges. This effect is not very great at power frequencies but is large at high frequencies. Also, the shape of the iron where the magnetic circuit turns a corner will influence the flux distribution.

3. We have tacitly assumed that there is perfect electric insulation between laminations, and this condition is never achieved in practice. Also, the degree of insulation will vary from place to place in the core due to accidental differences in assembly.

4. The laminations must be bound together by some means other than the adhesion of the insulating material, and it is common practice to bolt them together. These bolts must be insulated from the laminations because their lengths will be in a direction, in general, which is perpendicular to the flux. Differences of assembly and insulation of the bolts will cause appreciable differences in the eddy current losses in various machines. For greater detail, an advanced text on electrical machinery should be consulted.

Equation (15–4–8), however, tells us some very important facts about eddy current power loss for machines which have an approximately sinusoidal variation of flux with time. In the first place, the loss varies directly as the square of the thickness of the laminations. This functional relationship puts a premium on the use of thin laminations, but if the laminations are too thin the cost of construction and handling for assembly becomes excessive. Hence economics, as much as physics, determines the choice of thickness. In the second place, the power loss varies directly as the square of the frequency f of the alternating current. This is one of the many reasons why power frequencies are low and why some areas which have heavy industries use 25 cycles/sec instead of 60 cycles/sec for the a-c lines. At higher communication frequencies, h must be decreased to compensate for the increase in f even though the cost of manufacture is increased. In some cases, h is markedly decreased by using powdered iron mixed with an insulating resin for the core. At still higher frequencies, iron cores must be abandoned entirely.

The value of P varies inversely as the electrical resistivity ρ of the core material. The type of core material is dictated by its magnetic, rather than its electrical, properties. However, much progress has been made in developing ferromagnetic alloys which have better magnetic properties than iron but also have a higher electrical resistivity than iron.

Usually the values of B_m and v for a particular machine are dictated by the requirements of the magnetic circuit of that machine and cannot be altered to minimize eddy current loss.

We have considered, in some detail, the eddy current loss in the iron core of a machine which operates on alternating current in order to illustrate the type of discussion which is involved. However, this is just a single, but very important, illustration of a broad subject which is of considerable significance in many parts of electrical engineering.

15–5 A D-C GENERATOR

In Sec. 3–6 we discussed a simple a-c generator that consisted of a plane coil rotating in a uniform magnetic field. You are urged to review Sec. 3–6 as an introduction to the present discussion.

1. SIMPLE D-C GENERATOR. If the wires from H and J of Fig. 3–6–1 were connected to a split commutator (instead of slip rings), such as the one shown in Fig. 13–8–1 (c) for a motor, we can see that the connection of the rotating

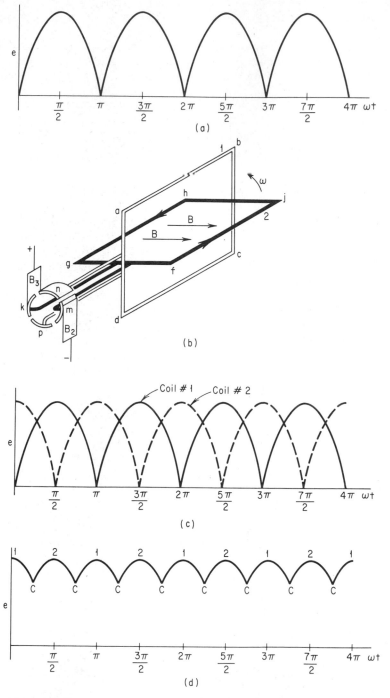

Figure 15–5–1. Simple d-c generator. (a) Emf of a single coil generator with a two segment split ring commutator. (b) Armature with two coils and four segment commutator. (c) Half wave rectified a-c from coils 1 and 2 separately. (d) Output voltage of the generator shown in (b).

coil to the outside circuit would be reversed each time that the emf in the coil reversed. Thus, the emf applied to the outside circuit would vary with time as shown in Fig. 15–5–1 (a). Hence, the emf applied to the outside circuit is direct (in one direction only) although an alternating emf is still induced in the coil. However, the direct emf obtained in this fashion is a full-wave rectified alternating emf, and is not a steady direct emf. For most purposes, when direct current is used, a more nearly steady direct emf is desirable and often imperative.

Now suppose that we add a second coil to the rotating system as shown in Fig. 15–5–1 (b) so that we now have the two coils, $abcd$ (call it coil 1) and $ghjf$ (call it coil 2), mounted with their planes at right angles to each other, rotating together, and insulated from each other. The split ring commutator has four segments, k, m, n, and p. Coil 2 is connected to the diametrically opposite segments k and m, while coil 1 is connected to the remaining two segments p and n. The brushes, B_2 and B_3 are mounted on the frame so that they remain at rest, and they rub against the commutator segments as the commutator turns under them. At the moment of the picture, the brushes are in contact with segments k and m, and thus are electrically connected to coil 2, while coil 1 is electrically insulated from the outside circuit.

Imagine that a uniform magnetic field is directed horizontally toward the right, as shown by the vector which represents B, all through the region where the coils are rotating. You can show that the emf of the generator will be as shown graphically in Figs. 15–5–1 (c) and (d). The number above each maximum point shows the coil that is connected to the brushes during the corresponding section of the curve, and the points marked with c's are the points where one pair of commutator segments leaves the brushes and the next pair rotates into contact with them.

From this discussion, you can see that the addition of more coils at various angles with respect to the coils shown in Fig. 15–5–1 (b), and each coil with its own pair of commutator segments, can result in a generator which supplies a more nearly steady direct emf to the external circuit. There will always be some emf ripple because there cannot be an infinite number of coils.

The generator discussed here would not produce an emf of sufficient magnitude to be of commercial value because it would not be practical to secure a sufficiently large total magnetic flux in the region where the armature rotates. This is because the armature has no iron core and thus the air gap in the magnetic circuit (see Chapter XVII) is too large. Thus, a generator of this type always has the coils wound on an iron core, and usually the wires of the windings are embedded in slots in the iron. The iron core must be laminated in order to minimize eddy current losses.

2. A MORE PRACTICAL D-C GENERATOR. As pointed out above, a d-c generator and a d-c motor have the same fundamental construction. Hence, we may take over the drum armature motor of Sec. 13–8 (shown in Fig. 13–8–2), drive it with an engine, and use it as a d-c generator. You are urged to review the construction of the drum armature motor as an introduction to our discussion here.

Figure 15–5–2 shows the same drum winding as does Fig. 13–8–2 (b), but this time the machine is being used as a generator. Compare the windings in these two figures and verify that they are the same. In Fig. 15–5–2 the armature is being driven counterclockwise by the engine, so the face conductors on the right side of the armature are moving upward, and the ones on the left side are moving downward. Application of Fleming's left-hand rule to the conductors on the right face of the armature will show you that positive charges will be forced down in these conductors, as shown by the crosses in the small circles which represent the conductors. Similarly on the left side, positive charges are forced up in the face (or active) conductors, as shown by the dots in the small circles which represent these conductors. Thus, the crosses and dots in the small circles indicate the senses of the induced emf's. Notice that the emf is always directed into the page on the right and out of the page on the left regardless of the position of the armature in its rotation.

In the center of Fig. 15–5–2, the commutator segments and brushes, B_1

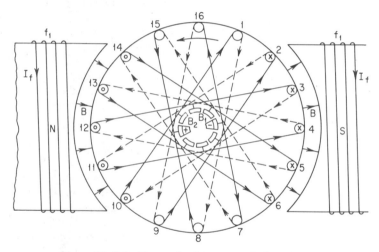

Figure 15–5–2. Two-pole, drum wound, d-c generator.

and B_2, are shown. The commutator is turned inside out for ease in drawing. Actually, the commutator is mounted on the armature shaft out in front of the picture and the brushes rub on the outside (not inside) surfaces of the commutator segments. Note that the connection of the commutator segments is the same as if the brushes rubbed directly on the face conductors as shown in Fig. 13–8–2 (b). Of course, the brushes remain at rest and the commutator turns under them.

Now imagine that brushes B_1 and B_2 are connected to an external circuit so that the induced emf causes a current to flow through the armature windings and through the external circuit. The arrows on the armature end connections of Fig. 15–5–2 show the senses of the currents in the armature windings, as do the dots and crosses in the small circles which represent the active face conductors. Follow the directions of these currents through the winding and note that (as in the corresponding motor) there are two paths, of equal resistance, in parallel through the armature. Notice also that this connection puts half of the face conductors in series in one path, and the other half in series in the other path, and these two paths in parallel. Thus, the emf of the generator that is applied to the external circuit is half of the sum of the emf's induced in all 16 face conductors.

Now let us derive a formula which we may use to compute the emf induced in this two-pole drum armature generator. The term "two-pole" is used here because the generator has two magnet poles, marked N and S in Fig. 15–5–2. We shall assume that the armature is rotating with a constant angular velocity ω and let v represent the linear speed of each face conductor. Also, for this simple theory, we shall assume that the magnetic flux density B is radial and of constant magnitude in the active region (under the pole faces) and zero outside of this region. Thus, $B = 0$ at conductors 1, 15, 16, 7, 8, and 9 at the moment which Fig. 15–5–2 represents. Hence, at this moment, all active conductors (i.e., all conductors except these six) are moving with constant speed v perpendicular to a magnetic field of constant magnetic flux density B. If we let l represent the length of each active conductor, we have from (15–1–9), $\mathscr{E}_1 = vBl$, where $\mathscr{E}_1$ is the constant emf induced in each active conductor. The face conductors are uniformly and closely spaced on the face of the armature (only a few are shown), so the number of active conductors is essentially constant as the armature rotates. Let N represent the total number of active conductors (10 in Fig. 15–5–2), and we have for the total emf $\mathscr{E}$ of the generator

$$\mathscr{E} = \tfrac{1}{2}NvBl \qquad (15\text{–}5\text{–}1)$$

where the factor $\tfrac{1}{2}$ enters due to the two paths in parallel in the armature as explained above. Let r be the radius of the armature and $v = \omega r$, so $\mathscr{E} = \tfrac{1}{2}N\omega rBl$. If n represents the number of revolutions of the armature per second, $\omega = 2\pi n$ and

$$\mathscr{E} = \pi rNnBl \qquad (15\text{–}5\text{–}2)$$

Equation (15–5–2) applies to the special generator that we have described in connection with Fig. 15–5–2. A book* that treats d-c machinery in greater detail should be consulted for other types of d-c generators and for the many important practical considerations.

The emf of (15–5–2) developed by this generator is essentially constant, although there will be some emf ripple because there cannot be an infinite number of conductors on the armature. A constant emf, of course, depends upon n and B remaining constant, and they cannot always be held constant* as the load on the generator changes. Direct current generators usually furnish their own field current (I_f in Fig. 15–5–2) and the common types of connections of the field coils to the brushes are shunt and compound as shown in Fig. 13–8–3 for the d-c motor. A generator which furnishes its own field current is said to be self-excited, and for the characteristics of a self-excited generator see a book on d-c machinery. Also, for practical alternators, consult a book† on alternating current machinery.

---

* For example, C. L. Dawes, *Electrical Engineering*, Vol. I, *Direct Currents* (New York: McGraw-Hill Book Co., Inc., 1937), pp. 352–475.

† For example, T. C. McFarland, *Alternating Current Machinery* (New York: D. Van Nostrand Co., Inc., 1948).

PROBLEMS

15–1 Derive (15–1–9) by use of the law of conservation of energy and Kirchhoff's second law. (a) First derive it under the conditions that R is the total resistance of the circuit in Fig. 15–1–1 and that resistance is the only circuit element present which can convert electrical energy into some other form of energy. (b) Second derive it under the conditions that there is a motor in series in the line from J to G in Fig. 15–1–1 and that $\mathscr{E}_M$ is the back emf of the motor. Let R, again, represent the total resistance of the circuit.

15–2 The wire AD in Fig. 15–1–1 is 2.00 m long and has a velocity of 50.0 cm/sec toward the right. The magnetic flux density is perpendicular to the page in the direction shown and is the earth's magnetic field which, at that place, has a magnitude of 6.00×10^{-5} wb/m². The circuit has a total resistance of 1.20×10^{-5} ohm. Substitute units with numerical quantities and show that proper units result for the answer. (a) What emf is induced in the wire? [*Ans:* 6.00×10^{-5} v.] (b) What is the electric field intensity in the wire? (c) What force does each electron in the wire experience because of the motion of the wire in the magnetic field? [*Ans:* 4.80×10^{-24} newton.] (d) What force must an external agency exert in order to keep the wire moving at this constant velocity? [*Ans:* 6.00×10^{-4} newton.] (e) Compute the rate at which the external agency is doing work and compare with the rate at which electrical energy is being converted into heat energy.

15–3 At a place where the earth's magnetic field has a flux density of 8.50×10^{-5} wb/m² and a dip angle (angle with the horizontal) of 70°, a railway train is traveling 60 miles per hour on a horizontal track and is going in the magnetic north direction. (a) What emf is induced in the 4 ft 8½ inch length of axle between each pair of wheels? Which end of the axle is the positive terminal of the source? [*Ans:* 3.10×10^{-3} v, west.] (b) On a wet day when the ground from rail to rail has a high conductivity, the total resistance of the circuit for each axle is 0.0010 ohm. How much extra force, in pounds, must the locomotive of a freight train exert because of the emf's induced in the 400 axles of its cars? [*Ans:* 0.032 lb.]

15–4 A horizontal straight copper bar, 2.00 m long, lies across the top of a freight car and points directly at one wire of a d-c power line which is at the same elevation as the top of the freight car. The power wire has its length parallel to the track. The length of the bar is perpendicular to the length of the power wire and it is 2.50 m from the near end of the bar to the wire. The current in the power wire is 400 amp. The train has a speed of 40.0 meter/sec parallel to the power wire and is traveling in a direction opposite to the current in the wire. What emf is induced in the copper bar and which end of the bar is positive? [*Ans:* $\mathscr{E} = 1.88 \times 10^{-3}$ v with far end of bar positive.]

15–5 An automobile, with a straight vertical radio antenna 2.00 m long, is traveling at 60.0 miles/hr, with the antenna vertically below a d-c power wire which is carrying a current of 200 amp. The velocity of the car is parallel with the length of the wire, and in the direction of the current in the wire. It is 2.50 m from the top of the antenna to the wire. What emf is induced in the antenna and which end of the antenna is positive? [*Ans:* 6.33×10^{-4} v, upper end.]

15–6 A very long solenoid is wound on a nonferromagnetic material and has an area of cross section A, and N/L turns of wire per unit length. A sinusoidal alternating current $i = I_m \sin \omega t$ flows through the windings of the solenoid. A secondary coil with n turns is wound around the center of the solenoid, and the turns of the secondary are bunched close together at the center. Show that the equation of the emf induced in the secondary coil is

$$e = \mu_0 N A n I_m \omega [\sin (\omega t - \pi/2)]/L$$

15–7 Refer to Problem 14–2 and imagine that the rectangle referred to there is a rectangular loop of wire. If the current flowing in the long straight wire is given by $i = I_m \sin \omega t$, where $I_m = 150$ amp and $\omega = 377/\text{sec}$, what is the equation of the emf induced in the wire rectangle? [*Ans:* $e = \mathscr{E}_m \sin (\omega t - \pi/2)$ where $\mathscr{E}_m = 9.08 \times 10^{-3}$ v.]

15–8 The current through a toroidal winding is $i = I_m \sin \omega t$. The toroid is wound on a nonferromagnetic core with an area of cross section A. The mean radius r_1 of the toroid is large compared with the radial distance across the core. A secondary coil of n turns is wound on the toroid and the ends are connected together through a resistor. The total resistance of the secondary circuit is R_2. Show that the quantity of charge, Q, which flows through the secondary circuit during a positive half cycle of the secondary current is

$$Q = 2n\mu_0 N A I_m / R_2 2\pi r_1$$

15–9 For the situation described in Problem 15–6 show that the mutual inductance M between the solenoid and its secondary coil is given by $M = \mu_0 A n N/L$. Derive this formula in two different (but closely related) ways.

15–10 In Problem 15–7 what is the mutual inductance M between the straight wire and the rectangular loop of wire? [*Ans:* 1.60×10^{-7} henry.]

15–11 What is the mutual inductance M between the primary toroidal winding and the secondary wound on it in Problem 15–8?

15–12 A coil, call it the *secondary coil*, with N turns of wire has its two terminals connected through a resistor to form a complete circuit. The total resistance of the circuit, including that of the secondary coil, is R and its total constant self-inductance is L. This secondary coil is located near another circuit, call it the *primary circuit*, in such a way that magnetic flux lines from the primary circuit link the secondary coil. At time $t = 0$, Φ_0 magnetic flux lines link the secondary coil; and at time t_1, Φ_1 magnetic flux lines link the secondary coil. Let $Q =$ the quantity of electricity that flows through the secondary circuit during the flux change. Prove that $Q = N(\Phi_1 - \Phi_0)/R$.

15–13 If a sinusoidal current flows through the windings of an electromagnet which has a ferromagnetic core, the magnetic flux produced by the magnet varies approximately sinusoidally with time under proper conditions. This relationship is approximate because of the hysteresis of the ferromagnetic material (we shall study hysteresis in Chapter XVII) and under some conditions it is a bad approximation.

Suppose that the magnetic flux density between the pole pieces of the General Electric betatron (described in Sec. 15–3) is given by the equation $\bar{B} = \bar{B}_m \sin \omega t$ where $\bar{B}$ is the space average (over the face of the orbit) of the instantaneous values of the magnetic flux density through the orbit.

Here $\bar{B}_m$ is the maximum value of $\bar{B}$ and has the magnitude $\bar{B}_m = 0.800$ wb/m²; ω is the angular frequency of the alternating current in the winding of the magnet and has the value $\omega = 377$ radians/sec. (a) Show that the emf induced in the electron orbit is given by emf $= \pi r_0^2 \bar{B}_m \omega \cos \omega t$, where $\pi r_0^2 \bar{B}_m \omega = 666$ volt. (b) Show that the electric field intensity at the electron orbit is $E = E_m \cos \omega t$, where $E_m = 126$ volt/meter. (c) Let W_1 represent the kinetic energy acquired by an electron in one trip around the orbit. Show that W_1 as a function of time is

$$W_1 = 1.07 \times 10^{-16} \text{ joule cos } 377\, t$$

(d) Let $\overline{W}_1$ represent the time average kinetic energy acquired by an electron in one trip around the orbit. The time average is to be taken for the first quarter cycle of the alternating current which flows in the winding of the magnet, since this is the only part of the cycle during which the electrons are accelerated. Hence the time average is to be taken from $t = 0$ to $t = \pi/2\omega$. (See Sec. 4–9 where we first computed a time average.) Show that $\overline{W}_1 = 2\omega q r_0^2 \bar{B}_m = 6.78 \times 10^{-17}$ joule, where q is the charge on an electron. Check this result against the statement in Sec. 15–3 that an electron acquires, on the average, 420 ev of energy in each trip around the orbit. (e) In the betatron, the electrons are promptly accelerated to such a high velocity that one may assume, to a fair approximation, that the electrons travel with the velocity of light $c = 3 \times 10^8$ m/sec for all their trips around the orbit. This, obviously, is not a correct assumption, for the electrons never do reach the velocity of light; but, using this assumption, show that the total distance d traveled by an electron during the total time that it is being accelerated is $d = c\pi/2\omega = 776$ miles. (f) Using the result from (e), show that the number n of trips which the electron makes around the orbit is $n = c/4\omega r_0 = 2.38 \times 10^5$. (g) Using the total number of trips that an electron makes around the orbit and [from part (d)] the average energy that an electron acquires per trip around the orbit, compute the total energy acquired by an electron. Check your result against the rating of this betatron.

15–14 A large electromagnet, which has 60 cycles/sec sinusoidal alternating current flowing in its windings, has 100 ft³ of laminated silicon steel in its core. The maximum magnetic flux density in the steel is 10,000 gausses. The laminations are 0.014 in. thick (29 gauge sheet steel was used) and the electrical resistivity of this silicon steel is 60×10^{-8} ohm meter. (a) If K is 1.5, what is the average power loss due to eddy currents in the core? Substitute units with numerical quantities and show that the proper unit results for the answer. [*Ans:* 4.0 kw.] (b) The density of this silicon steel is 474 lb/ft³. What is the eddy current power loss per pound for the above magnet?

15–15 A certain transformer core is made up of sheet steel laminations 0.020 in. thick. At a maximum magnetic flux density of 0.85 wb/m² on a 60 cycle/sec sinusoidal a-c line, it is found that the eddy current power loss is 550 w. If another transformer, of the same design and volume of core material, is built of 0.014 in. thick laminations of the same sheet steel, what will its eddy current power loss be at a maximum magnetic flux density of 1.1 wb/m² on the same a-c line? [*Ans:* 450 w.]

15–16 A certain transformer core is made up of silicon steel laminations 0.0245 in. thick. At a maximum magnetic flux density of 0.57 wb/m² on a 60 cycle/sec sinusoidal a-c line, the eddy current power loss is found to be 150 w. What thickness of laminations of the same silicon steel must be used in another transformer of the same design and volume of core in order to have no more than 100 w eddy current power loss at a maximum magnetic flux density of 0.68 wb/m² on a 500 cycles/sec sinusoidal a-c line? [*Ans:* 0.002 in.]

15–17 Refer to Sec. 15–4 and carry out the derivation of an eddy current power loss formula, but this time use the sketch in Fig. 15–P–1 for the calculation. In this figure it is assumed that the shaded circuit shown as *gdfk* is a possible eddy current circuit. Also, whatever the value of *x*, it is assumed that the eddy currents flow the full length *l* and then across top and bottom paths, which are along *gd* and *fk*. Assume at the outset that the resistances of the end paths *dg* and *fk* may be neglected with respect to the resistances of the side paths *df* and *gk*. (a) Show that the derivation on this basis gives the eddy current power loss formula

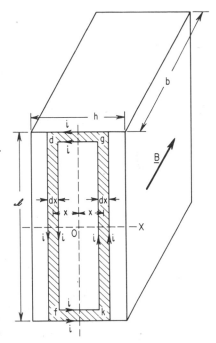

$$P = (\pi^2/6\rho)B_m^2 f^2 v h^2$$

which is one that is often encountered. (b) Note that this formula is the same as (15–4–7) except for the 6 in the denominator of this formula, where an 8 appears in the denominator of (15–4–7). Point out qualitatively the difference in the two derivations which leads to the different numerical factors in the two cases. Both derivations involve approximations, most of which are the same for both. But, where the

Figure 15–P–1. Sketch for calculation of eddy current power loss.

approximations differ in the two derivations, which do you consider to be a closer representation of the actual physical situation? Why? (c) Some iron cores are made up of a bundle of soft iron wires bound tightly together but insulated from each other. The long dimension of each wire is, of course, parallel to the flux lines. Let r_0 represent the radius of each wire, and derive the eddy current power loss formula, for a core of this type,

$$P = \pi^2 r_0^2 v f^2 B_m^2 / 4\rho$$

15–18 A copper disk of radius *R* is rotating with a constant angular velocity ω about an axis through its center and perpendicular to its face. There is a uniform magnetic field of magnetic flux density *B* directed perpendicular to the face of the disk (i.e., parallel to the axis of the disk) all through the region. Prove that the emf induced between the periphery of the disk and the axis of the disk is given by $\mathcal{E} = \omega B R^2 / 2$.

15–19 A two-pole drum wound d-c generator is rotating at 30 revolutions/sec, driven by a steam turbine. The armature has a radius of 20 cm and has 300 face conductors, 60% of which are active. Each active conductor is 40 cm long. The emf of the generator is 500 v. (a) What is the magnetic flux density at the armature of the generator? Substitute units with numerical quantities and show that the answer comes out in proper units. [*Ans:* 0.37 wb/m².] (b) If the generator is furnishing 40 amp to a circuit, what horsepower must the steam turbine furnish to the generator? Neglect losses in the generator. (c) If each of the parallel paths through the armature has a resistance of 0.55 ohm, what is the terminal potential difference of the generator and what power is being delivered to the external circuit?

15–20 Figure 15–P–2 shows a schematic circuit diagram of a two-pole drum wound d-c generator *G*, like the one in Fig. 15–5–2, charging a battery B_b. The generator has its field coils connected in shunt, as shown by *f* in Fig. 15–P–2. The engine driving the generator is shut off but the electric circuit remains as shown. What happens? Draw a diagram of the drum winding and commutator, like Fig. 15–5–2, and illustrate your answer in detail by use of this diagram.

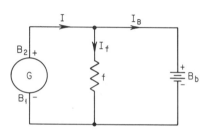

Figure 15–P–2. Generator *G* charging a battery B_b. *f* is the shunt field of the generator.

15–21 A two-pole drum wound generator, like the one in Fig. 15–5–2, is connected to an external circuit whose total resistance is 4.50 ohms. The armature has 180 face conductors of which 67% are active, and the resistance of the armature between brushes is 0.500 ohm. The radius of the armature is 10 cm and the armature is being driven by a gasoline engine at 1800 revolutions/min. The length of each face conductor is 15 cm and the flux density under each pole face is 0.800 wb/m². What is the magnetic force on the active conductors against which the gasoline engine must work? [*Ans:* 44 lb.]

15–22 A two-pole drum wound motor, like the one shown in Fig. 13–8–2, has 320 face conductors on its armature, 80% of which are active. The radius of the armature is 13.0 cm and the armature is turning at 1200 revolutions/min. The length of each active conductor is 30.0 cm and the magnetic flux density under each pole face is 0.750 wb/m². The potential difference across the terminals of the motor is 485 v and the resistance between brushes is 0.500 ohm. What torque is the motor developing? [*Ans:* 112 newton meter.]

15–23 A helicopter is hovering in a region where the vertical component of the earth's magnetic field is 5.52×10^{-5} wb/m². If the length of each metal rotor blade on the propeller is 4.55 m from hub to tip and if the propeller is rotating at 33.3 rev/sec, what emf is induced in each propeller blade from hub to tip?

MAGNETIC PROPERTIES

OF MATERIALS

16-1 MAGNETIC PROPERTIES ARE DUE TO MOTIONS OF ELECTRONS IN ATOMS

In Sec. 1–1 we summarized very briefly the essential features of the nuclear atom model and we have used this atom model for numerous explanations of electrical behavior of matter. We now wish to use it as a basis for a theory of the magnetic properties of matter.

In the nuclear atom model, the extranuclear electrons are in continual motion about the nucleus, and each electron can be considered as moving in some kind of a path about the nucleus. These paths are called orbits, and an electron moving in an orbit is the equivalent of a tiny loop of current. In Sec. 13–7 we have considered the magnetic field produced by a current loop and have defined the magnetic moment of such a loop. Thus, in our theory, we shall consider that each electron in its orbital motion about the nucleus produces a magnetic field and has a magnetic moment as if it were a tiny loop of current.

It is believed, from experimental and theoretical results, that an electron in an atom also rotates about an axis through the electron, very much as if it were a spinning sphere of electric charge, and this behavior is called *electron spin*. It turns out from results in atomic physics that we must not take too literally the picture of an electron as a spinning sphere of charge, but the concept of electron spin has become firmly embedded in physical theory. One of the important reasons for the belief that electrons have spin is contained in the electronic explanation of the magnetic properties of matter which we are now considering. We shall consider this reason briefly at the end of the present section.

When an electron spins, there is a charge in motion and thus an electric current which produces a magnetic field. We may also look upon electron spin as the equivalent of a tiny current loop which has a magnetic moment. By this theory, the resultant magnetic moment of an atom is the vector sum of the orbital and spin magnetic moments of the electrons which are part of the atom. To the best of our knowledge, all the magnetic properties of bulk matter can be attributed to the orbital motions and spins of the electrons of the atoms which make up the matter. (Nuclear spins also produce magnetic moments, but the nuclear magnetic moments are so small that the properties of bulk matter are unaffected by them.*)

The magnetic behavior of various kinds of matter can be divided into three classifications: (1) diamagnetism, (2) paramagnetism, and (3) ferromagnetism. We shall consider the physical basis for each very briefly and then propose additional theory which permits solution of physical problems.

1. DIAMAGNETISM. An electron revolving in an orbit about the nucleus of an atom has orbital angular momentum p. Also, because it is a charge in motion, it is the equivalent of a current flowing in a tiny current loop and thus has an orbital magnetic moment, as we have noted previously. Let us represent this orbital magnetic moment by M_r and derive the relationship between M_r and p. For simplicity, we shall assume that the electron is moving in the circular orbit shown in Fig. 16–1–1.

Let $-q$ be the charge on the electron, m be its mass, ω its angular velocity of revolution, and v its linear velocity in the orbit. If we let i represent the equivalent current in the loop and T be the time for one revolution of the electron, then

$$i = q/T = q\omega/2\pi$$

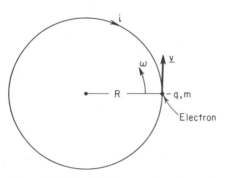

From (13–7–1), the magnetic moment of a current loop is $M = IA$, where A is the area of the face of the orbit. The current i in Fig. 16–1–1 is in the opposite sense around the loop to that of the electron motion, so the vector which represents A is perpendicular to the page and directed into the page. Thus (13–7–1) becomes, for this case

Figure 16–1–1. Electron moving in a circular orbit about a nucleus.

$$M_r = q\omega A/2\pi \quad (16\text{–}1\text{–}1)$$

and M_r is directed perpendicular to the page and into the page.

Now let us write the expression for the orbital angular momentum p of the electron. Angular momentum is equal to moment of inertia times the angular velocity. The moment of inertia of a point mass m revolving in a circle of radius R is mR^2, so

$$p = mR^2\omega \quad (16\text{–}1\text{–}2)$$

where the vector which represents ω is in the direction of the thumb of the right hand when the fingers point in the direction of revolution of the electron. Thus, p is represented by a vector, in Fig. 16–1–1, perpendicular to the page and directed up out of the page. Hence the vectors which represent M_r and p are oppositely directed. From (16–1–1) and (16–1–2) we can write

$$M_r = -qp/2m \quad (16\text{–}1\text{–}3)$$

where the fact that M_r and p are oppositely directed is implied by the negative

* See, for example, Felix Bloch, *Am. Scientist*, **48**, pp. 48–62, Jan., 1955, in particular p. 50.

sign before q, and where we have made use of the fact that $A = \pi R^2$. It can be shown that (16-1-3) continues to hold even if the orbital motion is not in a circular path.

In order for the electron to remain in the orbit, the nucleus must exert a force of attraction on the electron, and this force of attraction must furnish the required centripetal force $m\omega^2 R$. Thus the force F_n that the nucleus exerts on the electron is

$$F_n = m\omega^2 R \qquad (16\text{-}1\text{-}4)$$

Now imagine that a magnetic field of flux density B is turned on in Fig. 16-1-1 and that B is perpendicular to the page and directed up out of the page. While the magnetic flux through the orbit is increasing, an electric field exists in the orbit and, by Lenz's law, its sense will be such as to oppose the increase of the flux linking the orbit. Thus, the angular velocity of the electron in the orbit is increased, just as it was in the betatron (see Sec. 15-3). The electric field which accelerates the electron lasts only during the increase in the magnetic flux Φ linking the orbit. However, subsequent to the change in Φ, the electron continues to revolve at its new higher angular velocity as long as Φ remains constant. Let us compute the increase in the angular velocity of the electron.

The magnetic field exerts a magnetic force F_m on the electron given by (13-1-9) as $F_m = qv \times B$. From Fig. 16-1-1, F_m is directed radially inward along R, since q is a negative charge. Because v is perpendicular to B, the magnitude of F_m is $F_m = qvB$. Using the fact that $v = \omega_1 R$, then $F_m = q\omega_1 RB$, where ω_1 represents the new angular velocity. The total force which the attraction of the nucleus must now furnish is $m\omega_1^2 R - q\omega_1 RB$. Equate this to the force which the nucleus exerts, as given by (16-1-4), and we have $m\omega^2 R = m\omega_1^2 R - q\omega_1 RB$ or, letting $\Delta\omega = \omega_1 - \omega$,

$$\Delta\omega = qB\omega_1/m(\omega_1 + \omega)$$

Even for the strongest magnetic fields which are achieved in the laboratory, ω_1 differs but little from ω, so we may replace $\omega_1 + \omega$ by $2\omega_1$. Hence

$$\Delta\omega = qB/2m \qquad (16\text{-}1\text{-}5)$$

Note that $\Delta\omega$ is independent of both R and ω within the approximation that we have made. As mentioned before, $\Delta\omega$ is an increase in angular velocity of the electron for the case that we have solved. If the electron in Fig. 16-1-1 had been going in the opposite sense around the orbit (with B still directed out of the page), the angular velocity of the electron would have been decreased as required by Lenz's law. The magnitude of the decrease in ω in such a case is also given by (16-1-5) (see Problem 16-1).

It can be shown that (16-1-5) gives the change in the angular velocity of the electron even when the plane of the orbit is not perpendicular to B. [You will notice that this assumption has not explicitly been used in deriving (16-1-5).] In this case $\Delta\omega$ becomes a velocity of precession of the angular momentum vector about the direction of the field. Thus, *all* electron orbits in an atom precess, and hence the *whole* atom precesses about the direction of the magnetic field with the precessional velocity given in (16-1-5). The result is an additional orbital angular momentum Δp of the whole atom, given by $\Delta p = J\Delta\omega$, where J is the effective moment of inertia of all the electrons of the atom. Putting the value of $\Delta\omega$ from (16–1–5) into this expression for Δp and noting that Δp and B are in the same sense (i.e., out of the page), we have

$$\Delta p = JqB/2m \tag{16–1–6}$$

From (16–1–3) we know that this change in angular momentum Δp will result in a change in orbital magnetic moment ΔM_r given by $\Delta M_r = (-q/2m)\Delta p$. Hence, using Δp from (16–1–6),

$$\Delta M_r = -Jq^2B/(2m)^2 \tag{16–1–7}$$

This ΔM_r is an induced magnetic moment and, as we have seen from Lenz's law, it is in a direction opposite to that of the applied magnetic field. This latter fact is shown in (16–1–7) by the minus sign, which is independent of the sign of q since q is squared.

Now consider a particular kind of material each of whose atoms has a zero net magnetic moment when no external magnetic field is applied. This means that the spin and orbital magnetic moments of the electrons of each atom add vectorially to zero in the absence of an applied magnetic field. When a magnetic field is applied, the induced magnetic moment of each atom is given by (16–1–7), and it is in a direction opposite to that of the applied field. Hence, *the resultant magnetic flux density in the vicinity of the atom is smaller than that due to the applied field alone and thus smaller than it would have been if the material had been absent and the space empty.* This behavior is called a *diamagnetic* behavior because the presence of the material has weakened the magnetic field.

2. PARAMAGNETISM. In the explanation of diamagnetism we have chosen an atom whose resultant magnetic moment is zero when no external magnetic field is applied. If, however, we consider another kind of atom in which the magnetic moments, of the electron spins and orbital motions, do not add to zero, that atom will have a net magnetic moment built into it. Such an atom is said to be paramagnetic. In this case we may consider that the atom is a single tiny current loop with a net magnetic moment. When an external magnetic field is applied to a material made up of paramagnetic atoms, each atom experiences a torque due to the applied field. We have seen in Sec. 13–7 that this torque tends to turn the current loop toward a position where its magnetic field is parallel and in the same direction as that of the field imposed on it. Thus, each atom tends to turn so that its magnetic field strengthens the applied field in which it is immersed, and the resultant magnetic field has a greater magnetic flux density than it would have had with the material absent. The diamagnetic effect is still present in each atom but, if a net strengthening of the field results for a particular material, the paramagnetic effect predominates for that material.

Paramagnetic strengthening of the field, which depends on a particular orientation of the atoms, is opposed by thermal agitation because thermal agitation tends to produce random orientation. Thus, the net effect on the field due to the paramagnetic behavior of the atoms is an inverse function of temperature.

3. FERROMAGNETISM. Ferromagnetic materials are those which show an abnormally large paramagnetic behavior, often making the resultant magnetic flux density thousands of times larger than that of the external applied field. Thus, each ferromagnetic atom has a large resultant magnetic moment. For example, it is believed that the uncompensated spins of four electrons in the M shell of an iron atom are chiefly responsible for the ferromagnetic properties of iron. As we have pointed out several times, only iron, nickel, cobalt, gadolinium, and certain alloys are ferromagnetic. The vast majority of materials are either diamagnetic or paramagnetic. The behavior of ferromagnetic materials is much more complicated than that of diamagnetic or paramagnetic materials and much more important practically. In fact, in engineering, diamagnetic and paramagnetic properties find little application; but electrical engineering would be hard pressed for the solutions to many problems if it were not for ferromagnetic properties. We shall devote the next chapter to a study of some phases of ferromagnetism.

Let us consider very briefly one piece of experimental evidence for the electronic explanation of ferromagnetism. This is evidence which shows that electron spin is more important than electron orbital motion, at least in the explanation of ferromagnetism.

As we have seen, an electron moving in an orbit has mechanical angular momentum as well as a magnetic moment. Similarly, a spinning electron has both mechanical angular momentum and a magnetic moment. In the case of orbital electron motion, we have computed the ratio of magnetic moment to angular momentum, and the result is given in (16–1–3). It is also possible to compute the same ratio for electron spin.* It turns out that a spinning electron has just twice as big a value for this ratio as has an electron moving in an orbit. Barnett,* in an experimental study of a phenomenon since called the Barnett effect, was able to make a direct measurement of this ratio for ferromagnetic materials and found a value almost that for a spinning electron. The conclusion, for ferromagnetic materials at least, is that the spinning electron makes the major contribution to the magnetic properties of these materials. We say "major contribution" because his values were enough below that required for a spinning electron to show that the orbital electrons probably make some contribution. For most purposes, however, the contribution due to orbital electrons is neglected in a discussion of ferromagnetism.

Also of great importance, Barnett's experiment shows that the charges, whose motions are responsible for the magnetic properties of matter, are negative charges. This result lends great weight to the proposed electron theory explanation of magnetic properties of matter.

16–2 AMPERIAN CURRENTS; B INSIDE A MATERIAL MEDIUM

In order to build a theory of the magnetic properties of matter, we propose the hypothesis that materials affect magnetic fields as if their atoms contained

* See, for example, S. J. Barnett, "Gyromagnetic and Electron-Inertia Effects," *Rev. Mod. Phys.*, **7**, 129 (1935).

circuits like the current loop discussed in Sec. 13–7. By this hypothesis then, we may replace the orbital motions and spins of the electrons in an atom by a fictitious loop of current whose magnetic moment is equal to the resultant magnetic moment of the atom. For this purpose we cannot take the magnetic moment of an isolated atom, but rather that of an atom under the conditions imposed by its surrounding neighbor atoms. This requirement is essential because the atom will be perturbed by interactions with its neighbors. For a diamagnetic material, the current in the equivalent loop is zero when there is no applied field. Since there is no resistance in these equivalent current loops, the current flows continually without need for energy from an outside source. The currents in these loops are called Amperian loop currents because Ampere first suggested their usefulness.

When no external magnetic field is imposed on a paramagnetic material

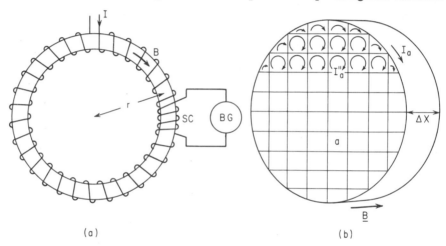

(a)   (b)

Figure 16–2–1. (a) Toroid with a material medium for its core. (b) Cross section through the core (to a much larger scale) showing schematically the Amperian current loops due to the atoms. The senses of the arrows are opposite to that of the motions of electrons since the arrows represent current. I_a on the surface of the core is the same as I_a'' if Δx is one atomic diameter.

or on an unmagnetized ferromagnetic material, the Amperian current loops are randomly oriented and produce no net magnetic field for the block of material. However, in the presence of an external magnetic field, each Amperian current loop experiences a torque which tends to align the magnetic moment of the current loop with the applied field. The greater the magnetic flux density of the applied field, the greater the torque on each current loop and the more complete the alignment. In the case of a diamagnetic material, the applied field induces a magnetic moment opposite to the applied field, and the greater the magnetic flux density of the applied field, the greater the induced magnetic moment.

In Fig. 16–2–1 (a) is shown a toroidal winding on a core material, and for the moment we shall consider that the material is paramagnetic. The radius of the toroid is large compared with the radial distance across its core. Thus, we may look upon the magnetic flux density, due to the conduction current I in the winding, as essentially constant across the cross section of the core. This means that the magnetic field in the core is uniform, and thus all parts of the core are exposed to the same magnetic flux density. Further, we shall consider that the core material is homogeneous and thus responds to the applied field in the same way at all points. With these conditions satisfied, the degree of alignment of the Amperian current loops will be the same through-out the core material, and the core material is said to be uniformly mag-netized. We shall limit our quantitative discussion to uniformly magnetized material.

Figure 16–2–1 (b) shows a cross section of the core to an enlarged scale, and shows schematically the equivalent Amperian current loops of the atoms of the core material. The Amperian current loops are only partially aligned but their magnetic moments have a resultant magnetic moment parallel to the applied magnetic flux density B and in the same direction as B. The other components of the magnetic moments of the loops are randomly oriented. Let us divide the resultant magnetic moment parallel to B by the number of current loops in the cross section and thus obtain the average component (parallel to B) of magnetic moment per loop. The result in the core material is the same as if each loop were oriented so that its component of magnetic moment parallel to B were equal to this average value. Let I_a'' represent the current in each loop which, flowing around the loop in the plane of the cross section of the core in Fig. 16–2–1 (b), would produce this average component of magnetic moment parallel to B. If the current loops were all completely aligned with their magnetic moments parallel to B, then I_a'' would be the actual equivalent current I_a' in each loop.

We see, in Fig. 16–2–1 (b), that I_u'' flows in opposite senses along each boundary of an Amperian loop except along the boundaries on the periphery of the core. Hence, the current loops are the equivalent of a fictitious current I_a'' flowing around the periphery of the core. This fictitious current is called an Amperian current. Thus, in this model, the effect of the core material is the same as if the Amperian current were flowing around the surface of the core, everywhere parallel to the conduction current in the wire winding on the core. For the paramagnetic core material considered for the picture in Fig. 16–2–1 (b), the Amperian current is in the same sense as the conduction current and adds its magnetic effect to that of the conduction current. We shall use this same result for ferromagnetic materials and shall see that the Amperian current often has many thousands of times as much magnetic effect as the conduction current and continues after the conduction current is shut off. This latter statement means that the Amperian current loops (and thus the atoms) retain some alignment after the external applied field is removed, and this is the basis for the magnetism of permanent magnets. In paramagnetic materials, the alignment changes with the applied field and no alignment remains when the applied field is shut off, so no Amperian current flows when the applied field is shut off.

If the core material is diamagnetic, we must think of the induced magnetic moment in each atom as being opposite to the field and thus the Amperian current flows in a direction opposite to that of the conduction current. Thus, the resultant flux density in the core is less than the flux density that the conduction current alone would produce there.

The Amperian current on the surface of materials in a magnetic field is the analogue of the surface polarization charges on dielectrics in an electric field. In dielectrics, however, the surface polarization charges always weaken the applied field, whereas, in the magnetic case, only diamagnetic materials weaken the applied magnetic field. Paramagnetic and ferromagnetic materials strengthen the magnetic fields in which they are placed.

It must be remembered that the Amperian current is simply a useful theoretical fiction that is introduced to simplify our thinking about a complicated situation. Our theory says that the magnetic behavior of materials is the same as if each atom were an Amperian current loop, and the behavior of a uniformly magnetized material is the same as if the Amperian surface current were flowing.

1. B INSIDE A MATERIAL MEDIUM. Let us now define *magnetic flux density B inside a material medium as a vector quantity that shall be computed from the total distribution of conduction currents, displacement currents, and Amperian currents in exactly the same way as it was computed in empty space, using conduction currents only.* Thus, B inside a material medium becomes a theoretical tool for purposes of calculation, not a quantity defined as directly measurable by experiment. Remember that B in empty space was defined as directly measurable, in principle at least, since it was defined in terms of the magnetic force on a moving charge. For B in a material medium, however, we have the method to be discussed in Sec. 16–10 that permits us to measure change of magnetic flux through a search coil by use of a ballistic galvanometer and thus permits us to calculate the average change in B over the face of the search coil. This method applies when a coil has a material medium in its core, for example, the toroid in Fig. 16–2–1. Here the change in magnetic flux through the search coil SC can be measured by use of the ballistic galvanometer BG. Thus, B inside a material, as defined above, is not as abstract as at first appears.

From the above definition of B at interior points in a material medium, we may carry over at once the methods that we have learned for computing B at points in empty space. However, we must now take account of all Amperian currents which contribute to the flux density at the point, as well as the contribution from conduction and displacement currents. Thus Ampere's law, as given in (14–1–4), is immediately available. If we let dB be an element of magnetic flux density at a point in a material medium, then by Ampere's law

$$dB = \frac{\mu_0 I}{4\pi} \frac{dl \times i_r}{r^2} + \frac{\mu_0 I_a}{4\pi} \frac{dl_a \times i_r}{r^2} \qquad (16\text{--}2\text{--}1)$$

where the first term on the right applies to the conduction current I in the wires of circuits and to the displacement current, and the second term on the right applies to the Amperian current I_a. Here dl_a is an element of path length along the Amperian current and is directed in the sense of the Amperian current. All statements made in Sec. 14–1, and illustrated in various calculations in Chapter XIV, apply here for the use of Ampere's law.

Similarly, this definition of **B** makes Ampere's line integral law of (14–8–5) available for calculation of **B**. However, now the current on the right side of Ampere's line integral law must contain the Amperian current as well as the conduction and displacement currents. Thus, we write the law as

$$\oint \boldsymbol{B \cdot ds} = \mu_0(I + I_a) \qquad (16\text{–}2\text{–}2)$$

where I is the net conduction current (plus displacement current if any) and I_a the net Amperian current which cut through the surface bounded by the path of integration. The permeability of empty space, μ_0, still appears here because we have let the Amperian current I_a take account of the properties of the material medium. Let us restate Ampere's line integral law in words for this more general case. The law says: *the line integral of* **B·ds** *around any imaginary closed path is equal to* μ_0 *times the net total current, Amperian plus conduction plus displacement, which cuts through the surface bounded by the path of integration.*

The **B** computed in this fashion for an interior point in a material medium is a space average of a function which is fluctuating considerably from point to point in an atom and between atoms. This space average is over a volume which is large compared with the volume of an atom but small in terms of ordinary dimensions. For example, when we said that B is uniform in the core material of the toroid of Fig. 16–2–1, we referred to this space average **B**, not the microscopic field within atomic dimensions. This situation is the same as the one discussed in Sec. 11–2 for **E** inside a dielectric.

2. Toroid. As an example of the use of (16–2–2) for calculation of **B** inside a material, apply it to the special case of the toroid in Fig. 16–2–1. You can show (see Problem 16–2) with a derivation like the one used to obtain (14–9–2) that the magnitude of **B** in the material of the core is

$$B = \mu_0 NI/2\pi r + \mu_0 I_a/2\pi r \qquad (16\text{–}2\text{–}3)$$

In arriving at (16–2–3) we think of a sheet of current, whose total magnitude is I_a, flowing around the surface of the core parallel with the conduction current in the wires. Then $I_a/2\pi r$ is the number of amperes per unit length of the core due to the Amperian current, and $NI/2\pi r$ is the number of ampere turns per unit length of the core due to the conduction current in the winding.

16–3 INTENSITY OF MAGNETIZATION $\mathscr{I}$

It is convenient, for the purposes of the theory of material media, to introduce a vector quantity called *intensity of magnetization* $\mathscr{I}$ of the material medium and *defined as the vector sum per unit volume of the magnetic moments of the Amperian current loops.* The vector quantity $\mathscr{I}$ is often called simply the *magnetization,* and is analogous to the polarization vector **P** (see Sec. 11–3) in the theory of dielectrics but, of course, has a completely different physical significance.

In (13–7–1) we defined the magnetic moment M of a current loop as $M = IA$ where I is the current flowing in the loop and A is the area of the face of the loop. As in Sec. 16–2, let I'_a represent the equivalent current in each Amperian current loop. Remember that the Amperian surface current I_a

equals I_a' only if all Amperian current loops are completely aligned with their magnetic moments parallel with the applied field and if one considers a distance of only one atomic diameter along the length of the core. Then the magnetic moment M of an Amperian current loop is

$$M = I_a'a \qquad (16\text{–}3\text{–}1)$$

where a is the area of the face of the loop. You will recall that the direction of the vector which represents a is determined by the right-hand rule applied to the current flowing in the loop. Since the direction of motion of electrons is opposite to that of the flow of current, the fingers of the right hand point in the sense opposite to the electron motion when the thumb points in the direction of the vectors which represent a and M.

Now consider a small volume ΔV of a material where ΔV contains many atoms but is small compared with ordinary dimensions. Magnetization $\mathscr{I}$ is a point function in the same sense that B is a point function. Thus we want ΔV to be small enough so that we may consider that B is uniform throughout ΔV even though B is not uniform throughout the whole region under consideration. By definition, $\mathscr{I}$ is the vector sum of M for all the Amperian loops in ΔV, divided by ΔV, or

$$\mathscr{I} = \sum I_a'a/\Delta V = \sum M/\Delta V \qquad (16\text{–}3\text{–}2)$$

This relationship is a general definition of $\mathscr{I}$.

Next we wish to relate the magnitude of $\mathscr{I}$ to the Amperian surface current I_a under the special conditions of Fig. 16–2–1, where the material is homogeneous and isotropic and the magnetization is uniform because the magnetic flux density in the core material is uniform. Let ΔV represent the volume shown in Fig. 16–2–1 (b), where the volume has the area of cross section A of the core for its face and a depth Δx into the page. The Amperian current I_a flowing around the periphery of the core has a magnetic moment I_aA, and this magnetic moment must be equal to the $\sum M$ in (16–3–2) in order that the Amperian current I_a shall be the equivalent of the Amperian current loops contained in ΔV. Thus (16–3–2) becomes, for the magnitude of $\mathscr{I}$

$$\mathscr{I} = I_aA/A\,\Delta x = I_a/\Delta x$$

But $I_a/\Delta x$ is the Amperian linear surface current density on the surface of the core, i.e., it is the Amperian current per unit length along the surface of the core. Let us represent $I_a/\Delta x$ as j_a, and

$$\mathscr{I} = j_a \qquad (16\text{–}3\text{–}3)$$

To repeat, note carefully that Δx in Fig. 16–2–1 is measured along a line at right angles to I_a, so that j_a is the Amperian current which flows across unit length of the surface, where the unit length is taken along a line perpendicular to the direction of flow of the Amperian current. Thus arises the name "linear surface current density." Substitution of units into either (16–3–2) or (16–3–3) shows that $\mathscr{I}$ has the unit of ampere/meter.

Equation (16–3–3) tells us that the magnitude of the intensity of magnetization is equal to the Amperian linear surface current density when the magnetization is uniform. We shall confine our quantitative discussion to the simple cases where the magnetization is uniform, and an advanced text should be consulted for the general case.*

16–4 MAGNETIC FIELD INTENSITY H INSIDE A MATERIAL MEDIUM

For interior points of a material medium we need a more general definition of magnetic field intensity H than the one that we introduced earlier in Sec. 14–2 for empty space. Since we introduced H as a vector-point function to be used for computational purposes, we are free to generalize its definition provided that the general definition will reduce to the special one under the free space conditions imposed on the special one. The general definition is

$$H = B/\mu_0 - \mathscr{I} \qquad (16\text{–}4\text{–}1)$$

In empty space there is no material medium to become magnetized, so $\mathscr{I}$ is zero. Also, from (14–2–3), and our earlier definition of H, $B = \mu_0 H$ in empty space, so the definition of H in (16–4–1) becomes the same as our earlier definition of H in Sec. 14–2 under the free space conditions imposed there.

1. H IN A TOROID. Using the general definition of H in (16–4–1), let us compute the magnitude of H for points inside the core material of the toroid of Fig. 16–2–1. Note that this is a special case because we are using the special conditions imposed by the toroid. We shall assume that the core material is isotropic (same properties in all directions) so that B, H, and $\mathscr{I}$ are parallel. Further, we assume that the material is homogeneous, and thus uniformly magnetized in the toroid, so that we may use the result in (16–3–3).

In (16–2–3) we have the equation for the magnetic flux density B in the core material of the toroid. Put (16–2–3) into (16–4–1), and the magnitude of H is

$$H = NI/2\pi r + I_a/2\pi r - \mathscr{I}$$

But, as pointed out following (16–2–3), $I_a/2\pi r$ is the Amperian linear current density on the surface of the core material, so $I_a/2\pi r = j_a$. And, from (16–3–3), $j_a = \mathscr{I}$. Hence, H in a toroid becomes

$$H = NI/2\pi r \qquad (16\text{–}4\text{–}2)$$

Compare (16–4–2) with (14–9–5), and we see that H is the same whether the toroid has a material medium or empty space for its core. Thus, for the special case of a toroid, the H in the core material depends only on the conduction current in the wire winding and not at all on the Amperian current due to the core material. This is a convenient and important situation because, in the special case of a toroid, we can calculate H directly from the measured current in the winding, the counted number of turns of wire, and the measured radius of the toroid. Thus, for the toroid, H is that property of currents in conductors which produces magnetization of the material in the core of the toroid. Although, in general, ferromagnetic materials are not isotropic, we shall use this result when the toroid has a ferromagnetic core.

* For example, R. M. Whitmer, *Electromagnetics*, 2d ed. (London: Prentice-Hall, International, Inc., 1962), pp. 203–6.

2. *H* IN AN INFINITE SOLENOID. As a second example of the use of the general definition of *H*, let us compute the magnitude of *H* in the core material that fills the space inside the winding of a solenoid of infinite length. In other words, the length of the solenoid is very large compared with its diameter, and we shall confine our attention to points which are far removed from the ends. Figure 16–4–1 shows the solenoid in cross section, and the dots and crosses in the circles, which represent the wires in cross section, show the senses of the conduction currents in the wires. Since *B* is uniform in the region under consideration, and the core material is homogeneous, the magnetization of the core is uniform in the region which interests us. Again we shall consider that the core material is isotropic, so that *B*, *H*, and $\mathscr{I}$ are parallel.

Let us apply Ampere's line integral law to the imaginary path *edcf* where side *ed* is in the core material and parallel with the magnetic flux lines, ends *dc* and *fe* are perpendicular to the sides of the solenoid and thus perpendicular to the flux lines, and side *cf* is outside the solenoid. Along side *ed*, *B* is constant and parallel to *ds*. If we think of a sheet of current flowing around the solenoid, instead of individual wires carrying current, *B·ds* is zero at all points along sides *dc* and *fe* because *B* is perpendicular to *ds* at all points.

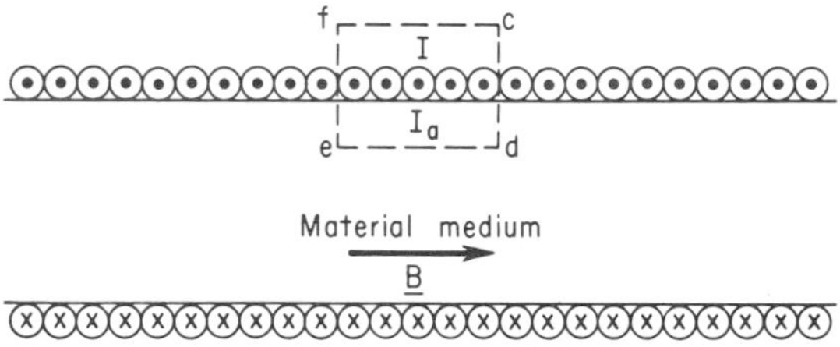

Figure 16–4–1. Solenoid of infinite length with a material medium filling its core.

We imagine that the wires are very closely spaced so that this requirement is essentially satisfied, as was the case when we derived formulas for the solenoid earlier. Along *cf*, *B* is zero for an infinite solenoid (see Problem 14–22). Let *l* be the distance from *e* to *d*, and from the above,

$$\oint \boldsymbol{B}\cdot \boldsymbol{ds} = B \int_0^l ds$$

Let *n* represent the number of turns of wire per unit length of the solenoid, and *I* be the current in each wire. Then *nlI* represents the net conduction current which cuts through the surface bounded by the path of integration. Let I_a represent the net Amperian current which cuts through the surface bounded by the path of integration, and I_a is parallel to *I*. Then Ampere's line integral law of (16–2–2) becomes

$$B \int_0^l ds = \mu_0(nlI + I_a) \quad \text{or} \quad B = \mu_0 nI + \mu_0 I_a/l \qquad (16\text{–}4\text{–}3)$$

Equation (16–4–3) gives the magnetic flux density in the core material of the infinite solenoid.

Now, to obtain H in the core material, put (16–4–3) into the general definition of H in (16–4–1) and for the magnitude of H we have $H = nI + (I_a/l) - \mathscr{I}$. But I_a/l is the Amperian linear current density (i.e., the Amperian current per unit length) on the surface of the core material, so $I_a/l = j_a$. But, by (16–3–3), $j_a = \mathscr{I}$, so

$$H = nI \qquad (16\text{–}4\text{–}4)$$

From (14–7–5) and from the fact that $B = \mu_0 H$ for empty space, we see that the H of (16–4–4) in the material medium of the core of the solenoid is the same as it is for empty space in the core. Again this is a convenient situation because H is that magnetic field intensity produced by the conduction current in the winding only, without reference to the Amperian currents. We may measure I and count the number of turns of wire per unit length n and compute H in the core material for this special case.

Although we have shown in two special cases that H in the core material is that H produced by the conduction current in the winding only, without reference to the Amperian currents, this situation is not a general one. For example, you can readily see that it is not general if you place the path *cfed* near the end of the solenoid and attempt to apply the above argument. It turns out that the result is valid only when all surfaces of the material medium are everywhere parallel to the magnetic flux lines; or any surfaces perpendicular to the magnetic flux lines are so far removed that they do not influence the argument at the point under consideration. We shall have a little more to say about this problem in the next chapter (see last part of Sec. 17–7), but for the moment it is sufficient to know that we can compute H in the core material of a toroid or infinite solenoid from directly measurable quantities.

16–5 MAGNETIC SUSCEPTIBILITY, PERMEABILITY, AND RELATIVE PERMEABILITY

1. MAGNETIC SUSCEPTIBILITY. A quantity which is often used to describe the magnetic properties of a material is the *magnetic susceptibility*, which is represented by the Greek letter χ, and defined by the equation

$$\chi = \mathscr{I}/H \qquad (16\text{–}5\text{–}1)$$

Thus χ is the ratio of the intensity of magnetization of the material to the magnetic field intensity which established the magnetization. Since the units of $\mathscr{I}$ and H are the same, χ is a dimensionless factor which represents the magnetic properties of the material. For all materials, except the few ferromagnetic ones, $\mathscr{I}$ is directly proportional to H, and χ is a constant (at a given temperature) for the particular material. This statement is true for the moderate fields usually attained in the laboratory. If the material is diamagnetic, $\mathscr{I}$ has a direction opposite to that of H, and χ is negative. Diamagnetic susceptibilities are essentially independent of temperature. For paramagnetic materials, χ is positive, since $\mathscr{I}$ is in the same direction as H. Table 16–1 gives the values of χ for several diamagnetic and paramagnetic materials. The second column lists the temperature of the substance at which the measurement was made.

In principle at least, we could measure magnetic susceptibilities of para-magnetic and diamagnetic materials by the use of the apparatus in Fig. 16–2–1 (a). The material to be studied can be used as the core of the toroid, and a measured current sent through the winding. We have shown that (16–4–2) gives H in the core material of a toroid and that all quantities in (16–4–2) are measurable. Thus the denominator of (16–5–1) is known and depends only on the conduction current and geometry of the circuit.

As we have stated, for paramagnetic and diamagnetic materials $\mathscr{I}$ is proportional to H, so when H goes to zero the magnetization of the material goes to zero, which in turn means that the magnetic flux in the core goes to zero. Hence, by opening the switch in the circuit which supplies the conduction current I in the winding, the flux change in the core is equal to the flux in the core when the conduction current had the value I. As explained in Sec. 16–10, the first throw of the ballistic galvanometer, BG, can be used to measure the flux change in the core and thus, from the above, BG can be used to measure the flux Φ in the core when the current I was flowing and the magnetic field intensity H existed in the core. With Φ known and the area of cross section A of the core known, the average B in the core can be computed from $B = \Phi/A$. If the radius of the toroid is large, B is essentially uniform. From (16–2–3) and (16–3–3)

$$B = \mu_0 NI/2\pi r + \mu_0 \mathscr{I}$$

TABLE 16–1*

SUSCEPTIBILITIES FOR SOME PARAMAGNETIC AND DIAMAGNETIC
MATERIALS

Substance	Temp., °C	χ
Air (gas)	20	0.037×10^{-5}
Aluminum	18	2.2×10^{-5}
Bismuth	18	-16.6×10^{-5}
Carbon		
(diamond)	20	-2.2×10^{-5}
(graphite)	20	-9.9×10^{-5}
Cerium	18	$130. \times 10^{-5}$
Copper	18	-0.96×10^{-5}
Ferric chloride	20	$306. \times 10^{-5}$
Helium (gas)	20	-0.000098×10^{-5}
Hydrogen (gas)	20	-0.00021×10^{-5}
Lead	-18	-1.7×10^{-5}
Mercury	18	-3.2×10^{-5}
Oxygen (liquid)	-219	$488. \times 10^{-5}$
(gas)	20	0.18×10^{-5}

Values for gases are at 1 atm pressure.

* Computed from values given in the *Handbook of Chemistry and Physics*, 32d ed., (Cleveland: Chemical Rubber Publishing Co.), pp. 2167–77. Values given there are specific susceptibility, which is susceptibility per unit mass instead of per unit volume as defined here. Also values given there are for emu system, which is not a rationalized system.

All terms in this equation are known except $\mathscr{I}$, so $\mathscr{I}$ may be computed. Thus both H and $\mathscr{I}$ are known and χ may be computed for the core material, using the definition of χ in (16–5–1). This measurement exploits the fact that, in the special case of a toroid, H is due to the conduction current only and can be readily computed from measurable quantities.

Actually the best ballistic galvanometers are not sensitive enough to make the above method practical for measurement of χ for diamagnetic and para-magnetic materials. Thus indirect methods are used, and you should consult a book on magnetism if you wish to explore the topic further.* However, the method is used extensively for measuring the properties of ferromagnetic materials, as we shall see later. For these ferromagnetic materials, χ is posi-tive, a function of temperature, and a complicated function of H, since $\mathscr{I}$ is a complicated function of H.

2. PERMEABILITY. Put the value of $\mathscr{I}$ from (16–5–1) into the definition of H in (16–4–1), and for the magnitude of H we have

$$B = \mu_0(1 + \chi)H \qquad (16\text{–}5\text{–}2)$$

In (16–5–2) the coefficient of H is called the *permeability* of the medium and is represented by μ, so by definition,

$$\mu = \mu_0(1 + \chi) \qquad (16\text{–}5\text{–}3)$$

Since χ has no unit, the unit of μ is the same as μ_0, i.e., weber/ampere meter. Since 1 weber = 1 volt second (see Sec. 3–3), 1 wb/amp m = 1 v sec/amp m. From the definition of the henry as a unit of self-inductance (see Sec. 3–7) or of mutual inductance (see Sec. 8–4), 1 henry = 1 volt sec/ampere. Thus 1 wb/amp m = 1 henry/m and you will often find both μ and μ_0 expressed in the mks system with the unit henry/meter.

From (16–5–3) and (16–5–2),

$$B = \mu H \qquad (16\text{–}5\text{–}4)$$

and this equation is probably the most used relationship between B and H in the solution of practical problems, especially in ferromagnetism. Equation (16–5–4) is often used as the defining equation for μ.

Since μ_0 and 1 in (16–5–3) are both constants, it follows from our previous comments regarding χ that μ is temperature-dependent for paramagnetic and ferromagnetic materials but essentially independent of temperature for diamagnetic materials. Also μ is a constant which is a characteristic of a given diamagnetic material or paramagnetic material at constant temperature. But for ferromagnetic materials, μ is a complicated function of H even at constant temperature, and in crystalline materials B and H may not be parallel. We shall study some of the features of this functional relationship in the next chapter.

3. RELATIVE PERMEABILITY. Another quantity which is frequently used to describe the magnetic properties of a material is *relative permeability*, which is represented by μ_r and is defined by the equation

$$\mu_r = \mu/\mu_0 \qquad (16\text{–}5\text{–}5)$$

* For example, S. R. Williams, *Magnetic Phenomena* (New York: McGraw-Hill Book Co. Inc., 1931), pp. 93–103.

From this definition it is obvious why μ_r is called relative permeability, since for a particular medium it expresses μ relative to μ_0. Of course, μ_r is a pure number and has the same numerical value for a given material in any system of units. In particular, it is the same as the quantity called permeability in the absolute electromagnetic system of units (emu), and values of permeabilities of materials are often listed in this system. Values of permeability in the emu system may be used for μ_r in the mks system. (Some authors call μ_r the permeability and represent it by μ, so you need to note the definition of permeability when reading various texts.)

Of the three quantities (χ, μ, and μ_r) introduced to describe a magnetic material, any one would be sufficient, because they are related by the equations (16–5–3), (16–5–5) and from these,

$$\mu_r = 1 + \chi \qquad (16\text{–}5\text{–}6)$$

Hence, if any one of these three is given for a particular material, the other two may be computed. However, all three are used in various calculations and you need to be familiar with all three.

16–6 NUMERICAL EXAMPLE

Let us consider a numerical example which will illustrate some of the methods of calculation, using the quantities that we have introduced into the theory.

The toroid shown in Fig. 16–2–1 (a) is 15.0 cm in mean radius, has an area of cross section of 3.00 cm², and the core is of soft iron. The toroid is uniformly wound with 900 closely spaced turns of wire. The iron core is demagnetized initially and, when the switch is closed sending a steady direct conduction current of 0.0292 amp through the wire, the ballistic galvanometer deflection shows a flux change of 10.5×10^{-6} wb.

(a) What is the average flux density in the iron? Since the iron was initially demagnetized (we shall discuss methods of demagnetizing ferromagnetic materials in Sec. 17–2) the change in flux is equal to the flux, so $B = \Phi/A = 3.50 \times 10^{-2}$ wb/m².

(b) What is the average magnetic field intensity in the iron? Remember that for the toroid, H is determined only by the conduction current and geometry of the circuit [see (16–4–2)] and not at all by the properties of the core material. However, H is responsible for the magnetization produced in the core material, because H is due to the conduction current, and the conduction current sets up the magnetic field which magnetized the core material. $H = NI/2\pi r = 27.9$ amp turns/m.

(c) What is the permeability of the iron under these conditions? Since B has been computed in (a) from the measured change in flux and H has been computed in (b) from the conduction current and geometry of the circuit, we may compute μ from (16–5–4), $\mu = B/H = 1.26 \times 10^{-3}$ wb/amp m, or $\mu = 1.26 \times 10^{-3}$ henry/meter.

(d) What is its relative permeability? $\mu_r = \mu/\mu_0 = 1000$.

(e) What is the magnetic susceptibility of the iron under these conditions? $\chi = \mu_r - 1 = 999$.

(f) What is its intensity of magnetization? $\mathscr{I} = \chi H = 27,900$ amp/meter.

(g) What is the Amperian linear current density? $j_a = \mathscr{I} = 27{,}900$ amp/m. Compare this with 27.9 amp/meter for the H due to the conduction current in the winding.

16–7 SELF-INDUCTANCE OF A TOROIDAL WINDING

In (3–9–2) we showed that the self-inductance L of an inductor is equal to the number of magnetic flux linkages of the inductor with itself when unit current flows through the inductor, or $L = N\Phi/I$ where $N\Phi$ is the number of flux linkages when the current is I. Let us apply this general equation for L to the special case of a toroid. If the radius r of the toroid is large compared with the radial distance across its core, we have seen that the magnetic flux through the core can be computed from $\Phi = BA$, to a very good approximation. But from (16–5–4), $B = \mu H$, so $\Phi = \mu HA$. Put the value for H (in the core of a toroid) from (16–4–2) into this expression and we have

$$\Phi = \mu ANI/2\pi r \qquad\qquad (16\text{–}7\text{–}1)$$

All these magnetic flux lines in (16–7–1) link all the N turns of wire on the toroid, so this value of Φ may be substituted for Φ in (3–9–2), and we have for the self-inductance of the toroid,

$$L = \mu AN^2/2\pi r \qquad\qquad (16\text{–}7\text{–}2)$$

For a given toroid, the area of cross section A, the number of turns N, and the mean radius r are all measurable constants. Also, if the material of the core is either paramagnetic or diamagnetic, μ is constant. Hence for such a toroid, L is a constant which can be computed from the above constants. Thus, such a toroid may be used as an inductor of known self-inductance, in the self-inductance bridge of Sec. 8–2, and unknown inductors may be measured in terms of it.

In Sec. 3–7 we said that the self-inductance of an inductor is constant for a circuit of fixed geometry if there are no ferromagnetic materials about. This toroidal inductor, with a paramagnetic or diamagnetic material in its core, is an example which illustrates that statement.

The permeability μ of a nonferromagnetic material differs but little from the permeability μ_0 of free space (see Problem 16–3), so the self-inductance of a coil with a nonferromagnetic core is essentially the same as if the core were empty space. If, however, the core is a ferromagnetic material, μ may have many hundreds of times the magnitude of μ_0 [see for example part (d) in Sec. 16–6]. Thus the self-inductance of an inductor with a ferromagnetic core may have many hundreds of times as large a value for L as if it had empty space for a core. Further, μ is a complicated function of H for a ferromagnetic material, so the self-inductance of an inductor with a ferromagnetic core is not constant, but is a complicated function of the current flowing in its winding.

From (16–5–5), $\mu = \mu_r\mu_0$, so (16–7–2) may be written

$$L = \mu_r\mu_0 AN^2/2\pi r \qquad\qquad (16\text{–}7\text{–}3)$$

For empty space $\mu_r = 1$. Thus, if we let L_0 be the self-inductance of a certain toroid with empty space for its core, and L represent the self-inductance of the same toroid with a particular material for its core, we may obtain from (16–7–3),

$$\mu_r = L/L_0 \qquad (16\text{–}7\text{–}4)$$

Equation (16–7–4) is analogous to (12–1–5), in which we showed that the relative dielectric constant of a given material is equal to the capacitance of a certain capacitor with that material between its plates to the capacitance of the same capacitor with empty space between its plates.

16–8 ENERGY DENSITY IN A MAGNETIC FIELD

In (5–1–10), we showed that the energy in the magnetic field of a self-inductance L due to a current I flowing in the winding is $\frac{1}{2}LI^2$. This formula was derived under the condition that there is no ferromagnetic material near the inductor. Now we wish to compute the magnetic energy per unit volume, i.e., energy density, in the magnetic field of such an inductor. We shall use the special case of a toroidal inductor, because the calculation is easy in this case, since the magnetic field is confined to the core of the toroid. Let W represent the energy of the magnetic field in the core, and we have, from (5–1–10),

$$W = \tfrac{1}{2}LI^2 \qquad (16\text{–}8\text{–}1)$$

From (3–9–2), $I = N\Phi/L$ for any self-inductor and, for a toroid whose mean radius r is large compared with the radial distance across its core, $\Phi = BA$. Hence, for the toroid,

$$I = NBA/L \qquad (16\text{–}8\text{–}2)$$

Put (16–8–2) into (16–8–1) and then substitute formula (16–7–2) for the L of a toroid, and we have

$$W = 2\pi r A B^2/2\mu \qquad (16\text{–}8\text{–}3)$$

Let v represent the volume of the core of the toroid, and $v \approx 2\pi r A$. Hence, the magnetic energy density of the magnetic field is

$$\text{energy density} = W/v = \tfrac{1}{2}B^2/\mu \qquad (16\text{–}8\text{–}4)$$

From (16–5–4), $B = \mu H$, so (16–8–4) can be written in either of the following equivalent forms:

$$\text{energy density} = \tfrac{1}{2}HB = \tfrac{1}{2}\mu H^2 \qquad (16\text{–}8\text{–}5)$$

Energy density, in the mks system, has the unit of joule/meter^3, and you can show that this unit results by substitution of units into any one of the equivalent equations above for energy density.

We have derived (16–8–4) for the special case of the uniform field in the core of a toroid. However, it is a general formula and may be used to compute magnetic energy density whether the field is uniform or not. In the case of a nonuniform field, (16–8–4) gives the energy density in a small volume over which B may be considered to be uniform, and the energy density varies from point to point in the field.

You should compare these formulas for magnetic energy density with (12–5–2) and (12–5–3) for the energy density in an electric field and note that they are of the same form.

16–9 AMPERE'S CIRCUITAL LAW

1. LINE INTEGRAL OF $\mathscr{I}$. Consider that the rod, shown in cross section as *ghkm* in Fig. 16–9–1, is located in a uniform magnetic field and, as a result, has a uniform intensity of magnetization $\mathscr{I}$. The direction of $\mathscr{I}$ is shown by the vector labeled $\mathscr{I}$ in the figure. The equivalent Amperian surface currents associated with the magnetization of the rod are indicated by the use of dots and crosses. The rod is in empty space.

Let us evaluate the line integral, $\oint \mathscr{I} \cdot d\mathbf{s}$ around the closed imaginary path *edcf*. Along *ed*, $\mathscr{I}$ is parallel to $d\mathbf{s}$ and of constant magnitude. Along *fe*, and *dc*, $\mathscr{I}$ is everywhere perpendicular to $d\mathbf{s}$. Along *cf*, $\mathscr{I}$ is zero, because the space is empty and there is nothing to magnetize. Let *l* represent the distance from *e* to *d*, and we have $\oint \mathscr{I} \cdot d\mathbf{s} = \mathscr{I} \int_0^l ds = \mathscr{I}l$. But, from (16–3–3), when the magnetization is uniform, $\mathscr{I}$ is equal to the linear surface density j_a of Amperian current, so $\oint \mathscr{I} \cdot d\mathbf{s} = j_a l$. If we let I_a be the total Amperian current which cuts through the surface bounded by the path of integration,

$$\oint \mathscr{I} \cdot d\mathbf{s} = I_a \qquad (16\text{–}9\text{–}1)$$

Although we derived (16–9–1) under the special condition of a uniform

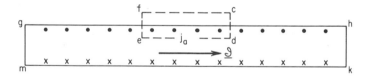

Figure 16–9–1. Material rod which has a uniform intensity of magnetization.

intensity of magnetization, and for a special path, it turns out to be true in general.* In the general case, I_a includes the volume density of Amperian current which results from a nonuniform intensity of magnetization, as well as the linear surface density of Amperian current.

2. AMPERE'S CIRCUITAL LAW. Now let us consider Ampere's line integral law as given in (16–2–2). This law is a general one and we shall consider a general case (not one limited to the conditions of Fig. 16–9–1). Write (16–2–2) as

$$\oint \mathbf{B} \cdot d\mathbf{s}/\mu_0 = I + I_a \qquad (16\text{–}9\text{–}2)$$

From the general definition of H given in (16–4–1), secure the value of B/μ_0 and put it into (16–9–2), with the result that $\oint \mathbf{H} \cdot d\mathbf{s} + \oint \mathscr{I} \cdot d\mathbf{s} = I + I_a$. But, using (16–9–1), this becomes

$$\oint \mathbf{H} \cdot d\mathbf{s} = I \qquad (16\text{–}9\text{–}3)$$

Equation (16–9–3) is known as *Ampere's circuital law*, and is completely general in its validity, although we derived (16–9–1) under special conditions. The law says that *the line integral of $\mathbf{H} \cdot d\mathbf{s}$ around any closed path is equal to*

* See R. M. Whitmer, *Electromagnetics*, 2d ed. (London: Prentice-Hall, International, Inc., 1962), pp. 203–6.

the net conduction current plus displacement current which cuts through the surface bounded by the path of integration without any reference to the Amperian current. This relationship is a particularly useful one for many computations, due to the very fact that the Amperian current is not included, as it is in Ampere's line integral law for B. In the next chapter we shall consider cases where the displacement current is either zero or negligible, and (16–9–3) will permit us to make computations in terms of the measurable conduction current.

The $\oint H \cdot ds$ around a closed path is called the *magnetomotive force* mmf around the path. This usage arose because (as stated in Sec. 14–5) H, in the emu system of units, is often defined as force per unit pole. Looking upon H in this fashion, $\oint H \cdot ds$ is the work done by the magnetic field in moving a unit pole around the closed path and thus becomes analogous to emf.

16–10 MEASUREMENT OF CHANGE OF MAGNETIC FLUX BY THE USE OF A BALLISTIC GALVANOMETER

In Sec. 13–6 we discussed the ballistic galvanometer and pointed out that the maximum deflection of the first throw is a measure of the quantity of charge Q that flows through it. You are urged to review Sec. 13–6 at this point, and we shall assume in our discussion that the ballistic galvanometer is being used as outlined there.

If the magnetic flux that links a search coil changes from Φ_0 to Φ_1, an emf is induced in the circuit and a quantity of charge Q flows around the circuit. In Problem 15–12 you proved that Q is related to the flux change by the equation

$$Q = N(\Phi_1 - \Phi_0)/R \tag{16–10–1}$$

where N is the total number of turns of wire on the search coil which the flux lines link and R is the total resistance of the circuit including that of the coil, galvanometer, and any series resistors (imagine, for example, that the circuit is the one in Fig. 16–2–1 (a) containing the search coil SC and the galvanometer BG).

Hence, *the maximum deflection of the first throw of the ballistic galvanometer is proportional to the change in the magnetic flux linking the search coil* provided the current flow is completed in a time that is short compared to the period of the galvanometer. Thus, if N and R are known, and the galvanometer has been calibrated so that Q can be computed from the maximum deflection of its first throw, the galvanometer may be used to measure the change in the magnetic flux linking the search coil. Section 20–3 tells how to use a ballistic galvanometer and search coil to explore a magnetic field and Sec. 20–4 describes one kind of fluxmeter.

PROBLEMS

16–1 In the paragraph immediately following (16–1–5), it is stated that (16–1–5) also gives the magnitude of the change in angular velocity of the electron in the case where the electron is going around the orbit in the opposite sense to that shown in Fig. 16–1–1, but with B still directed out of the page. Prove that this statement is correct; i.e., derive (16–1–5) for this case where $\Delta\omega$ is the decrease in the angular velocity of the electron in the orbit.

16–2 Derive (16–2–3) by the method suggested in the text.

16–3 (a) Compute the permeability and relative permeability of the paramagnetic and diamagnetic materials air, aluminum, bismuth, and copper listed in Table 16–1. Present the results in tabular form, including the magnetic susceptibility. Head each column with the proper units for the entries in that column. (b) In Sec. 14–2, when making computations for magnetic fields in free space due to currents, we stated that we would make no serious error in the value of B if we considered that any of the nonferromagnetic materials were near the circuits. In the light of the values of μ obtained in part (a), what is your conclusion about the validity of this remark?

16–4 The magnetic moment of an electron in the first allowed Bohr orbit (the one closest to the nucleus) of the hydrogen atom is

$$M_r = qh/4\pi m \qquad (16\text{–P–}1)$$

where q is the magnitude of the charge on the electron, m is the mass of the electron, and h is Planck's constant (see Appendix A–5 for the value of h). The value of M_r in (16–P–1) is known as the *Bohr magneton*, has the numerical value 9.27×10^{-24} amp m^2, and is the unit in which atomic magnetic moments are often measured.

In Bohr's model of the hydrogen atom (see Problems 9–16 and 10–15) the only orbits allowed are the ones given by Bohr's quantum condition that the angular momentum $p = nh/2\pi$, where n must be an integer and is (for circular orbits) the orbit number, starting with $n = 1$ for the allowed orbit closest to the nucleus. From the discussion in Sec. 16–1, derive the formula in (16–P–1), imposing Bohr's quantum condition where needed.

16–5 Consider the numerical example solved in Sec. 16–6. If the core of the toroid were bismuth (instead of iron), compute (a) the intensity of magnetization; (b) the Amperian current density. What is the direction of the Amperian current relative to the conduction current in the wires? [*Ans:* (b) -4.63×10^{-3} amp/m.] (c) Assume that, to six significant figures, H is known to be 27.9 amp/m, and A is known to be 3 cm^2. What are the magnetic flux in the bismuth core and the magnetic flux in the empty space of an identical toroid which has no core but has the same conduction current in the winding? What is the percentage difference? [*Ans:* about 0.016 %.]

16–6 A solenoid, that is very long compared with its diameter, has 1000 closely spaced turns of wire per meter of length and an area of cross section of 6.00 cm^2. The core of the solenoid is filled by a silicon steel rod which is initially demagnetized. A coil of 100 turns of wire is wound over a short region near the center of the solenoid and connected through a series resistance to a ballistic galvanometer. The total resistance of the ballistic galvanometer circuit is 5000 ohms. When a switch in the solenoid circuit is closed, and a steady direct current of 0.0334 amp is sent through the solenoid winding, the initial ballistic galvanometer deflection (after correction for logarithmic decrement) shows that a charge of 9.00×10^{-7} coulomb flowed through the ballistic galvanometer circuit. Draw a circuit diagram showing both the solenoid circuit and the ballistic galvanometer circuit. (a) What is the magnetic flux in the silicon steel core when the current of 0.0334 amp is flowing through the solenoid windings? [*Ans:*

4.5×10^{-5} wb.] (b) What is the permeability of the silicon steel under these conditions? [*Ans:* 2.25×10^{-3} henry/m.] (c) What is its intensity of magnetization? [*Ans:* 59,800 amp/m.] (d) How does the linear Amperian current density compare with H in magnitude? [*Ans:* j_a is 1790 times as much as H.] (e) The total resistance of the solenoid circuit is 50 ohms. What total electric energy is required of the battery in the solenoid circuit, after the magnetic field is established, to maintain the magnetization in the silicon steel for half an hour?

16–7 Derive the formula $L = \mu n^2 l A$ for the self-inductance L of a solenoid whose length l is very large compared with its diameter. Here n is the number of turns per unit length on the solenoid, and A is the area of cross section of the solenoid. Point out the approximation made in the derivation.

16–8 Derive the magnetic energy density formulas, (16–8–4), and (16–8–5), by the use of the very long solenoid of Problem 16–7.

16–9 Refer to the coaxial transmission line of Problem 14–24 and shown in Fig. 14–P–3, where the current I is flowing down into the page in the central rod and up out of the page in the outer cylinder. Consider that $R_2 - R_1$ is very large compared with R_1, so that flux linkages inside the central rod may be neglected. Also consider that the outer copper cylinder is of negligible radial thickness, so that flux linkages inside the copper of the cylinder may be neglected. The insulating material between the central copper rod and the coaxial cylinder is either paramagnetic or diamagnetic (or a mixture) and, as far as their magnetic properties are concerned for the purposes of this problem, they and the copper may be treated as empty space to a very good approximation. Derive the formula

$$L = (\mu_0 l/2\pi) \ln (R_2/R_1)$$

for the self-inductance L of a length l of this coaxial line. The radius of the outer cylinder is R_2.

16–10 In Problem 16–9 consider that R_1 is not negligible with respect to $R_2 - R_1$, so that the magnetic flux linkages inside the central rod may not be neglected. All other conditions remain as stated in Problem 16–9. (a) Using (16–8–4) for the magnetic energy density, compute the magnetic energy in a length l of the central copper rod. (b) Using the fact that the energy in the magnetic field of a self-inductance is equal to $\frac{1}{2}LI^2$, show that the self-inductance L_R due to the magnetic field inside the central rod alone is given by $L_R = \mu_0 l/8\pi$. (c) Compute the energy of the magnetic field in the region between the central copper rod and outer copper cylinder for a length l of the coaxial cable. From this result compute the self-inductance L_S of the coaxial cable due only to the space between the central rod and the outer cylinder, and check your result against the answer to Problem 16–9. (d) Show that the total self-inductance L of the coaxial cable is

$$L = \mu_0 l[1/4 + \ln (R_2/R_1)]/2\pi$$

16–11 Derive the formula

$$L = \mu_0 l[1/4 + \ln (d/R)]/\pi$$

for the self-inductance L of a length l of a two-wire transmission line. Each copper wire has a radius R, and there is a distance d between the centers of the two wires. The wires are parallel, and assume that d is large compared with R. Also assume that the magnetic properties of both the air between the wires and the copper of the wires can be satisfactorily accounted for by treating them the same as empty space in this regard.

16–12 In Fig. 16–2–1 (a) the toroid has a core made of a doughnut of lucite which has an area of cross section of 78.8×10^{-4} m^2 and a mean radius of 0.655 m. Consider that the permeability of lucite is the same as that of empty space within the accuracy of calculation in this problem. There are 4820 closely spaced turns of wire on the toroid to serve as the primary winding, and the resistance of this winding is 50.1 ohms. The primary leads from the toroid, shown at the top of the figure in Fig. 16–2–1 (a) are connected to a circuit with a battery, resistor, and switch in series. The battery has an emf of 10.5 volts and a negligible internal resistance. The resistor has a resistance of 5.4 ohms and the switch and wires have negligibly small resistances. The magnetic flux density in the core of the toroid, when the current in the primary is 0.190 amp, is to be measured by closing the primary switch and reading the first throw of the ballistic galvanometer *BG*, which has a period of 15.0 sec. (a) Can the primary circuit respond fast enough to make this a satisfactory method? (b) If the toroid core were a ferromagnetic material with an average relative permeability of 1500 under the conditions of the experiment (instead of the lucite), could the primary circuit respond fast enough? If your answer is "no" in either case, tell how the conditions could be improved but do not change the toroid or the current in the primary at which *B* is to be measured.

chapter

XVII

FERROMAGNETIC

MATERIALS

17–1 MAGNETIZATION CURVE

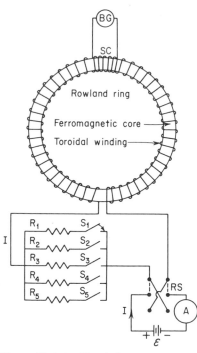

Figure 17–1–1. Circuit for determination of magnetization and hysteresis curves for a sample of ferromagnetic material.

In Sec. 16–5 we pointed out that the permeability μ of a ferromagnetic material is a complicated function of H, and now we wish to learn more about this functional relationship from experimental measurements. As illustrated in the numerical example of Sec. 16–6, under suitable circumstances we may measure* B, compute H, and then calculate μ, since it is the ratio B/H. Again we shall have the ferromagnetic specimen in the form of a toroid with a closely spaced toroidal wire winding. Then, as we have shown in Sec. 16–4, we may compute H from readily measurable quantities. Also, the radius of the toroid will be large compared with the radial distance across the cross section of its core, so that B will be essentially uniform in the core. A toroid used in this fashion is often called a Rowland ring, because Rowland used it extensively for early research on the magnetic properties of ferromagnetic materials.

Figure 17–1–1 shows the Rowland ring and its associated circuit for the experiment that we now wish to perform. Here SC is a search coil attached

* See Sec. 20–4 for one type of fluxmeter which is often more convenient than a ballistic galvanometer for measurement of magnetic flux change.

444

to a ballistic galvanometer *BG*, and this combination will be used to measure magnetic flux changes in the core (see Sec. 16–10); $\mathscr{E}$ is a battery that furnishes the magnetizing current *I*, and the ammeter *A* reads the magnitude of *I*. By use of the switches S_1, S_2, S_3, S_4, and S_5, any number of resistors R_1, R_2, R_3, R_4, and R_5, may be put in parallel in the circuit. By the use of these switches, the current *I* may be changed in steps from zero to the maximum that the battery and circuit resistance will permit. Switch *RS* is a reversing switch that we shall not use in the present experiment. The ferromagnetic core material is initially demagnetized (see Sec. 17–2 for a method that may be used to demagnetize such a core).

First, in this experiment we wish to secure data so that we may plot a curve of the magnetic flux density *B* against magnetic field intensity *H*. Both *B* and *H* are to be the values for the interior of the core material. Such a curve is called a magnetization curve for the material of the core.

The ferromagnetic core in the ring is called the magnetic circuit, or path followed by the magnetic flux lines, and *H* is often called the *magnetizing force*, not only in this magnetic circuit but also in more complicated magnetic circuits, some of which we shall consider later. Although *B* is the fundamental magnetic quantity, the magnetizing force *H* is taken as the independent variable for the magnetization curve because it may be computed directly from the measured current *I*, number of turns of wire on the toroid, and radius of the toroid, as we have seen in (16–4–2).

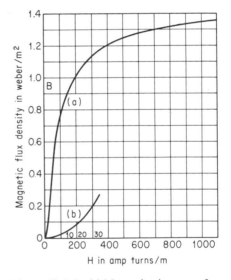

Figure 17–1–2. (a) Magnetization curve for a typical silicon steel used for transformer cores. (b) Enlarged section of the curve at small values of *B* and *H*.

Now let us outline the procedure by means of which we shall obtain the data for the magnetization curve.

1. Close S_1 and read the deflection of *BG*. Leave S_1 closed. From the calibration and reading of *BG* and the known number of turns of wire on the search coil, compute the magnetic flux increase in the core. Since the flux was initially zero, the flux change is equal to the flux Φ_1 in the core after the change. From the known area A_1 of cross section of the core, compute the average value of B_1 in the core. From the reading of the ammeter *A* and the known constants of the toroid, compute H_1 by the use of (16–4–2). Plot the value of B_1 against H_1 in Fig. 17–1–2.

2. Close switch S_2, read *BG*, and compute the increase $\Delta\Phi_2$ in the magnetic flux in the core. The flux Φ_2 now present in the core is the flux Φ_1 present before the change, plus $\Delta\Phi_2$. Compute B_2 and H_2 and plot the value of B_2 against H_2 in Fig. 17–1–2. Leave S_2 closed.

3. Repeat the above procedure in steps until all five switches are closed, and in each step plot the point on the graph in Fig. 17–1–2. Actually we need many more points than five in order to secure a well-defined magnetization curve, so we need many more resistors in parallel and many more switches. Care must be taken that a switch once closed is not opened again, since we must go progressively from zero magnetizing current to the maximum without any decrease in the current along the way.

Figure 17–1–2 shows the result obtained, and is the magnetization curve for the core material being tested. Remember that the curve starts with the core material demagnetized and is taken for progressive increases in H without any decreases. The curve* in Fig. 17–1–2 is for a typical silicon steel used for transformer cores.

Notice, on the magnetization curve, that B increases slowly at first as H increases, then the curve rises steeply in a region where small changes in H

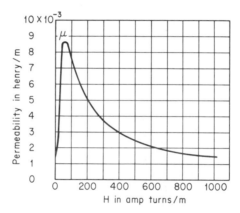

Figure 17–1–3. Permeability as a function of magnetic field intensity for the magnetization curve of Fig. 17–1–2.

produce large changes in B. Next the "knee" of the magnetization curve is reached, where the curve bends, i.e., the rate of change of B with respect to H, decreases. Finally the slope of the curve becomes small as the ferromagnetic material approaches saturation. In Problem 17–3, you will see that most of the magnetic flux density in the core is due to the intensity of magnetization of the core material for the entire magnetization curve shown in Fig. 17–1–2. For example, at the point where H is 480 amp turns/m, $\mathscr{I}$ is 1×10^6 amp/m, or $\mathscr{I}$ is about 2000 times the value of H. This means that, while H is responsible for the alignment of the Amperian current loops, the Amperian current loops contribute most of the magnetic flux density in the core. At saturation, all the Amperian current loops have their magnetic moments aligned parallel with the applied field, and any further increase in B is due entirely to an increase in H.

The permeability μ of the ferromagnetic material at any point on the

* Data taken from *U.S.S. Electrical Steel Sheets, Engineering Manual No. 3*, Carnegie-Illinois Steel Corporation, 1949, by courtesy of United States Steel.

magnetization curve is the ratio B/H at that point, or it is the slope of a straight line drawn from the origin to the point. Figure 17–1–3 shows a plot of μ as a function of H for the magnetization curve of Fig. 17–1–2. We have stated several times that μ is a complicated function of H for ferromagnetic materials, and the curve in Fig. 17–1–3 shows this functional relationship for one kind of material, at constant temperature, and under the particularly simple conditions used to obtain the magnetization curve. Even here the functional relationship is not simple. We shall see that there are further complications in this functional relationship.

CURIE TEMPERATURE. When any ferromagnetic material is heated to a sufficiently high temperature, it ceases to be ferromagnetic and becomes paramagnetic. The temperature at which a material makes this change is known as the Curie temperature for that material. The Curie temperature for iron is about 770° C, for nickel about 358° C, and for cobalt about 1120° C.

When a ferromagnetic material is in a strong, constant, external magnetic field and the temperature of the material is increased, the magnetic flux density B in the material decreases as the temperature increases, and B falls abruptly to essentially that of the external field as the Curie temperature is approached. On the other hand, if the constant external applied magnetic field is weak, B first increases as the temperature increases and then decreases, again falling to essentially that of the external field at the Curie temperature. Thus, the permeability of the material, even at constant H, is a complicated function of the temperature of the material. Fortunately, for most ferromagnetic materials used in the cores of machines, μ does not change appreciably over the temperature range to which the machine is subjected. However, some ferromagnetic alloys, which have been developed for special purposes, have Curie temperatures in the range from 40° C to 160° C. Such materials are used in instruments where magnetic temperature sensitivity is desired.

17–2 HYSTERESIS

Let us return to the experiment which we were performing in the last section, where we used the equipment in Fig. 17–1–1. We demagnetize the ring and start over again, using the following procedure.

1. Progress up the magnetization curve Oab of Fig. 17–2–1 to the point where B in the core is 1 wb/m². The procedure is the same as before and the magnetic flux density B_b, in the core, is known when the point b is reached.

2. Open switch S_1 and compute the decrease ΔB in the flux density. Compute the new value of the flux density B_1 in the core, knowing B_b and ΔB. From the ammeter reading compute the new value of H_1 and plot B_1 against H_1 in Fig. 17–2–1.

3. Continue this procedure in steps until all the numbered switches are opened and I is equal to zero, so H is equal to zero. *The experimentally determined values of B do not follow back down the magnetization curve.* At the point where H equals zero, B has the value B_R, and the ferromagnetic core material has retained much of its magnetic flux density, i.e., the Amperian current loops have retained much of their alignment. Therefore, B_R is called

the residual flux density or, more often, the *retentivity*. Sometimes the term *remanence* is used. The behavior of the ferromagnetic material, whereby the *B-H* curve is different for decreasing *H* than for increasing *H*, is called *hysteresis*.

4. Now reverse the switch *RS* of Fig. 17–1–1 and close S_1. A current is now flowing through the toroidal winding in the opposite sense to its former value. By the same method as above, plot the section of the curve from B_R to H_C. At H_C the magnetic flux density in the core is zero, and a magnetic field intensity H_C was required to produce this state. This H_C is called the *coercive*

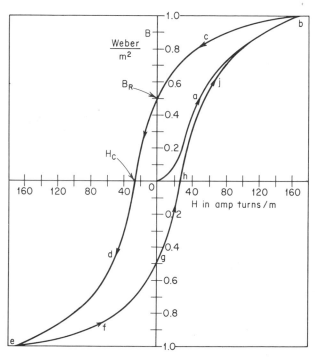

Figure 17–2–1. Magnetization curve and normal hysteresis loop for a sample of silicon steel.

force or, sometimes, the *coercivity*. Coercive force H_C is, of course, in a direction opposite to that of *B*.

5. Continue closing the numbered switches, making the appropriate readings and calculations in each step, until the magnetic flux density is again 1 wb/m² , but now in the opposite direction to that at *b*. The path $H_C de$ in Fig. 17–2–1 will be followed in the process. It will be found that *H* at *e* is equal in magnitude but opposite in direction to *H* at *b*.

6. Open the numbered switches, one at a time, take the appropriate readings, and the path *efg* is followed. At *g*, the value of *H* is again zero, and the retentivity is the same as B_R above.

7. Reverse *RS*, close the numbered switches one at a time, and follow the

path *ghj* back to the starting point at *b*. At *h*, the coercive force is the same in magnitude as H_C on the left of the origin.

The entire cycle of the curve $bCB_RH_Cdefghjb$ is called a *hysteresis loop*, and the arrowheads on the curve show the sense of progression around the loop. It is called a *normal* hysteresis loop because it was obtained by using values of *H* which are symmetrical on the two sides of the zero value for *H*. Since *B* is not a single-valued function of *H*, the curve shows still further the complications in the functional relationship between μ and *H* for a ferromagnetic material (see Problem 17–4).

On the hysteresis loop, the intensity of magnetization $\mathscr{I}$ no longer depends on *H* alone; it depends also on the previous magnetic history of the specimen, as does *B*. Thus the simple relationship $\mathscr{I} = \chi H$ of (16–5–1) loses its meaning and is of no use for the calculation of $\mathscr{I}$. The normal hysteresis loop is only one step more complicated than the magnetization curve, and yet $\mathscr{I}$ is not even a single-valued function of *H* for the hysteresis loop. However, the general definition of *H* in (16–4–1) is valid and may be used to compute $\mathscr{I}$ if *H* and *B* are known. If the material may be treated as isotropic so that *H*, *B*, and $\mathscr{I}$ are parallel, the calculation is simple for the ring specimen of Fig. 17–1–1 and the data obtained in this experiment.

If a hysteresis loop is started from a different point (corresponding to *b* in Fig. 17–2–1) on the magnetization curve, a different hysteresis loop is obtained. If the starting point is below *b* on the magnetization curve, the hysteresis loop lies inside the one drawn and has lower values for both B_R and H_C. Conversely, if the starting point is above *b*, the hysteresis loop lies outside the one drawn and has higher values for both B_R and H_C. If the specimen is carried to saturation on the magnetization curve before the hysteresis loop is started, B_R and H_C have unique values for a particular sample of material.

For a particular hysteresis loop, *H* should be reversed many times between fixed maximum positive and negative values in order to get the material well established on that loop. Otherwise the shape of the loop may be influenced by the previous magnetization of the material. A sinusoidal alternating current of fixed maximum value, flowing in the magnetizing windings, automatically establishes a particular hysteresis loop in a short time. A curve drawn through the tips of a series of hysteresis loops for a given material is called the *normal magnetization curve* for that material. This magnetization curve is the same as the one discussed in Sec. 17–1 except for slight deviations at values of *H* in the neighborhood of zero.

A material which is to be used to make a permanent magnet must have a high retentivity B_R, so that it will produce a strong magnetic field. It must also have a high coercive force H_C, so that it will not have its magnetization altered in relatively weak magnetic fields. For example, alnico 5, which is a good material for permanent magnets, has a value of B_R equal to 1.25 wb/m^2 and a value of H_C equal to 44,000 amp turns/m.

METHOD OF DEMAGNETIZING A SAMPLE. We have seen that a ferromagnetic material retains some of its magnetization after the magnetizing field has been shut off. Thus, such a material cannot be demagnetized simply by reducing the magnetizing field to zero. It can be demagnetized, however, if the magnetizing field is initially large and then is continuously reversed as it is reduced to zero. For example, in Fig. 17-1-1 the ring may be demagnetized by continuous reversal of RS as the current is gradually and continuously reduced to zero. The same result can be obtained by use of an alternating current which starts with a large magnitude and is gradually reduced to zero. In either case the initial current for demagnetizing the ring should be at least as large as the current which originally magnetized the ring.

In the process of demagnetizing the specimen, the magnetization of the ferromagnetic material is carried around progressively smaller hysteresis cycles, as the current is gradually reduced, until at zero current the hysteresis cycle is one very close to the origin.

17-3 ENERGY LOSS DUE TO HYSTERESIS

In the past we have considered inductors with nonferromagnetic cores. For such inductors, the electrical energy converted to energy in the magnetic field during the rise of the current is all reconverted into electrical energy when the current decreases to zero. If the core material is ferromagnetic, however, some of the magnetic energy is converted irreversibly into heat as a result of the hysteresis behavior. Work is done in aligning the Amperian current loops but not all of the energy is recovered because, as we see from the hysteresis loop, some work must be done to remove the alignment. There is a kind of internal friction against which the alignment, and removal of alignment, must be made. Let us now compute the net amount of electrical energy in one hysteresis cycle, which is converted to magnetic energy but is not reconverted to electrical energy. We shall think in terms of the Rowland ring of Fig. 17-1-1, but let us assume that the main winding on the ring is connected to a sinusoidal alternating emf, so that the core material goes continuously around the hysteresis loop, not in steps as would be the case with the d-c circuit shown in Fig. 17-1-1. The result is the same in either case, but the thinking is easier in terms of the a-c case.

Let e represent the instantaneous emf of self-induction set up in the toroidal winding due to the rate of change of i, where i is the instantaneous current flowing in the winding. Also, let dW represent the element of energy which is transferred from the electric circuit to the magnetic field of the toroid in an element of time dt. When i is increasing in magnitude, e is in an opposite sense to that of i, and electrical energy is being converted into magnetic energy so, by the above convention as to sign, dW is positive during an increase in the magnitude of i. When i is decreasing in magnitude, e is in the same sense as i, and magnetic energy is being converted into electrical energy so, by the above convention as to sign, dW is negative during a decrease in the magnitude of i. For any infinitesimal length of time dt, we have

$$dW = ie\, dt \qquad (17-3-1)$$

But, by Faraday's law,

$$e = N\, d\Phi/dt = NA\, dB/dt \qquad (17-3-2)$$

where N is the number of turns of wire on the ring, Φ is the instantaneous value of the total magnetic flux through the core, B is the instantaneous magnetic flux density, and A is the area of cross section of the core. We omit the minus sign in Faraday's law as written in (17–3–2) because we took account of the sense of e when we defined dW and set up (17–3–1).

Put (17–3–2) into (17–3–1) and we have

$$dW = NAi\, dB \qquad (17–3–3)$$

But, from (16–4–2) for a toroid, $Ni = 2\pi rH$, where r is the radius of the toroid. Put this value of Ni into (17–3–3) and $dW = 2\pi rAH\, dB$. However, $2\pi rA = v$, where v is the volume of the core, so

$$dW = vH\, dB \qquad (17–3–4)$$

Let W represent the net energy input to the magnetic field during one cycle, i.e., W is the energy that is not re-covered by the electric circuit. Then

$$W = v\oint H\, dB \qquad (17–3–5)$$

where $\oint$ means that the integration is to be carried completely around one cycle of changes of H and B. In (17–3–5) each magnitude of H is to be multiplied by the associated infinitesimal change in B, and the sum of these products taken for the complete cycle of changes of H and B. In general, no satisfactory analytical function can be written re-lating H and B for a cycle of changes in a ferromagnetic material. However, the hysteresis loop represents graphi-cally the functional relationship which exists and which is necessary for the evaluation of (17–3–5).

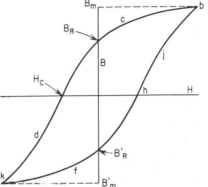

Figure 17–3–1. Calculation of energy loss due to hysteresis.

In Fig. 17–3–1, let B_m represent the maximum magnetic flux density in the core during the hysteresis loop, i.e., B_m is the magnitude of B at point b on the loop. Also, B'_m is equal in magnitude to B_m and is the magnitude of B at point k on the loop. Break the integral of (17–3–5) into the following parts for evaluation, after dividing by v.

$$W/v = \int_{B_m}^{B_R} H\, dB + \int_{B_R}^{B'_m} H\, dB + \int_{B'_m}^{B'_R} H\, dB + \int_{B'_R}^{B_m} H\, dB \qquad (17–3–6)$$

Along the part bCB_R of the loop, the magnetic field is decreasing, e is in the same sense as i, and energy is being fed from the magnetic field into the electric circuit. The first term on the right of (17–3–6) represents this energy per unit volume of the core and is the area (in units of B times H) between the curve bCB_R and the B-axis. From B_R to H_C on the loop, the magnetic field is still decreasing, so e is in the same sense as above; but now i has reversed, and e and i are in opposite senses. Thus, energy is now required of the electric circuit in order to reduce the magnetic flux density. Along the part of the loop H_Cdk, e and i are still in opposite senses and energy is still required from the electric circuit in order to build up the magnetic field in the reverse direction. The second term on the right side of (17–3–6) is the energy per unit volume of the core, required of the electric circuit along the part of the loop $B_R H_C dk$, and is the area between this curve and the B-axis. You can follow this type of argument on around the loop and show that the energy represented by the areas outlined by the letters $bCB_R B_m b$ and $B'_R fk B'_m B'_R$, is fed from the electric circuit into the magnetic field and subsequently fed from the magnetic field back into the electric circuit. However, the energy represented by the area enclosed in the loop is fed from the electric circuit into the magnetic field but is *not* returned to the electric circuit. Thus, (17–3–5) becomes

$$W = v \ (\text{``area'' enclosed in the hysteresis loop}) \qquad (17\text{–}3\text{–}7)$$

In (17–3–7), "area" must, of course, be in units of B times H.

As pointed out above, W is the net energy expended by the electric circuit as heat loss in hysteresis for one trip around the hysteresis loop. If the frequency of the alternating current flowing in the winding is f, the core material goes through the hysteresis cycle of changes f times per second and the power loss P due to hysteresis is

$$P = vf \ (\text{area enclosed in the hysteresis loop}) \qquad (17\text{–}3\text{–}8)$$

Note that the hysteresis power loss is in addition to the eddy current power loss discussed in Sec. 15–4. Both losses occur together in the ferromagnetic core of any a-c machine and in any part of a d-c machine (such as the rotating armature) in which the magnetic flux in a ferromagnetic material is changing.

Hysteresis and eddy current losses depend on different factors, as we have seen. The greatest contrast arises from the fact that the eddy current power loss varies directly as the square of the thickness of the laminations used in the core, whereas lamination of the core does not influence hysteresis power loss. Hence, figures cannot be given which compare the magnitudes of hysteresis and eddy current power losses in general. However, we may obtain some notion of their relative magnitudes from the fact that the hysteresis power loss is usually about twice the eddy current power loss in well-designed power transformers.

STEINMETZ' EQUATION. Steinmetz found an empirical relationship between the energy loss W for one cycle of the hysteresis loop and the maximum value B_m of the magnetic flux density during the cycle. His equation is

$$W = v\eta B_m^n \qquad (17\text{–}3\text{–}9)$$

where η is called the Steinmetz coefficient for the particular ferromagnetic material being used, and v is the volume of the core. Steinmetz found a value of 1.6 for n for the wide variety of materials that he tested. The newer ferromagnetic alloys, however, have values for n in the range* from 1.5 to 2.5, and n may not be constant for more than a limited range of values of B_m. Thus, Steinmetz' equation may be used for a particular material only when η

---

* M.I.T. Electrical Engineering Staff, *Magnetic Circuits and Transformers* (New York: John Wiley & Sons, Inc., 1943), p. 129.

and n are known for that material, and then only for the range of B_m for which n is known to be constant. Within these limitations, however, Steinmetz' equation is very useful for calculation, since it saves plotting the hysteresis loop for each new maximum value of magnetic flux density.

Using Steinmetz' equation, the power loss P due to hysteresis may be expressed as

$$P = \eta v f B_m^n \qquad (17\text{–}3\text{–}10)$$

where again v is the volume of the core and f is the a-c frequency in cycles/sec. As before, (17–3–10) assumes a normal hysteresis loop, so it assumes that H is varying cyclically between equal positive and negative values and that the flux density is uniform throughout the sample.

17–4 THE DOMAIN THEORY OF FERROMAGNETISM

We can give only a brief summary of the important and far-reaching domain theory of ferromagnetism. This theory has contributed much to an understanding of the magnetic properties of ferromagnetic materials in their simpler aspects, and is still the subject of considerable research for further understanding of the more complicated aspects. For a more complete picture, advanced texts* and journal articles should be consulted.

According to this theory, ferromagnetic materials are composed of small regions, called *domains*, each of which is magnetized to saturation even though no external field is applied. Hence, within each domain, the uncompensated electron spins have their magnetic moments aligned parallel to each other. Thus, we may consider that the hypothetical Amperian current loops have their magnetic moments aligned parallel to each other. All ferromagnetic materials are crystalline solids, and it is believed that strong interatomic forces in the crystals are responsible for the alignment of the uncompensated electron spins of all the atoms within each domain. The size of each domain in a single crystal is a complicated function of many factors, including the size and shape of the crystal, but domain sizes in general are in the range from 10^{-2} to 10^{-6} cm^3.

Roughly speaking, the size of a given domain is the result of a compromise between two effects, one tending to make the whole crystal into a single domain and the other tending to break down the domains entirely, leaving the uncompensated spins oriented at random. What tends to line up all the spins in a crystal is the strong interatomic force we have mentioned earlier, which seems to exist in all ferromagnetic materials, but which can be understood, if at all, only through difficult quantum-theoretical calculations. If this were all, a domain would extend over a whole crystal, or even a larger region, but there is another effect which tends to discourage the formation of large domains, and this is the setting up of large magnetic potential energies. Let us pass an imaginary plane through some domain, parallel to the direction of magnetization, dividing the domain into two parts which we can compare to

* For example, R. M. Bozorth, "Magnetism," *Rev. Mod. Phys.*, **19**, No. 1 (January, 1947), p. 29, and "Ferromagnetism," (New York: D. Van Nostrand Co., Inc., 1951). C. Kittel, "Physical Theory of Ferromagnetic Domains," *Rev. Mod. Phys.*, **21**, No. 4 (October, 1949), p. 541. Group of summary articles *Rev. Mod. Phys.*, **25**, pp. 1–352 (1953).

two magnets lying side by side, North to North and South to South. But if there were to be two such magnets and one were to let go of them, one magnet would at once reorient itself South to North and North to South relative to the other. Evidently, this would produce a state of lower potential energy than the first. Similarly, in a domain, this potential energy has a demagnetizing effect, tending to split any domain into parts with different directions of magnetization. The actual domain represents a compromise between aligning and disaligning forces.

Let us leave the domain concept for the moment and consider first the crystal structure and then the magnetic behavior of a large single crystal of iron. This discussion will serve as an example for all ferromagnetic crystals. The general ideas are the same for all even though the details differ markedly. An iron crystal is relatively simple, since it is a cubic crystal made up of cubical building blocks like the one in Fig. 17–4–1. There is an iron atom at each corner of this cubical building block, and one in the center of the cube. Because there is an atom at the center of the cube, the iron crystal is said to be a body centered cubic crystal. Three possible directions through the cube are indicated in Fig. 17–4–1, and are labeled with the usual crystallographic notation. Any cube edge is known as a 100 direction, a diagonal across any face is known as a 110 direction, and any cube diagonal is known as a 111 direction.

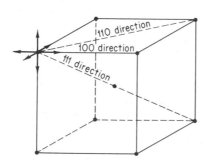

Figure 17–4–1. Unit cube in an iron crystal.

Now let us perform an experiment in which we secure data so that we may plot the magnetization curve for the large single crystal of iron made up of many such building blocks as the one in Fig. 17–4–1. It is called a single crystal because all the building blocks in it are arranged with their 100 directions parallel to each other. We start the experiment with the single crystal demagnetized and apply H parallel to a 100 direction in the crystal. We compute H and measure B much as we did for the magnetization curve in Fig. 17–1–2. From each measured value of B we compute B_F, where B_F is the magnetic flux density in the iron crystal due just to the iron (i.e., $B_F = B - \mu_0 H$). You will note from (16–4–1) that B_F is equal to μ_0 times the intensity of magnetization $\mathcal{I}$ in the iron. Then we plot the magnetization curve, using B_F as the ordinate and H as the abscissa. The result is the magnetization curve labeled 100 in Fig. 17–4–2. Next we demagnetize the crystal and repeat the experiment, except that this time H is applied parallel to the 110 direction. The resulting magnetization curve is the one labeled 110 in Fig. 17–4–2. Again we repeat the experiment, but with H parallel to the 111 direction, and the result is the magnetization curve labeled 111 in Fig. 17–4–2.

You will note how much more easily the single crystal of iron is magnetized to saturation when H is parallel to the 100 direction than in either of the other two directions. This direction in the crystal is called the *direction of easy magnetization.* Similarly the 110 direction is called the *direction of medium easy magnetization*, and the 111 direction is called the *direction of hard magnetization.* The direction of easy magnetization may be different, with regard to the crystal axes, for different kinds of ferromagnetic materials. For example, nickel has its direction of easy magnetization along the 111 direction, i.e., along the cube diagonal. (Nickel happens to be a cubic crystal also, but it is a face centered cubic for it has an atom in the center of each face as well as at each corner of the cube, but none in the center of the cube.)

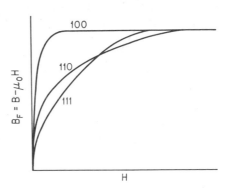

Now let us return to the domain theory. This theory says that the direction of easy magnetization in a crystal is the direction of actual magnetization in each domain in the crystal provided that there is no applied magnetic field and no strain.

Figure 17–4–2. Magnetization curves for the 100, 110, and 111 directions in an iron single crystal showing that 100 is the direction of easy magnetization in iron.

In the iron crystal there are six directions of easy magnetization (counting both senses along a cube edge) as shown by the six arrows at the upper left corner of the cube in Fig. 17–4–1. In an unmagnetized iron crystal, the domains are magnetized along these six directions more or less at random. Thus, in this state, the crystal as a whole has no net magnetic flux density. This situation is pictured for a single crystal of iron, by a highly schematic representation, in Fig. 17–4–3 (a) where the

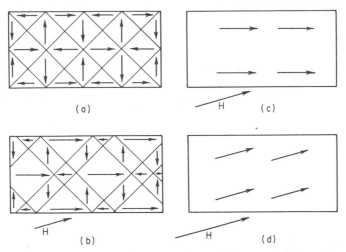

Figure 17–4–3. Changes in domains of an iron single crystal during magnetization, shown schematically. (a) Unmagnetized with no applied field. (b) Boundary displacements due to applied field. (c) Knee of magnetization curve. (d) Saturation.

domains are represented as if they were rectangular and as if they were in a two dimensional, instead of three dimensional, array. The domains are more likely to be long and slender, although a wide variety of shapes has been observed. In Fig. 17–4–3, the edges of the crystal are parallel to a 100 direction of the unit cube, the resultant magnetic moment in each domain has been represented by an arrow, and the arrows are all parallel to a 100 direction, i.e., parallel to one of the six directions of easy magnetization. In Fig. 17–4–3 (a), the magnetic moments form closed magnetic circuits inside the crystal in their orientations along these directions; thus the crystal has no net magnetic moment and no external net magnetic flux density.

Now apply a weak magnetic field directed from lower left to upper right on the page as shown by the vector labeled *H* in Fig. 17–4–3 (b). Those domains, which have their magnetic moments most nearly parallel to the applied *H*, grow in volume at the expense of their neighbors, as shown schematically in Fig. 17–4–3 (b). The result is a small net magnetic moment in the direction of the applied field, and the ferromagnetic material is contributing some magnetic flux. At this stage, if the weak applied field were removed, the boundaries would go back, essentially, to their original configuration, and the movement of the boundaries in a weak field is known as a *reversible boundary displacement*. Relatively little energy has gone into heat. On the magnetization curve of Fig. 17–4–4, the approximate range, over which reversible boundary displacements occur, is labeled.

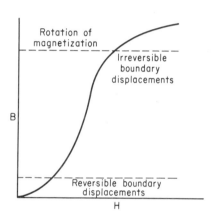

Figure 17–4–4. Magnetization curve with various regions identified with domain behavior.*

As the applied field becomes stronger, the boundaries continue to change, but now in an irreversible fashion, and the flux density in the iron increases rapidly for small changes in *H*. This region is also labeled on the magnetization curve of Fig. 17–4–4. In the latter stages of this part of the process, all the magnetic moments in the domains rotate so that they are parallel with that 100 direction which is most nearly parallel with the applied field. This situation is shown in Fig. 17–4–3 (c), and the limit of the region is at the knee of the magnetization curve. The curve has a knee because it is hard to rotate the direction of magnetization within a domain, i.e., a relatively larger change in *H* is required to produce a certain change in *B* than was required earlier in the magnetization process when boundary displacements alone were involved. The piece of iron is now essentially all one domain as shown in the figure.

As the applied field is increased still further, the magnetic moments of the domains gradually rotate until at saturation all the magnetic moments are

* C. Kittel, "Physical Theory of Ferromagnetic Domains," *Rev. Mod. Phys.*, **21** (October, 1949), p. 545.

parallel with the applied field. This condition at saturation is illustrated in Fig. 17–4–3 (d).

The ferromagnetic materials used industrially are polycrystalline. This means that a piece of the material is made up of a vast number of single crystals, and the little single crystals are randomly oriented in the piece. Each little single crystal contains, in general, many domains. The above discussion may be considered as a discussion of the behavior of the domains in each little single crystal of the polycrystalline piece.

When we say that each domain is magnetized to saturation, we are assuming that the energy of thermal agitation of the atoms is small enough so that it does not disturb the interatomic forces which hold the uncompensated electron spins in alignment within each domain. This is strictly true only at very low temperatures. However, for most ferromagnetic materials used industrially, it is essentially true in the neighborhood of room temperature. As the temperature of the material is increased, more and more of the electron spins break away from the alignment within a domain. When the Curie temperature is reached, the alignment within a domain has been lost and the material shows a paramagnetic, rather than ferromagnetic, behavior. Thus, the major magnetic difference between paramagnetic and ferromagnetic materials is the domain structure of the ferromagnetic materials, in addition to the fact that each ferromagnetic atom has a large intrinsic magnetic moment. The domain structure permits a relatively weak applied magnetic field to produce a very marked alignment of the magnetic moments in a piece of ferromagnetic bulk matter due to the interatomic forces which tend to line up the atomic magnetic moments. Without these interatomic forces, the magnetic moments would be oriented largely at random. Further, the material retains some of this alignment after the applied field is removed, thus giving us permanent magnets. On the other hand, a comparable applied magnetic field produces very little alignment of magnetic moments in a paramagnetic material. This is because the thermal agitation of the atoms tends to dominate their behavior, and the interatomic forces, which might produce alignment, are absent. Thus a very high magnetic field intensity, which is beyond those available in the laboratory, would be required to produce complete alignment, or saturation, in a paramagnetic material at ordinary temperatures.

1. EXPERIMENTAL EVIDENCE FOR DOMAIN STRUCTURE. We shall summarize very briefly two of the experimental methods which show that domains exist in ferromagnetic materials. The first, and by far the most important, is the *magnetic powder pattern technique*. Since each domain is magnetized to saturation it acts like a tiny magnet. Where two domains meet at the surface of an unmagnetized piece of ferromagnetic material, there will be a small local magnetic field outside the material. This is a region where some of the magnetic flux lines from one domain penetrate the surface before they enter the next domain, which has a different orientation of its magnetic moments. To find and study these boundaries between domains, the powder pattern technique is used. A liquid, that contains a colloidal suspension of a fine ferromagnetic powder, is spread on the surface to be studied. The particles of the powder have a size of the order of one one-millionth of a meter. These

ferromagnetic particles are attracted by the inhomogeneous magnetic fields at the boundaries between domains and concentrate on these boundaries. Under a microscope, the lines along which the particles concentrate can be seen. Hence, indirectly the domain boundaries can be seen and their behavior studied as an external magnetic field is applied. From this technique and modifications which arise from it, much of the experimental knowledge about behavior of domains during magnetization (see Fig. 17–4–3) has been obtained.

The second evidence, which we shall summarize briefly, comes from the *Barkhausen effect*. Suppose, in Fig. 17–1–1, that we wind a secondary coil on the ring and connect this secondary to an amplifier and loud speaker. Starting with the ring demagnetized, we slowly and continuously increase the current in the primary winding so that H is slowly and continuously increased. (This means that we do not use the numbered resistors and switches which would cause H to increase in steps, but rather use a rheostat so that we may increase the current continuously.) As the steep part of the magnetization curve is traversed, a succession of clicks is heard from the loud speaker. A click in the loud speaker means that an abrupt change has occurred in the magnetic flux linking the secondary coil on the ring, thus inducing a sizable emf of short duration in this secondary. A steady increase in the magnetic flux linking the secondary coil results in a steady emf which holds the diaphragm of the speaker but does not cause clicks. These clicks indicate sudden irregular changes in the magnetic flux linking the secondary. These sudden irregular changes in the magnetic flux linking the secondary are associated with the sudden irregular motion of the domain boundaries [see Fig. 17–4–3 (b)] as the favored domains grow at the expense of their neighbors. Thus, in the Barkhausen effect, we may say that we "hear" the domain boundaries shift. Very pronounced Barkhausen noise has been observed accompanying the motion of a single domain boundary.

17–5 MAGNETIC MOMENT OF A PERMANENT MAGNET

Let us consider a bar of ferromagnetic material which is magnetically very hard and is magnetized to saturation in a uniform magnetic field. A very intense magnetic field is required for this purpose. When the magnetic field is removed, the bar is left magnetized and the magnetization stabilizes below the retentivity point of the hysteresis curve of Fig. 17–2–1 in the region where μ is negative. We shall assume that the material is magnetically hard enough so that subsequent exposure to external magnetic fields will not alter the magnetization in the bar. This assumption is valid if the external magnetic field has a flux density which is small compared with that of the field used to magnetize the bar. We now have a permanent magnet with which we may experiment.

1. MAGNETIC MOMENT OF A PERMANENT MAGNET. We shall give an experimental definition of the magnetic moment of a permanent magnet. It is a definition which can be applied without making any special assumptions with regard to the magnetization in the magnet except that the applied magnetic field does not alter the magnetization of the magnet.

First, by means of a fine fiber, we suspend the magnet in the earth's magnetic field and find that the magnet always aligns itself with its long dimension (its axis) in an approximately north-south direction. This behavior is that of a compass needle. We mark the end of the magnet which is toward the north with an N and the end which is toward the south with an S. (As you know, these ends of the magnet are called the north and south poles of the magnet, respectively, and we shall have more to say about poles in the next section.)

Next we perform a systematic experiment in which we measure the torque τ on the magnet when it is immersed in a uniform magnetic field whose flux density B is known (see Fig. 17–5–1). The experiment should be performed in empty space but air will do. When the axis of the magnet makes a fixed angle β with the direction of $\boldsymbol{B}$, we find that the torque is independent of the axis of rotation selected, so we are dealing with a couple. Thus we may think in terms of two equal and oppositely directed forces acting on the magnet. Next we find that τ is directly proportional to $\sin \beta$ for a magnetic field of fixed flux density. Then, when we use magnetic fields with different flux densities, we find that τ is directly proportional to B. Hence we write

$$\tau = MB \sin \beta \qquad (17\text{–}5\text{–}1)$$

where M is a constant of proportionality. When we use different magnets we get different values of M, so we say that M "belongs" to the magnet and call it the *magnetic moment of the magnet*. From (17–5–1) $M = \tau/(B \sin \beta)$, and if $\beta = 90°$,

$$M = \tau/B \qquad (17\text{–}5\text{–}2)$$

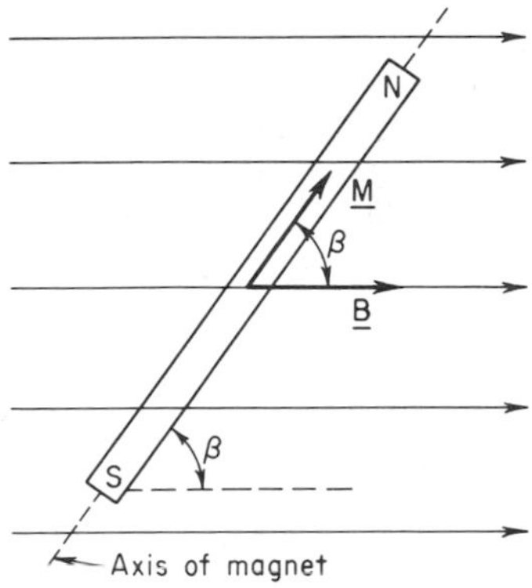

Figure 17–5–1. Permanent magnet in an applied external magnetic field; magnetic moment M of the magnet.

Hence we may state the general definition of M as: *the magnetic moment of a magnet is equal to the torque* (moment of force) *that the magnet experiences when its axis is perpendicular to a magnetic field of unit magnetic flux density in air.*

Let us say that M is a vector quantity whose direction is along the axis of the magnet in the sense from the S pole toward the N pole as shown by the vector which represents $\boldsymbol{M}$ in Fig. 17–5–1. Then we may express the torque on the magnet by means of the vector product

$$\boldsymbol{\tau} = \boldsymbol{M} \times \boldsymbol{B} \qquad (17\text{–}5\text{–}3)$$

The torque on the magnet, as drawn in Fig. 17–5–1, is such as to cause a clockwise rotation of the magnet (as viewed from above). Thus, according to the convention adopted in Sec. 13–2, Fig. 13–2–2, the vector that represents this torque is directed into the page and we see that (17–5–3) satisfies this previously adopted convention for representation of torque as a vector quantity.

By substitution of units into (17–5–2), you can show that the unit of M in the mks system is newton meter^3/weber, or the equivalent, ampere meter^2. Note that (17–5–3) is the same as (13–7–2) for the torque on a current loop and that the units of M for a magnet are the same as the units of M for a current loop.

2. Calculation of M for a bar magnet in terms of Amperian currents. The permanent magnet has a magnetic moment because the uncanceled magnetic moments of the electron spins in the ferromagnetic atoms were left with a high degree of alignment after the magnetizing field was removed. To put it another way, the domains were left with an alignment something like that of Fig. 17–4–3 (c), and we may think of equivalent Amperian currents as flowing around the surface of the magnet with their planes perpendicular to the axis of the magnet.

In Fig. 17–5–1 the magnet experiences a torque, due to the applied field, because the applied field exerts a net torque on the uncompensated electron spins in each atom, or, what is equivalent, the external applied field exerts a torque on the Amperian surface current as if the bar magnet were a solenoid with each of its turns a current loop like that of Sec. 13–7.

The actual magnetization of a bar magnet is, in general, a complicated affair, and calculations with respect to it are beyond the scope of this book. However, if we take an idealized case that no actual permanent magnet satisfies, we may calculate the magnetic moment of a bar magnet in terms of the Amperian currents and thence in terms of the intensity of magnetization $\mathscr{I}$. Let us assume, for this idealized case, that the bar magnet is uniformly magnetized throughout its volume, and let A represent the area of cross section of the bar. Let M_a represent the magnetic moment due to the Amperian current flowing around unit length of the bar, and as before, let j_a represent the Amperian linear surface current density. Then, from the definition of the magnetic moment of a current loop as given in (13–7–1), $M_a = j_a A$. Since the bar is uniformly magnetized, all these magnetic moments are parallel and in the same sense, so $M = \sum M_a = \sum j_a A = A \sum j_a$ where M is the total magnetic moment of the bar magnet due to the Amperian current. Let l represent the length of the magnet, and $\sum j_a = l j_a$, so

$$M = l A j_a \tag{17–5–4}$$

But from (16–3–3), $\mathscr{I} = j_a$, so

$$M = l A \mathscr{I} \tag{17–5–5}$$

Magnetization $\mathscr{I}$ is defined as the magnetic moment per unit volume of the magnet, and lA is the volume of the magnet, so it is to be expected that (17–5–5) will result for the total magnetic moment of the Amperian currents when the magnetization is uniform. In this simple case, (17–5–4) and (17–5–5) give the same magnetic moment for the bar magnet as does the experimental definition in (17–5–1). In a more general case, a similar relationship exists, but the intensity of magnetization must be summed vectorially over the volume.

17–6 MAGNETIC POLE STRENGTH OF A PERMANENT MAGNET

1. Definition in terms of M. If we dip an actual permanent bar magnet into iron filings or if we map the magnetic field of the magnet by use of iron filings

(in the manner that you have all performed the experiment in the elementary laboratory), we find a region near each end of the magnet where the iron filings experience a strong force of attraction and cling to the magnet. These regions are called the poles of the magnet, and are named north N and south S in the way that we outlined in the last section.

The iron filing map gives a graphic picture of magnetic flux lines, and tests conducted in the air about the magnet show that B and H are directed, in general, away from an N pole and toward an S pole. Before the theory of the magnetic properties of materials and the relationship between electricity and magnetism were as well understood as they are today, these poles were considered the source of magnetic effects and were given physical significance. We now believe that these poles are simply the regions where the magnetic flux lines, due to the uncompensated electron spins, emerge from the body of the magnet and produce magnetic effects outside the magnet. However, it is often convenient to treat magnet poles of permanent magnets as if they were the seats of magnetic effects and to assign them *pole strengths*. When we do this we let the fictitious poles replace the fictitious Amperian currents which, in turn, replaced the uncompensated electron spins, in our description of magnetic effects.

From the iron filing map of the field of a permanent magnet we may locate, more or less, the center of the region which we call the pole of the magnet. Having located the centers of both poles of the magnet, we may measure the distance between the centers and call the distance l, the length of the magnet. In general, l is not the geometric length of the magnet. However, if we have a very long slender bar magnet, the percentage error is small if l is taken as the geometric length.

The pole strength m of each pole of a magnet is defined as the quotient obtained when the magnitude of the magnetic moment M of the magnet is divided by the length l. Thus the defining equation for m is

$$m = M/l \qquad (17\text{-}6\text{-}1)$$

Equation (17–6–1) is a general definition of m and does not assume that the magnetization of the bar is uniform. From this defining equation, the unit of m is ampere meter^2/meter or ampere meter in the mks system.*

* If the magnetic moment of a current loop is defined by the Kennelly proposal as $M = \mu_0 IA$ (see footnote in Sec. 13–7), the magnetic moment M of a magnet comes out to be $M = \mu_0 \tau / B$ [in place of (17–5–2) here]; and, of course, has the same unit, of weber meter, as does the magnetic moment of a current loop when using the Kennelly proposal. As here in (17–6–1), $m = M/l$, so pole strength has the weber (or volt second) as its unit if the Kennelly proposal is followed. The Sommerfeld proposal is followed in this text. If we let m_K be the pole strength of a magnet expressed in Kennelly units (i.e., webers) and m_S be the pole strength of the same magnet expressed in Sommerfeld units (i.e., ampere meter), then $m_K = \mu_0 m_S$, where $\mu_0 = 4\pi \times 10^{-7}$ henry/meter. This relationship may be used to convert pole strength given in weber to the same pole strength given in ampere meter, or vice versa. Both Kennelly and Sommerfeld units belong to the mks system.

The unit pole (UP) in the absolute electromagnetic system of units (emu) was defined in Sec. 14–5 in the discussion of the basis for this system of units. Conversion of the pole strength of a certain pole, expressed in UP, to the pole strength of the same pole, expressed in ampere meter, can be made from the fact that there is 0.1 amp m/UP. Thus, if we let

When we take the pole point of view, we consider that an external magnetic field exerts a force F on each pole. The force on the N pole is in the direction of the applied field, and that on the S pole is in an opposite direction to that of the applied field. These two forces are to be of such magnitude that they would produce the actual torque experienced by the magnet. The situation is pictured in Fig. 17–6–1 where NS is the magnet, and the two forces F and F represent the fictitious forces acting on the fictitious poles. In the first part of the last section we saw from experiment that the torque on the magnet is independent of the axis of rotation selected, so that we must consider a couple to be acting on the magnet. These two equal and opposite forces, F and F, constitute such a couple.

From (17–5–1) the torque τ on the magnet is given by $\tau = MB \sin \beta$. From (17–6–1), $M = ml$, so

$$\tau = mlB \sin \beta \qquad (17\text{–}6\text{–}2)$$

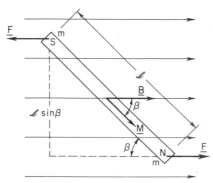

But, from Fig. 17–6–1, the torque τ produced by the forces F and F is

$$\tau = Fl \sin \beta \qquad (17\text{–}6\text{–}3)$$

and these two torques are the same torque. Hence

$$F = mB \qquad (17\text{–}6\text{–}4)$$

or, since the applied field is in air and $B = \mu_0 H$,

$$F = m\mu_0 H \qquad (17\text{–}6\text{–}5)$$

Figure 17–6–1. Permanent magnet in an applied external magnetic field; force F on each magnet pole.

Thus, from the pole point of view, each magnet pole in an applied field in air experiences a force given by (17–6–4) or (17–6–5). This relationship is often very useful.

2. RELATIONSHIP OF POLE STRENGTH TO INTENSITY OF MAGNETIZATION. Again, as in the last section, we can make a calculation if we select an idealized simple case. This time we wish to relate pole strength m to intensity of magnetization $\mathscr{I}$. We take the same idealized case as before, i.e., a uniformly magnetized permanent bar magnet. No actual bar magnet is ever uniformly magnetized, but this is a useful approximation which is simple enough for calculation.

Put the value of the magnetic moment of the bar magnet from (17–5–5) into (17–6–1), and

$$m = A\mathscr{I} \qquad (17\text{–}6\text{–}6)$$

---

m_{emu} be the pole strength of the pole expressed in UP, and m_S be the pole strength of the same pole to be expressed in ampere meter, we have

$$m_S = 0.1 \text{ amp m } m_{\text{emu}}/\text{UP}$$

Thus, there are

$$10^8 \text{UP}/4\pi \text{ weber}, \quad \text{or} \quad m_{\text{emu}} = 10^8 \text{UP } m_K/4\pi \text{ weber}$$

For a discussion of the relationship between choice of units and the method of teaching, see the Report of the Coulomb's Law Committee of the A.A.P.T., "The Teaching of Electricity and Magnetism at the College Level," *Am. J. Phys.*, **18**, pp. 1–25 (1950); particularly pp. 22–23 and the references given there.

This equation says that the pole strength of the magnet is the area of the end face of the magnet times the intensity of magnetization of the magnet in this simple case. From the fact that we are considering a uniformly magnetized bar we must picture the pole as being at the very end of the magnet and the flux lines as coming out of the end face of the magnet only. Otherwise, the magnetization would not be uniform all the way to the end of the bar. We know from our iron filing maps that this is not a very realistic picture for an actual bar magnet, but it is sometimes a useful approximation when dealing with this complicated situation.

The magnetic moment of a magnet, as defined in (17–5–1), is a quantity which can be determined experimentally from a torque measurement without making any simplifying assumptions, and is thus a more useful quantity for many calculations. However, both pole strength and magnetic moment will change in the presence of an external field unless the material of the magnet is very hard magnetically and the external field weak, so both m and M must be used with caution unless it is known that the external conditions do not appreciably alter them.

17–7 MAGNETIC FIELD INTENSITY H DUE TO A POINT MAGNET POLE

Let us consider a very long, slender, uniformly magnetized bar magnet. We want the magnet to be very long so that we may make calculations near its north pole and consider that its south pole is so far away that it does not influence our discussion. We want the magnet to be very slender so that its poles will be confined to very small regions, and we shall look upon them as point poles. Being uniformly magnetized, its poles will be at the ends. The magnet should be in empty space for this calculation, but we shall make no

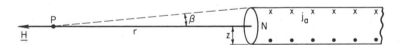

Figure 17–7–1. Calculation of magnetic field intensity H at a point P in air due to a point magnet pole.

serious error if it is in air. We wish to compute the magnetic field intensity H at a point P in the space outside the magnet due to the N pole of the magnet alone. The distance from the pole to the point is large compared with the small radius of cross section of the magnet.

Figure 17–7–1 shows the situation, where a short section of the magnet near the N pole is drawn, and the S pole is a great distance beyond the right edge of the page. In our thinking we may, for points outside the magnet, replace the magnet by a long slender solenoid. The solenoid must have nI ampere turns per unit length (n is the number of turns per unit length) such that $nI = j_a$, where j_a is the linear surface current density of Amperian current of the magnet. In (14–7–7) we showed that the magnetic field intensity H at any point on the axis of the solenoid is

$$H = \tfrac{1}{2}nI(\cos \alpha - \cos \beta) \qquad (17\text{–}7\text{–}1)$$

and we may write (17–7–1) as

$$H = \tfrac{1}{2} j_a (\cos \alpha - \cos \beta) \qquad (17\text{–}7\text{–}2)$$

for points on the axis outside the magnet. Here β is the angle designated in Fig. 17–7–1, and α is the angle between the axis and a line drawn from P to the periphery of the magnet at the S pole. Let r_s equal the distance from P to the S pole and, as shown on the figure, r is the distance from P to the N pole. From the figure, $\cos \beta = r(r^2 + z^2)^{-1/2} = (1 + z^2/r^2)^{-1/2}$. Similarly, $\cos \alpha = (1 + z^2/r_s^2)^{-1/2}$. Expand the right-hand sides of each of these equations by the binomial theorem and retain only the first two terms, since z is small compared to r and much smaller compared to r_s. Then $\cos \beta = 1 - z^2/2r^2$ and $\cos \alpha = 1 - z^2/2r_s^2$, and (17–7–2) becomes

$$H = (j_a \pi z^2 / 4\pi)(1/r^2 - 1/r_s^2) \qquad (17\text{–}7\text{–}3)$$

But $\pi z^2 = A$, where A is the area of the end face of the magnet. Also, from (16–3–3), $j_a = \mathscr{I}$; and from (17–6–6), $m = \mathscr{I} A$, so (17–7–3) becomes

$$H = (m/4\pi)(1/r^2 - 1/r_s^2) \qquad (17\text{–}7\text{–}4)$$

for on-axis positions of a magnetic dipole with point poles and for points where $r \gg z$. Now pass to the limit, for a very long magnet where $r_s \gg r$ so $1/r_s^2$ is negligible with respect to $1/r^2$, and (17–7–4) becomes

$$H = m/4\pi r^2 \qquad (17\text{–}7\text{–}5)$$

due to the single point pole of the magnetic dipole.

From the pole point of view, we consider that the magnet in Fig. 17–7–1 has a point pole at each end and that these point poles are the sources of the magnetic field of the magnet. The pole strengths $+m$ and $-m$ replace the Amperian currents for purposes of description of the behavior of the magnet and the field it produces, where $+m$ is associated with the north pole and $-m$ with the south pole. Field intensity H is a vector quantity and its direction is along a line drawn from P to the pole. The sense along this line is away from the pole if it is an N pole and toward the pole if it is an S pole. We have derived (17–7–5) for a point on the axis of the magnet only. However, by a more general treatment than the one given here, it can be shown that the magnetic field around a single point pole is spherically symmetrical, and that (17–7–5) is valid for points off the axis as well as for points on the axis of the magnet.

For most magnets, we must look upon each actual pole as a distribution of point poles throughout a volume. Then H at P is the vector sum of terms like (17–7–5), one for each point pole in the distribution. Also if there is a distribution of point poles in various magnets in the neighborhood, two poles for each magnet, we employ the same technique. Thus, in general, for H at P in free space due to a distribution of n point poles,

$$H = (1/4\pi) \sum_{i=1}^{n} m_i \mathbf{i}_{ri}/r_i^2 \qquad (17\text{–}7\text{–}6)$$

where the S poles have minus signs in this vector sum and the N poles have plus signs, and we define i_{ri} as a unit vector, at P, along the line drawn from m_i to P and directed away from m_i. Since $B = \mu_0 H$ in free space, we may write (17–7–6) in terms of B as

$$B = (\mu_0/4\pi) \sum_{i=1}^{n} m_i i_{ri}/r_i^2 \qquad (17\text{--}7\text{--}7)$$

Compare (17–7–7) with (9–6–18) for the analogous case in electrostatics.

1. FORCE EXERTED BY ONE POINT POLE ON A SECOND POINT POLE. Imagine that we have a point pole of strength m_1 at a distance r in empty space (air will do) from a second point pole of strength m_2. At pole 2, the magnetic field intensity H due to pole 1 is given by (17–7–5) as $H = m_1/4\pi r^2$. From (17–6–5), the force F which this field exerts on pole 2 is $F = m_2 \mu_0 H$, so

$$F = \mu_0 m_1 m_2/4\pi r^2 \qquad (17\text{--}7\text{--}8)$$

The force acts along the line between the two poles and is a force of repulsion if they are like poles and attraction if they are unlike poles. This formula* is known as Coulomb's law of force between point poles; it was discovered experimentally by Coulomb before a theory of magnetism existed. Equation (17–7–8) gives the direct force which one point pole exerts on a second point pole regardless of the medium in which the poles are immersed. The resultant forces on the poles may be altered by the intervening medium due to the uncompensated electron orbital motions and spins in the atoms of the medium, but this does not alter the fact that (17–7–8) gives the direct force.

Equation (17–7–8) is used as the experimental basic equation for one method of developing the whole mathematical theory of magnetism. However, we have elected to base the study of magnetism on the magnetic fields of currents. Even in the study of the magnetic properties of matter we replaced the uncompensated orbital and spin magnetic moments of electrons by magnetic moments of equivalent Amperian current loops and Amperian surface currents. Magnetic poles, however, are very useful concepts for many descriptions where it is not convenient to go all the way back to the uncompensated magnetic moments of electrons in the material. A great simplification of the problem often results when magnet poles are used in this fashion. We have used the magnet pole description in our discussion of several instruments and machines.

2. LINES OF H DUE TO POLES ORIGINATE ON N POLES AND TERMINATE ON S POLES. Consider the imaginary closed path $abcdea$ in Fig. 17–7–2, which shows an oversimplified drawing of lines of H for a permanent magnet. Apply Ampere's circuital law of (16–9–3) to this path, and

$$\oint H \cdot ds = 0 \qquad (17\text{--}7\text{--}9)$$

---

* If the Kennelly proposal is followed, (17–7–8) has the form $F = m_{1K} m_{2K}/4\pi\mu_0 r^2$, where m_{1K} and m_{2K} are the pole strengths of the two poles expressed in Kennelly units (i.e., weber). You can show this result directly from the material in the footnote in Sec. 17–6 following (17–6–1). In this formula, F is in newtons and r in meters, as it is in (17–7–8).

The zero appears on the right side of this equation because no conduction or displacement currents cut through the surface bounded by the path of integration. Only Amperian current cuts through this surface. But H is not zero, nor is it perpendicular to ds at all points on the path. Hence H must have a direction opposite to that of ds for enough of the path so that the sum around the closed path is zero. Outside the magnet, along path abc, we must consider that lines of H are directed in the sense shown by the arrowhead on the path in order to agree with our previously selected direction for H. Hence, inside the magnet, the lines of H are directed from N toward S as they are outside. Consequently, we must think of lines of H, which are due to poles, as originating on N poles and terminating on S poles both for the lines that stay inside the magnet and those that are outside the magnet.

The above contains the reason why there is a very limited number of cases

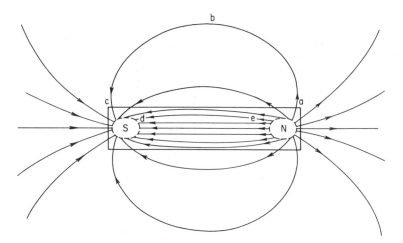

Figure 17–7–2. Some lines of H for a permanent bar magnet.

in which H can be computed from conduction current only. The limited number of cases includes *only* those cases (e.g., the toroid) where there are no poles or where the poles are so far away (e.g., the infinite solenoid filled with a ferromagnetic material) that they do not influence the discussion (see Sec. 16–4). The toroid (or an equivalent arrangement with no poles) is usually used for magnetization and hysteresis measurements so that H can be computed directly from measurable quantities.

In contrast with lines of H, lines of B are always closed lines (see footnote Sec. 14–3) whether they are due to poles (i.e., Amperian currents) or to conduction and displacement currents. Lines of H due to conduction and displacement currents are also always closed lines. This contrast between the nature of lines of H due to Amperian currents on the one hand and conduction and displacement currents on the other need not disturb us, because H was introduced as a useful vector quantity for calculation purposes and does not have the fundamental physical significance of B.

17–8 THE MAGNETOMETER

The magnetometer is an instrument used for the comparison of the magnetic flux densities of two magnetic fields at two different places in air. Strictly the magnetic fields should be in empty space but, as before, we can neglect the magnetic properties of air for practical purposes. As an example, we may use the magnetometer to compare the magnetic flux density of the earth's magnetic field at two different places on the earth's surface.

A magnetometer has a short permanent magnet suspended in a horizontal position by a silk fiber. The fiber selected is one that has a very little restoring torque when it is twisted, and we shall assume that it has zero restoring torque. Usually the suspended magnet is in a nonferromagnetic metal housing so that air currents will not disturb it, and a window is provided so that the motion of the magnet can be observed. If the experiment is performed in a room, the effect of air currents may be negligible and the magnet may be suspended in the open. The magnet must be one whose intensity of magnetization will not be altered by the magnetic field in which it is immersed.

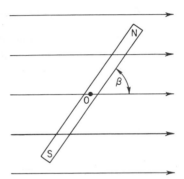

Figure 17–8–1 shows the magnet NS suspended in a horizontal position with the silk fiber attached at the center of mass O. The fiber is perpendicular to the page in this figure and its point of support is above the page. The lines drawn are the magnetic flux lines of the magnetic field, of flux density B, in which the magnet is immersed. The equilibrium position of the magnet is one in which its axis is parallel with the flux lines and its N pole is to the right of O. When the magnet is displaced an angle β from equilibrium, it will experience a restoring torque τ given by (17–5–1) as $\tau = -MB \sin \beta$ where we use the minus sign to indicate that the torque is a restoring torque.

Figure 17–8–1. Magnetometer magnet with its axis making an angle β with the flux lines of the magnetic field in which it is immersed. The magnetic field is uniform over the length of the magnet.

There is no requirement here that the poles of the magnet be point poles or even that we know or be able to find out their distribution in the magnet. It is required only that the magnet have a sufficiently large magnetic moment M for the purposes of the experimental measurements which follow, and that the magnetic moment is not altered by the magnetic field in which the magnet is immersed.

If β is small, we may replace $\sin \beta$ by β (expressed in radians) and have

$$\tau = -MB\beta \qquad (17\text{–}8\text{–}1)$$

Equation (17–8–1) says that the restoring torque is proportional to the angular displacement, and thus the magnet will oscillate back and forth about its equilibrium position in angular harmonic motion. It will be a damped angular harmonic motion, but the air damping is small. Thus we may use the formula from mechanics for the period T of an undamped angular harmonic motion, $T = 2\pi\sqrt{-\beta'/\alpha'}$ where β' is the angular displacement at a particular instant and α' is the angular acceleration at that instant.

Let J represent the moment of inertia of the bar magnet about the fiber as an axis of rotation. Use (17–8–1) as the unbalanced torque, since we are neglecting air friction and the restoring torque of the fiber. Then, from Newton's second law for rotational motion, $-MB\beta = J\alpha$, or

$$\beta = -J\alpha/MB, \quad \text{so} \quad T = 2\pi\sqrt{J/MB} \qquad (17\text{–}8\text{–}2)$$

If the periods T_1 and T_2, of oscillation of the same magnet are measured in two different fields of flux densities B_1 and B_2 we have

$$T_1/T_2 = \sqrt{B_2/B_1} \qquad (17\text{–}8\text{–}3)$$

Then, if the flux density of one field is known, that of the other may be computed without knowing either the magnetic moment or moment of inertia of the magnet.

This comparison assumes that the magnetic fields are horizontal, or at least it is the horizontal components that are being compared. If it is the earth's magnetic field that is being compared at two places, a dip needle will give the direction of the field, and B may be computed from a comparison of the horizontal components.

17–9 THE MAGNETIC CIRCUIT

The general problem of finding values of H and B in magnetized materials is very complicated, and one which we shall not attempt to solve. However, magnetic flux lines are always closed lines (see footnote Sec. 14–3) and this fact simplifies a class of problems, known as magnetic circuit problems, to a point where approximate solutions may be obtained without too much trouble. Fortunately this class of problems includes many which are very important in physics and engineering. We wish now to consider the method of attack on magnetic circuit problems and to solve a few simple ones.

A magnetic circuit is the region occupied by magnetic flux lines, and a magnetic circuit is always a closed path because magnetic flux lines are always closed lines. Although nothing flows along magnetic flux lines, we are helped considerably in thinking about magnetic circuits if we compare them to d-c electric circuits. In the comparison, magnetic flux is analogous to current, mmf (see latter part of Sec. 16–9) is analogous to emf, and we invent a quantity called *reluctance* which is analogous to resistance.

For an electric circuit we insulate the wires. There are no perfect electrical insulators, but the materials in common use are so good in this respect that we are usually justified in assuming that all current follows the wire paths that we provide. No such happy situation exists for magnetic circuits because there are no magnetic insulators. Magnetic flux lines will penetrate any medium. Hence, when we want flux lines to follow a particular circuit, the best we can do is to offer a path of high permeability and most of the flux lines will follow it. Any flux lines which do not follow the desired path are said to be *flux leakage* lines, and flux leakage is a much more serious problem in a well-designed magnetic circuit than are leakage currents in a well-designed electric circuit. A toroid, with the magnetizing windings closely spaced over the whole circumference of a soft ferromagnetic core has essentially all its magnetic flux confined to the core, as we have seen. If the conduction current that magnetizes the core were a sheet of current, instead of discrete currents in individual turns of wire, the magnetic flux would all be confined to the core. However, such a toroid cannot be realized in practice. Further, the wire-wound toroid described above does not meet all the other design requirements for instruments and machines, and thus more complicated magnetic circuits are required.

Figure 17–9–1 shows a slightly more complicated magnetic circuit made of a soft ferromagnetic material such as a good grade of transformer silicon steel. The magnetizing windings are concentrated on one small part of the magnetic circuit and some magnetic flux lines are shown by dotted lines. Three flux leakage lines are indicated, and only one of the many magnetic flux lines which follow all the way around the prescribed circuit is shown.

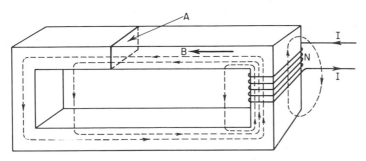

Figure 17–9–1. A ferromagnetic material forming a magnetic circuit. Three leakage flux lines are shown and, of the many flux lines which follow the prescribed magnetic circuit, only one is shown.

In order to solve magnetic circuits we make various assumptions, and the answers obtained for problems are good only to the extent that the assumptions are valid. First, we assume that all magnetic flux lines follow the prescribed circuit. (More rigorous calculations make approximate corrections for flux leakage.) Second, we assume that we may use an average value for the permeability μ and that we may take this value from the magnetization curve without worrying about the complicated changes in μ throughout a hysteresis cycle. Third, we assume that we may use average values of H and B over a cross section and throughout a length of the circuit for purposes of calculation.

If there are N turns of wire on the magnetic circuit (as in Fig. 17–9–1) and each carries a current I, we have for any path around the magnetic circuit

$$\oint \boldsymbol{H} \cdot \boldsymbol{ds} = NI \tag{17–9–1}$$

from Ampere's circuital law of (16–9–3). By our assumption, we may treat

H as an average value around the magnetic circuit. Hence if l is the average length around the magnetic circuit,

$$\oint \boldsymbol{H} \cdot \boldsymbol{ds} = Hl \qquad (17\text{–}9\text{–}2)$$

is the mmf for the circuit. Then, from (17–9–1) and (17–9–2),

$$Hl = NI \quad \text{or} \quad H = NI/l \qquad (17\text{–}9\text{–}3)$$

But $\Phi = BA = \mu HA$, where A is the area of cross section of the circuit (see Fig. 17–9–1). Hence, $\Phi = \mu NIA/l$. Let us write this equation as

$$\Phi = (NI)/(l/\mu A) \qquad (17\text{–}9\text{–}4)$$

Equation (17–9–4) is called the magnetic circuit equation where NI is the mmf and the denominator is called the *reluctance* $\mathscr{R}$ of the magnetic circuit. Thus, the magnetic circuit equation is written

$$\Phi = \text{mmf}/\mathscr{R} \qquad (17\text{–}9\text{–}5)$$

The analogous electric circuit equation for a d-c circuit, with only resistance and a source, is $I = \text{emf}/R$. If we write σ, the conductivity of a wire, as the reciprocal of ρ, the resistivity, we have for the resistance of a wire $R = l/\sigma A$ where l is the length of the wire and A its area of cross section. Thus we have a close analogy between resistance and reluctance

$$\mathscr{R} = l/\mu A \qquad (17\text{–}9\text{–}6)$$

However, the conductivity σ of a wire is independent of current at a fixed temperature, whereas the permeability μ of a ferromagnetic material is a complicated function of the flux density even though we have decided to use the μ obtained from the magnetization curve and ignore the complications of the hysteresis cycle.

1. Magnetic circuit with air gap. As a slightly more complicated case, let us consider a ferromagnetic circuit with an air gap in it, as shown in Fig. 17–9–2, where l_i is the length of the magnetic circuit in the ferromagnetic material and l_g is the length of the air gap. Let H_i be the value of H in the ferromagnetic material and H_g its value in the air gap. We have for the mmf

$$\text{mmf} = \oint \boldsymbol{H} \cdot \boldsymbol{ds} = H_i l_i + H_g l_g = NI \qquad (17\text{–}9\text{–}7)$$

Let A_g be the area of cross section of the magnetic circuit at the air gap. Area of the cross section of the air gap A_g will be somewhat larger than A, the area of cross section of the ferromagnetic part of the circuit, because the magnetic lines will spread out in the gap. The spreading of the flux lines is called fringing, and the fringing makes A_g rather indeterminate. If, however, l_g^2 is small compared with A, then A_g is nearly equal to A. Let B_g be the flux density in the gap and B_i be the flux density in the ferromagnetic material. Since the number of flux lines, Φ, is the same at all cross sections, $B_g = \Phi/A_g$ and $B_i = \Phi/A$. Since the permeability in the gap is essentially μ_0 and that in the ferromagnetic material is μ, we have

$$H_g = \Phi/\mu_0 A_g \quad \text{and} \quad H_i = \Phi/\mu A \qquad (17\text{–}9\text{–}8)$$

Put these values of H into (17–9–7), and obtain

$$\Phi = NI/(l_i/\mu A + l_g/\mu_0 A_g) = NI/(\mathscr{R}_i + \mathscr{R}_g) \qquad (17\text{–}9\text{–}9)$$

for the magnetic circuit equation. You will note that reluctances in series in a magnetic circuit add arithmetically as do resistances in series in an electric circuit. It can be shown (see Problem 17–20) that, for magnetic paths in parallel in a magnetic circuit, reluctances add by the reciprocal relation used for resistances in parallel in a d-c electric circuit.

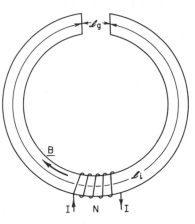

To see the disadvantage of even a small air gap in a magnetic circuit, let us compute the ratio of the reluctance of the air gap to the total reluctance, in Fig. 17–9–2, for a particular numerical example. Let us say that the length of the air gap is one-fiftieth of the length of the magnetic circuit in the ferromagnetic material or $l_i = 50l_g$. Also let us say that $A_g = A$ and that the relative permeability of the ferromagnetic

Figure 17–9–2. Magnetic circuit with an air gap.

material is 1500 under the existing conditions. Then, if $\mathscr{R}$ is the total reluctance of the circuit,

$$\mathscr{R} = \mathscr{R}_i + \mathscr{R}_g = 50l_g/1500\mu_0 A + l_g/\mu_0 A, \quad \text{or} \quad \mathscr{R}_g/\mathscr{R} = 30/31$$

Hence the air gap offers the major portion of the total reluctance, and a much larger mmf is required for the same magnetic flux than would be required if there were no air gap in the magnetic circuit. However, we know that air gaps are essential in the operation of such machines as motors and generators in order for the rotor to be free to turn. As we pointed out in the discussion of these machines, the air gaps are kept to the minimum necessary for mechanical clearance, and the reason now becomes apparent.

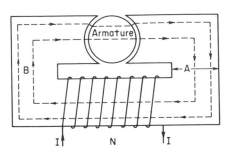

2. NUMERICAL EXAMPLE. Consider the magnetic circuit for the d-c motor shown in cross section in Fig. 17–9–3. Two representative magnetic flux lines are shown dotted in the magnetic circuit. The total average length of the

Figure 17–9–3. Magnetic circuit for a simple d-c motor.

magnetic circuit in the silicon steel used for the ferromagnetic part of the circuit (including the armature) is 1.5 m, and the area of cross section of the ferromagnetic part of the circuit is 250 cm². Each air gap is 0.30 cm long and may be considered to have the same effective area of cross section as the ferromagnetic material. The silicon steel is the same as that for which the magnetization and permeability curves were drawn in Fig. 17–1–2 and 17–1–3 (the magnetization curve is the one that you drew from the data in Problem 17–3). The magnetic flux density at the armature is 0.80 weber/m².

(a) What is the total reluctance of the magnetic circuit? Let $\mathscr{R}_g$ represent the reluctance of the two air gaps in series, and

$$\mathscr{R}_g = l_g/\mu_0 A_g = 19.1 \times 10^4 \text{ amp turns/wb}$$

The flux density in the steel must be the same as in the air gap, since the total flux Φ is the same and their areas of cross section are considered equal. From the magnetization curve of Fig. 17–1–2 (or the one for Problem 17–3) when $B = 0.80$ wb/m², $H = 110$ amp turns/m. Hence from Fig. 17–1–3 (or from $\mu = B/H$), $\mu = 7.3 \times 10^{-3}$ henry/meter.

$$\mathscr{R}_i = l_i/\mu A_i = 0.82 \times 10^4 \text{ amp turns/wb}$$

and $\mathscr{R} = \mathscr{R}_g + \mathscr{R}_i = 19.1 \times 10^4 + 0.82 \times 10^4 = 20 \times 10^4$ amp turns/wb

We write $\mathscr{R}$ as 20×10^4 amp turns/wb (instead of 19.9×10^4) because the accuracy of our information and method does not permit us to distinguish between the two numbers, and the former is easier to use.

(b) If there are 200 turns of wire on the field winding, what current I is flowing through the wires of the winding? Here $\Phi = BA = 0.020$ weber and mmf $= \Phi\mathscr{R} = 4000$ amp turns. But mmf $= NI$, so $I = \text{mmf}/N = 20$ amp.

(c) What flux density will be produced by a current of 25 amp flowing in the field winding? Because of the air gaps, this is not so simple a problem as the previous one. Such is the case because μ for the silicon steel depends on the flux density and the flux density is unknown. If there were no air gaps, the uniform area of cross section would permit us to use $Hl = \text{mmf}$ for the computation of H, and then we could read B from the magnetization curve. Thus we must solve this problem by a cut and try method.

We have seen above that the reluctance of the air gap is the dominant reluctance in the circuit, and this reluctance is not altered by a change in the flux density. Let us estimate, then, that the total reluctance of the magnetic circuit will not be altered markedly by a change of 25% in the magnetizing current, especially since we have flux densities near the knee of the magnetization curve. Hence, for a first try, let us assume that the total reluctance remains constant at 20×10^4 amp turns/weber, and compute the flux density that would result from a magnetizing current of 25 amp, i.e., $\Phi = \text{mmf}/\mathscr{R} = NI/\mathscr{R} = 0.025$ weber. Then $B = \Phi/A = 1.0$ weber/m².

With the above as a guide let us *guess* that the magnetic flux density will be 1.0 wb/m² when the magnetizing current is 25 amp and check our guess. From the magnetization curve of Fig. 17–1–2 (or Problem 17–3), when B is 1.0 wb/m², H is 187 amp turns/m. Thus, μ is 5.34×10^{-3} henry/m from $\mu = B/H$. Then $\mathscr{R}_i = l_i/\mu A_i = 1.12 \times 10^4$ amp turn/wb. Then $\mathscr{R} = \mathscr{R}_g + \mathscr{R}_i = 19 \times 10^4 + 1 \times 10^4 = 20 \times 10^4$ amp turns/wb, and $\Phi = BA = 1.0 \times 0.025 = 0.025$ wb. From this value of Φ we can compute the mmf from mmf $= \Phi\mathscr{R} = 0.025 \times 20 \times 10^4 = 5000$ amp turns.

This value of mmf checks with the $NI = 5000$ amp turns furnished by the magnetizing windings when the magnetizing current is 25 amp. Thus, within the accuracy of our calculation, the flux density is 1.0 wb/m² when the magnetizing current is 25 amp. If the two values of mmf had not checked, we would have revised our guess as to the value of B, in the light of our new information, and recomputed to test our guess. Usually the calculation will not check on the first try (see Problem 17–19), but the above example illustrates the method of approach.

PROBLEMS

17–1 Explain how the circuit in Fig. 17–P–1 can be used to calibrate a ballistic galvanometer BG, which is subsequently to be used to measure the change in the magnetic flux linking its search coil SC. In the calibration process SC is far removed from, while electrically in series with, the rest of the secondary circuit, so no magnetic flux from another part of the circuit links it. Derive the equation $Q = M\Delta i/R$, where R is the total resistance of the secondary circuit and Q is the quantity of electricity that flows in the secondary circuit due to the change Δi in the primary current. The secondary resistance R is large enough so that the galvanometer experiences only small damping. Outline a procedure which makes the equation a suitable one and discuss whether or not the logarithmic decrement need be measured and used. Specify the quantities you would plot as abscissa and as ordinate on your calibration curve.

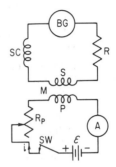

Figure 17–P–1. Calibration circuit for a ballistic galvanometer BG using a standard air-core mutual inductor M whose primary coil is P and secondary coil is S. The value of M is known from the dial reading.

17–2 You are to determine the magnetization curve of a ferromagnetic material which fills the core of a solenoid. The solenoid is *very* long compared to its diameter. Tell how you would carry out this experiment using the BG and search coil secondary circuit calibrated in Problem 17–1. Assume that the search coil is of suitable size and shape for the use that you specify for it. Draw the *complete* circuit diagram.

17–3 Table 17–1 gives the values of H and the corresponding values of B for the silicon steel magnetization curve plotted in Fig. 17–1–2. Plot the magnetization curve from these data over the range shown in Fig. 17–1–2. For each value of H, and its corresponding value of B, compute the permeability μ, relative permeability μ_r, susceptibility χ, and intensity of magnetization $\mathscr{I}$, and present the results in tabular form. (a) Show graphically the functional relationship between intensity of magnetization (as ordinate) and magnetic field intensity for all data in the table. Do this with two graphs on the same page, using the same scale for $\mathscr{I}$ in both. For the first graph adopt an enlarged scale for H, such as 1 cm on the graph paper represents 100 amp turns/m. For the second graph use a diminished scale, such as 1 cm on the graph paper represents 5000 amp turns/m. What is the value of H at which the silicon steel becomes saturated? In terms of Amperian current loops, what is meant by the saturation of the silicon steel? (b) What

TABLE 17–1

DATA FOR MAGNETIZATION OF A SAMPLE OF SILICON STEEL

(Courtesy of United States Steel)

H is in amp turn/m and B in wb/m²					
H	B	H	B	H	B
0.8	0.0008	79.6	0.660	2,000	1.42
3.2	0.0052	120	0.84	3,180	1.49
8.0	0.0192	159	0.94	4,780	1.55
15.9	0.060	240	1.08	6,380	1.60
23.9	0.140	318	1.16	7,960	1.65
31.8	0.240	477	1.24	15,800	1.81
47.8	0.410	637	1.28	20,000	1.86
63.6	0.540	800	1.32	31,900	1.94
71.6	0.610	1,580	1.41	79,600	2.03

is the magnetic flux density, due to the silicon steel only, at saturation of
the silicon steel? [*Ans:* 1.90 wb/m².]

17–4 Table 17–2 gives the data for the part of the hysteresis loop of Fig. 17–2–1,
which is labeled bcB_RH_Cde. Since the part bCB_R is the same (but inverted)
as the part efg, and the part B_RH_Cde is the same (but inverted) as the part
$ghjb$, the whole hysteresis loop can be plotted from these data. (a) Plot the
entire hysteresis loop and compare your curve with the one in Fig. 17–2–1.
Use the largest convenient scale that an $8\frac{1}{2}$ by 11 in. sheet of graph paper will
permit, since you will need the curve in Problem 17–7 for graphical analysis.
(b) Permeability (given by $\mu = B/H$) of a ferromagnetic material is not a
useful quantity for calculation in a situation any more complicated than
that described by a magnetization curve. However, it is interesting to see
the graphical representation of the functional relationship between μ and H
for a normal hysteresis loop. Compute the value of μ for a large number of
points distributed around the hysteresis loop and plot the curve showing
μ as a function of H.

TABLE 17–2

DATA FOR HYSTERESIS LOOP OF A SAMPLE OF SILICON STEEL

(Courtesy of United States Steel)

H is in amp turn/m and B in wb/m²					
H	B	H	B	H	B
171	1.000	0	0.490	− 32	−0.180
160	0.991	− 8	0.390	− 40	−0.330
140	0.980	−12	0.310	− 60	−0.570
120	0.961	−16	0.220	− 80	−0.705
100	0.935	−20	0.120	−100	−0.805
80	0.895	−24	0.040	−120	−0.880
60	0.844	−26	0.00	−140	−0.935
40	0.770	−27	−0.05	−160	−0.980
20	0.670	−28	−0.08	−171	−1.000

17–5 Compute the Amperian surface current density j_a for the silicon steel ring for each value of H and B given in Table 17–2 and, from these data, plot j_a as a function of H around the hysteresis loop.

17–6 Show that the "area" (in units of B times H) enclosed in the hysteresis loop has the unit of joules/m³.

17–7 (a) Find the hysteresis power loss per unit volume for the silicon steel of Problem 17–4 if it is used in the core of a transformer operating on 60 cycles/sec alternating current, and the transformer is so designed that the maximum flux density is 1.00 wb/m². [*Ans:* About 5600 w/m³.] (b) If the density of this silicon steel is 7.55 g/cm³, what is the hysteresis power loss in watts/pound? [*Ans:* About 0.34 w/lb.]

17–8 (a) Express the hysteresis energy loss, for one trip around the hysteresis loop, in terms of the intensity of magnetization $\mathscr{I}$ and the magnetic field intensity H. [*Ans:* $W = v\mu_0 \oint H \, d\mathscr{I}$.] (b) Determine the hysteresis energy loss per unit volume, for one trip around the hysteresis loop, using the result above and the curve plotted in Problem 17–5. Check your answer against the result obtained in Problem 17–7 for the same quantity.

17–9 A certain toroidal inductor wound on a wooden core has a self-inductance of 0.535 mh. An identical toroidal inductor wound on a core of silicon steel of the same kind as that referred to in Problem 17–3 has under a particular set of conditions, a self-inductance of 3.21 henrys. The mean circumference of each toroid is 0.654 m and each has 1200 turns of wire. What are the particular conditions, referred to above, which must be satisfied? [*Ans:* If you specify the correct conditions, the current in the winding of the toroid with the silicon-steel core must be either 0.0173 amp or 0.0565 amp.]

17–10 For the silicon steel of Problems 17–4 and 17–7, tests show that the exponent n of Steinmetz' equation has the value 1.6 in the range of B_m from 0.4 to 1.2 wb/m². (a) What is the value of the Steinmetz coefficient η for this material? (b) What is the hysteresis power loss in a transformer core, made of this silicon steel, when the maximum magnetic flux density in each cycle is 1.2 wb/m²? The volume of the core is 0.45 m³, and the transformer is operating on a 60 cycles/sec a-c line. [*Ans:* 3.4 kw.] (c) What would be the hysteresis power loss in the core of the same transformer operating with the same B_m but on a 25 cycles/sec a-c line?

17–11 An alnico magnet is uniformly magnetized with an intensity of magnetization of 1.0×10^6 amp/m. It is a cylindrical bar with an area of cross section of 1.80 cm² and a length of 20 cm. In the following, substitute units with numerical quantities and show that the proper unit results for the answer. (a) What torque will this magnet experience when its axis is at right angles to the earth's magnetic field at a place where B of the earth's field is 0.62×10^{-4} wb/m²? [*Ans:* 0.0022 meter newton.] (b) What is the pole strength of the magnet? (c) What force does the earth's field exert on each pole?

17–12 Two magnets, each 20 cm long, lie along opposite sides of a square in air and with their magnetic moments parallel but oppositely directed. The square is 20 cm on a side. The magnet on the upper side of the square has its magnetic moment directed toward the left and has a pole strength of

200 amp m. The magnet on the lower side of the square has a pole strength of 20 amp m. Assume that each of the four poles may be treated as a point pole and that the intensity of magnetization of neither magnet is altered by the presence of the other magnet. Use (17–7–7) to find the magnetic flux density at the center of the square. Substitute units with numerical quantities and show that the proper unit results for the answer. [*Ans:* 1.27×10^{-3} wb/m² parallel to the axes of the magnets and directed toward the right.]

17–13 A permanent cylindrical bar magnet made of platinum-cobalt alloy has a cross-sectional area of 0.50 cm² and a length of 30 cm. When it is at right angles to a magnetic field in air whose flux density is 0.045 weber/m², it experiences a torque of 0.243 meter newton. (a) If the magnet can be considered to be uniformly magnetized, what is its intensity of magnetization? [*Ans:* 36×10^4 amp/m.] (b) The platinum-cobalt alloy has a coercive force of 2.11×10^5 amp/m, which is among the highest for permanent magnets. Is it likely that the above external applied field will alter the intensity of magnetization of the magnet?

17–14 See footnotes in Secs. 17–6 and 17–7. (a) Starting with (17–7–8), show that the same formula in Kennelly units is $F = m_{1K}m_{2K}/4\pi\mu_0 r^2$. (b) A certain magnet has a pole strength of 20 amp m. Express this pole strength both in weber (Kennelly mks) and in UP (emu). Substitute units with numerical quantities and show that the proper unit results for the answer. [*Ans:* $m_K = 25.1 \times 10^{-6}$ wb, $m_{emu} = 200$ UP.] (c) The magnet in part (b) is 30 cm long. Express its magnetic moment in the emu system and also in Kennelly and Sommerfeld units in the mks system. Put the proper units on each of the three answers.

17–15 A magnet, whose magnetic moment is 0.600 amp m², is suspended by a torsionless silk fiber in the earth's magnetic field at a place where the horizontal component of the magnetic flux density is 150×10^{-7} wb/m². It is given a small displacement and oscillates with a period of 10.0 sec. (a) What is the moment of inertia of the magnet for rotation about an axis which is perpendicular to the axis of the magnet and through its center of mass? Substitute units with numerical quantities and show that the proper unit comes out in the answer. [*Ans:* 2.28×10^{-5} kg m².] (b) At another location in the earth's field the magnet has a period of 12.5 sec, and a dip needle shows that the dip angle (angle with the horizontal) is 63°. What is the magnetic flux density of the earth's field at this new location? [*Ans:* 0.212×10^{-4} wb/m².]

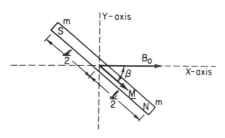

Figure 17–P–2. Bar magnet in a non-uniform magnetic field.

17–16 The non-uniform field in which the bar magnet of Fig. 17–P–2 is immersed has the value B_0 at the origin and is parallel to the X-axis everywhere along the X-axis. Over the limited region where the magnet is located, B increases in the positive x direction at the constant space rate $\partial B_x/\partial x$. On the X-axis, B_y is everywhere zero but the

Y-component of B increases on either side of the X-axis with the constant space rate $\partial B_y/\partial y$ where $\partial B_y/\partial y = -\partial B_x/\partial x$. $B_z = 0$ and $\partial B_z/\partial z = 0$ everywhere in the region under consideration. Show that the net force of *translation* on the bar magnet is given by $F = i\,\partial B_x/\partial x\,M\cos\beta + j\,\partial B_y/\partial y\,M\sin\beta$, where $M = ml$ is the magnitude of the magnetic moment of the magnet [see (17–6–1)]. (Compare with Fig. 17–6–1 where the magnet experiences a rotational torque but no translational force.) What is the direction of this force in the situation pictured? What would be its direction if the magnet were turned so the N and S poles were interchanged in Fig. 17–P–2?

17–17 A single well-collimated beam of silver atoms is projected perpendicular to the page and down into the page along the Z-axis in Fig. 17–P–2. (The whole region of the experiment is inside a well-evacuated container.) It is observed that the non-uniform magnetic field of Fig. 17–P–2 splits the single beam of silver atoms into two well-defined and separate beams of atoms. One of the two beams goes to the left of the origin in the figure and one to the right. The deflection of one of these two beams is found experimentally to be due to a net translational force given by $F = i\,\partial B_x/\partial x\,M$ and the other by $F = -i\,\partial B_x/\partial x\,M$. Each silver atom has an effective magnetic moment M of one Bohr magneton [see (16–P–1) of Problem 16–4]. What is the meaning of the fact that there are two well-defined and separate beams of silver atoms and that their deflections can be accounted for by the net translational forces given above, instead of simply a broadening of the incoming beam by the field? The reasoning in Problem 17–16 and its interpretation here is the basis for the famous Stern-Gerlach* experiment and its significance.

17–18 A magnetic circuit is made up entirely of the silicon steel of Problem 17–3. The average length of the circuit is 1.2 m, and the area of cross section is uniform throughout the length and has a value of 100 cm². The magnetizing winding has 150 turns of wire. (a) What magnetizing current must flow in the winding in order to have a magnetic flux density of 0.30 wb/m² in the silicon steel? [*Ans:* 0.32 amp.] (b) What is the magnetic flux through the core if the magnetizing current is 1.5 amp? [*Ans:* 0.010 wb.]

17–19 A magnetic circuit has a mean length of 3.0 m of the silicon steel of Problem 17–3 and an air gap of 0.10 cm length. The area of cross section is 100 cm² and the air gap may be treated as having the same area. There are 500 turns of wire on the magnetizing winding. (a) What is the current in the magnetizing winding if the flux density in the air gap is 0.43 wb/m²? [*Ans:* 1.0 amp.] (b) What is the flux density in the air gap if the magnetizing current is 3.0 amp? [*Ans:* 1.05 wb/m².]

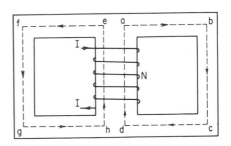

Figure 17–P–3. Magnetic circuit with two branches in parallel.

17–20 Using the magnetic circuit in Figure 17–P–3 show that $1/\mathscr{R}$

* See any book on atomic physics, for example Weidner and Sells, *Elementary Modern Physics* (Boston: Allyn and Bacon, Inc., 1960), pp. 235–36.

$= 1/\mathscr{R}_1 + 1/\mathscr{R}_2$, where $\mathscr{R}_1$ is the reluctance of the path *abcda*, $\mathscr{R}_2$ is the reluctance of the path *efghe*, and $\mathscr{R}$ is the equivalent reluctance of the two branches in parallel.

17-21 The magnetizing winding on the center leg of the magnetic circuit in Fig. 17–P–3 has 1000 turns, and the flux density in this center leg is 1.2 wb/m². The area of cross section of the center leg is 103 cm² and that of each side branch is 51.5 cm². The mean length of each path, *abcda* and *efghe*, is 91 cm. The magnetic circuit is made of the same silicon steel as that of Problem 17–3. What is the current flowing in the magnetizing winding? [*Ans:* 0.36 amp.]

17-22 (a) Show that the total magnetic energy in a magnetic circuit is $\frac{1}{2}\mathscr{R}\Phi^2$. (b) What is the total magnetic energy in the magnetic circuit of Problem 17–19, part (b)? Substitute units with numerical quantities and show that the proper unit results for the answer. [*Ans:* 7.9 joules.] (c) How much of the energy of part (b) is in the air gap? In the silicon steel? [*Ans:* In air gap, 4.4 joules.]

17-23 In Sec. 17–9 just prior to (17–9–1) we made three assumptions concerning magnetic circuits and, on the basis of these assumptions, we set up the method of calculation for magnetic circuits. List the three assumptions and under each one enumerate the ways in which the actual conditions in a magnetic circuit may differ from the ideal conditions postulated by that assumption.

THE SINGLE-PHASE

XVIII

TRANSFORMER

18–1 INTRODUCTION

A transformer is an instrument of many uses, some of which we shall point out in this chapter. However, its greatest use probably arises from the fact that it can step alternating voltages either up or down, and we shall be chiefly concerned with this property. First let us look at the construction of a simple transformer and see qualitatively how it can have a voltage output from its secondary that differs from the voltage input to its primary.

Figure 18–1–1 shows a schematic diagram of a simple transformer. It consists of the primary winding P which is connected to the a-c line, the secondary winding S which is connected to the load, and the ferromagnetic material which makes up the magnetic circuit. Both P and S are wound on the ferromagnetic material as shown in Fig. 18–1–1 and insulated electrically from it. The magnetic circuit is the link between P and S. We shall confine our attention to transformers which have ferromag-

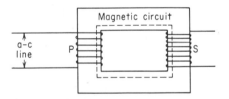

Figure 18–1–1. Schematic diagram of a transformer showing the primary winding P and the secondary winding S. These windings are on a ferromagnetic core which makes up the magnetic circuit and are electrically insulated from the magnetic circuit and from each other.

netic material for their magnetic circuits, although air core transformers have a wide field of usefulness in communication circuits.

Since the primary is connected to an a-c line, the current in P is continually changing in a cyclic fashion. This changing current sets up a changing mmf, which causes the magnetic flux in the core to change cyclically. The changing flux induces emf's in both the primary and the secondary windings. The emf induced in the primary is the familiar emf of self-induction, and that induced in the secondary is the equally familiar emf of mutual induction. Either coil might be used as the primary and the other as the secondary. The ferromagnetic material in the core adds the magnetic flux due to its Amperian current loops to that of the conduction current in the winding, and as we have seen, a large core flux results from a relatively small conduction current.

Consider the situation when the secondary has an open circuit and thus no secondary current flows although a secondary emf exists. A primary current flows because the primary offers a complete circuit, and this primary current (at zero secondary current) is called the *exciting current*. We shall represent the rms (or effective) value of the exciting current by I_E and its instantaneous value by i_E. The magnitude of the exciting current is such that, at every instant, the primary emf of self-induction plus the $i_E R_1$ drop in potential is (by Kirchhoff's second law) equal to the applied line voltage at that instant. Here R_1 is the resistance of the wires of the primary winding. As stated above, it is the changing mmf (due to the changing i_E) which causes the changing flux linkages with the secondary and thus induces the secondary emf.

Since the magnitude of the secondary emf is determined by Faraday's law, it depends on both the number of turns of wire on the secondary and the rate of change of the magnetic flux linking the secondary. Thus for a given rate of change of flux, the secondary emf may be made either large or small by making the number of turns of wire on the secondary either large or small. This is the physical reason why the emf of the secondary can differ from the primary voltage. If the transformer delivers a secondary emf which is larger than the primary line voltage, the transformer is said to be a step-up transformer. Conversely, if the secondary emf is smaller than the applied line voltage, the transformer is said to be a step-down transformer. Let us see briefly some of the reasons why the ability of a transformer to change voltage is important.

Because of insulation problems and hazards to personnel, alternating current for power distribution systems is usually generated at relatively low voltage. Alternators for such distribution systems usually have emf's in the range from 6600 to 13,200 v. On the other hand, for power distribution to loads far removed from the generating station, it is essential that high line voltage (and corresponding low line current) be used in order to minimize $I^2 R$ power loss on the distribution line. (The saving due to high-voltage transmission was illustrated in a small way for direct current by Problem 2–42, and the same principle applies here much magnified in its commercial importance.) As an example of a very high line voltage, the transmission line from Hoover Dam to Los Angeles is a 287,000 v line, and in the caption for Fig. 10–7–3 we pointed out some of the design work now going on for high voltage lines. For shorter distances of transmission, the voltage of the line is much below this value. In almost any case a step-up transformer is required between the alternator and the line. When it comes to consumption, the voltage again must be low for reasons of insulation and safety of personnel. It may be a few hundred volts in a factory, and 120 v is common in a home. Hence, a transformer (usually several) is required between the line and the load. Alternating current distribution is used so extensively today because the transformer makes it easy to change the voltage wherever a change is required. The structural simplicity, dependability, and efficiency of a transformer are also important factors in the role that the transformer has played in the growth of a-c power distribution and use.

In addition to power distribution, transformers have a wide variety of uses in communication networks and elsewhere. It is probable that the transformer is more widely used than any other single kind of electrical machine. In Problem 18–1 you are asked to list uses of the transformer which have come to your attention.

As we have seen, the physical reason why the secondary emf of a transformer can differ from the applied line voltage is a simple one. However, in a quantitative discussion of transformer theory, certain complications arise, which we enumerate here. Ideally, all magnetic flux lines link all turns of both the primary and the secondary. But, as we pointed out in Sec. 17–9 (see Fig. 17–9–1), even the best magnetic circuit has some magnetic flux leakage. This means that there are magnetic flux lines which link some or all of the primary turns but do not link the secondary turns. Similarly, when a current flows in the secondary, there are magnetic flux lines which link some or all of the secondary turns but do not link the primary turns. A few such flux leakage lines are shown in Fig. 18–1–2.

Also, ideally, all electrical power delivered as input to the primary of the transformer is delivered as electrical power output from the secondary. However, in actual transformers, there is power loss in both windings due to the I^2R heating in the copper of the wires and known as the copper loss. Further, there are hysteresis and eddy current power losses in the ferromagnetic core as we have seen in Secs. 15–4 and 17–3, and such losses are known as core losses. Additional complications arise because of the hysteresis behavior in the ferromagnetic core in that the flux in the core lags behind the mmf and is not a single-valued function of the mmf.

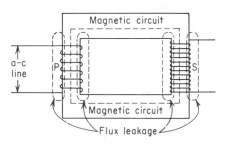

Figure 18–1–2. Magnetic flux leakage lines in the magnetic circuit of a transformer.

Further, the distributed capacitance of the windings causes complications. For all these reasons, a general, detailed, and exact mathematical treatment of the theory of a transformer is extremely complex.

However, the situation is not so dark as would appear from the above. Very satisfactory answers can be obtained for many problems by ignoring all these complications and considering that the transformer is ideal. This type of treatment is permissible in such problems because transformer design has minimized the above complications in the following manner:

1. By proper choice of structural design of the magnetic circuit and by proper location and winding of the primary and secondary coils, flux leakage can be kept to a small fraction of the total flux.

2. The resistances of the wires which make up P and S can be kept small enough so that the IR drop in potential is small compared with the applied voltage on the primary side and with the induced emf on the secondary side.

3. Ferromagnetic materials, with small areas enclosed in their hysteresis loops, have been developed to minimize hysteresis loss.

4. Proper lamination of the core minimizes eddy current loss. The success

of (2), (3), and (4) is shown by the fact that most transformers have efficiencies at full load in the range from 90 to 99%.

5. The fact that the hysteresis loop has small area also means that the magnetic flux does not lag seriously behind the mmf and becomes more nearly a single-valued function of the mmf.

6. At power frequencies and the lower communication frequencies, the effect of the distributed capacitance of the windings is negligibly small. At the higher frequencies, however, the distributed capacitance may make the transformer behave in a very different fashion from that predicted by simple theory. Our discussion will have to do with transformer behavior at low frequencies only.

In those problems where the accuracy required does not permit the transformer to be considered ideal, methods have been developed to correct approximately for the deviation of a real transformer from the ideal. The extent and nature of the correction to be made depends on the demands of the problem. Thus the mode of attack is essentially one of successive approximations, with experience often telling the computer which of the above listed factors requires the most attention in a particular situation.

Our discussion will be one in which we consider an ideal transformer first and then use some of the methods by which ideal transformer theory is corrected to take approximate account of the behavior of real transformers. Our treatment is limited to the simpler and more important aspects of single phase transformers with ferromagnetic cores and you should consult a book devoted primarily to transformers when more difficult problems arise.*

18–2 IDEAL TRANSFORMER

For an ideal transformer it is assumed that:

1. The electrical power input to the primary is equal to the electrical power output from the secondary. Thus the copper losses and core losses are negligible.

2. All magnetic flux lines are confined to the designated ferromagnetic circuit and link all primary and all secondary turns. Thus the flux leakage is negligible.

3. The permeability of the core material is so high that a negligibly small mmf will establish the required flux in the core. Thus the exciting current is negligibly small and we shall neglect it in the equations at the same time that we use it for explanations.

4. There is no lag of the magnetic flux behind the mmf, and the flux is a linear function of the mmf.

5. There is no distributed capacitance in the windings.

Further, we shall use a sinusoidal alternating voltage applied to the primary and thus, under these ideal conditions, the currents that flow in both primary and secondary circuits are sinusoidal alternating.

It will be convenient if we collect together in one place the definitions of the symbols that we shall use. Let us adopt the following notation:

---

* For example, M.I.T. Electrical Engineering Staff, *Magnetic Circuits and Transformers* (New York: John Wiley & Sons, Inc., 1943).

v_1, V_{1m}, and V_1 represent, respectively, the instantaneous, maximum, and rms (or effective) values of the applied primary voltage. e_1, $\mathscr{E}_{1m}$, and $\mathscr{E}_1$ represent, respectively, the instantaneous, maximum, and rms values of the emf of self-induction induced in the primary. i_1, I_{1m}, and I_1 represent, respectively, the instantaneous, maximum, and rms values of the primary current. i_E, I_{Em}, and I_E represent, respectively, the instantaneous, maximum, and rms values of the primary exciting current. The exciting current in the ideal transformer is the primary current required to establish the necessary flux in the core and is assumed to be negligibly small. i_1', I_{1m}', and I_1' represent, respectively, the instantaneous, maximum, and rms values of the load current. The load current is the additional primary current that flows because a load is connected to the secondary. For an ideal transformer, this is the same as the primary current, since the exciting current is assumed to be negligible. N_1 represents the number of primary turns of wire. R_1 represents the resistance of the wire in the primary turns, and is assumed to be zero for an ideal transformer. ϕ_1 represents the phase angle between the primary current and

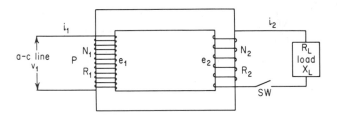

Figure 18-2-1. Ideal transformer with its primary connected to a sinusoidal a-c line and secondary connected to a load. P and S would actually be wound on the same leg of the magnetic circuit in order to minimize flux leakage, but are shown on separate legs for ease in drawing.

primary applied voltage. P_1 represents the time average electric power input to the primary.

Φ and Φ_m represent, respectively, the instantaneous and maximum values of the magnetic flux in the core. For the ideal transformer all this flux links all turns of the primary and secondary and is called the mutual flux.

e_2, $\mathscr{E}_{2m}$, and $\mathscr{E}_2$ represent, respectively, the instantaneous, maximum, and rms values of the emf induced in the secondary. i_2, I_{2m}, and I_2 represent, respectively, the instantaneous, maximum, and rms values of the secondary current. N_2 represents the number of turns of wire on the secondary. R_2 represents the resistance of the secondary winding, and is assumed to be zero for an ideal transformer. ϕ_2 represents the phase angle between the secondary current and secondary emf. P_2 represents the time average electric power output from the secondary.

Figure 18-2-1 shows a schematic diagram of the ideal transformer which we shall consider, and some of these quantities are designated on the figure.

1. VOLTAGE EQUATION FOR AN IDEAL TRANSFORMER. From Faraday's law, the emf of self-induction in the primary is

$$e_1 = -N_1 \, d\Phi/dt \qquad (18\text{-}2\text{-}1)$$

Since R_1 is zero and thus there is no i_1R_1 drop in potential, the applied line voltage is equal in magnitude and opposite in phase to e_1 at every instant. Hence

$$v_1 = N_1 \, d\Phi/dt \qquad (18\text{–}2\text{–}2)$$

Note carefully that the step from (18–2–1) to (18–2–2) changes the argument from one containing the emf of self-induction in the primary to one containing the applied primary voltage. Also, from Faraday's law,

$$e_2 = -N_2 \, d\Phi/dt \qquad (18\text{–}2\text{–}3)$$

where the $d\Phi/dt$ term is the same in (18–2–3) as it is in (18–2–1) and (18–2–2),

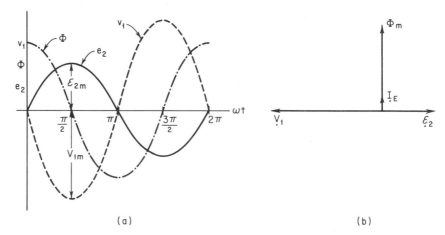

(a)   (b)

Figure 18–2–2. (a) Curves for an ideal transformer showing Φ, e_2 and v_1 as functions of time, with e_2 taken as the reference for measurement of phase. (b) Vector diagram showing the same phase relationships. I_E is assumed to be negligible for an ideal transformer but is indicated to show its phase.

because the same flux links both P and S in the ideal transformer. Divide (18–2–2) by (18–2–3), and

$$v_1/e_2 = -N_1/N_2 \qquad (18\text{–}2\text{–}4)$$

The minus sign in (18–2–4) means that v_1 and e_2 are opposite in phase (e_1 and e_2 have the same phase) as shown by Fig. 18–2–2 (a) where e_2 is taken as the reference for measurement of phase. Since we have assumed that the exciting current is sinusoidal, the mmf is sinusoidal. Then, since we have assumed that the flux is a linear function of the mmf for an ideal transformer, the flux is sinusoidal and is so drawn in Fig. 18–2–2 (a). The curves for e_2 and v_1 have been drawn to satisfy the requirements of (18–2–2), (18–2–3), and (18–2–4). In Fig. 18–2–1, the turns are drawn so that $N_1 = 2N_2$, and this ratio has been used in drawing Fig. 18–2–2. (Solve Problem 18–2 at this point.)

Since (18–2–4) is valid at every instant, it is valid at the instant when the voltage curves in Fig. 18–2–2 (a) attain their maximum values, or

$$V_{1m}/\mathscr{E}_{2m} = -N_1/N_2, \quad \text{so} \quad V_1/\mathscr{E}_2 = -N_1/N_2 \qquad (18\text{–}2\text{–}5)$$

Equation (18–2–5) is the much-used and very convenient transformer equation relating the primary and secondary voltages by the turns ratio. Notice that it is strictly true only for an ideal transformer, for we had to assume ideal transformer conditions in order to derive it. (Answer Problem 18–3 at this point.)

Since v_1 is sinusoidal and under ideal transformer conditions, Φ and e_2 are also sinusoidal, we may represent the situation of Fig. 18–2–2 (a) by use of the sort of vector diagrams employed in Chapters VII and VIII.

Let us assume that the switch SW in the secondary circuit of the transformer of Fig. 18–2–1 is open, so that no secondary current is flowing and thus the only current is the exciting current in the primary. We may draw the vector diagram of Fig. 18–2–2 (b) to represent the conditions. Although we assume that the exciting current is negligibly small we shall draw a very short vector to represent it in order to show its phase relationship to the other quantities.

2. REASON FOR A FERROMAGNETIC CORE AT LOW FREQUENCIES. If no ferromagnetic material were used for the magnetic circuit, the core loss would be zero, and any transformer would represent an ideal transformer in this respect. However, in other respects a real transformer would differ markedly from the ideal. For example, the flux leakage would be large if a medium of high permeability were not used for the magnetic circuit, and the very useful equation expressed in (18–2–5) would not be even an approximation to the actual conditions.

However, there is a more important reason for the use of a ferromagnetic core at power frequencies. Without such a core, the primary exciting current required to produce sufficient magnetic flux would be prohibitively large. We can see that this is the case by the following argument. Under ideal transformer conditions we can expresss the flux in the core, as shown by the curve in Fig. 18–2–2 (a), by the equation

$$\Phi = \Phi_m \cos \omega t \quad \text{and} \quad d\Phi/dt = -\Phi_m \omega \sin \omega t \qquad (18\text{–}2\text{–}6)$$

Then, from (18–2–2), the relationship between the applied line voltage and the flux is

$$v_1 = -N_1 \Phi_m \omega \sin \omega t \qquad (18\text{–}2\text{–}7)$$

But the amplitude of (18–2–7) must be the maximum value of the applied line voltage, so

$$V_{1m} = N_1 \Phi_m \omega = 2\pi f N_1 \Phi_m \qquad (18\text{–}2\text{–}8)$$

gives the relationship between the maximum value of the applied line voltage and the maximum value of the flux required in the core. Using the magnetic circuit equation of (17–9–4), this becomes

$$V_{1m} = 2\pi f N_1^2 I_{Em}/\mathscr{R} \qquad (18\text{–}2\text{–}9)$$

Thus, for a transformer with a fixed number N_1 of primary turns which is to operate on a line with a fixed voltage and frequency, the bigger the reluctance of the magnetic circuit the bigger the exciting current must be in order to establish the flux required by (18–2–8). Since a soft ferromagnetic material has a much higher permeability than a nonferromagnetic material, it will offer a path of much lower reluctance. Thus, much less primary exciting current will be required to establish the required flux, if the magnetic circuit is made of a soft ferromagnetic material, than will be required if it is made of a nonferromagnetic material. The magnitude of the exciting current is of vital importance commercially, for power transformers on a distribution line, because the primary is connected continuously whether power is taken from the secondary or not.

The fundamental physical reason behind this argument is, of course, that the ferromagnetic material adds many thousands of times as much magnetic flux as that set up by the exciting current alone. A very small exciting current can control the very large magnetic flux due to the core material, and a transformer with such a core becomes more nearly ideal. (Answer Problem 18–7 as an alternate explanation.)

3. CURRENT EQUATION FOR AN IDEAL TRANSFORMER. With the switch SW open in the secondary circuit of Fig. 18–2–1, the primary current is I_E. There is no power input to the primary of an ideal transformer with SW open because there is no power output from the secondary and no power is used by the transformer itself. The fact that there is no power input to the primary is shown both by the fact that I_E is 90° out of phase with V_1 [see Fig. 18–2–2 (b)] and the fact that I_E is negligibly small.

Now let us close SW, and the secondary emf causes a secondary current to flow. There is now a power output from the secondary circuit to its load; consequently, from conservation of energy, there must be a power input to the primary. In order to have a power input to the primary, I_{1m} must have increased when the secondary current started to flow, and I_{1m} must be less than 90° out of phase with V_{1m}. Let us approach this argument from another point of view and, to simplify the discussion, we shall assume that V_{1m} is constant, as it would be (very nearly) for a well regulated power transmission line.

In the first place, the applied line voltage is determined by the line, both in its maximum value and its variation with time. It is not determined by the transformer behavior, for a well-regulated line where V_{1m} is constant as we have assumed. In the second place, at every instant and on the average, the emf of self-induction in the primary must be equal and opposite to the applied line voltage, in accord with Kirchhoff's second law. Equation (18–2–8) tells the value that Φ_m must have to satisfy this requirement and, with $V_{1m}, 2\pi, f$, and N_1 fixed, Φ_m must keep a fixed value regardless of the secondary current.

When a secondary current flows, it sets up an mmf, whose maximum value is $\text{mmf}_{2m} = N_2 I_{2m}$, and this mmf would alter Φ_m if nothing happened to counteract it. But Φ_m cannot change, so a primary current I'_{1m} (in addition to I_E) must flow, and its magnitude and phase must be such that Φ_m remains constant. This requires that the mmf due to I'_{1m} must be equal and opposite to mmf_2, or

$$\text{mmf}'_{1m} = -\text{mmf}_{2m} \tag{18–2–10}$$

But $\text{mmf}'_{1m} = N_1 I'_{1m}$, so (18–2–10) becomes $N_1 I'_{1m} = -N_2 I_{2m}$. Divide both sides by $\sqrt{2}$, and

$$N_1 I'_1 = -N_2 I_2, \quad \text{or} \quad I_2/I'_1 = -N_1/N_2 \qquad (18\text{–}2\text{–}11)$$

Current I'_1 is called the *primary load current* because it is the current that flows in the primary as a result of the load that has been connected to the secondary. The minus sign in (18–2–11) shows that I'_1 and I_2 are opposite in phase, as they must be in order that their mmf's shall be opposite in phase.

Since, for an ideal transformer, we assume that I_E is negligible, I'_1 is the total primary current, I_1, and (18–2–11) becomes

$$I_2/I_1 = -N_1/N_2 \qquad (18\text{–}2\text{–}12)$$

which is the very convenient and much-used transformer equation relating primary and secondary currents. Because of this relationship, it is often said that a transformer "transforms" the current in a circuit. Note that (18–2–12) applies strictly only to an ideal transformer, because we used the ideal transformer conditions for its derivation. (Solve Problems 18–5 and 18–8 at this point.)

Let us redraw the vector diagram of Fig. 18–2–2 (b) and add to it the vectors which represent the primary and secondary currents. The magnitude and phase of I_2 are determined by $\mathscr{E}_2$ and the impedance of the secondary circuit. Let us assume that the load in Fig. 18–2–1 is the equivalent of a resistor and inductor in series, so that I_2 lags $\mathscr{E}_2$ by the angle ϕ_2.

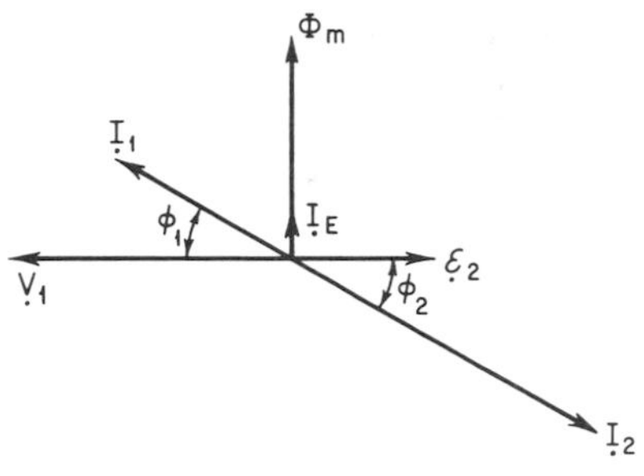

Primary load current I_1 is opposite in phase to I_2 so, once I_2 is known in

Figure 18–2–3. Vector diagram for an ideal transformer. I_E is assumed to be negligible for an ideal transformer but is indicated to show its phase.

magnitude and located on the vector diagram, I_1 can be drawn. The magnitude of I_1 must be related to that of I_2 by (18–2–12). Figure 18–2–3 shows the resulting vector diagram, again drawn for the turns ratio of the transformer sketched in Fig. 18–2–1. In the diagram ϕ_1 and ϕ_2 show the primary and secondary phase angles, and $\phi_1 = \phi_2$.

From the argument used here, Φ_m remains constant, and any magnetic flux produced by I_2 is neutralized by the counter flux produced by I'_1. Thus it is convenient to think of I_{Em} as producing Φ_m, as being in phase with Φ_m, and having the same magnitude regardless of any changes there may be in I_2 with the corresponding changes in I'_1.

4. Power equation for an ideal transformer. Since, for an ideal transformer we assume that there are no power losses, $P_1 = P_2$ or

$$I_1 V_1 \cos \phi_1 = I_2 \mathscr{E}_2 \cos \phi_2 \qquad (18\text{–}2\text{–}13)$$

where $\phi_1 = \phi_2$ from the argument that resulted in the vector diagram of Fig. 18–2–3.

5. EQUIVALENT PRIMARY CIRCUIT DIAGRAM FOR AN IDEAL TRANSFORMER. In circuit analysis it is often convenient to replace a transformer and its secondary load by an equivalent primary circuit. The equivalent circuit is to be such that the primary current, voltage, and power factor remain the same in the equivalent circuit as they are in the actual circuit. Let us work out such an equivalent circuit for an ideal transformer and its load. Figure 18–2–4 (a) shows the actual circuit where the schematic diagram of a transformer has been replaced by the usual symbol (shown at T) used for an iron core transformer. The secondary load has a resistance R_L and reactance X_L and, to be explicit, let us assume that the reactance is inductive. Here Z_L is the complex impedance, and we shall use the complex number notation of Chapters VII and VIII in this argument.

Let us represent the ratio of the number of secondary turns N_2 to the number of primary turns N_1 by n, so that

$$n = N_2/N_1 \qquad (18\text{–}2\text{–}14)$$

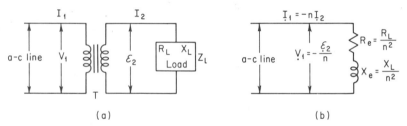

Figure 18–2–4. An ideal transformer and its secondary load. (a) Schematic diagram of actual circuit. (b) Equivalent primary circuit diagram.

Then, from (18–2–5), $V_1 = -\mathscr{E}_2/n$ (18–2–15)

and, from (18–2–12), $I_1 = -nI_2$ (18–2–16)

Let Z_e represent the equivalent complex impedance of the transformer and its load as defined above. Then

$$Z_e = V_1/I_1 = \mathscr{E}_2/n^2 I_2 \qquad (18\text{–}2\text{–}17)$$

But $Z_L = \mathscr{E}_2/I_2$ from Fig. 18–2–4 (a), so (18–2–17) becomes

$$Z_e = Z_L/n^2 = R_L/n^2 + jX_L/n^2 \qquad (18\text{–}2\text{–}18)$$

If the secondary reactance were capacitive, the argument would be the same, but the second term on the right would have a minus sign.

Equation (18–2–18) tells us that current and power factor of the primary circuit would be the same, with the same applied voltage, if the transformer and its load were removed and replaced by a resistance of R_L/n^2 in series with a reactance X_L/n^2. Figure 18–2–4 (b) shows the diagram of this equivalent primary circuit, where R_e is the equivalent resistance, X_e is the equivalent reactance, and X_L is assumed to be inductive. This procedure is often called "reflecting the secondary circuit into the primary."

From (18–2–18) and the equivalent primary circuit diagram of Fig. 18–2–4 (b) which results from it, it is often said that a transformer "transforms" the impedance of its secondary circuit into an equivalent impedance in its primary circuit. This property is frequently useful when it is necessary to change the equivalent impedance of a part of a network. Impedance *matching*, used to secure maximum power transfer from an a-c source to a load, is an important illustration of this use, as you will show when you solve Problems 18–11, 18–12, and 18–13.

Since the ideal transformer and its load have been converted into an equivalent simple series circuit, you may use the methods of Sec. 7–7 for the solution of ideal transformer problems.

18–3 AN APPROACH TO REAL TRANSFORMERS BY SOME CORRECTIONS TO IDEAL TRANSFORMER THEORY

As we pointed out in Sec. 18–1, the problem presented by a real transformer is approached by the process of successive corrections to ideal transformer theory. We shall now indicate some of the more obvious and simple corrections and arrive at a result which is usually sufficiently accurate at power frequencies and the lower audio frequencies.

1. CORRECTION FOR CORE LOSS AND MAGNETIZING CURRENT ONLY. First we shall assume that the transformer is ideal in all respects except for the hysteresis and eddy current power losses in the core. Also we shall take account of the fact that a primary current is required to establish the core flux Φ_m, and thus shall not assume that the magnetizing current is negligibly small.

The hysteresis and eddy current losses convert electrical energy into heat energy in the core, so they suggest the use of an equivalent circuit in which a current flows through a resistance. We shall call this equivalent resistance R_C, and the rate at which heat is developed in R_C is to be the same as the rate at which heat is developed in the core due to hysteresis and eddy current losses. We have seen, for a given transformer, that Φ_m, and thus B_m, remain constant whatever the changes in I_2 may be, if the applied primary voltage is constant. Equations (15–4–8) and (17–3–10), respectively, give us the eddy current and hysteresis power loss formulas. From these formulas we observe that, for a given transformer on a fixed frequency line, the power loss is constant if B_m is constant. Hence, the core loss is independent of the load on the transformer if V_1 is constant. This fact suggests that we want a constant current flowing through R_C. Since the applied line voltage is constant, we can secure this condition by connecting R_C across the line in parallel with the primary of an ideal transformer, and the power loss in R_C will take account of the core loss. Resistor R_C is shown connected in this fashion in the equivalent circuit diagram of Fig. 18–3–1, where a current I_C is assumed to be flowing through R_C. The connection assures us that I_C will be independent of I_2, if V_1 is independent of I_2 as assumed.

A current must flow through the primary winding in order to establish the core flux, and this current is constant in magnitude, since Φ_m is constant in magnitude. Also this current is $90°$ behind V_1 in phase, as we have seen in

Figs. 18–2–2 (b) and 18–2–3. This situation suggests that we connect a pure inductance X_m across the line in parallel with the primary of the ideal transformer as shown in Fig. 18–3–1. This is an iron core inductance, as shown by the symbol for X_m in Fig. 18–3–1, and thus its inductance is not constant through a cycle of changes of the current. Hence, the current through it will not be sinusoidal even though the applied voltage is sinusoidal. However, to a good approximation for most cases, we may assume an equivalent sinusoidal

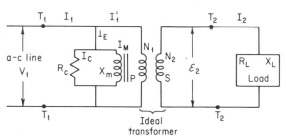

Figure 18–3–1. Equivalent circuit for correction of ideal transformer theory to account for core loss and magnetizing current.

current I_M and use vector methods. Thus, we assume that X_m is constant and that I_M is constant and sinusoidal in its variations with time. Here I_M is called the *magnetizing current.*

The exciting current I_E was defined as the current which flows in the primary when the secondary current is zero. In the ideal transformer, I_E was the same as I_M and negligible in magnitude. Now, in the equivalent circuit diagram of Fig. 18–3–1, I_E becomes the vector sum of I_C and I_M, while I_1' is the primary load current as before. The total primary current is I_1 and an ammeter connected in the primary circuit would read I_1. From the equivalent circuit in Fig. 18–3–1, I_1 is the vector sum of I_1' and I_E; and $I_1 = I_E$ if $I_2 = 0$, so that $I_1' = 0$.

In Fig. 18–3–1, T_1 and T_1 are the primary terminals of the transformer, while T_2 and T_2 are the secondary terminals. The equivalent circuit between the primary terminals and the secondary terminals in Fig. 18–3–1 replaces the actual transformer when we correct ideal transformer theory to take account of core loss and magnetizing current only. For the part of the circuit labeled "Ideal Transformer" we apply the ideal transformer theory derived in Sec. 18–2.

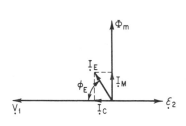

Figure 18–3–2. Vector diagram for circuit in Figure 18–3–1 when $I_2 = 0$.

Now let us redraw the vector diagram of Fig. 18–2–3 and add to it the features of the equivalent circuit in Fig. 18–3–1. First we shall have $I_2 = 0$ and, with an ammeter and sensitive wattmeter in the primary circuit, we shall determine I_E and its phase angle. The component of I_E which is in phase with V_1 is I_C, and the component of I_E which is 90° out of phase with V_1 (i.e., in phase with Φ_m) is I_M. This situation is shown by the vector diagram in Fig. 18–3–2.

Next we close a switch in the secondary circuit of Fig. 18–3–1, so that a current I_2 flows. Immediately the primary load current I_1' is established opposite in phase to I_2 and with a magnitude determined by the turns ratio as given by (18–2–11). Currents I_2 and I_1' are shown in Fig. 18–3–3, where

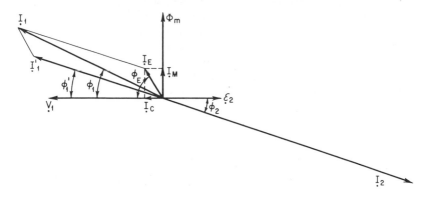

Figure 18–3–3. Vector diagram for the circuit in Fig. 18–3–1 when I_2 is not zero.

$\phi_1' = \phi_2$. The magnitudes of I_2 and of ϕ_2 are, of course, determined by $\mathscr{E}_2$ and the secondary load impedance composed of R_L and X_L. That is,

$$I_2 = \mathscr{E}_2/(R_L + jX_L) \qquad (18\text{–}3\text{–}1)$$

Then, as stated above, $\qquad I_1' = -N_2 I_2/N_1 \qquad (18\ 3\ 2)$

The primary current I_1 may now be computed from

$$I_1 = I_1' + I_E \qquad (18\text{–}3\text{–}3)$$

In Fig. 18–3–3, the magnitude of I_E is exaggerated with respect to I_1, because for a good transformer with an appreciable fraction of its rated load, I_E would be very small compared with I_1'.

2. ADDITIONAL CORRECTIONS FOR RESISTANCES OF WINDINGS AND FOR LEAKAGE FLUX. Again we shall confine our discussion to cases where the frequency is low enough so that the distributed capacitance of the windings has a negligible effect and the resistances of the windings are essentially those measured by d-c methods. However, we wish to add further corrections to the ideal transformer theory so that we may take approximate account of the resistances of the windings and of the primary and secondary leakage flux. As before, we can make the corrections most easily in terms of an equivalent circuit.

For the equivalent circuit, the resistance R_1 of the primary winding is simply a resistance R_1 in series with the primary of an ideal transformer. Similarly the resistance R_2 of the secondary winding is simply a resistance R_2 in series with the secondary of the ideal transformer. We shall assume, as stated above, that we can measure these resistances by use of a d-c method (say a Wheatstone bridge) applied to the actual transformer and, after making any necessary temperature corrections, we can use the measured values in an equivalent circuit for transformer calculations.

The primary leakage flux links the primary turns but does not link the secondary turns. Thus it enters into the production of an emf of self-induction in the primary, but is not a part of the mutual flux which produces an emf in the secondary. This situation suggests that the equivalent circuit should contain a self-inductance in series with the primary of the ideal transformer as a means of correction. Similarly a self-inductance in series with the secondary of the ideal transformer is suggested as a means of correcting for secondary leakage flux. The amount of leakage flux in each winding is found to be a function of the current in the winding, and thus the self-inductances used for correction are not strictly constant as the load changes. However, it turns out

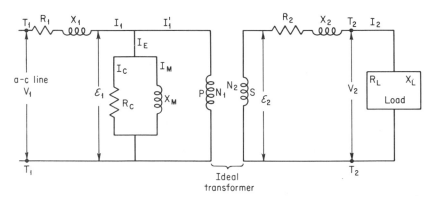

Figure 18–3–4. Equivalent circuit for correction of ideal transformer theory to account approximately for core loss, magnetizing current, resistances of windings, and flux leakage.

that a very good approximation is obtained if they are treated as constants, and we shall treat them as such.

Figure 18–3–4 shows the equivalent circuit diagram of Fig. 18–3–1, redrawn to include the circuit elements which correct approximately for leakage flux and primary and secondary resistances. In Fig. 18–3–4, the resistance of the primary winding is R_1, and X_1 is the inductive reactance due to the primary flux leakage. Similarly, R_2 is the resistance of the secondary winding and X_2 is the inductive reactance due to the secondary flux leakage. The secondary terminal potential difference V_2 is less than $\mathscr{E}_2$ because of the drops in potential in R_2 and X_2.

In Fig. 18–3–4, R_1 and X_1 have been placed to the left (i.e., on the line side) of the parallel combination of R_C and X_m. We can see the reason for placing them here, rather than on the right of the R_C and X_m combination, by the following. In the actual transformer, all primary current, I_1, flows through the primary winding. Thus, I_1 flows through R_1 and X_1 in the actual transformer, so it must flow through them in the equivalent circuit diagram. If R_1 and X_1 were to the right of the R_C and X_m combination, only the I_1' part of I_1 would flow through them, and the above requirement would not be satisfied. To put the argument another way, I_E flows through R_1 and X_1 in the actual transformer, so R_1 and X_1 in the equivalent circuit must be so placed that I_E flows through them. The equivalent circuit, as drawn in Fig. 18-3-4, satisfies this requirement. We shall continue to assume that the line characteristics are good enough so that V_1 is constant, independent of the load on the transformer.

The rms value of the emf of self-induction in the primary due to the mutual flux in the core is $\mathscr{E}_1$. It does not include the emf of self-induction due to the primary leakage flux; this latter emf is accounted for by the use of X_1. It is $\mathscr{E}_1$, not V_1, which is now related to $\mathscr{E}_2$ by the simple turns ratio formula

$$-\mathscr{E}_1/\mathscr{E}_2 = -N_1/N_2 \qquad (18\text{-}3\text{-}4)$$

as you can show directly from (18-2-1) and (18-2-3) for the part of the equivalent circuit (in Fig. 18-3-4) which is labeled "Ideal Transformer." Equation (18-2-5) is valid only under conditions where R_1 and X_1 are negligible, so that $\mathscr{E}_1$ may be considered to be equal, and opposite in phase, to V_1. From Fig. 18-3-4,

$$V_1 = -\mathscr{E}_1 + I_1(R_1 + jX_1) \qquad (18\text{-}3\text{-}5)$$

and the turns ratio formula applies only to the $-\mathscr{E}_1$ part of (18-3-5). Since $\mathscr{E}_1$ is in phase with $\mathscr{E}_2$ as shown by (18-3-4) (they both depend upon the same rate of change of mutual flux), we retain the minus sign on $\mathscr{E}_1$ because we wish to plot it on the primary side of the vector diagram. Equation (18-3-5) shows that, with V_1 constant, $\mathscr{E}_1$ changes as I_1 changes. However, we shall assume that we may obtain sufficient accuracy if we consider that I_E remains constant in magnitude and phase, and that the equivalent impedance of R_C and X_m in parallel remains constant as the load on the transformer changes. This means that we neglect the drop in potential across R_1 and X_1 for purposes of the exciting current only. We do not neglect this drop in potential for other features of the circuit. This procedure is justified only because I_E is such a small fraction of I_1 for any reasonable load on the transformer.

The remainder of the notation in Fig. 18-3-4 is the same as that in Fig. 18-3-1, and has the same meaning as that assigned to it earlier.

Let us redraw the vector diagram of Fig. 18-3-3 and add to it the new features presented by the equivalent circuit diagram of Fig. 18-3-4. We shall elect to put $\mathscr{E}_2$ along the plus axis of reals as before. Our guiding equations, in addition to those used for Fig. 18-3-3, are (18-3-4), (18-3-5), and the following, which we can write at once from Fig. 18-3-4:

$$V_2 = \mathscr{E}_2 - I_2(R_2 + jX_2) \qquad (18\text{-}3\text{-}6)$$

$$V_2 = I_2(R_L + jX_L) \qquad (18\text{-}3\text{-}7)$$

$$I_2 = \mathscr{E}_2/[R_2 + R_L + j(X_2 + X_L)] \qquad (18\text{-}3\text{-}8)$$

Fig. 18-3-5 shows the vector diagram for Fig. 18-3-4. For convenience in proportioning the drawing, we assume that we are dealing with a step-up transformer which has $1\frac{1}{2}$ times as many secondary turns as primary turns.

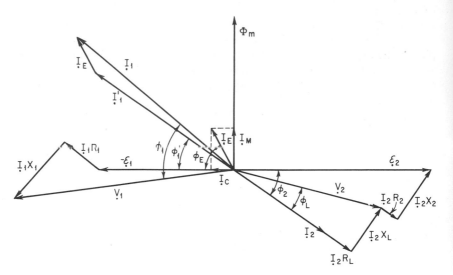

Figure 18–3–5. Vector diagram for the equivalent circuit diagram of Fig. 18–3–4. The effect of the nonideal characteristics of the transformer are exaggerated.

We shall also exaggerate the nonideal features in order that their contributions to the vector diagram shall be readily visible. You should give considerable thought to Fig. 18–3–5 to see how it satisfies the requirements of the equivalent circuit diagram of Fig. 18–3–4 and the associated equations.

3. EQUIVALENT PRIMARY CIRCUIT DIAGRAM. Let us apply the theory developed at the end of Sec. 18–2 for the equivalent primary circuit of an ideal transformer to the circuit diagram of Fig. 18–3–4. We shall reflect the part labeled "Ideal Transformer," and everything to the right of it into the primary circuit. The theory developed in Sec. 18–2 applies to the ideal transformer, and we may look upon R_2 and X_2 as part of the secondary load along with R_L and X_L. Using (18–2–14), (18–2–15), (18–2–16), and (18–2–18) and the method suggested by Fig. 18–2–4, we may at once draw and label the circuit diagram

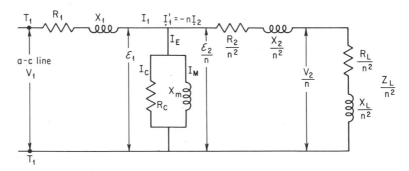

Figure 18–3–6. Equivalent primary circuit for the circuit diagram in Fig. 18–3–4.

in Fig. 18-3-6, which is the equivalent primary circuit for Fig. 18-3-4. Now, however, (18-2-15) becomes

$$-\mathscr{E}_1 = -\mathscr{E}_2/n \qquad\qquad (18\text{-}3\text{-}9)$$

and (18-2-16) becomes $\qquad I_1' = -nI_2 \qquad\qquad\qquad (18\text{-}3\text{-}10)$

while (18-2-18) is replaced by

$$Z_e = R_L/n^2 + jX_L/n^2 + R_2/n^2 + jX_2/n^2 \qquad (18\text{-}3\text{-}11)$$

In Fig. 18-3-7, let us draw the vector diagram for the circuit of Fig. 18-3-6 and elect to put the primary load current, I_1' along the plus axis of reals. This vector diagram permits us to represent both the primary and secondary

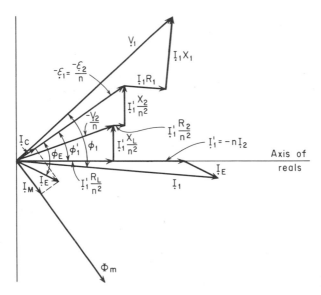

Figure 18-3-7. Vector diagram for the circuit in Fig. 18-3-6. The primary load current, I_1', is arbitrarily placed along the positive axis of reals. The effects of the nonideal characteristics of the transformer are exaggerated.

quantities on the same side, and shows their interrelations very clearly. You should study Fig. 18-3-7 very carefully and relate each part of the vector diagram both to the circuit diagram in Fig. 18-3-6 and the vector diagram in Fig. 18-3-5. For this latter comparison, you will find it instructive to trace Fig. 18-3-7 on a piece of tracing paper and then superimpose the tracing on Fig. 18-3-5 with the vectors for Φ_m along the same line. Compare the vectors which correspond in the two diagrams and account for those that do not correspond.

It is possible to determine,[*] experimentally, approximate values for X_1 and X_2 for a particular transformer. With R_1, R_2, X_1, X_2, and I_E known, the equivalent circuit diagram permits solution of most practical transformer problems with sufficient accuracy. At frequencies high enough so that the

---

[*] M.I.T. Electrical Engineering Staff, *op. cit.*, pp. 352-55.

effect of the distributed capacitance becomes important, the approximation given here is not adequate.

Since the transformer and its load have been reduced to an equivalent series-parallel circuit in Fig. 18–3–6, you may now apply the methods learned in Sec. 8–1 to the solution of transformer problems.

PROBLEMS

18–1 List at least ten different uses of the transformer.

18–2 Refer to Fig. 18–2–2, (a) Write an equation for the magnetic flux, in the core of the ideal transformer, which will satisfy the curve drawn for Φ. (b) Assume that no secondary current is flowing and write an equation for the exciting current in the primary as a function of time for the ideal transformer. Using the magnetic circuit equation, obtain a relationship between Φ_m and I_{Em}. (c) From the equation that you have written for Φ, obtain equations for v_1 and e_2 as functions of time, and show that the curves drawn for these quantities are correct in phase with respect to the curve drawn for Φ. (d) Show from your equations that i_E lags 90° behind v_1 and explain why this is true for an ideal transformer.

18–3 Enumerate the ideal transformer assumptions which entered into the derivation of the much-used transformer equation of (18–2–5) and explain briefly how each entered into the derivation. Which of the ideal transformer assumptions were not used in the derivation of this equation?

18–4 (a) A transformer has an area of cross section of 0.0129 m² in its core, and 700 turns of wire on its primary. It is designed to operate on a 2300 v 60 cycles/sec line. What is the required maximum magnetic flux density in its core? [*Ans:* 0.954 wb/m².] (b) How many secondary turns must be wound on the core in order to have a secondary emf of 120 v?

18–5 Enumerate the ideal transformer assumptions that were used either directly or indirectly in the derivation of (18–2–12). Which assumptions were not used?

18–6 An ideal transformer induces a maximum emf per cycle of 56.6 v per turn, and its primary is connected to a 22,000 v 60 cycles/sec sinusoidal a-c line. A wattmeter in the primary reads 940 kw. The secondary current is 454 amp, with a lagging power factor of 0.940. (a) How many turns are there on the primary? On the secondary? (b) What are the equivalent primary resistance and reactance for the transformer and its load? [*Ans:* R_e = 456 ohms, X_e = 166 ohms.] (c) What must be the area of cross section of the magnetic circuit if the magnetic flux density is not to exceed 1.00 wb/m²? [*Ans:* 0.150 m².]

18–7 As an alternative to the explanation, in Sec. 18–2, of why a ferromagnetic core is desirable for a transformer operating on a low frequency a-c line, consider the effect of the ferromagnetic core on the self-inductance of the primary. Explain why a smaller exciting current is possible under these conditions than would be possible with a diamagnetic or paramagnetic material used in the core.

18–8 An ideal transformer, for which the turns ratio is $N_2/N_1 = 0.01$, has an equivalent primary circuit diagram, for the transformer and its secondary load, of $R_e = 4500$ ohms and $X_e = 2500$ ohms inductive. The primary of the transformer is connected to a 12,000 v 60 cycles/sec sinusoidal a-c line. (a) What is the complex expression for the impedance of the secondary load? (b) What would an ammeter in the secondary circuit read? In the primary circuit? [*Ans: I_2* = 233 amp.] (c) If the transformer has an area of cross section of 0.010 m² for its magnetic circuit and was designed so that the maximum magnetic flux density in the core would not exceed 0.80 weber/m² at this load, how many turns were wound on the primary and secondary? [*Ans: N_1* = 5620 turns.]

18–9 Starting with the voltage equation of (18–2–4) and the fact that for an ideal transformer the electrical power input to the primary at every instant must equal the electrical power output from the secondary at that instant, derive the current equation of (18–2–12). Then show, from the same conservation of energy line of argument, that the phase angles in the primary and secondary must be equal for an ideal transformer.

18–10 An ideal transformer has its primary connected to a 13,200 v sinusoidal a-c power line. The secondary circuit is delivering 150 amp at 110 v, and the secondary power factor is 0.8 with I_2 lagging. (a) What is the current in the primary? (b) What is the turns ratio for the transformer? (c) Draw the equivalent primary circuit diagram for this transformer and its load, and put numerical values on the circuit elements shown. [*Ans: Z_e* = 8450 + $j6320$.]

18–11 An a-c source has a constant complex emf $\mathscr{E}_s$ and an internal complex impedance $Z_s = R_s + jX_s$ (i.e., it is a source that does not have a maintained terminal potential difference). Assume that R_s and X_s are constants. The source is connected to a load that has a complex impedance $Z_L = R_L \pm jX_L$. Assume that you may adjust Z_L at will. Show that maximum power is transferred from the source to the load if the impedance of the load is adjusted to a value such that it is the conjugate complex of the internal impedance of the source, i.e., that $R_s = R_L$ and $X_s = -X_L$. Consult your solution to Problem 2–21.

18–12 The secondary load on an ideal transformer is $Z_2 = 32.0 + j48.0$ at 60 cycles/sec frequency. The turns ratio of the transformer is $n = N_2/N_1 = 4$. The primary is to be connected to a sinusoidal 60 cycle/sec a-c source of 120 volts emf and 2.00 ohm internal resistance. Using the result of the proof in Problem 18–11 and the equivalent primary circuit diagram of Fig. 18–2–4, find what reactance should be connected in series with the source in order to match it to the transformer and load, and thus have maximum power transfer from the source to the load. [*Ans: X_s* = 3.00 ohm capacitive.]

18–13 A load with an impedance of $Z_L = 1200 - j1600$ at 1000 cycles/sec is to be matched to a 1000 cycle/sec sinusoidal a-c source of emf $\mathscr{E}$ whose impedance is $Z_s = 13.3 + j14.5$. What ideal transformer should be selected, how should it be connected, and what adjustment should be made in its primary circuit, in order to have maximum power transfer from the source to the load?

18–14 The primary circuit of an ideal transformer has a 60 cycle/sec sinusoidal a-c source with 220 volts rms emf, a resistance of 50.1 ohms and an inductive reactance of 40.5 ohms all in series. The turns ratio of the transformer is $n = N_2/N_1 = 10$. What capacitance connected across the secondary coil of the transformer will put the equivalent primary circuit in series resonance? [*Ans:* 0.654 μf.]

18-15 Table 18-1 gives the data for the normal magnetization curve (see Sec. 17-2) of a typical sample of transformer silicon steel. This is a different grade of silicon steel than the one for which data is given in Problem 17-3. (a) Plot the normal magnetization curve. (b) A small toroid ring transformer, using this silicon steel for its core, has 250 turns on its primary and is connected to a 120 v 60 cycles/sec a-c line. The cross sectional area of the core is 0.00300 m², and the mean length of the magnetic circuit is 0.800 m. The transformer is to be looked upon as ideal except that the magnetizing current is not to be considered negligible.

TABLE 18-1

DATA FOR NORMAL MAGNETIZATION CURVE OF A TYPICAL
TRANSFORMER SILICON STEEL

(Courtesy of United States Steel)

H in amp turns/m, B in wb/m²					
H	B	H	B	H	B
10	0.043	80	0.765	200	1.085
20	0.160	90	0.813	220	1.110
30	0.305	100	0.852	240	1.130
40	0.440	120	0.915	260	1.150
50	0.545	140	0.968	280	1.163
60	0.628	160	1.012	300	1.180
70	0.703	180	1.050		

(1) What is the maximum value of the emf of self-induction induced in the primary? (2) What is the maximum rate of change of the magnetic flux in the core? [*Ans:* 0.68 wb/sec.] (3) What is the maximum value of the flux in the core? (4) What is the maximum value of H in the core? (5) What would an ammeter in the primary circuit read when no secondary current is flowing? [*Ans:* 0.13 amp.]

18-16 A certain transformer core, made of the silicon steel for which data is given in Problem 18-15, has an area of cross section of 250 cm² and a mean length of 100 cm. The maximum flux density in the core is to be 0.900 weber/m². There are 1100 turns of wire on the primary and 110 turns on the secondary. The transformer is to be used on a 60 cycles/sec sinusoidal a-c line. (a) What maximum value of mmf must the primary turns supply when there is no load on the secondary? What magnetizing current must flow? [*Ans:* $I_M = 0.0732$ amp.] (b) For what primary voltage is the transformer designed? [*Ans:* 6600 v.] (c) A load is connected to the secondary of the transformer, and an ammeter in the secondary circuit reads 100 amp, while the secondary power factor is 0.800 with the current lagging. The transformer may be considered ideal except for the magnetizing current. What will an ammeter in the primary read if it can be read to three significant figures? Sketch the vector diagram and label all vectors. [*Ans:* 10.0 amp.]

18-17 Published data show that the silicon steel of Table 18-1 has a total core loss (due to both hysteresis and eddy currents) of 0.400 w/lb at $B_m = 0.900$

wb/m² and $f = 60$ cycles/sec when the core laminations are 29 gauge
sheets (sheets 0.014 in. thick). The density of this steel is 7.55 g/cm³.
Consider again the transformer of Problem 18–16 and look upon it as an
ideal transformer except for core loss and magnetizing current. (a) What
would an ammeter read in the primary circuit if $I_2 = 0$? The ammeter is
one which reads 100 ma full scale. (b) The primary ammeter is replaced
by the previous one of higher range, and the secondary load of Problem
18–16, part (c), is connected. Using $\mathscr{E}_2$ along the plus axis of reals, write
the vector equations for I_1', I_E, and I_1. What does the primary ammeter
read? [*Ans:* $I_1 = -8.03 + j6.07$.]

18–18   A certain transformer may be considered ideal except for core loss and
magnetizing current. It is designed to deliver 110 v secondary emf when
the primary is connected to a 660 v sinusoidal 60 cycles/sec a-c line. If the
secondary emf is taken along the plus axis of reals, the primary exciting
current is given by $-0.130 + j0.487$, and the secondary current is given
by $11.59 - j3.11$. (a) Sketch the complete vector diagram like the one in
Fig. 18–3–3. Find I_1 and the phase angle between I_1 and V_1. [*Ans:* 2.3 amp,
26°.] (b) What are the values of R_C and X_m in the equivalent circuit diagram
of Fig. 18–3–1 for this transformer? What is the power loss in the core?
[*Ans:* $P_{\text{core}} = 86$ w.] (c) The core of the transformer is made of the silicon
steel whose magnetization data are given in Table 18–1, Problem 18–15.
The magnetic circuit is uniform in cross-sectional area and has a mean
length of 0.625 m. There are 210 turns on the primary. What is the maximum value of the magnetic flux density in the core? What is the area of
cross section of the core? [*Ans:* $B_m = 1.12$ wb/m², $A = 0.0105$ m².]

18–19   The data on the name plate of a certain 60 cycles/sec transformer indicates
that it is a 4400 v to 220 v step-down transformer. Tests show that
$R_1 = 3.55$ ohms, $X_1 = 5.00$ ohms, $R_2 = 0.00888$ ohm, and $X_2 = 0.0125$
ohm. The core loss of the transformer at rated primary voltage is 200 w, and
the exciting current is 0.46 amp. The transformer secondary is connected
to a load which is equivalent to 1 ohm resistance and 0.5 ohm inductive
reactance. When 4400 v sinusoidal alternating current is applied to the
primary, a current of 192 amp flows in the secondary circuit. (a) Draw the
equivalent primary circuit diagram of Fig. 18–3–6 and label it with all
known constants. (b) Consider first that $I_2 = 0$ and find the equivalent
admittance of R_C and X_m in parallel. Assume that this admittance remains
constant when the secondary load is applied. [*Ans:* $Y_E = 10.4 \times 10^{-6} -
j104 \times 10^{-6}$.] (c) With the secondary current of 192 amp flowing, put I_1'
along the plus axis of reals as in Fig. 18–3–7, and find $-V_2/n$ and $-\mathscr{E}_1$.
What is the terminal potential difference of the secondary? [*Ans:* $-V_2/n =
3840 + j1920$, $-\mathscr{E}_1 = 3874 + j1968$. (d) Compute I_1 and I_1. [*Ans:*
$I_1 = 9.85 - j0.39$.] (e) Compute V_1 and V_1. The value of V_1 should check
with the applied primary voltage within slide rule error. Sketch the vector
diagram, like the one in Fig. 18–3–7, for this transformer and its load.
(f) What is the power input to the transformer? [*Ans:* 38 kw.]

18–20   A small step-down transformer connected to a 120 v 60 cycles/sec sinusoidal a-c line has a core loss of 20 w, and draws an exciting current of
0.800 amp. The resistance of the primary winding is 0.325 ohm and that of
the secondary winding is 0.00100 ohm. The turns ratio is 20 to 1. Assume
that the transformer has no leakage reactance. When the secondary is

connected to a pure resistance load of 0.0590 ohm: (a) What will an ammeter in the primary circuit read? [*Ans:* 5.15 amp.] (b) What will an ammeter in the secondary read and what is the efficiency of the transformer? [*Ans:* $I_2 = 98.8$ amp.]

18-21 A small step-up transformer, with a 2 to 1 turns ratio, is to be used in the laboratory to supply 10.0 amp secondary current at 60 cycles/sec to an inductive load whose power factor is 0.800. Calculation shows that a secondary terminal potential difference of 200 v will be required in order to have 10 amp flow through the load. By test it is found that $R_1 = 0.300$ ohm, $R_2 = 1.300$ ohms, $X_1 = 0.405$ ohm, and $X_2 = 1.510$ ohms. With no load on the secondary, the following data for the transformer are obtained.

Applied voltage (volt)	Core loss (watts)	Exciting current (amperes)
60	6.3	0.400
80	10.6	0.500
100	15.6	0.620
120	21.2	0.740
140	27.2	0.870

(a) Plot curves for the core loss and exciting current, each as a function of applied primary voltage. (b) Put I_1' along the plus axis of reals, as in the vector diagram of Fig. 18-3-7, and find $-\mathscr{E}_1$ and $\mathscr{E}_1$ when the secondary load is connected and the primary applied voltage is adjusted so that 10 amp flow in the secondary load. [*Ans:* $-\mathscr{E}_1 = 86.5 + j67.6$.] (c) Using the curves for part (a), find the exciting current, core loss, I_1, and applied primary voltage V_1 under the conditions required by part (b). [*Ans:* $I_1 = 20.5$ amp, $V_1 = 120$ v.]

THE ELECTROMAGNETIC FIELD

by David Park

19–1 INTRODUCTION

Most of the discussion of electric and magnetic fields so far in this book has been limited essentially to situations in which either there is no time variation or the time variation is slow enough so that it may be replaced by a sequence of static situations. Here a knowledge of Coulomb's law of electrostatics and the right-hand rule for the magnetic field produced by a given current is enough to give at least an intuitive sense of the physical facts.

But as soon as the fields vary in time, deeper relationships begin to emerge. This is because, as we emphasized in the discussion of Faraday's law in Sec. 15–2, a changing magnetic field gives rise to an electric field. Conversely, as we pointed out in the study of Maxwell's hypothesis in Sec. 14–10, a changing electric field gives rise to a magnetic field.

The goal of this chapter is to study these interrelations in some detail. The most important result of this study is the possibility of having such fields completely detached from their sources and propagating freely in empty space. These *electromagnetic waves*, as they are called, travel at an invariable velocity of about 2.998×10^8 m/sec, and can be identified, in their various frequency ranges, as radio waves; infra-red, visible, and ultra-violet light; x-rays; and gamma-rays.

Because of the fundamental complexity of the relationships between electric and magnetic fields, we are obliged to discuss them in a mathematical manner, and because these fields are represented as vectors, we shall pause first to give some basic definitions and derive some basic theorems in vector calculus.

19–2 THE DIVERGENCE OF A VECTOR

In Sec. 10–11 we introduced the symbol for divergence. Here we shall start afresh and then relate our findings to this earlier usage.

Suppose that G represents a vector whose components $G_x(x, y, z, t)$ etc., are defined at each point of space and at each instant of time. We define the *flux* of G through a surface A (see Fig. 19–2–1) by the equation

$$\text{flux of } G \text{ through } A = \int_{>\to} G \cdot dA \qquad (19\text{–}2\text{–}1)$$

where the sign on the integral is symbolic of the open area in Fig. 19–2–1. Thus, if G, for example, represents an electric field E, the flux of G through A is, in conformity with our usage in Sec. 9–7, equal to the total number of electric lines of force passing through A. It will be noted that, since the vector element dA may be taken to point to either side of the surface, we are obliged to choose arbitrarily one side or the other, and this choice is denoted by the normal vector n in the figure.

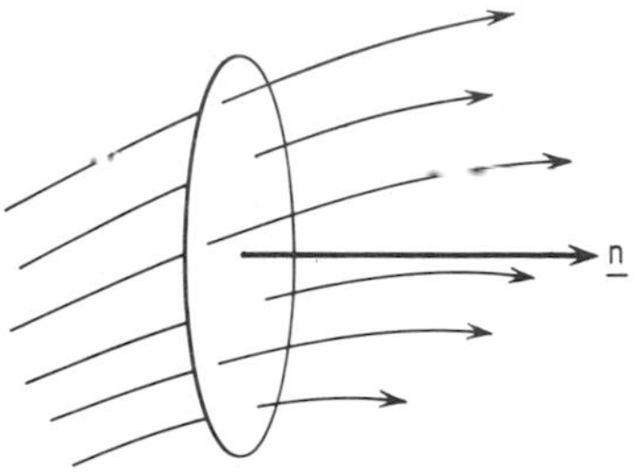

Suppose now that A is a closed surface. We then choose n to be the outward normal and can speak of the *net outward flux* of G through the surface (as we did in the special case of Gauss's theorem in Sec. 9–8):

$$\text{net outward flux of } G = \int_{\bigcirc\rightarrow} G \cdot dA$$

$$(19\text{--}2\text{--}2)$$

Figure 19–2–1. Flux of a vector quantity G through an area A, having a normal n.

where the sign on the integral means that the surface is closed and that the direction of the normal vector is chosen to point outwards. The three situations in Figs. 19–2–2 (a), (b), and (c) may be distinguished from each other. In (a), as argued in Problem 9–34, the integral in (19–2–2) is zero, and we can say that the lines of G are continuous. (This is why the term "*net* outward flux" is used.) In (b), some lines go straight through, while some originate and terminate there. The integral then gives the net number of lines. In (c) there are no lines incident from outside. In cases (b) and (c) we say that the vector G has a *divergence*. The familiar example of this, as pointed out above, is

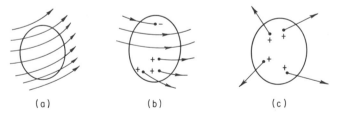

        (a)   (b)   (c)

Figure 19–2–2. Ways in which flux lines can enter and leave a region of space.

found in Gauss's theorem (9–8–10), in which the net outward flux of E is proportional to the charge q enclosed within the surface:

$$\int_{\bigcirc\rightarrow} E \cdot dA = q/\varepsilon_0 \qquad (19\text{--}2\text{--}3)$$

An example of situation (a) is a charge-free region of an electric field or, by (14–3–7), any field of magnetic induction whatever, since

$$\int_{\bigcirc\rightarrow} B \cdot dA = 0 \qquad (19\text{--}2\text{--}4)$$

Let us now apply Gauss's theorem to an infinitesimal element of volume dv in a region in which there is a charge density ρ. In (19–2–3) we can write q as $\rho \, dv$, so that on dividing by dv,

$$\lim_{dv \to 0} (1/dv) \int_{\circlearrowright} \boldsymbol{E} \cdot d\boldsymbol{A} = \rho/\varepsilon_0 \qquad (19\text{–}2\text{–}5)$$

where dv is the volume enclosed in the surface over which the integration is to be performed. The left side of (19–2–5) is the *net outward flux per unit volume*, which is defined as the *divergence of* $\boldsymbol{E}$, written div $\boldsymbol{E}$. Thus (19–2–5) [which is the same as (10–11–6)] is

$$\text{div } \boldsymbol{E} = \rho/\varepsilon_0 \qquad (19\text{–}2\text{–}6)$$

which may be called the *infinitesimal form* of Gauss's theorem just as (19–2–3) is the finite form, and we write the general *definition* of the divergence of an arbitrary vector $\boldsymbol{G}\,(x, y, z, t)$ as

$$\text{div } \boldsymbol{G} \overset{\text{def}}{=} \lim_{dv \to 0} (1/dv) \int_{\circlearrowright} \boldsymbol{G} \cdot d\boldsymbol{A} \qquad (19\text{–}2\text{–}7)$$

Starting from this definition, which the preceding remarks were merely intended to explain, we can now prove two very useful theorems. Theorem 1 states, for a finite volume, that

$$\int \text{div } \boldsymbol{G} \, dv = \int_{\circlearrowright} \boldsymbol{G} \cdot d\boldsymbol{A} \qquad (19\text{–}2\text{–}8)$$

where the surface of integration on the right is that which encloses the finite volume on the left. The proof of this theorem is best seen from a picture, which we draw in two dimensions for convenience in Fig. 19–2–3. The integral on the right is the sum of the net outward fluxes from all the volume elements dv. But the flux out of the volume a, for example, flows into adjacent volume elements; so the sum of all the interior fluxes is zero and we are left only with surfaces such as the bottom of b, where the flux passes through the outer surface. Thus when the contributions from all the volume elements dv are summed together, only those from the outer surface remain. Thus we have proved (19–2–8), which is, of course, closely related with (19–2–3) via (19–2–6).

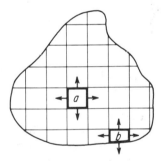

Figure 19–2–3. The outward flux from a reappears as inward flux in adjacent elements, while that from the lower edge of b contributes to the flux leaving the entire region.

Theorem 2 states that if Cartesian coordinates are used, there are the simple formulas for div $\boldsymbol{G}$ given in (10–11–5), namely:

$$\text{div } \boldsymbol{G} = \partial G_x/\partial x + \partial G_y/\partial y + \partial G_z/\partial z = \boldsymbol{\nabla} \cdot \boldsymbol{G} \qquad (19\text{–}2\text{–}9)$$

The proof of this follows at once from Sec. 10–11, where it was shown by direct calculation that, integrated over an infinitesimal cube of dimensions dx, dy, dz,

$$\int_{\circlearrowright} \boldsymbol{E} \cdot d\boldsymbol{A} = (\partial E_x/\partial x + \partial E_y/\partial y + \partial E_z/\partial z) \, dx \, dy \, dz$$

Replacing E by G and $dx\,dy\,dz$ by dv, we have

$$\lim_{dv\to 0}\ (1/dv)\int_{\circlearrowleft\to}G\cdot dA = \partial G_x/\partial x + \partial G_y/\partial y + \partial G_z/\partial z$$

which was to be proved. Combining the two theorems, we have

$$\int \nabla\cdot G\,dv = \int_{\circlearrowleft\to}G\cdot dA \qquad\qquad (19\text{–}2\text{–}10)$$

where G is any vector and the integrations are over any region of space and the surface bounding it. This theorem, closely related to Gauss's theorem of electrostatics, is also often known as Gauss's theorem, but for reasons of clarity we shall refer to it below as the *divergence theorem*. It will be noted that we have really done nothing here except to re-state, in more general language, the results already derived in Sec. 10–11.

19–3 THE CURL OF A VECTOR

We have seen in the preceding paragraph how to characterize a vector which tends to *diverge*; we shall now discuss one which tends to *circulate*. In the most general terms, a *divergent vector field* is one which becomes more or less intense as one travels along the lines of flux of the vector (Fig. 19–3–1), while

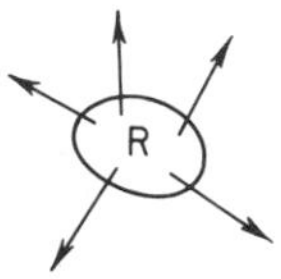

Figure 19–3–1. A vector field which is divergent in the region R.

Figure 19–3–2. A vector field with circulation around the path P.

a circulating vector field is one whose intensity changes as one travels perpendicularly to the lines of flux (Fig. 19–3–2). It is of course possible for a vector field to possess both properties at once. The reason for the word *circulation* is seen if we consider the dotted curve in Fig. 19–3–2. The flux at the top, tending clockwise around the loop, is stronger than that at the bottom, tending counterclockwise. There is, thus, a net clockwise circulation, where we define the circulation as

$$\text{circulation of } G \text{ around a path } P \overset{\text{def}}{=} \oint G\cdot ds \qquad (19\text{–}3\text{–}1)$$

The line integral is around the path P in one direction or the other (we have to specify which).

The example already familiar from Sec. 14–8 and 14–10 is the production of circulation in a magnetic field by the flow of a current, analogous to the production of divergence in an electric field by the presence of charge, and given by

$$\oint B\cdot ds = \mu_0 I \qquad\qquad (19\text{–}3\text{–}2)$$

Ampere's line integral law is analogous to Gauss's theorem, and we wish now to find its infinitesimal form, analogous to (19–2–6). To this end we consider the quantity known as the *curl* of B defined as

$$\text{curl } B = \lim_{dA \to 0} (1/dA) \oint B \cdot ds \qquad (19\text{–}3\text{–}3)$$

or, in words, the circulation per unit area, where the integration is around the circumference of the element of area dA.

Let us now apply Ampere's line integral law to find the field produced by a narrow filament of current flowing through the area dA. At the position of the loop, we define the *current density j* as the current per unit area flowing through the loop in Fig. 19–3–3. (Since we shall not refer to $\sqrt{-1}$ in this chapter, and since we are going shortly to make j a vector, there should be no confusion in notation. This use of j is analogous to its use in the quantity j_D

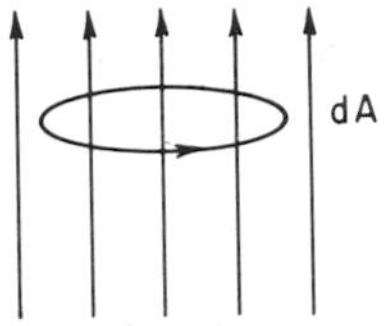

Figure 19–3–3. Flux of current through an element of area perpendicular to it.

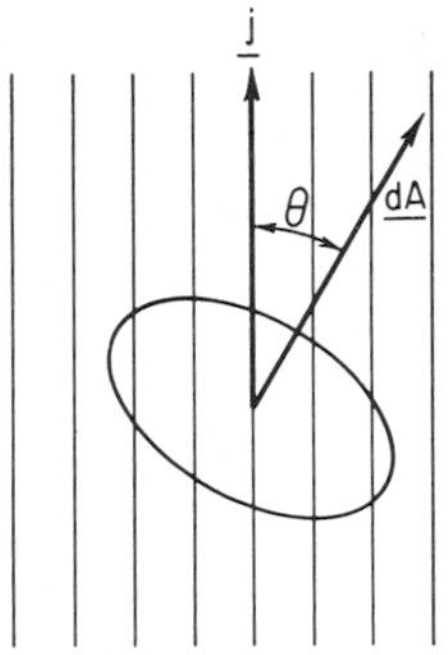

Figure 19–3–4. Flux of current through an area oblique to it.

in Sec. 14–10 and j_c in Sec. 13–1.) Then, for integration around the infinitesimal loop of area dA, (19–3–2) gives

$$\oint B \cdot ds = \mu_0 j \, dA \qquad (19\text{–}3\text{–}4)$$

or, by (19–3–3),
$$\text{curl } B = \mu_0 j \qquad (19\text{–}3\text{–}5)$$

Now we must take into account that the current has a direction in space and that the right side of (19–3–5) should, therefore, be a vector. This suggests that curl B should also be a vector, corresponding to the fact that the infinitesimal surface whose area in (19–3–3) is dA has an orientation in space described by a vectorial dA. Suppose that dA is oblique to the current as in Fig. 19–3–4. Then, as in Sec. 14–10, we see that the number of amperes passing through the loop is $j \cos \theta \, dA$, or $j \cdot dA$; this is what the right-hand side of (19–3–4) should be. To derive the vector form of (19–3–3) let us take curl B to be a vector, and define it by the relation

$$\lim_{dA \to 0} (\text{curl } B) \cdot dA \overset{\text{def}}{=} \oint B \cdot ds \qquad (19\text{–}3\text{–}6)$$

Then (19-3-4) becomes

$$\oint B \cdot ds = (\text{curl } B) \cdot dA = \mu_0 j \cdot dA$$

and since this is true for any infinitesimal magnitude and direction of dA, we can conclude that

$$\text{curl } B = \mu_0 j \qquad (19\text{-}3\text{-}7)$$

Generalizing (19-3-6), we define the curl of an arbitrary vector G by the relation

$$\lim_{dA \to 0} (\text{curl } G) \cdot dA \overset{\text{def}}{=} \oint G \cdot ds \qquad (19\text{-}3\text{-}8)$$

where (as with B) the direction of the normal to dA and the direction in which the perimeter of the path is traversed are related by the right-hand rule as in Fig. 19-3-3.

We are now ready to prove two theorems analogous to those which followed the definition (19-2-7). The first is the finite form of the infinitesimal equation (19-3-8). Let us form the surface integral $\int_{>\to} (\text{curl } G) \cdot dA$ by adding together the line integrals taken around each of the area elements dA. In doing so we encounter again a situation like the one shown in Fig. 16-2-1 (b). The circulations around adjacent elements of area cancel each other except at the periphery, where they add up to give a line integral around the periphery, $\oint G \cdot ds$. We conclude that

$$\int_{>\to} (\text{curl } G) \cdot dA = \oint G \cdot ds \qquad (19\text{-}3\text{-}9)$$

where the direction of ds and that of dA are related by the right-hand rule and where the area no longer needs to be a plane, but can be any surface bounded by the given perimeter.

As a simple corollary, let us suppose that the surface is closed, so that it has no rim. Then the right side of (19-3-9) is zero, and we have

$$\int_{\circ\to} (\text{curl } G) \cdot dA = 0$$

Applying the divergence theorem, (19-2-8), to this gives $\int \text{div} (\text{curl } G) \, dv = 0$ for any volume whatever, and can be true only if*

$$\text{div curl } G = 0 \qquad (19\text{-}3\text{-}10)$$

The second theorem to be proved is the one which gives an explicit way of calculating curl G when the components of G are known. In Cartesian coordinates, it states that

$$\text{curl } G = \nabla \times G \qquad (19\text{-}3\text{-}11)$$

* To see this, let us consider the general case in which an integral taken over an arbitrary volume vanishes, i.e., $\int f(x, y, z) \, dv = 0$. Suppose we want to know whether f is zero at a certain point P whose coordinates are x_0, y_0, and z_0. Reduce the volume of integration to an infinitesimal region centered on P. Then $f(x, y, z)$ will be approximately constant at the value of $f(x_0, y_0, z_0)$ over the region and may be taken outside the integral giving $f(x_0, y_0, z_0) \int dv = 0$; so, since the integral is not zero, $f(x_0, y_0, z_0)$ must be. But P may be any point whatever, so $f(x, y, z)$ therefore vanishes everywhere.

meaning that the X-component of curl G, according to the ordinary rule (see Sec. 13–1) for cross-product, is given by

$$(\text{curl } G)_x = (\partial/\partial y)G_z - (\partial/\partial z)G_y \qquad (19\text{-}3\text{-}12)$$

and similarly for the other two components. To prove this, we return to the definition (19–3–8) and consider an element of area, Fig. 19–3–5, which is in the YZ-plane, so that dA has only the X component $\Delta y\, \Delta z$. We have from (19–3–8)

$$\Delta y\, \Delta z\, (\text{curl } G)_x = \oint G \cdot ds \qquad (19\text{-}3\text{-}13)$$

and we must now evaluate the line integral.

Let the path be a square with one corner at an arbitrary point (x_0, y_0, z_0) as shown in Fig. 19–3–5 and let $y = y_0 + \eta$, $z = z_0 + \zeta$. At points near (x_0, y_0, z_0), the value of $G_y(x_0, y, z)$ is given by Taylor's theorem in y and z,

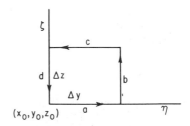

Figure 19–3–5. Integration around an infinitesimal path in the YZ-plane.

$$G_y(x_0, y, z) = G_y(x_0, y_0 + \eta, z_0 + \zeta)$$
$$= G_y^{(0)} + \eta\, \partial G_y^{(0)}/\partial y + \zeta\, \partial G_y^{(0)}/\partial z + \cdots$$

where the superscripts mean that G_y and its derivatives are evaluated at (x_0, y_0, z_0), and similarly for G_z. Integrating around the four sides of the square, we now find the sum of four contributions.

Side a. $\qquad\qquad \displaystyle\int_{(a)} G \cdot ds = \int_0^{\Delta y} G_y\, d\eta \quad$ since $dx = dz = 0$

Along this side, $\zeta = 0$, so that the integral is

$$\int_0^{\Delta y} (G_y^{(0)} + \eta\, \partial G_y^{(0)}/\partial y)\, d\eta = G_y^{(0)}\, \Delta y + \tfrac{1}{2}\, \partial G_y^{(0)}/\partial y\, (\Delta y)^2$$

Side b. Along this side, $\eta = \Delta y$ and $ds = d\zeta$.

$$\int_{(b)} G \cdot ds = \int_0^{\Delta z} (G_z^{(0)} + \Delta y\, \partial G_z^{(0)}/\partial y + \zeta\, \partial G_z^{(0)}/\partial z)\, d\zeta$$
$$= G_z^{(0)}\, \Delta z + \partial G_z^{(0)}/\partial y\, \Delta y\, \Delta z + \tfrac{1}{2}\, \partial G_z^{(0)}/\partial z\, (\Delta z)^2$$

Side c. Along this side $\zeta = \Delta z$, and $ds = -d\eta$.

$$\int_{(c)} G \cdot ds = -\int_0^{\Delta y} (G_y^{(0)} + \eta\, \partial G_y^{(0)}/\partial y + \Delta z\, \partial G_y^{(0)}/\partial z)\, d\eta$$
$$= -G_y^{(0)}\, \Delta y - \tfrac{1}{2}\, \partial G_y^{(0)}/\partial y\, (\Delta y)^2 - \Delta y\, \Delta z\, \partial G_y^{(0)}/\partial z$$

Side d. Here, $\eta = 0$ and $ds = -d\zeta$.

$$\int_{(d)} G \cdot ds = -\int_0^{\Delta z} (G_z^{(0)} + \zeta\, \partial G_z^{(0)}/\partial z)\, d\zeta$$
$$= -G_z^{(0)}\, \Delta z - \tfrac{1}{2}\, \partial G_z^{(0)}/\partial z\, (\Delta z)^2$$

The value of $\oint \boldsymbol{G} \cdot \boldsymbol{ds}$ is obtained by adding these four contributions together. Most of the terms cancel, and we find

$$\oint \boldsymbol{G} \cdot \boldsymbol{ds} = (\partial/\partial y \, G_z^{(0)} - \partial/\partial z \, G_y^{(0)}) \, \varDelta y \, \varDelta z$$

Putting this into (19–3–13) gives

$$(\text{curl } \boldsymbol{G})_z = \frac{\partial}{\partial y} G_z - \frac{\partial}{\partial z} G_y$$

where we have left off the superscripts because the place at which the curl is evaluated may be at any value of (x, y, z). This completes the proof of (19–3–12), and the remaining two components of (19–3–11) are established the same way.

Combining the two theorems (19–3–9) and (19–3–11) gives

$$\int_{)\rightarrow} (\boldsymbol{\nabla} \times \boldsymbol{G}) \cdot \boldsymbol{dA} = \oint \boldsymbol{G} \cdot \boldsymbol{ds} \qquad (19\text{–}3\text{–}14)$$

a vector identity usually called *Stokes's theorem*. We are now going to use this and the divergence theorem to transform the basic laws governing the electromagnetic field into the form of differential equations.

19–4 MAXWELL'S EQUATIONS

Rather than discuss the general theory of the electromagnetic field in arbitrary media, we can see the most important features of it if we restrict attention to regions of free space in which various charges and currents are moving around. In this case the four field quantities $\boldsymbol{B}$, $\boldsymbol{D}$, $\boldsymbol{E}$, and $\boldsymbol{H}$ may be expressed in terms of two, which we shall take to be $\boldsymbol{E}$ and $\boldsymbol{B}$, with the other two given by

$$\boldsymbol{D} = \varepsilon_0 \boldsymbol{E}, \qquad \boldsymbol{H} = \boldsymbol{B}/\mu_0 \qquad (19\text{–}4\text{–}1)$$

For the purposes of electromagnetic theory, the basic facts about the electromagnetic field are 5 in number:

(a) *Gauss's theorem*, which is expressed in differential form by (19–2–6).

(b) *The magnetic analog of Gauss's theorem*, obtained from (19–2–4). Since there is no magnetic charge, we have

$$\boldsymbol{\nabla} \cdot \boldsymbol{B} = 0 \qquad (19\text{–}4\text{–}2)$$

(c) *Ampere's line integral law*, which in vector terms is given by (19–3–7) with $\boldsymbol{j}$ the density of the total current, conduction plus displacement. In Sec. 14–10, we have seen that the displacement current density is, for the free-space situation considered here,

$$\boldsymbol{j}_D = \partial \boldsymbol{D}/\partial t = \varepsilon_0 \, \partial \boldsymbol{E}/\partial t \qquad (19\text{–}4\text{–}3)$$

so that we can write (19–3–7) as

$$\boldsymbol{\nabla} \times \boldsymbol{B} = \mu_0(\boldsymbol{j}_c + \varepsilon_0 \, \partial \boldsymbol{E}/\partial t) \qquad (19\text{–}4\text{–}4)$$

where j_c is the conduction current density in amperes per square meter

(d) *Faraday's law of electromagnetic induction*, given by (15-2-4). We can use Stokes's theorem to re-express the left side of this equation so that

$$\oint E \cdot ds = \int_{>\rightarrow} (\nabla \times E) \cdot dA = - \int_{>\rightarrow} (\partial B/\partial t) \cdot dA$$

where both surface integrals are over the same surface, arbitrary in size, shape, and orientation. We conclude that the integrands must therefore be equal and

$$\nabla \times E = -\partial B/\partial t \qquad (19\text{-}4\text{-}5)$$

This is the infinitesimal form of Faraday's law.

(e) *The conservation of electric charge.* Let us imagine that a closed region in space contains a charge q and that a conduction current density j_c flows outward through the boundary of the region. The total rate at which charge is leaving the region is the surface integral of $j_c \cdot dA$, and if charge can be neither created nor destroyed, this must be the rate at which q decreases. Thus

$$\int_{\text{O}\rightarrow} j_c \cdot dA = -dq/dt \qquad (19\text{-}4\text{-}6)$$

Now express q in terms of the charge density $\rho(x, y, z, t)$ inside the region. The right side of (19-4-6) is

$$-d/dt \int \rho \, dv = - \int (\partial\rho/\partial t) \, dv \qquad (19\text{-}4\text{-}7)$$

if we assume that the boundary of the region is fixed in space so that ρ is the only thing that is changing. We can use the divergence theorem to rewrite the left side of (19-4-6) as a volume integral, so that

$$\int \nabla \cdot j_c \, dv = - \int (\partial\rho/\partial t) \, dv$$

From this, since the volume of integration is arbitrary and the same on both sides, we conclude as before that the integrands are equal and that the conservation of electric charge is expressed by the law

$$\nabla \cdot j_c = -\partial\rho/\partial t \qquad (19\text{-}4\text{-}8)$$

Now let us gather together the various differential equations which we have found:

$$
\left.
\begin{aligned}
\nabla \cdot E &= \frac{\rho}{\varepsilon_0} & \text{(A)} \\[4pt]
\nabla \cdot B &= 0 & \text{(B)} \\[4pt]
\nabla \times B &= \mu_0 \varepsilon_0 \frac{\partial E}{\partial t} + \mu_0 j_c & \text{(C)} \\[4pt]
\nabla \times E &= -\frac{\partial B}{\partial t} & \text{(D)} \\[4pt]
\nabla \cdot j_c &= -\frac{\partial \rho}{\partial t} & \text{(E)}
\end{aligned}
\right\} \qquad (19\text{-}4\text{-}9)
$$

These are Maxwell's equations for the electromagnetic field, derived in essentially the present form in 1865, and they contain all the information necessary to characterize the field, its generation, its propagation through space, and its final absorption.

The most obvious feature of these equations is the complexity of the relationships they represent. There are, however, some connections between the equations which make them easier to understand. Let us, for example, take the divergence of both sides of (C). By (19–3–10) we have

$$0 = \mu_0 \varepsilon_0 \, (\partial/\partial t) \, \nabla \cdot E + \mu_0 \nabla \cdot j_c \qquad (19\text{–}4\text{–}10)$$

because the order of differentiation is immaterial. Cancelling the μ_0's and expressing $\nabla \cdot E$ by means of (A) gives

$$0 = \partial \rho / \partial t \; | \; \nabla \cdot j_c$$

which is the conservation law (E). This law is therefore built into Maxwell's theory, but only if the current j in (19–3–7) is taken to include the displacement current, and it is the immediate reason for adopting Maxwell's hypothesis. The ultimate reason is, as we said in Sec. 14–11, that the entire theory agrees with experiment when the displacement current is included.

Since (E) is contained in (A) and (C), we shall generally omit it from further consideration. The number of equations remaining, if we count each vector equation as three, is

$$\text{(A) (B) (C) (D)}$$
$$1 + 1 + 3 + 3 = 8$$

whereas E and B comprise only 6 quantities and are therefore over-determined by the equations. Since this fact leads to some question as to what the extra two equations are for, we digress for a moment to discuss it. Let us take the time derivative of the quantity $\nabla \cdot E - \rho/\varepsilon_0$. The use of (E) and (19–4–10), which came from (C), shows easily that

$$(\partial/\partial t)(\nabla \cdot E - \rho/\varepsilon_0) = 0 \qquad (19\text{–}4\text{–}11)$$

and we can show analogously that

$$(\partial/\partial t)(\nabla \cdot B) = 0 \qquad (19\text{–}4\text{–}12)$$

Suppose now that the field is such that at some initial moment (A) and (B) are satisfied. Equations (19–4–11) and (19–4–12) show that they will automatically go on being satisfied as a consequence of (C) and (D) without our having to think of them again. As an extreme example, suppose that the region of space in which we are interested is initially empty of charges, currents, and fields, so that (A) and (B) are satisfied trivially. If now charges move in so that the fields are established, they will automatically continue to obey (A) and (B), as long as the 6 equations (C) and (D) are satisfied. Maxwell's equations then, are really 6 equations in 6 unknowns, (A) and (B) being in the nature of initial conditions. Still, however, the equations (19–4–9) represent interrelations whose physical content is very involved; therefore our next step must be to try to form some conception of it by considering an extremely simple special case.

19-5 ELECTROMAGNETIC WAVES

The main obstacle to grasping the physical content of Maxwell's equations and to solving them is the way in which the 6 variables are entangled together. We must therefore look for situations in which they can be disentangled, so that we can concentrate on solving for one unknown at a time. This is not hard to do if (a) we consider the propagation of fields in empty space where j_c and ρ are zero and (b) we use Cartesian coordinates. The equations to be solved are then

$$
\left.
\begin{array}{ll}
\mathbf{\nabla \cdot E} = 0 & \text{(A$'$)} \\
\mathbf{\nabla \cdot B} = 0 & \text{(B$'$)} \\
\mathbf{\nabla \times B} = \mu_0 \varepsilon_0\, \partial E/\partial t & \text{(C$'$)} \\
\mathbf{\nabla \times E} = -\partial B/\partial t & \text{(D$'$)}
\end{array}
\right\}
\qquad \text{(19-5-1)}
$$

where the asymmetry of the minus sign in (D$'$) should again be noted. Let us take the curl of both sides of (D$'$),

$$
\mathbf{\nabla \times (\nabla \times E)} = -\frac{\partial}{\partial t}(\mathbf{\nabla \times B})
$$

To simplify the left side, we use the easily verified relation (see Problem 19-4) that for any vector G expressed in Cartesian coordinates

$$
\mathbf{\nabla \times (\nabla \times G)} = \mathbf{\nabla(\nabla \cdot G)} - \nabla^2 G \qquad \text{(19-5-2)}
$$

where the first term on the right means that we first find the divergence $\mathbf{\nabla \cdot G}$ and then take the gradient of it, while the second term is a vector whose three components are $\nabla^2 G_x$, $\nabla^2 G_y$, and $\nabla^2 G_z$. We have therefore

$$
\mathbf{\nabla(\nabla \cdot E)} - \nabla^2 E = -(\partial/\partial t)(\mathbf{\nabla \times B})
$$

The first term of this vanishes by (A$'$), while the right-hand side is simplified by (C$'$) to give

$$
\nabla^2 E - \mu_0 \varepsilon_0\, \partial^2 E/\partial t^2 = 0 \qquad \text{(19-5-3)}
$$

and in exactly the same way,

$$
\nabla^2 B - \mu_0 \varepsilon_0\, \partial^2 B/\partial t^2 = 0 \qquad \text{(19-5-4)}
$$

Each of the 6 field components has its separate equation, all of which are identical, and the disentanglement is complete. The simplicity of the result makes it obvious why we elected to express the fundamental properties of the field in differential form.

The equation satisfied by the components of E and B is known as *d'Alembert's equation*, and it is the basic mathematical expression of a wave. Suppose for example that E lies parallel to the Z-axis and it varies only along the Y-axis. Then (19-5-3) reduces to

$$
\frac{\partial^2 E_z}{\partial y^2} - \mu_0 \varepsilon_0 \frac{\partial^2 E_z}{\partial t^2} = 0 \qquad \text{(19-5-5)}
$$

If this is to represent a wave of E_z, this means that E_z must fluctuate periodically in space and time as a wave does. Leaving complicated waveforms for later mention, we can represent the simplest type of traveling wave in the manner of Fig. 19–5–1, where the solid line represents the value of E_z everywhere at some time, say $t = 0$, and the dotted line shows E_z at a time t, a little later. This represents a wave traveling to the right in the direction of the Y-axis. Now we must write the expression for E_z as a function of y and t. The solid line of Fig. 19–5–1 is represented by the formula $E_z = E_m \sin(2\pi y/\lambda)$, which oscillates through a complete cycle as y varies from 0 to λ. The dotted curve is represented by a formula of the same kind, in which, however, the origin of the wave is shifted a distance δ, $E_z = E_m \sin[2\pi(y - \delta)/\lambda]$. Now, how big is δ? If the wave is traveling with a constant velocity c, then δ is the distance it travels in time t between the two snapshots of Fig. 19–5–1, or $\delta = ct$. Thus

$$E_z(y, t) = E_m \sin[2\pi(y - ct)/\lambda] \tag{19–5–6}$$

(or one could also use a cosine instead of the sine). Direct substitution of this

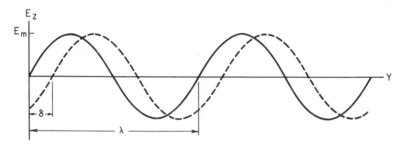

Figure 19–5–1. The form of a simple sinusoidal wave at two successive instants of time. (The dotted curve shows the wave at the later instant.) The wavelength of the wave is λ, and its amplitude is E_m.

into (19–5–5) shows that the equation is satisfied for all values of λ provided only that

$$c = 1/\sqrt{\mu_0 \varepsilon_0} \tag{19–5–7}$$

With the known values of ε_0 and μ_0 this gives

$$c = 2.9978 \times 10^8 \text{ m/sec} = 186,300 \text{ mi/sec} \tag{19–5–8}$$

and we see that all forms of electromagnetic radiation travel through space at the same fundamental speed. You are asked in Problem 19–5 to show that the units of c computed from (19–5–7) are indeed those of a velocity.

The remarkable thing about this result is that (19–5–8) corresponds very closely to the known value of the speed of light. In Maxwell's time this speed had already been measured with considerable accuracy, and the close coincidence with this theoretical speed was very surprising, since it had not generally been thought that light had anything to do with electromagnetism. One was forced to conclude that light might be an electromagnetic wave of the sort we have been discussing. In the years since Maxwell's discovery this possibility has hardened into a certainty, and we can add to the list x-rays, γ-rays of radioactivity, and radio waves, all of which seem to travel at precisely the same velocity c in a vacuum and which differ only in being waves of greater or smaller wavelengths.*

Equation (19–5–7) is generally regarded as the high point in the physics of the nineteenth century and, indeed, as one of the great scientific achievements of mankind. We must add though that such discoveries are never made in isolation. The idea, without any numbers attached, had been suggested in general terms by Faraday in a paper, "Thoughts on Wave-Vibrations," written several years earlier. A relation equivalent to (19–5–7) had been discovered experimentally, with no logic whatever to explain it, as early as 1849, and the Maxwell theory itself has only gradually evolved to the form in which it is here presented. In fact Maxwell's first derivation, in 1861, was based on an elaborate theory of the mechanical properties of the ether which has, essentially, no physical connection whatever with the more modern derivation, much like this one, which he published four years later.

Equation (19–5–6) represents a field of infinite extent, propagating in a straight line. The surfaces of constant phase (i.e., the wave fronts) are infinite planes perpendicular to the Y-axis. Such a *plane wave*, as it is called, is of course an idealization, but it provides an accurate and simple picture of what is going on in any part of a real electromagnetic wave at points far enough from the source so that the wave fronts do not curve very much in a distance of a few wavelengths. Closer than this, the fields are related in a rather involved way, therefore we shall not attempt to discuss them.

Next we must find the value of B. This can best be done from (D′). The only derivative of E contributing to the curl is $\partial E_z/\partial y$; therefore, only $\partial B_x/\partial t$ is different from zero,

$$\partial B_x(y, t)/\partial t = -\partial E_z/\partial y$$

So, using (19–5–6) for E_z,

$$\partial B_x(y, t)/\partial t = -(2\pi E_m/\lambda) \cos [2\pi(y - ct)/\lambda]$$

B_x can be found from this as an indefinite integral

$$B_x(y, t) = -(2\pi E_m/\lambda) \int \cos [2\pi(y - ct)/\lambda] \, dt$$

plus any arbitrary function of y alone. (To see this, differentiate it with respect to t.) Since a wave is not going to involve components which are constant in time, we conclude that the arbitrary function is zero. On performing the integration, we find

$$B_x(y, t) = (E_m/c) \sin [2\pi(y - ct)/\lambda]$$

Thus B_x is again of the form

$$B_x(y, t) = B_m \sin [2\pi(y - ct)/\lambda], \quad \text{with} \quad B_m = E_m \sqrt{\mu_0 \varepsilon_0} \quad (19\text{–}5\text{–}9)$$

and in general, $$B_x(y, t) = \sqrt{\mu_0 \varepsilon_0} \, E_z(y, t) \qquad (19\text{–}5\text{–}10)$$

The spatial relationship between the two waves is shown in Fig. 19–5–2.

* A detailed chart of the entire electromagnetic spectrum is contained in the issue of *Electronics* for March, 1954.

Another way to write the relationship between the electric and magnetic field strengths is to introduce $H_m = B_m/\mu_0$, so that

$$E_m = \sqrt{\mu_0/\varepsilon_0}\, H_m \qquad (19\text{–}5\text{–}11)$$

The quantity $\sqrt{\mu_0/\varepsilon_0}$ is, like c, a universal constant, and on working out its magnitude and units one finds $\sqrt{\mu_0/\varepsilon_0} = 377$ ohms approximately, which leads to its somewhat loose designation as the *wave resistance of free space*. We shall see in the next section what (19–5–10) means physically.

If the electromagnetic wave is propagating in a medium whose permeability is μ and whose permittivity is ε, then the whole argument goes through as before with the replacement of these quantities for μ_0 and ε_0. In particular, the speed of propagation comes out to be

$$c_{\text{medium}} = 1/\sqrt{\mu\varepsilon} \qquad (19\text{–}5\text{–}12)$$

The general solutions of (19–5–1) include all kinds of disturbances

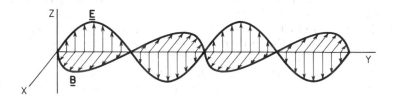

Figure 19–5–2. Plane electromagnetic wave moving toward the right along the Y-axis. B lies always 90 clockwise from E if one looks in the direction of propagation.

propagating at the speed c, and of these the plane waves are merely the simplest. But the simplicity of our result and the ease with which the equations were disentangled should not obscure the fact that only a special case of Maxwell's equations has been solved, in which the relation of the fields to their sources is ignored. The reader who attempts to tackle this problem by the methods used above will be disappointed. It is necessary to use a different and more sophisticated mathematical procedure.*

The reader will have noted that the electromagnetic waves discussed here are transverse, in that the directions of E and B are perpendicular to the direction of motion of the waves. We can show very easily, as follows, that the divergence conditions of (19–5–1), (A′) and (B′), imply that this will always be so. Suppose a plane wave moves along the Y-axis so that E depends only on y. Then (A′) says that

$$\partial E_x/\partial x + \partial E_y/\partial y + \partial E_z/\partial z = \partial E_y/\partial y = 0$$

since E is independent of x and z. But now we see the E_y must be independent of y also; so it must be constant in space or zero. Since constant fields do not

---

* W. T. Scott, *The Physics of Electricity and Magnetism* (New York: John Wiley & Sons, Inc., 1959), pp. 478–504.

interest us in this connection, we conclude that $E_y = 0$ and that the wave must therefore be transverse. The same applies to B, and finally the discussion above shows that E and B will always be perpendicular to each other as well as perpendicular to the direction of propagation.

19–6 ENERGY IN THE ELECTROMAGNETIC FIELD

In Secs. 12–5 and 16–8 we have discussed the idea that electric and magnetic fields can have energy. If a charge is moved in an electric field with the performance of work, one says in the language of elementary physics that the charge has acquired potential energy. But, in fact, nothing about the charge itself has changed, and the attribution to it of a changed property strikes some students as a little mysterious. The thing that has changed is the field, which depends on the entire arrangement of charges present, and it is often more convenient, as well as more logical, to say that the work has gone into building up the energy of the field. If we adopt this point of view, then we must be careful not to talk any more of the energies of the charges, for that would be to count the same thing twice. The idea of field energy gains strength from our knowledge that radiation (and, as we shall see, the energy it transports) which is emitted from a radiating source only appears at the receiver after a certain interval of time during which it was in transit, and the simplest way to regard this fact is to think of the energy lost by the radiator as stored in the field itself and traveling with it during this period. If this is true, we should expect that the energy of the field, being conserved, should satisfy a conservation law exactly analogous to (19–4–9) (E) describing the conservation of electric charge. That is, if $U(x, y, z, t)$ is a scalar which represents the energy density of the field at a given point and if $P(x, y, z, t)$ is a vector giving the energy transported per second past that point through a unit area normal to the direction of P, we would expect them to satisfy a relation of the form

$$\partial U/\partial t + \boldsymbol{\nabla} \cdot \boldsymbol{P} = 0 \qquad (19\text{–}6\text{–}1)$$

The electric and magnetic energy densities of static fields have already been found in (12–5–3) and (16–8–4).*

$$U_e = \varepsilon_0 E^2/2, \quad U_m = B^2/2\mu_0 \qquad (19\text{–}6\text{–}2)$$

There is of course no guarantee that these formulas continue to hold for changing fields, but let us nevertheless write U in (19–6–1) as $U_e + U_m$ and see what happens. We have

$$U = \tfrac{1}{2}(\varepsilon_0 \boldsymbol{E} \cdot \boldsymbol{E} + \boldsymbol{B} \cdot \boldsymbol{B}/\mu_0) \qquad (19\text{–}6\text{–}3)$$

so that $\qquad \partial U/\partial t = \varepsilon_0 \boldsymbol{E} \cdot \partial \boldsymbol{E}/\partial t + (1/\mu_0)\boldsymbol{B} \cdot (\partial \boldsymbol{B}/\partial t)$

Taking the time derivatives from (19–4–9) (C) and (D) we find

$$\partial U/\partial t = (1/\mu_0)[\boldsymbol{E} \cdot (\boldsymbol{\nabla} \times \boldsymbol{B}) - \boldsymbol{B} \cdot (\boldsymbol{\nabla} \times \boldsymbol{E})] - \boldsymbol{E} \cdot \boldsymbol{j}_c \qquad (19\text{–}6\text{–}4)$$

---

* The derivation of these expressions is discussed in more detail by D. Park, *Am. J. Phys.*, **24**, 78 (1956).

To simplify this, we use the vector identity (see Problem 19–7)

$$\boldsymbol{\nabla \cdot (F \times G)} = \boldsymbol{G \cdot (\nabla \times F)} - \boldsymbol{F \cdot (\nabla \times G)} \qquad (19\text{–}6\text{–}5)$$

so that (19–6–4) becomes

$$\partial U / \partial t = (1/\mu_0)[\boldsymbol{\nabla \cdot (B \times E)}] - \boldsymbol{E \cdot j_c} = -(1/\mu_0)[\boldsymbol{\nabla \cdot (E \times B)}] - \boldsymbol{E \cdot j_c}$$

Introducing the abbreviation

$$\boldsymbol{P} = (1/\mu_0)\boldsymbol{E \times B} = \boldsymbol{E \times H} \qquad (19\text{–}6\text{–}6)$$

we can rewrite the last equation as

$$\partial U / \partial t + \boldsymbol{E \cdot j_c} + \boldsymbol{\nabla \cdot P} = 0 \qquad (19\text{–}6\text{–}7)$$

If there are no currents present, (19–6–7) is exactly of the desired form (19–6–1) and this is why $\boldsymbol{P}$ is significant. But if moving charges are present, then the energy of the field is no longer conserved, since it can be transferred out of the field in the form of work done on the charges. One can easily convince oneself (see Problem 19–8) that $\boldsymbol{E \cdot j_c}$ is exactly the rate at which the field energy per unit volume is depleted by such a process. Thus (19–6–7) represents the conservation of electromagnetic energy in its most general form, and the vector $\boldsymbol{P}$ given by (19–6–6) represents a directed flow of power through space. These facts were first discovered in 1884 by John Henry Poynting, and $\boldsymbol{P}$, with the units of watts/m², is known as Poynting's vector.

Let us look again at the plane waves described by (19–5–6) and (19–5–9). The instantaneous electric and magnetic energy densities are

$$U_e = \tfrac{1}{2}\varepsilon_0 E_m^2 \sin^2 [2\pi(y - ct)/\lambda]$$

$$U_m = (1/2\mu_0) B_m^2 \sin^2 [2\pi(y - ct)/\lambda]$$

Taking the time average energy densities (as we did in Sec. 4–11), we have at any point in space $\bar{U}_e = \varepsilon_0 E_m^2/4$, $\bar{U}_m = B_m^2/4\mu_0$, $\bar{U} = \bar{U}_e + \bar{U}_m$, where, of course, the energy densities will be in joules/m³. Substituting (19–5–10) for B_m in $\bar{U}_m$ shows that in a plane wave $\bar{U}_e = \bar{U}_m$, so the energy of the field is equally divided between its electric and magnetic components. This is the physical content of (19–5–10), and the average energy density may be written as

$$\bar{U} = \varepsilon_0 E_m^2/2 = B_m^2/2\mu_0 \qquad (19\text{–}6\text{–}8)$$

or, in terms of the rms values of the field strengths,

$$\bar{U} = \varepsilon_0 E^2 = B^2/\mu_0$$

Again the Poynting energy flux calculated from (19–5–6) and (19–5–9) is, as expected, directed along the Y-axis, and using (19–6–6) you can show that it is equal to

$$P_y = \sqrt{\varepsilon_0/\mu_0}\, E_m^2 \sin^2 [2\pi(y - ct)/\lambda] \qquad (19\text{–}6\text{–}9)$$

and the time average is

$$\bar{P}_y = \tfrac{1}{2}\sqrt{\varepsilon_0/\mu_0}\, E_m^2$$

in the units of watts/m². With (19–6–8) and (19–5–7), it follows that

$$\bar{P}_y = c\bar{U} \tag{19–6–10}$$

The intensity of electromagnetic wave is thus proportional to the square of the amplitude of the wave, a relationship which is characteristic of all kinds of wave motion.*

It is easy to see what the relation (19–6–10) means. Consider the arrangement shown in Fig. 19–6–1 in which a plane wave of limited extent (though owing to diffraction such a wave will never be quite plane) falls on a black surface which absorbs all of it. Draw a cylinder of length l, area A, and volume V, and suppose it contains a quantity of energy W, flowing towards the right with velocity v. At the end of a time l/v

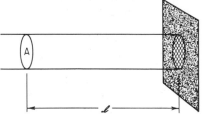

Figure 19–6–1. A beam of light of cross section A incident on a black screen.

this energy will all have flowed into the surface; so the mean power per unit area is

$$\bar{P} = \frac{W}{(l/v)A} = \frac{Wv}{Al} = v\frac{W}{V}$$

or v times the energy per unit volume in the beam. Comparison with (19–6–10) shows that the electromagnetic wave carries its energy at the speed c, a result which though not surprising was by no means obvious, since there are various kinds of waves which transport energy at a speed different from their wave velocity.

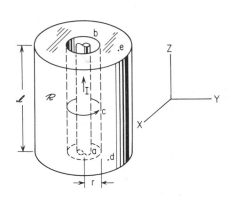

Figure 19–6–2. To find the Poynting flux in the vicinity of a current-carrying segment of wire.

As an example of the application of Poynting's theorem in a field which is not of the form of a wave, let us consider the flow of power in the space surrounding the segment ab, in Fig. 19–6–2, of a very long straight wire of finite resistance carrying a steady current I. We shall apply Poynting's theorem, $P = E \times H$, to the region $\mathscr{R}$, a cylinder from which the volume occupied by the wire has been cut out.

Let us first calculate the power flowing through the inner boundary of $\mathscr{R}$ towards the wire. Evaluating it at the typical point c in the YZ-plane, we wish to find the component $P_y =$

* See Halliday and Resnick, *Physics for Students of Science and Engineering* (New York: John Wiley & Sons, Inc., 1960), p. 406.

$E_z H_x - E_x H_z = E_z H_x$ since H has no Z component. The value of E_z at c near the wire is given by

$$E_z = V/l \qquad (19\text{-}6\text{-}11)$$

where V is the potential difference between the ends a and b of the segment of wire. (To see this, imagine that a test charge q' is carried from a to b through c, requiring an amount of work $q'V = q'E_z l$.) The magnetic field intensity at c is in the negative X direction and is given by (14-3-6) as

$$H_x = -I/2\pi r \qquad (19\text{-}6\text{-}12)$$

Thus we find $\qquad P_y = E_z H_x = -IV/2\pi rl$

in watts/m^2, where the negative sign denotes a flow toward the left. To find the total power flowing into the wire, we let c lie near the surface and integrate over the whole area of the wire, $2\pi rl$. We thus find a flow of energy into the wire equal to IV as required by Joule's law. It is not the result that is significant but the reasoning used to obtain it. We have considered the electrons moving in the wire only as a guide for an electromagnetic field in space which carries all the energy in the circuit. The Joule heat in the wire appears only because the existence of a voltage drop produces a small inward flow of energy which, being conserved, appears in the form of heat.

An interesting conclusion regarding the electric field around a current-carrying wire can be drawn from our results. The true significance of a differential relation such as (19-4-8) or (19-6-1) lies in the integral conservation law (19-4-6) or

$$\int_{\circlearrowright} \mathbf{P} \cdot d\mathbf{A} = -\frac{dW}{dt}, \qquad W = \int U\, dv \qquad (19\text{-}6\text{-}13)$$

to which it is equivalent. Let us apply this to the region $\mathscr{R}$. If a constant current is flowing, all the fields are steady and U is a constant. Thus the time derivative in (19-6-13) is zero, and the vanishing of the surface integral shows that just as much power flows into $\mathscr{R}$ as flows out of it. We have just seen that an amount IV flows out through the inner surface. Further we can take the outer surface to be at an enormous distance, so all the fields vanish and no power flows through it. There remain the top and the bottom, and we see that there must be a flux of field energy parallel to the wire. (It flows in through one end of $\mathscr{R}$, and what does not pass into the wire goes out through the other.) The Poynting vector evaluated at the point d in Fig. 19-6-2 must therefore have a Z component

$$P_z = E_x H_y - E_y H_x = -E_y H_x$$

since H_y is zero at d. This shows that the electric field around the wire has a radial component $E_y = E_r$ at point d. We see further that, since the flow out through the top must be less than that in through the bottom, the value of E_r must vary along the wire, being smaller at e than at d. It can be shown* that this radial field is in fact due to a very slight surface charge which forms itself

---

* A. Sommerfeld, *Electrodynamics* (New York: Academic Press, Inc., 1952), sec. 17. With a little care you will be able to follow this clear and interesting discussion.

on the surface of a current-carrying wire. On working out the magnitudes, one finds that the field energy is exactly conserved.

The reader should note with care that we do not observe experimentally the conservation of charge and of energy at each individual point of space, but only over finite regions. Suppose now we have the device shown in Fig. 19–6–3, where a bar magnet is balanced on a dry cell. Clearly nothing is changing, so no energy flows at all. Yet there is E and B at every point of space and P is not zero. The Poynting vector is in this case entirely fictitious, a mathematical accident, as can be seen from (19–6–13), where, since dW/dt is zero for any region of space in the neighborhood of the apparatus, the integral of P over any closed surface must vanish. Most numerical calculations in Maxwell's theory involve finally the determination of an energy or a power;

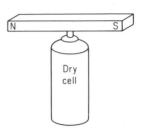

Figure **19–6–3.** In this arrangement, the Poynting flux is clearly fictitious.

so it is really the value of a surface integral of P that counts, as in the last example, and this integral will always turn out to be correct. Only in a field of radiation at great distances from the source is it safe to interpret P as a power flow.

19–7 SOME CONSEQUENCES OF MAXWELL'S THEORY

In order to illustrate some of the applications of the foregoing ideas, we shall consider several examples of the behavior of light with which you will already be familiar.

1. POLARIZATION OF ELECTROMAGNETIC WAVES. It is clear from what we have said that when the wavelength and direction of motion of an electromagnetic wave have been given, the wave is still not completely specified. One must give, in addition, the plane in which one of the field vectors lies, the other being determined thereby as in Fig. 19–5–2, and also the amplitude of the oscillations of one of the field vectors, the other then being determined by (19–5–10). Two plane waves which are alike except for the direction of their E and B vectors are still physically different. If their wavelength puts them in the range of visible light, they can be distinguished by means of a piece of Polaroid or a Nicol prism; whereas anyone who has experimented turning a dipole radio antenna at different angles to get the loudest possible signal has actually been at work aligning the dipole so that it lies parallel to the E vector of the incoming wave. The plane which contains the E vector of a polarized beam is usually called the *plane of vibration*. Of course, not all light waves are polarized, though most radio waves are, but the nearly unpolarized light coming from an electric lamp, for example, may be regarded as a superposition of waves polarized in all different directions.

2. THE REFRACTION OF LIGHT. It has long been known, and the proof is in any elementary text, that if a light wave moves from a region in which its

velocity is greater into one in which it is less, the direction of the beam is refracted towards the normal to the interface. Snell's law says that

$$\sin i/\sin r = n \qquad (19\text{–}7\text{–}1)$$

where i is the angle of incidence, r is the angle of refraction (measured between the beam and the normal), and n is the index of refraction, defined as the ratio of the greater velocity to the smaller one. Let us suppose for definiteness that the beam passes from air (essentially a vacuum) into water, whose permittivity is ε and whose permeability is essentially that of air. We have mentioned before that Maxwell's theory applies to any suitable dielectric (we shall see in the next paragraph what "suitable" means) with the replacement of ε_0 by ε and μ_0 (if necessary) by μ. In our case, the speed of light in the water is $1/\sqrt{\mu_0\varepsilon}$; so the ratio of the velocities in air and water is

$$n = \sqrt{\varepsilon/\varepsilon_0} = \sqrt{\varepsilon_r} \qquad (19\text{–}7\text{–}2)$$

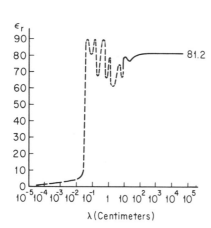

Figure 19–7–1. Values fo ε_r for water at various wavelengths. The irregularities in the middle of the graph are the effects of resonances in the molecular structure of water, and the curve is dashed here because, for some of these wavelengths, water is so opaque (i.e. absorbs so much of the incident radiation) that the ideas of this chapter are hardly applicable. Along the lower part of the curve there are still resonances, but between them are intervals over which water seems to be perfectly transparent. These regions of transparency are indicated by longer dashes. The data summarized here are for room temperature and were obtained chiefly from *Properties of Ordinary Water-Substance* compiled by N. E. Dorsey (New York: Reinhold Publishing Corp., 1940).

by (11–5–14), where ε_r is the relative dielectric constant of water. Note however, that the relevant values of ε_r are not those given in Table 11–1, for ε_r is a function of the frequency at which it is measured, and the values in Table 11–1 are for constant voltages. In Fig. 19–7–1 are values of ε_r for water at various wavelengths of electromagnetic radiation.

It would appear from what we have said that, at least over a suitable range of wavelengths, all dielectrics should be transparent, since the equations by which we have discussed the electromagnetic theory hold in the interior of any dielectric. But one of the assumptions in the discussion was that the dielectric considered would be *homogeneous*, and this property is actually possessed by relatively few substances. A piece of ordinary glass is essentially homogeneous, and so is a sample of pure water or alcohol. The reason why these are transparent and why a piece of fine clay, for example, which might be pure aluminum silicate, is not, is that under ordinary circumstances aluminum silicate does not occur as a homogeneous mass. A sample of clay, however fine, is composed of microscopic crystalline bits, and the opacity of the clay is due to the reflection of the light from the surfaces of the crystals. (Even so, good porcelain is rather translucent.)

On the other hand, consider a piece of an electric conductor, say a sample of metal. In the interior of this the conditions for the propagation of a Maxwellian wave cannot be met. Essentially, we cannot have an electric field inside a piece of metal, for a current would at once flow and neutralize it. If the conductivity of the metal is finite, the light incident from outside penetrates a very short distance into a conductor, and is nearly all reflected. The fact of penetration can be verified if one holds a piece of gold leaf up to the light. It is so thin that some of the light gets through.

We shall discuss below in greater detail the normal reflection of light from plane surfaces of metal or dielectric. For a more complete treatment, see a text on physical optics.*

3. METALLIC REFLECTION. In the discussion which follows, we shall assume that the metal under consideration is a perfect conductor. Under ordinary circumstances, no metal is a perfect conductor, but almost all are good enough so that what we shall say is applicable.

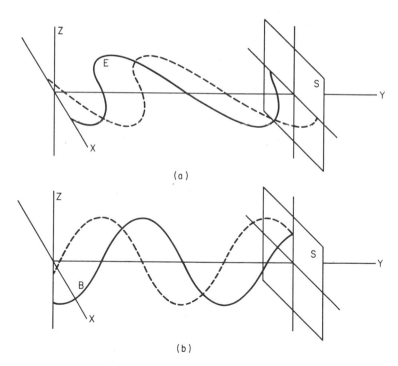

(a)

(b)

Figure 19-7-2. Incident (solid) and reflected (dashed) waves of E and B in reflection from a conducting surface, S.

---

* An excellent text is F. A. Jenkins and H. E. White, *Fundamentals of Optics*, 3d ed. (New York: McGraw-Hill Book Company, Inc., 1957); also C. L. Andrews, *Optics of Electromagnetic Spectrum* (Englewood Cliffs, N.J.: Prentice-Hall, Inc., 1960).

In Chapter XI we have discussed the behavior of the electric field on the two sides of a plane interface between two media, and (11–8–2) expresses the fact that the tangential component of E must change continuously as the boundary is crossed. But inside a perfect conductor, E would be zero, so the tangential component of E must vanish just outside the metal surface also. Suppose now that the electromagnetic wave of Fig. 19–5–2 is incident normally on a flat metal surface. Here E is entirely tangential to the surface, and therefore must vanish there. But this clearly does not happen if the light wave goes on and enters the surface. Therefore, the wave can neither be transmitted nor absorbed at the surface—in fact, the only way in which the boundary condition can be satisfied is if the incident wave gives rise to another wave which starts at the metallic surface with an E which is always equal and opposite to that of the incident wave. Such a wave is the reflected wave, equal in amplitude and frequency to the incident one and moving in the opposite direction. The situation is shown in Fig. 19–7–2 (a). This reflection is analogous to that of a sound wave at the end of a closed organ pipe.

Let us now look at the B vector in the incident and reflected waves. The rule for the direction of B relative to E is given in the caption of Fig. 19–5–2. From this it follows that, while the E vectors cancel at the interface, the B vectors add there, producing a varying magnetic field. This is shown in Fig. 19–7–2 (b). A more general discussion, extended to the case in which the incidence of the ray is not normal, leads to the familiar law of reflection: the angles of incidence and reflection are equal. These elementary remarks lead to no conclusions that are not obvious; they are included only to show how simple optical phenomena can be discussed in terms of the electromagnetic theory.

4. REFLECTION FROM THE SURFACE OF A DIELECTRIC. It is a matter of common experience that no sample of dielectric is "perfectly" transparent in the sense that all the light incident on the surface passes through. Rather, from any air-dielectric interface, unless it has been prepared in a very special way, a certain fraction of the light incident is always reflected—in fact, we always see two

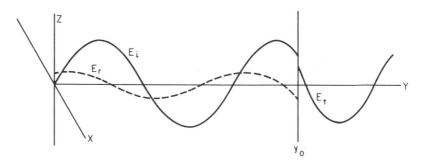

Figure 19–7–3. The E-waves of light passing from one transparent substance to another. E_i, E_r, and E_t, are instantaneous magnitudes of E in the incident, reflected, and transmitted parts respectively. The region to the left of the interface, y_0, is characterized by ε_1 and μ_0, and that to the right by ε_2 and μ_0.

reflections from any sheet of glass, one from each face. As before, we shall consider only normal incidence, since the more general case, though it introduces no new physical considerations, is rather more elaborate mathematically.

Let us assume that the magnetic properties of the two media are essentially those of the vacuum: $\mu_1 = \mu_2 = \mu_0$. Figure 19-7-3 shows the situation, where in the interests of clarity we have omitted the B-wave. The boundary condition to be satisfied is (11-8-1). At every instant, E is to be continuous at the boundary, or

$$E_i' + E_r' = E_t' \qquad (19\text{-}7\text{-}3)$$

where for simplicity of notation we denote by a prime the value which a field variable takes on at y_0 the position of the interface. Similarly, (16-9-3) implies that since there are no surface currents flowing, the tangential component of H, which is here its whole value, is also continuous at y_0. Let the path of integration in Ampere's circuital law (16-9-3) be the loop $abcd$ in Fig. 11-8-1. The vanishing of the line integral tells us that the contributions to $\oint H \cdot ds$ from the two sides of the boundary are equal and opposite; hence the tangential components of H are equal and in the same sense. Remembering that, as in the last section, if E does not change its direction at reflection H does, we have, at the boundary,

$$H_i' - H_r' = H_t' \qquad (19\text{-}7\text{-}4)$$

The solution of the problem consists in solving (19-7-3) and (19-7-4) under the condition (19-5-11), which in this case gives

$$\sqrt{\mu_0}\, H_i' = \sqrt{\varepsilon_1}\, E_i'$$
$$\sqrt{\mu_0}\, H_r' = \sqrt{\varepsilon_1}\, E_r'$$
$$\sqrt{\mu_0}\, H_t' = \sqrt{\varepsilon_2}\, E_t'$$

Multiply (19-7-4) by $\sqrt{\mu_0}$ and substitute these.

$$\sqrt{\varepsilon_1}\,(E_i' - E_r') = \sqrt{\varepsilon_2}\, E_t'$$

From (19-7-3), $\qquad \sqrt{\varepsilon_1}\,(E_i' + E_r') = \sqrt{\varepsilon_1}\, E_t'$

Add these equations. $\quad 2\sqrt{\varepsilon_1}\, E_i' = (\sqrt{\varepsilon_1} + \sqrt{\varepsilon_2})E_t'$

or $\qquad E_t' = 2\sqrt{\varepsilon_1}\, E_i'/(\sqrt{\varepsilon_1} + \sqrt{\varepsilon_2}) = 2E_i'/(1 + \sqrt{\varepsilon_2/\varepsilon_1}) \qquad (19\text{-}7\text{-}5)$

To identify the square root, let us consider the speed of light in the two media:

$$c_1 = 1/\sqrt{\mu_0\varepsilon_1}, \quad \text{and} \quad c_2 = 1/\sqrt{\mu_0\varepsilon_2}$$

whence $\qquad \sqrt{\varepsilon_2/\varepsilon_1} = c_1/c_2 = n_{12} \qquad (19\text{-}7\text{-}6)$

the *relative index of refraction* of the two media. Now (19-7-5) gives us the relation between the incident and transmitted beams in terms of this experimentally measurable number:

$$E_t' = \frac{2}{1 + n_{12}}\, E_i' \qquad (19\text{-}7\text{-}7)$$

Substitution of this into (19–7–3) gives us the strength of the reflected wave,

$$E'_r = \frac{1 - n_{12}}{1 + n_{12}} E'_i \tag{19–7–8}$$

$$= \frac{c_2 - c_1}{c_2 + c_1} E'_i \tag{19–7–9}$$

Let us define the reflection coefficient of this surface as the ratio of the power reflected from the surface to that incident on it. We can use (19–6–9) to write this as

$$R = P_r/P_i = E'^2_r/E'^2_i = [(1 - n_{12})/(1 + n_{12})]^2 = [(c_2 - c_1)/(c_2 + c_1)]^2 \tag{19–7–10}$$

The last way of writing this shows that R depends only on the difference of c_1 and c_2, but not on which is larger. Thus we get the important result that from whichever direction the light is (normally) incident on the surface, the fraction reflected is the same.

A typical sample of glass has an index of refraction with respect to air of about 1.5 at ordinary wavelengths of light. This gives $R = (0.5/2.5)^2 = 4\%$, so the fractional power reflected from the two surfaces of a plate of glass as light goes through it normally is in the neighborhood of 8%. This reflection is occasionally troublesome, particularly in the design of cameras, microscopes, and other optical instruments where the stray light that reflects from the lenses and gets trapped in this way in the spaces between them may diffuse through the instrument and fog the image. Measures can be taken to overcome this tendency,* by coating the lenses with suitable transparent substances (the bluish color of the lenses of an expensive camera is due to this coating), but the reflection cannot be completely eliminated in any way.

Let us now examine briefly the question of the *phase* of the reflected light, supposing that the light (see Fig. 19–7–3) is incident from air onto a denser medium, such as glass. In this case $n_{12} > 1$, and, in (19–7–8), E'_r and E'_i have opposite signs but are otherwise proportional. That is, if we write

$$E_i = E_m \sin [2\pi(y - c_1 t)/\lambda] \tag{19–7–11}$$

whence

$$E'_i = E_m \sin [2\pi(y_0 - c_1 t)/\lambda]$$

then

$$E'_r = -\frac{n_{12} - 1}{n_{12} + 1} E_m \sin \left[\frac{2\pi}{\lambda} (y_0 + c_1 t)\right]$$

$$= \frac{n_{12} - 1}{n_{12} + 1} E_m \sin \left[\frac{2\pi}{\lambda} (y_0 + c_1 t) + \pi\right] \tag{19–7–12}$$

so that we may say that the phase of the light is changed 180° by the act of reflection. If, on the other hand, the light passes from glass to air, $n_{12} < 1$, E'_r and E'_i have the same sign, and no change of phase occurs. The existence of the change of phase can be inferred experimentally from the arrangement

* K. Blodgett, *Phys. Rev.*, **55**, 391 (1939).

known as *Lloyd's mirror*,* and it follows also from a theoretical argument due
to Stokes.†

This finishes our discussion of some of the applications of Maxwell's
theory in the field of optics. Nothing has been done here at all completely, but
it has perhaps sufficed to indicate the range and fertility of these relatively
simple ideas.

19–8 RELATIVE MOTION

In this section we shall discuss some of the things which are found when we
regard the same phenomena from different systems of reference. Some of them
are already familiar. If for example we walk with velocity v through a magnetic field carrying a suitably oriented pair of probes connected to a voltmeter, we find a voltage developed. The elementary way to describe this fact
is to say that a voltage is induced when a wire "cuts magnetic flux lines." But
such a formulation is unsatisfactory. For one thing, there is really no such
thing as a flux line; it is a convenient though somewhat slippery‡ abstraction,
so this formulation gives no hint of why or how the induced voltage comes
about. We therefore look a little more deeply and find, as we did in Chapters
III and XV, that the reason why a voltage is induced is that an electric charge
q moving through a magnetic field experiences a force $qv \times B$, and it is this
force that tends to drive electrons along the wire.

But this must not be regarded as *the* explanation of electromagnetic induction. Suppose for example that we hold the probes still and move the magnet
at the velocity $-v$. The same voltage is induced, but our explanation of the
fact is entirely different. Now the probes are at rest in a magnetic field which
changes in time as the magnet goes past. The electric field is explained by
(19–4–5) as an effect of the changing magnetic field.

There is nothing really wrong with giving a choice of two different explanations of a phenomenon depending on the viewpoint, but it is unpleasing to
one's sense of the economy of nature, for all experience shows that when two
things move relative to one another, physical consequences arise only from
their relative motion and do not depend on any supposition that one thing is
moving while the other is standing still.

Reflections like these were the starting point of Einstein's theory of relativity in 1905. We cannot here enter into any profound discussion of relativity, but there are a number of ideas in the theory which are not hard to get
at and which throw considerable light on the fundamental nature of the
various physical phenomena discussed in this book. To this end, let us see
what happens when we consider certain phenomena from systems of reference
which are in motion relative to each other.

The problem to be solved is this: Suppose there are two observers,
O and O', and O' is moving with respect to O at a velocity v. Observer O uses
various instruments and determines that there are fields present equal to

---

* Jenkins and White, op. cit., p. 238.
† *Ibid.*, Sec. 11–8, p. 199.
‡ J. Slepian, *Am. J. Phys.*, **19**, 87 (1951).

E and *B*. Observer O′ measures the same fields and finds the values *E*′ and *B*′. Are *E*′ and *B*′ the same as *E* and *B*, and if not, how do they differ?

We have two facts to guide us towards the answer. The first is that whereas a charged particle at rest is acted upon only by an electric field, in motion it responds also to a magnetic field. Suppose now that there is a particle of charge *q*, at rest with respect to O′ and therefore moving at velocity *v* with respect to O. Observer O′ can use it to measure the electric field *E*′, for the particle experiences a force *qE*′. But for O, if a magnetic field is also present, the force on the moving charge will be $q(E + v \times B)$, by (15–1–1). Since O′ and O measure the same force on the same particle,* we conclude that

$$E' = E + v \times B \qquad (19–8–1)$$

The second basic point is contained in the relation (19–5–10). If O sees a beam of light move through space with $B = E\sqrt{\mu_0\varepsilon_0}$, then as seen by O′ it is still a beam of light, even though its direction, due to aberration, and its frequency, due to Doppler effect, may have changed; therefore $B' = E'\sqrt{\mu_0\varepsilon_0}$. Since the various vectors all point in different directions, it is easier not to worry about the components and write merely

$$B^2 = \mu_0\varepsilon_0 E^2, \qquad B'^2 = \mu_0\varepsilon_0 E'^2 \qquad (19–8–2)(a)(b)$$

Let us suppose that the velocity *v* is not very great, so that the second term in (19–8–1) is much smaller than the first. Then we can omit its square in squaring *E*′, so that

$$E'^2 = E^2 + 2E\cdot(v \times B) \qquad (19–8–3)$$

Now let us suppose that $B' = B + K$ with *K* small, so that omitting K^2,

$$B'^2 = B^2 + 2K\cdot B \qquad (19–8–4)$$

We have from (19–8–2)(b)

$$B^2 + 2K\cdot B = \mu_0\varepsilon_0[E^2 + 2E\cdot(v \times B)]$$

so that, using (19–8–2)(a), $K\cdot B = \mu_0\varepsilon_0 E\cdot(v \times B)$. The last term can be transformed by the vector identity $F\cdot(G \times H) = (F \times G)\cdot H$ for any three vectors (see Problem 19–16), so that

$$K\cdot B = \mu_0\varepsilon_0(E \times v)\cdot B \qquad (19–8–5)$$

The relation was derived by studying a beam of light. We shall now assume that it is a general equation which gives *K* in all circumstances, even if *B* and *E* may be chosen quite independently of each other. Then (19–8–5) can be true only if

$$K = \mu_0\varepsilon_0 E \times v = -\mu_0\varepsilon_0 v \times E \qquad (19–8–6)$$

The transformations connecting the fields as seen by the two observers are thus

$$E' = E + v \times B \qquad (19–8–7)$$

and

$$B' = B - \mu_0\varepsilon_0 v \times E \qquad (19–8–8)$$

* A more sophisticated analysis shows that this is not exactly true, but the discrepancy is of the order of v^2/c^2, which is very small under ordinary circumstances and of the same order as other terms which we shall neglect throughout this treatment.

These relations are only approximate. We have neglected terms of the order of v^2 in their derivation, and there are in addition other corrections of the order of v^2 and higher which represent characteristically relativistic effects arising from the Lorentz transformation formulas. All these we ignore.

As we have seen, (19–8–7) describes the response of a particle to electric and magnetic fields. Now let us see what (19–8–8) has to say. It will be convenient to start by writing it as $\boldsymbol{B} = \boldsymbol{B}' + \mu_0\varepsilon_0 \boldsymbol{v} \times \boldsymbol{E}$ and then noting that since by (19–8–7), $\boldsymbol{v} \times \boldsymbol{E}$ differs from $\boldsymbol{v} \times \boldsymbol{E}'$ only by a term of order v^2, we can write

$$\boldsymbol{B} = \boldsymbol{B}' + \mu_0\varepsilon_0 \boldsymbol{v} \times \boldsymbol{E}' \qquad (19\text{–}8\text{–}9)$$

to the same accuracy as the rest of our equations. This is just the inverse of (19–8–8). It says, as one might expect, that the transformation which takes us from O′ back to O is the same as that which took us from O to O′ except that $\boldsymbol{v}$ has been replaced by $-\boldsymbol{v}$.

Suppose now that a charge dq is stationary with respect to O′ and moves past O with velocity $\boldsymbol{v}$. As seen by O′, it produces a Coulomb field

$$d\boldsymbol{E}' = dq\,\boldsymbol{i}_r/4\pi\varepsilon_0 r^2 \qquad (19\text{–}8\text{–}10)$$

where $\boldsymbol{i}_r$ is a unit vector pointing away from the charge, and produces no magnetic field. But according to (19–8–9), as seen by O, there is a magnetic field

$$d\boldsymbol{B} = \mu_0\varepsilon_0 \boldsymbol{v} \times d\boldsymbol{E}' = \mu_0\,dq\,\boldsymbol{v} \times \boldsymbol{i}_r/4\pi r^2 \qquad (19\text{–}8\text{–}11)$$

This formula has been known for many years. If we replace the charged particle by an equivalent element of current of length $d\boldsymbol{l}$, we have

$$\boldsymbol{v}\,dq = (d\boldsymbol{l}/dt)\,dq = (dq/dt)\,d\boldsymbol{l} = I\,d\boldsymbol{l}$$

because dt is the length of time it takes dq to go a distance $d\boldsymbol{l}$. Thus the field due to this element of current is

$$d\boldsymbol{B} = \mu_0 I\,d\boldsymbol{l} \times \boldsymbol{i}_r/4\pi r^2 \qquad (19\text{–}8\text{–}12)$$

and this is exactly Ampere's law as given in equation (14–1–4). We have the remarkable conclusion that the reason why Ampere's law looks somewhat like Coulomb's law is that it *is* Coulomb's law as seen from a different coordinate system.

As we have said above, (19–8–7) is the equation which describes how a magnetic field affects a moving charge. We have just seen that (19–8–8) describes how a moving charge produces a magnetic field. All physical effects of a magnetic field are ultimately accounted for by (19–8–7) (we have already mentioned, for example, the explanation of induced emf's), while all the known ways of producing magnetic fields (except, perhaps, the fields associated with the magnetic moments of elementary particles) involve (19–8–12). Thus we have produced an explanation of ordinary magnetic phenomena entirely in terms of the relative motions of charges and observers, and not involving any ideas of absolute motion or rest as do the explanations outlined at the beginning of this section. The equations (19–8–7) and (19–8–8), on which the new interpretation is based, have not, of course, been derived rigorously; the best approach is to study the transformation properties of Maxwell's equations under changes of coordinate system. But the above relations, modified to take into account relativistic phenomena which manifest themselves when v approaches the speed of light, are the basis of the relativistic theory of electric and magnetic fields, and they, together with Coulomb's law, sum up most of what is known concerning the basic phenomena of electricity and magnetism.

PROBLEMS

19–1 Prove that for any vector G, $\int_{\circlarrow} (\nabla \times G) \cdot dA = 0$ when the integration is over an arbitrary closed surface.

19–2 (a) Prove by direct differentiation that for any vector G and any scalar S, $\nabla \cdot (\nabla \times G) = 0$ and $\nabla \times (\nabla S) = 0$. (b) Prove the second of these identities by means of the divergence theorem and Stokes's theorem without performing any differentiations. (The first is proved in the text.)

19–3 Prove that if the vectors F and G satisfy $\int_{)\rightarrow} F \cdot dA = \int_{)\rightarrow} G \cdot dA$, when the integration on each side is over the same, arbitrary, non-closed surface, then $F = G$.

19–4 Prove Equation (19–5–2).

19–5 Show that the units of c as defined in (19–5–7) are those of a velocity.

19–6 Evaluate the magnitude and units of the "wave resistance of free space" defined in (19–5–11), and show that if c were exactly 3×10^8 m/sec, its value would be exactly 120π.

19–7 Prove the identity (19–6–5).

19–8 Show that if a conduction current j_c flows in the presence of an electric field E, the field does work on the current at a rate $E \cdot j_c$ per unit volume.

19–9 The potential difference between any two points in an electrostatic field E is independent of the path joining them. Show that this is equivalent to the statement that curl $E = 0$. Show that the curl of the coulomb field of a point charge is zero. Can one infer from this that the curl of any electrostatic E is zero?

19–10 The sun delivers an energy of 1.94 calories/cm²/min at the top of the earth's atmosphere. Find the energy density of the radiation at the sun's surface. (The sun's diameter is 1.39×10^6 km, and its mean distance from the earth is 149×10^6 km.)

19–11 In Sec. 19–6 we calculated the power flow in the field around a resistive wire. Discuss qualitatively the flow around a battery or other source of emf. Does this discussion help to clarify the essential nature of an emf?

19–12 (a) Calculate the rms values of E and B in the light 1.00 m from an electric lamp consuming 60 w, if 10% of this power is turned into light. (b) An antenna consisting of a straight length of wire 3.00 m long is used to receive the signal from a station broadcasting 10.0 kw at 800 kc, 100 km away. If the antenna is oriented so as to have induced in it the maximum possible voltage, what is the rms potential difference between its ends?

Assume that the angular distribution of the radiation is such that the antenna receives five times as much power as it would if the transmitter transmitted equally in all directions.

19–13 Write down formulas for the incident and reflected waves of B and E in Fig. 19–7–2, In what direction does Poynting's vector point in each case?

19–14 Prove that the total power leaving the surface at y_0 in Fig. 19–7–3 is equal to that arriving there.

19–15 Suppose that the two dielectrics of Fig. 19–7–3 have different μ's as well as different ε's What form would (19–7–10) take?

19–16 Prove that for any three vectors F, G, and H, $F \cdot (G \times H) = (F \times G) \cdot H$.

19–17 Consider two identical parallel wires carrying equal currents in the same direction. According to the law of interacting currents, they should attract each other. But the electrons in the two wires are stationary with respect to each other, and therefore should repel. How is this apparent contradiction settled?

19–18 Two identical beams of electrons travel parallel to each other through free space. Will they tend to move together or apart? Why?

19–19 To understand better the relation between Ampere's law (14–1–4) for the formation of a magnetic field and the Lorentz equation (15–1–1) for the effect of a magnetic field on a moving charge, consider the arrangement shown in Fig. 19–P–1, which shows a magnet (solenoid or iron bar) of pole strength m in the vicinity of a straight wire carrying a current I. Assume, as we did in Sec. 17–6, that magnetic poles (analogously to electric poles) are acted upon by a force given in (17–6–4) as $F = mB$ and that they produce a field given by $B = \mu_0 mr/4\pi r^3$, as you can show from (17–7–5). Calculate the force exerted by the current element dl on the pole m. By Newton's third law this determines the force exerted by the pole on the current element; from this deduce (15–1–1).

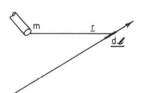

Figure 19–P–1. For calculating the force exerted on a current element by a magnet pole of strength m.

19–20 In a region empty of charges and currents, a changing magnetic induction B induces an electric field E whose components are

$$E_x = \tfrac{1}{2}yf(t), \quad E_y = -\tfrac{1}{2}xf(t), \quad E_z = 0$$

where $f(t)$ is independent of x, y, and z. Sketch the electric lines of force in this field. Now use the appropriate Maxwell equations to find out the B which caused it. Do B and E satisfy the rest of Maxwell's equations? What restrictions must be imposed on the function $f(t)$? Can you explain in a simple way the reason for these restrictions?

INSTRUMENTS

We have discussed a number of electrical instruments earlier, notably in Chapter XIII. Here we shall discuss a few more. This is not a text on electrical measurements, so we shall not pretend anything even approximating coverage of important electrical instruments. Our purpose, rather, is to illustrate further the use of the basic first principles presented in the text, and instruments are admirably suited to this end. In the selection of examples, we limit ourselves to some important instruments in the d-c and low-frequency a-c range and leave the sophisticated instruments to books* devoted to electrical measurement.

20–I THE D-C POTENTIOMETER

A potentiometer is an instrument for measuring an unknown emf, or potential difference, by balancing it against a known potential difference. The known potential difference is due to the flow of current through calibrated resistances. We shall first review the simple slide-wire potentiometer that is usually used in elementary laboratories. The theory of this simple instrument is basic for all potentiometers. Then we shall discuss one of the many types of potentiometers commonly used in electrical measurements laboratories. The potentiometer has a wide field of usefulness and is one of the more trustworthy and accurate instruments.

SIMPLE POTENTIOMETER. Figure 20–1–1 shows a schematic diagram of a simple potentiometer in which WW' represents the slide wire, so-called because of the sliding contact C. A ruler MM', calibrated in centimeters and subdivided into millimeters, is mounted as shown. The driving battery B sends a current continuously through the slide wire while the instrument is in use. The magnitude of this current may be adjusted by use of the rheostat Rh.

In a branch circuit below, WW' is a standard cell whose emf $\mathscr{E}_s$ is

---

* For example, Stout, M. B., *Basic Electrical Measurements* (Englewood Cliffs, N.J.: Prentice-Hall, Inc., 1950). Michels, W. C., *Electrical Measurements and Their Applications* (Princeton, N.J.: D. Van Nostrand Co., Inc., 1957). Harris, F. K., *Electrical Measurements* (New York: John Wiley & Sons, Inc., 1952).

accurately known, a battery whose emf $\mathcal{E}$ is to be measured, a protective resistance PR, a galvanometer G, and a tap key K. By means of the double pole double-throw switch S, either $\mathcal{E}_s$ or $\mathcal{E}$ may be connected in series in this branch circuit. Note the polarity of B relative to $\mathcal{E}_s$ or $\mathcal{E}$, whichever one is connected into the circuit.

The value of $\mathcal{E}_s$ is known, and the magnitude of $\mathcal{E}$ is to be determined in terms of $\mathcal{E}_s$. Let us say, to be explicit, that the emf $\mathcal{E}_s$ is 1.019 v, which is a common emf for a Weston standard cell. The measurement of $\mathcal{E}$ is made as follows: Close S so that $\mathcal{E}_s$ is in the branch circuit, adjust PR to a large value (about 50,000 ohms), set C at the position on WW' that corresponds in significant figures to the emf of the standard cell (i.e., set C at 101.9 cm as shown in Fig. 20–1–1), and then close K momentarily and note the direction of deflection of the galvanometer. In general the deflection will be large on this first try, but PR is in the circuit to protect the galvanometer from an excessive current and to protect the standard cell, since a standard cell will be ruined if more than a tiny current flows through it. The current through a

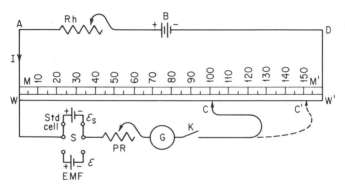

Figure 20–1–1. Simple slide wire potentiometer.

standard cell should not exceed 100 μa, and this current only momentarily. If the current through the standard cell exceeds this value appreciably, the cell must be set aside for several days or weeks to recover and then it must be tested for constancy of emf before use again. If its emf does not recover or is unsteady, the cell must be discarded. Hence great care is imperative in the use of a standard cell.

Adjust Rh to a value such that G shows little or no deflection when K is closed, then gradually decrease PR and make fine adjustments of Rh to the condition such that there is no deflection of G when K is closed and when PR is zero.

A zero reading of G when K is closed means that no current is flowing through the galvanometer branch, which in turn means that the potential difference between W and C is equal to the emf $\mathcal{E}_s$ of the standard cell. At this setting all the current I from B is flowing through the slide wire WW'; also, by the above setting of Rh, you have adjusted I to such a magnitude that the potential drop from W to C is equal to $\mathcal{E}_s$. Let us give this particular value of I the name I_s. As mentioned before, WW' has a uniform resistance per unit length; hence, with I_s flowing through WW', WW' has a uniform potential drop per unit length. In the specific numerical example we are using, it has a potential drop of 1.019 v in 101.9 cm or 0.01000 v/cm. The setting of Rh that we have just made is called *standardizing the potentiometer* to make it direct reading. Note that I_s must have a very definite value when the potentiometer is standardized, but we do not need to know this value of I_s. Also note that WW' must have a uniform resistance per unit length, but for measurement purposes we do not need to know this resistance per unit length.

Now we wish to measure the emf $\mathscr{E}$ of the unknown battery. Throw switch S to the contacts for $\mathscr{E}$ (thus removing $\mathscr{E}_s$ from the circuit), set PR back at its maximum value, leave Rh alone, and adjust C to a position (such as C') where G shows no deflection when K is closed. Decrease PR slowly and at the same time make fine adjustments of the position of C' until there is no deflection of G when K is closed even when PR is equal to zero. This means that the potential drop from W to C' is equal to the emf $\mathscr{E}$. Read the position C' on the ruler, multiply this reading by the potential drop per unit length of WW'; this is the emf of $\mathscr{E}$. To apply our numerical example, suppose that C' is 150.7 cm; then $\mathscr{E} = 150.7$ cm $\times$ .01000 v/cm $= 1.507$ v. The instrument is direct reading, for we merely move the decimal point to secure the value of $\mathscr{E}$.

The above assumes that I remained constant at I_s while the measurement of $\mathscr{E}$ was being made, which in turn assumes that the emf of B and the resistance of the loop $BAWW'DB$ both remained constant. After the current has been flowing through this loop for some time and temperature equilibrium has been reached, the resistance of the loop usually remains sufficiently constant. However, the driving battery B will fluctuate somewhat in emf and, if it is a freshly charged storage battery, its emf will decrease slowly but continuously for many hours. Thus, in general, I will not remain constant at I_s, and immediately after the C' position has been determined the standardization must be repeated. If there has been an appreciable change, C' must be redetermined. In any potentiometer, this process may have to be repeated several times before a good value of C' is secured, and the repetition cannot be done either quickly or easily with the simple potentiometer shown in Fig. 20–1–1.

One important feature of any potentiometer is that at balance no current flows through the branch circuit where the unknown is located. Thus the unknown battery is neither supplying nor receiving energy when the measurement is made, and its terminal potential difference is equal to its emf. Hence the potentiometer measures the emf of the battery. Contrast this situation with that encountered when a D'Arsonval voltmeter is connected across the terminals of a battery.

A MORE CONVENIENT AND PRECISE POTENTIOMETER. The simple potentiometer is rarely used, except for instructional purposes, because it is bulky, inconvenient, and its design does not permit the desired precision. We shall discuss the Leeds and Northrup type K–1 potentiometer as an example of a more precise and convenient instrument. The fundamental theory is the same as that for the simple slide-wire potentiometer, so we shall be concerned chiefly with the features that permit greater accuracy and convenience. The calibration of almost any electrical measuring instrument depends, directly or indirectly, on an accurate potentiometer reading of a d-c voltage somewhere along the chain of measurements that lead to its calibration. Hence it is worth our while to consider an accurate potentiometer before we consider other meters.

Figure 20–1–2 shows the simplified schematic circuit diagram of the Leeds and Northrup type K–1 potentiometer. The parts have been lettered in Fig. 20–1–2 to agree, as far as possible, with the corresponding parts in Fig.

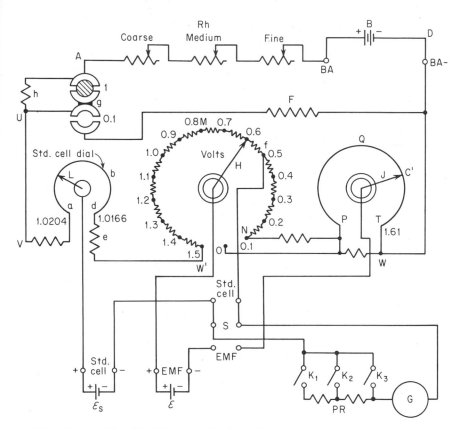

Figure 20–1–2. Simplified diagram, Leeds and Northrup type K–1 potentiometer.

20–1–1. The slide wire WW' has been replaced by 15 resistors, each of 5.0000 ohms, around the circle $W'MN$ and the shunted circular slide wire PQW. This shunted circular slide wire has a resistance of 5.5000 ohms. Now follow the main driving circuit, which corresponds to the loop $BAWW'DB$ in Fig. 20–1–1. In Fig. 20–1–2 this main driving circuit is $BAUabdeW'$-$MNPQTWDB$, and when the rheostat is set just right the battery B sends the standard current I_s through this driving circuit. When I_s flows in this circuit there is a drop in potential of 0.10000 v in each of the 15 resistors in the circle $W'MN$ and a drop in potential of 0.11000 v in the slide wire PQT. Thus there is a drop in potential of 1.61000 v between W and W'. This explains the number 1.61 written on the diagram at T. This means that I_s must have the value $I_s = 1.61000/80.5000 = 0.0200000$ amp.

Notice that the branch circuit below the main driving circuit in Fig. 20–1–2 is the same as the corresponding one in Fig. 20–1–1 except that the unknown battery (when it is in the circuit) has its positive terminal connected to arm H and its negative terminal connected to arm J, via the galvanometer circuit, and both arms can rotate. Another difference is that the standard cell (when it is in the circuit) has its negative terminal connected, via the galvanometer circuit, to the 0.5 v position of the circle $W'MN$ and its positive terminal connected to arm L of the $STD\ CELL\ DIAL$.

Now let us outline the standardization and use of this potentiometer. First set arm L on the dial position that corresponds to the known emf of the standard cell and leave it there. (For example, if the emf is 1.01884 v, set arm L on this position and the resistance along the path $LbdeW'M$ to f is 50.9420 ohms so that, when the current I_s flows, the potential difference between L and f will be equal to the emf of the standard cell.) Close S on the standard cell side and adjust Rh to such a value that the galvanometer G shows no deflection when K_1, then K_2, then K_3 is closed. (See Sec. 13–4 for galvanometer damping.) The potentiometer is now standardized and the current I_s is flowing in the driving circuit. The position of L is not changed, unless a different standard cell is used, so you may switch S to the standard cell position at any time and check the standardization without changing any other setting on the instrument. Thus the standardization may be checked quickly and easily and must be checked sufficiently frequently so that you know that the driving current is I_s when a measurement of an unknown is made.

Now switch S to the unknown emf position so that $\mathscr{E}$ is in series in the branch circuit. Leave Rh alone and adjust arms H and J for balance. The calibration markings at the positions of H and J then give a direct reading of the emf $\mathscr{E}$. The slide wire gives the subdivision of the 0.1 v steps on the circle $W'MN$, and the reading of the potentiometer is the sum of the readings indicated by arms H and J.

At g on the diagram, in Fig. 20–1–2, are two metal blocks with tapered holes and a tapered metal plug. During the above discussion the metal plug was inserted in hole 1 and all the driving current went through the three circles b, M, and Q as pointed out above. If, however, the metal plug is removed from hole 1 and put in hole 0.1, the main driving circuit is shunted by F and resistor h is put in series in the driving circuit. With this setting, I_s is not altered and one-tenth of I_s flows through the three circles b, M, and Q. Hence the potential drop across each resistor is one-tenth of its prior value, and any reading taken for an unknown must be multiplied by 0.1. The plug must always be in hole 1 before checking against the standard cell.

Leeds and Northrup types K–2 and K–3 potentiometers are similar to the K–1 except that they have an additional range for which the multiplier is 0.01, a circuit arrangement making it unnecessary to return to the 1 range when checking against the standard cell, and other important features which lead to greater accuracy, dependability, and ease of reading. For other types and makes of potentiometers and for details about standard cells, see a book on electrical measurements.*

CALIBRATION OF AN AMMETER. With a good potentiometer, standard cell, and some auxiliary apparatus, it is possible to calibrate many of the instruments used in electrical measurements. An ammeter, such as the D'Arsonval type, which is suitable for use on direct current, may be calibrated very easily. Figure 20–1–3 shows the auxiliary equipment needed, in addition to the potentiometer, for calibration of an ammeter. Here A is the ammeter that is to be calibrated, B is a battery to send a current I through the series circuit shown, Rh is a rheostat for the control of I, and R_s is a suitable standard known resistor. There are two sets of terminals on the standard resistor. The T_C terminals are the current connections, while the T_P terminals are the potential connections.

The calibration is very simple. Standardize the potentiometer and check the standardization frequently. Set the current through the ammeter so that its pointer is at a selected point on the scale, balance the potentiometer, and read the potential difference across R_s. With R_s and the potential drop across R_s known, I can be computed and the error of the ammeter noted. This

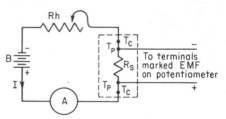

Figure 20–1–3. Auxiliary circuit for calibration of an ammeter.

procedure can be repeated for as many points on the ammeter scale as desired.

CALIBRATION OF A VOLTMETER. If a voltmeter has a range less than 1.6 v, it is obvious how the voltmeter may be calibrated directly by use of a potentiometer. If, however, the range of the voltmeter is greater than 1.6 v, a known fraction of the potential difference must be measured. Resistance boxes, especially designed for this purpose, are called *volt boxes* and are calibrated high-resistance potential dividers. A volt box is shown in Fig. 20–1–4 as VB. The resistance between T_1 and T_2 is an accurately known and labeled fraction (say one one-hundredth) of the total resistance between the two T_V terminals. Similarly the resistance between T_1 and T_3 is an accurately known fraction (say one-tenth) of the total resistance between the two T_V terminals. Sometimes the multiplying factor, instead of the fraction, is marked on the box. For example T_3 would be marked "10" if T_1 to T_3 were one-tenth of the total resistance.

The auxiliary circuit for calibration of the voltmeter is also shown in

---

* Stout, M. B., *Basic Electrical Measurements* (Englewood Cliffs, N.J.: Prentice-Hall, Inc., 1950), pp. 140–61. See also Harris, F. K., *Electrical Measurements* (New York: John Wiley & Sons, Inc., 1952), pp. 144–90.

Fig. 20–1–4, where B is a battery and PD is an uncalibrated potential divider used to regulate the voltage applied to the voltmeter V that is to be calibrated. The voltmeter calibration may be made quickly and simply using this circuit.

MEASUREMENT OF POWER WITH A POTENTIOMETER. The power input to a load on a d-c line may be measured indirectly by a potentiometer by using an ammeter and a voltmeter that have been calibrated on the potentiometer (see Sec. 20–8 for error of connection). Or the power may be measured directly. In this latter case, a standard resistor (like the one shown in Fig. 20–1–3) is connected in series with the load, and a volt box (like the one shown in Fig. 20–1–4) is connected across the load. Successive potentiometer measurements give values from which the current flowing through the load and the potential difference across the load may be computed, and then the

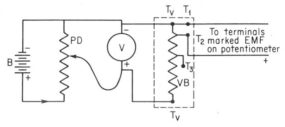

Figure 20–1–4. Auxiliary circuit for calibration of a voltmeter.

power supplied to the load may be determined. (Again see Sec. 20–8 for error of connection.)

20–2 THE KELVIN DOUBLE BRIDGE. RESISTIVITY. TEMPERATURE COEFFICIENT OF RESISTANCE

KELVIN DOUBLE BRIDGE. In Example C, Sec. 2–4, we discussed the Wheatstone bridge used for measurement of the resistance of an unknown resistor in terms of the resistances of known resistors. If the resistance of a resistor is much less than 1 ohm, the Wheatstone bridge does not yield very accurate results. This loss of accuracy is due to the contact resistances, at the places where the unknown is connected to the bridge, being comparable with the magnitude of the unknown and being in series with the unknown.

The Kelvin double bridge minimizes the effect of this source of error by placing the contact resistances in series with the higher resistances in the ratio arms of the bridge. We wish to consider the theory and use of the Kelvin double bridge, which also makes its measurements by a comparison method, but for unknown resistances of 1 ohm or less.

Figure 20–2–1 shows a schematic circuit diagram of the Kelvin bridge. Here lk is the rod or bar of metal, a part of whose resistance is to be determined. It is held in a rack with four terminals l, p', p, and k. The current leads l and k are heavy binding posts or lugs fastened securely to the ends of the specimen, since at final balance a current of 10 to 25 amp flows in this part of the circuit. The potential terminals p' and p are usually knife edges with screws to hold them firmly in place against the metal bar lk. Only very small currents flow through these potential contacts. The resistance measured is that between p' and p. Resistor mj is a standard variable low resistance (range from zero to 0.0101 ohm) that also has current terminals at m and j and potential terminals t' and t. The known resistance is between the potential terminals t' and t; A, B, a, and b are standard adjustable resistances, contained in a double ratio box so arranged that the resistance ratio A/B is always the same as the resistance ratio a/b.

The yoke of the bridge Y is a heavy copper rod or bar that carries the current of several amperes from j to k; G is the galvanometer and $\mathcal{E}$ is the driving battery. For balance, the resistance ratios in the ratio box and the magnitude of R are adjusted so that no current flows through the galvanometer. The resistance between t' and t is R, and the resistance X, of the part of the unknown that is measured, is that between p' and p. Note that the contact resistances at m, j, k, and l do not enter into either the resistance of the standard R or of the unknown X. Also note that the contact resistances at t', t, p' and p are in series with the relatively high resistances of B, b, A, and a, respectively, and not in series with either R or X.

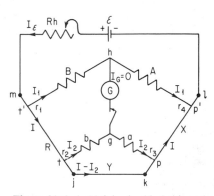

Let us assume that the bridge is balanced and compute the balance conditions. With no current through G, points h and g are at the same potential, so the potential drop from t' to h equals the potential drop from t' to t to g. Also the potential drop from h to p' equals the potential drop

Figure 20–2–1. Kelvin double bridge.

from g to p to p'. Thus if we let the letters beside the resistances represent the magnitudes of the resistances, we may write

$$I_1 B = IR + I_2 b \quad \text{and} \quad I_1 A = IX + I_2 a \qquad (20\text{–}2\text{–}1)$$

Also the potential difference from t to p is the same along the path tgp as it is along the path $tjYkp$, so we have

$$(I - I_2)Y = I_2(a + b) \qquad (20\text{–}2\text{–}2)$$

Solve these equations for X and obtain

$$X = AR/B + bY(A/B - a/b)/(a + b + Y) \qquad (20\text{–}2\text{–}3)$$

If $A/B = a/b$, this becomes

$$X = AR/B \qquad (20\text{–}2\text{–}4)$$

which is the usual equation used to compute X when the ratio A/B and the magnitude of R are known.

Let $r_1, r_2, r_3,$ and r_4 (see Fig. 20–2–1) represent the contact resistances and the resistances of the lead wires to the terminals of the ratio box, at t', t, p, and p', respectively. Each of these unknown resistances must be small compared with the known resistance in series with it in order to make the above approximation a good one. Since there will be some residual in the term $(A/B - a/b)$, the resistance Y of the yoke is made small by using a copper rod with secure connections at j and k. Thus, in (20–2–3) the term $bY/(a + b + Y)$ is much less than unity, and it is a multiplier of the residual of $A/B - a/b$. Hence in a well-connected bridge, the error is small if we use (20–2–4) in place of (20–2–3).

The Kelvin double bridge is capable of greater precision than the above approximations permit, by the use of secondary balances. These secondary balances make A/B more nearly equal to a/b. Thus, if more precision is required, consult a book* on electrical measurements where these secondary balances are described and the theory discussed.

Since R and X are low resistances, I must be a large current in order to secure appreciable potential differences between t' and t and between p and p'. It is fairly common practice to use a battery current $I_\mathscr{E}$ of 5 amp in the preliminary stages of securing a balance and then to increase $I_\mathscr{E}$ to about 20 or 25 amp for the final adjustment. Hence $\mathscr{E}$ must be a battery that will supply this magnitude of current without damage to it.

In Fig. 20–2–1, lk is the metal bar that is the unknown, but, as pointed out above, X is its resistance between points p and p' (not its total resistance). Thus the length between p and p' must be measured in order to know the length of the specimen that is associated with the resistance measured. If the area of cross section of the bar is determined and the length and resistance are known, the resistivity of the material of the bar may be computed as we shall see in the next paragraph.

RESISTIVITY. As a result of experiment, we know the resistance R of a metallic conductor of a given kind of material to be directly proportional to the length L of the conductor and inversely proportional to the area A of cross section of the conductor, provided that the temperature of the conductor is constant. If we let ρ represent the constant of proportionality, we may express this relation as

$$R = \rho L/A \quad \text{or} \quad \rho = RA/L \qquad (20\text{–}2\text{–}5)$$

Constant ρ is called the resistivity of the material of which the conductor is made. Equation (20–2–5) is the defining equation for ρ.

The Kelvin double bridge is well suited to the measurement of resistivities of various metallic conducting materials. Table 20–1 gives some representative values of resistivities of various common materials. In this table, resistivities are expressed in ohm meters as required by (20–2–5) for the mks system of units. If the centimeter is used as a unit of length in (20–2–5), ρ will be in ohm centimeters (it is more common to find resistivity expressed in these units). A conversion from one system to the other can be made very quickly by using the fact that there is 10^{-2} meter/cm.

* Harris, F. K., *Electrical Measurements* (New York: John Wiley & Sons, Inc., 1952), pp. 282–88.

TABLE 20–1*

RESISTIVITIES AND TEMPERATURE COEFFICIENTS

Approximate values near room temperature

Material	Resistivity ρ in ohm-meter	Temperature Coefficient α_{t_1} in $°C^{-1}$	Base Temp t_1 $°C$
Aluminum (commercial)	2.83×10^{-8}	0.0039	18
Brass (hard drawn)	8.2×10^{-8}	0.002	20
Carbon	3500×10^{-8}	-0.0005	
Constantan (Cu 60%, Ni 40%)	49×10^{-8}	0.000002	25
Copper (standard commercial annealed)	1.7241×10^{-8}	0.00393	20
Gold	2.44×10^{-8}	0.0034	20
Iron	10×10^{-8}	0.0050	20
Manganin		0.000006	12
(Cu 84%, Mn 12%, Ni 4%)	44×10^{-8}	0.000000	25
Mercury	94×10^{-8}	0.00089	20
Molybdenum	5.7×10^{-8}	0.0033	25
Nichrome	100×10^{-8}	0.0004	20
Nickel	7.8×10^{-8}	0.006	20
Platinum	10×10^{-8}	0.003	20
Silver (electrolytic)	1.51×10^{-8}	0.0038	20
Steel (Si 4%)	62×10^{-8}	0.0008	20
Tungsten	5.51×10^{-8}	0.0045	18

* From *Handbook of Physics and Chemistry*, 32d ed. (Cleveland: Chemical Rubber Publishing Co.), pp. 2132–41.

TEMPERATURE COEFFICIENT OF RESISTANCE. Experiment shows that the resistance of any conductor changes with temperature. For metals, the resistance increases as the temperature increases, but for carbon and some semiconductors, the resistance decreases as the temperature increases. The resistance may be expressed approximately as a function of temperature by the equation

$$R_t = R_0(1 + \alpha t + \beta t^2 + \cdots) \qquad (20\text{–}2\text{–}6)$$

where R_t is the resistance of the conductor at the temperature t and R_0 is the resistance of the conductor at $0°C$. For metallic conductors, β and the coefficients of the higher powers of t are numerically small, so the terms beyond the first power of t may be neglected unless t is large. Hence, for moderate temperatures, (20–2–6) is written

$$R_t = R_0(1 + \alpha t) \qquad (20\text{–}2\text{–}7)$$

or
$$\alpha = (R_t - R_0)/R_0 t \qquad (20\text{–}2\text{–}8)$$

The *temperature coefficient* of resistance α is defined by (20–2–8) as the

change in resistance per unit of resistance per degree change in temperature.
Any temperature scale may be used and α, for a given material, will have a
different numerical value for each different temperature scale. It is common
practice to use the centigrade scale, so α usually has the unit $(°C)^{-1}$. Since the
unit of resistance cancels, it makes no difference what unit is used for resistance so long as it is the same unit in the numerator and denominator of
(20–2–8).

As (20–2–8) is written, it is based on the resistance R_0 of the conductor
at $0°C$, and the correct numerical value for α will be obtained only if the
resistance at $0°C$ is used for R_0 in both numerator and denominator. Since it is
more common to measure resistances of samples at room temperature it
might be better to write

$$\alpha_{t1} = (R_t - R_{t1})/R_{t1}(t - t_1) \qquad (20\text{–}2\text{–}9)$$

where α_{t1} is the coefficient based on the resistance R_{t1} of the conductor at the
temperature t_1 and, as before, R_t is the resistance of the conductor at the
temperature t. You can readily show (see Problem 20–7) that

$$\alpha_{t1} = \alpha/(1 + \alpha t_1) \qquad (20\text{–}2\text{–}10)$$

thus you can compute the temperature coefficient α_{t1} based on the resistance
R_{t1} if the coefficient α based on R_0 is known, or vice versa.

Table 20–1 gives values of α_{t1} for some representative conducting materials
and gives, with each value, the temperature t_1 at which the initial resistance
R_{t1} was measured; thus the temperature given is the base temperature for the
measurement.

20–3 USE OF A BALLISTIC GALVANOMETER AND SEARCH COIL TO EXPLORE A MAGNETIC FIELD

The ballistic galvanometer with a search coil offers a convenient means of
exploring a region to determine first whether or not there is a magnetic field
in the region and, second, the mag-
nitude and direction of B in the
field. We are thinking now of an
arrangement, such as that in Fig.
20–3–1, whereby the search coil is
free to move in the region that we
wish to explore. For example,
imagine that the region is in air. We
use the apparatus pictured in Fig.
20–3–1, where the ballistic galvanometer and the search coil are connected electrically by means of a

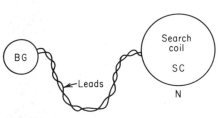

Figure 20–3–1. Ballistic galvonometer used to
explore a magnetic field. Search coil is free so
it can be moved about in the field.

flexible twisted pair of leads so that, within limits, the search coil may be
moved about as desired. The leads are a twisted pair so that the emf's
induced in the leads, as they move about in the magnetic field, will be
equal and opposite and the only net emf will be that induced in *SC*. In Sec.
16–10 we have discussed the theory which permits measurement of magnetic flux with a ballistic galvanometer.

First let us determine whether or not there is a magnetic field in the region. If the galvanometer shows a deflection when SC is turned a quarter turn about an axis in the plane of the coil, there must be a magnetic field in the region. If it shows no deflection, try several other starting positions for the plane of the coil, since the first try of a quarter turn of SC may have been one in which the flux linking the coil was first increased and then decreased an equal amount, or the axis of rotation was along the flux lines, so that the net change in the flux linking the coil was zero. If no starting position can be found such that a quarter turn of the coil will produce a deflection of BG, then either there is no magnetic field in the region or the magnetic field is of such a low magnetic flux density that the apparatus is not sufficiently sensitive to detect it.

Now let us say that we have found that there is a magnetic field in one region and have found another region nearby where there is no magnetic field. We select a particular point P in the region where there is a magnetic field and we wish to determine the magnitude and direction of B at this point. Place SC at P and, when BG has stopped at its zero, snatch SC to the region where there is no field and read the first throw of BG. Repeat for all possible initial orientations of the plane of SC at P and locate the orientation (call it O) that produces the largest first throw of BG when SC is snatched to the region of no field. Then B is normal to the face of the coil when the coil is in orientation O at the point P. This statement follows from the fact that there must be a maximum magnetic flux through the face of SC, when it is in orientation O at P, in order to have a maximum change in magnetic flux, when SC is snatched to the region of zero field.

From this experiment, we know the line along which B points, but we do not know which way B points along this line. This latter point can be settled by Lenz's law. A ballistic galvanometer can deflect either direction from its zero position depending on the direction of flow of current through it, and an auxiliary experiment can be performed to determine the direction of flow of current associated with each direction of deflection of BG. The direction of winding of SC can be known so, for a deflection of BG in a particular direction, the direction of flow of the induced current in SC can be known. Determine the direction of flow of the induced current in SC when SC is snatched from P to the region where there is no field. During the process of snatching the coil, the magnetic flux through the coil is decreasing so, by Lenz's law, the induced current will flow in such a direction as to oppose this decrease. Thus the induced current flows in a direction such that it produces magnetic flux in the same direction as that of the field from which it is snatched. Hence, with the coil at P and in the orientation O, encircle SC with the fingers of the right hand, point the fingers in the direction of the induced current, and the thumb will point in the direction of B of the field being explored. We now know the direction of B at P.

Using the magnitude of the first throw of BG, when SC is snatched from the orientation O at P, and the calibration of BG, calculate Q. Then use (16–10–1) to compute Φ_0 (Φ_1 is zero since there is no flux through SC when it is at the end of its motion in the region of zero field). Let A represent the area of the face of SC and have $B = \Phi_0/A$. The B calculated in this manner is, of course, the average value of B over the face of SC when SC is at P. If, however, A is small, this calculation will yield a good approximation of the magnitude of B at P. We now know both the magnitude and direction of B at P.

This process can be repeated for as many points in the field as desired, and the field can be mapped as completely as the situation demands. This method of exploring a magnetic field is a useful alternate to the one outlined in Sec. 3–2, in which we used the magnetic force on a moving positive charge to define the magnitude and direction of the magnetic flux density of a field.

For the calibration of a ballistic galvanometer by means of a standard mutual inductor, see Problem 17–1; for the use of a shunted ballistic galvanometer, consult a text* on electrical measurements.

20–4 THE FLUXMETER

As the name implies, the fluxmeter is an instrument that is designed to measure the change in the magnetic flux that links with its search coil. It has two advantages over the ballistic galvanometer used for this purpose. First, the flux change does not need to take place as rapidly as it does with the ballistic galvanometer, and second, the portable fluxmeter has a scale that is calibrated so that the flux change can be determined with a minimum of calculation. On the other hand, a high-sensitivity ballistic galvanometer can be used to measure smaller flux changes than can a portable fluxmeter.

Like the ballistic galvanometer, the fluxmeter is a radial field galvanometer of the D'Arsonval type (see Sec. 13–4, Fig. 13–4–1). There is only one fundamental difference between the two. The fluxmeter coil is mounted in such a way that there is, as nearly as possible, zero restoring torque on its coil when the coil is deflected from its zero position. You will recall, from Sec. 13–6, that the theory of the ballistic galvanometer depends on a restoring torque that is proportional to the angular deflection of the coil. Since the two instruments differ in this important respect, it is easier to derive the theory of the fluxmeter from a fresh start than to adapt the ballistic galvanometer theory.

We shall confine our discussion to a portable fluxmeter (such as the one manufactured by the Sensitive Research Instrument Corporation), although the non-portable type is not essentially different except for the features that have to do with portability. You can most readily visualize the essential parts of the instrument by reference to Fig. 13–5–1, Sec. 13–5, which shows the construction of the D'Arsonval type of moving coil instrument used for d-c ammeters and voltmeters. Remove the hairsprings which serve as current leads and supply the restoring torque for the moving coils, and replace them with current leads that offer a very minimum of restoring torque. Also wind the coil on a non-conducting coil form. The instrument now has the essential features of a fluxmeter. The restoring torque can never be made zero, so the coil will always drift slowly back toward its zero position. If it were not for this slow drift of the coil, the flux change could continue as long as desired and the meter would measure the flux change properly. We shall assume that the restoring torque is zero in our discussion and ignore the drift of the coil.

* For example, Stout, M. B., *Basic Electrical Measurements* (Englewood Cliffs, N.J.: Prentice-Hall, Inc., 1951), pp. 367–69.

The moving coil of the meter and the search coil that is attached to it are both of low resistance, so the moving coil is heavily damped and stops fairly promptly after the flux change in the search coil ceases. In order to return the coil to its zero after a reading, a current is sent through the coil from an auxiliary battery that is installed just for this purpose, and the battery is disconnected as soon as the coil has reached its zero. The battery is *not* in the coil circuit when a flux reading is taken.

Figure 20–4–1 shows the schematic circuit diagram that we need for derivation of the fluxmeter formula. It shows a search coil SC connected to the fluxmeter F. We imagine that, due to some event outside of the circuit, the magnetic flux linking SC is changing at a rate $d\Phi/dt$ and the emf, e_{SC}, that this changing flux induces in SC, is sending a current i through the fluxmeter coil. Hence the fluxmeter coil is experiencing a torque τ and is turning. As the fluxmeter coil turns in the magnetic field of its own permanent magnet, an emf e_F is induced in this coil. Because of Lenz's law, e_F is in a direction opposite to that of e_{SC}. Also, the circuit has self-inductance L, and an emf of self-induction is set up that opposes the change of the current. The initial flux through SC is Φ_0 and the final flux is Φ_1. From Faraday's law, the

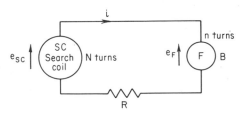

Figure 20–4–1. Fluxmeter F connected to a search coil SC.

instantaneous emf induced in SC has the magnitude $e_{SC} = N\, d\Phi/dt$ and we shall consider e_{SC} as positive and adapt the signs on other emf's accordingly.

From (15–1–8), the motional emf induced in the n turns of wire on the fluxmeter coil is given by $e_F = 2nvBl$, since there are $2n$ straight wires in series, each of length l, and moving with a velocity v perpendicular to B. Here, of course, B is the magnetic flux density of the field of the permanent magnet in the fluxmeter at the place where the side wires of the fluxmeter coil are situated. B is radial and has the same magnitude for all positions of the coil as the coil turns. But $v = \omega r$, so $e_F = 2n\omega rBl$. However, $A = 2rl$ and $\omega = d\alpha/dt$, where A is the area of the face of the fluxmeter coil, r is its half width, and α is its angular displacement, so

$$e_F = n\omega AB = nAB\, d\alpha/dt \qquad (20\text{–}4\text{–}1)$$

Then, by Kirchhoff's second law applied to the loop in Fig. 20–4–1, we have

$$N\, d\Phi/dt - L\, di/dt - nAB\, d\alpha/dt = iR \qquad (20\text{–}4\text{–}2)$$

where R is the total resistance of the circuit. But, from (13–4–1), Sec. 13–4, the instantaneous torque τ on the fluxmeter coil due to the current i flowing in the wires of the coil is $\tau = niAB$. Put the value of i from (20–4–2) into this equation and we have

$$\tau = (nAB/R)(N \, d\Phi/dt - L \, di/dt - nAB \, d\alpha/dt) \qquad (20\text{–}4\text{–}3)$$

The frictional torque in the fluxmeter is so small that we assume it negligible. As mentioned before, the restoring torque on the fluxmeter coil is the bare minimum that construction will permit; so we assume that it is zero for purposes of our derivation. Hence (20–4–3) gives the unbalanced torque on the fluxmeter coil.

By Newton's second law for rotational motion, the unbalanced torque equals the moment of inertia times the angular acceleration so

$$\tau = J \, d\omega/dt \qquad (20\text{–}4\text{–}4)$$

where J is the moment of inertia of the fluxmeter coil about its axis of rotation and ω is the instantaneous angular velocity of the fluxmeter coil. Equate the values of τ in (20–4–3) and (20–4–4) and remove the common dt, and we have

$$nAB(N \, d\Phi - L \, di - nAB \, d\alpha)/R = J \, d\omega \qquad (20\text{–}4\text{–}5)$$

Now integrate from a time just before the flux through the search coil started to change to a time just after it has completed the change. Current i is zero both before and after the change. Also ω is zero both before and after the change, because, as pointed out before, the coil motion is heavily damped. Let α_0 represent the angular position of the fluxmeter coil before the change of flux in the search coil started, and α_1 its position after the change ended. Then from (20–4–5)

$$nAB\left(N \int_{\Phi_0}^{\Phi_1} d\Phi - L \int_0^0 di - nAB \int_{\alpha_0}^{\alpha_1} d\alpha\right)\Big/R = J \int_0^0 d\omega$$

from which
$$N(\Phi_1 - \Phi_0) = nAB(\alpha_1 - \alpha_0) \qquad (20\text{–}4\text{–}6)$$

Equation (20–4–6) is the desired equation for the fluxmeter and says that the change in the angular position of the fluxmeter coil is directly proportional to the change in the magnetic flux linkages with the search coil. Since the pointer of the fluxmeter is fastened directly to the fluxmeter coil, the change in pointer position on the scale of the fluxmeter is directly proportional to the change in the magnetic flux linkages with the search coil. Thus the scale of the meter can be calibrated to read change in magnetic flux linkages directly. Equation (20–4–6) says that the scale is linear. There is nothing in the theory that requires that the flux change in the search coil be made rapidly. Thus, as pointed out earlier, it is only the slow drift of the fluxmeter coil toward its zero position that limits the length of time over which the meter will read change of flux linkages accurately.

The fluxmeter is calibrated by the use of a standard magnetic flux source, such as a very long standard solenoid using accurately controlled currents. The reading of the instrument must be divided by the number of turns of wire on the search coil in order to secure the change in magnetic flux $(\Phi_1 - \Phi_0)$ linking the search coil.

SHUNTED FLUXMETER. A fluxmeter may be made into a multirange instrument by the use of appropriate shunts; therefore we wish now to consider the theory involved in shunting a fluxmeter. Since we saw previously that the emf of self-induction contributed no net result, we shall ignore it in the present discussion. The discussion takes the same form as for the unshunted flux-meter except that now we must take account of the parallel path through the shunt.

Figure 20–4–2 shows a schematic diagram of the circuit that we must consider, where R_S is the resistance of the shunt, R_{SC} is the resistance of the search coil plus any resistance that may be in series with the search coil, and R_F is the resistance of the fluxmeter coil. The remainder of the symbols are self-explanatory. Set up Kirchhoff's second law for loop $ADGHJKA$

$$N \, d\Phi/dt - nAB \, d\alpha/dt = (i_F + i_S)R_{SC} + i_F R_F \qquad (20\text{–}4\text{–}7)$$

Set up the same law for loop $GDJHG$

$$nAB \, d\alpha/dt = -i_F R_F + i_S R_S \qquad (20\text{–}4\text{–}8)$$

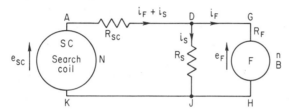

Figure 20–4–2. Shunted fluxmeter. R_S is the shunt across the fluxmeter F. SC is the search coil.

Solve for i_S in (20–4–8), substitute it in (20–4–7), and solve for i_F

$$i_F = (N \, d\Phi/dt - nABR'' \, d\alpha/dt)/R' \qquad (20\text{–}4\text{–}9)$$

where $R' = R_F + R_{SC} + R_F R_{SC}/R_S$, and $R'' = (R_S + R_{SC})/R_S$. Since i_F is the current flowing in the fluxmeter coil, the value of i_F in (20–4–9) may be sub-stituted for i in (13–4–1) in order to secure the torque on the fluxmeter coil due to this current. Hence the torque τ on the fluxmeter coil due to the current i_F is

$$\tau = nAB[N \, d\Phi/dt - nABR'' \, d\alpha/dt]/R' \qquad (20\text{–}4\text{–}10)$$

and (20–4–10), for the shunted fluxmeter, corresponds to (20–4–3) for the unshunted meter, except that the $L \, di/dt$ term has been omitted in the present argument. As before, we shall neglect the frictional torque and the slight restoring torque on the fluxmeter coil. Thus (20–4–10) may be looked upon as the unbalanced torque acting on the fluxmeter coil due to the changing flux in the search coil.

Now follow the same argument as that used from (20–4–4) through (20–4–6) and obtain

$$N(\Phi_1 - \Phi_0) = nAB(1 + R_{SC}/R_S)(\alpha_1 - \alpha_0) \qquad (20\text{–}4\text{–}11)$$

which is the formula for the shunted fluxmeter within the accuracy of the approximations that we have made. Notice that (20–4–11) differs from (20–4–6) only by the presence of the shunting factor $(1 + R_{SC}/R_S)$ in (20–4–11).

As an example, the Sensitive Research Instrument Corporation Model FM multirange fluxmeter has five ranges for which the multiplying factors are 1, 3, 10, 30, and 100, respectively; thus it has one unshunted range and four shunts with different resistances. A selector switch permits selection of the desired shunt. The multiplying factors are the values of $(1 + R_{SC}/R_S)$ for the shunt selected, and the scale reading is multiplied by the factor to obtain the value of $N(\Phi_1 - \Psi_0)$. Since each shunt in the instrument has a definite fixed resistance (see Problem 20–13), R_{SC} must have a corresponding definite fixed resistance in order that the factor $(1 + R_{SC}/R_S)$ shall have the numerical value stamped on the face of the meter for that selector switch position. The Model FM multirange fluxmeter requires that R_{SC} be 15 ohms. Hence a search coil of more than 15 ohms cannot be used with this meter if the calibration is to have meaning. If the search coil has a resistance less than 15 ohms, its resistance must be measured and then enough resistance added in series to bring the total to 15 ohms. In the use of the meter, search coils are wound as needed to fit the conditions of the experiment at hand. The fact that the resistance of the search coil must not exceed 15 ohms is rarely a handicap.

20–5 THE ELECTRODYNAMOMETER VOLTMETER AND AMMETER FOR DIRECT AND ALTERNATE CURRENTS

D'ARSONVAL TYPE METERS. In Sec. 13–5, we discussed the D'Arsonval type of d-c ammeter and voltmeter and, in Sec. 20–1, showed how such meters may be calibrated on steady direct current. The calibrations on the scales always refer to steady d-c values.

If a meter of this type is used on cyclically fluctuating direct current, the pointer reading on the scale will show the time average of the first power of the instantaneous current where the time average is taken over one cycle of the fluctuation (or over any whole number of cycles). For this statement to be true, the time for a cycle of fluctuations must be short compared with the period of the meter, so that the moving coil system of the meter cannot follow the individual changes in the cycle of the current. The above statement concerning the pointer reading follows from the fact that the moving coil system will take up an equilibrium position where the time average turning torque is equal to the restoring torque of the hairsprings; and the time average turning torque is directly proportional to the time average of the instantaneous current flowing in the moving coil.

If a sinusoidal alternating current is sent through the moving coil of a D'Arsonval type meter, the time average torque is zero, since the time average current is zero. Thus a D'Arsonval type of ammeter or voltmeter reads zero when connected in a sinusoidal a-c circuit regardless of the magnitude of the alternating current or voltage. If, however, there is a d-c component superposed on the alternating current, the D'Arsonval meter will read the time average of the first power of the instantaneous direct current without reference to the alternating current. Care must be taken in such connections because the alternating current may be large enough to burn out the meter even though the pointer of the meter is reading well below the limit of the scale.

In the D'Arsonval type meter, the magnetic field is furnished by a permanent magnet so the field remains in the same direction all the time. Thus when the current in the moving coil reverses, the torque on the moving coil reverses. This is the physical reason why the meter reads zero on alternating current when the positive and negative half cycles of the alternating current are symmetrical.

THE ELECTRODYNAMOMETER TYPE METER. The electrodynamometer type of meter overcomes the difficulty, presented above for alternating current, by replacing the permanent magnet by an electromagnet. Figure 20–5–1 (a) shows the schematic circuit diagram, where A and A represent the field coil

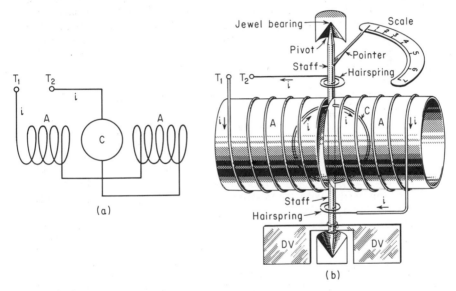

Figure 20–5–1. Electrodynamometer. (a) Schematic circuit diagram. (b) Schematic structural diagram.

that replaces the permanent magnet, and C is the moving coil. Figure 20–5–1 (b) shows a schematic structural diagram, and comparison with Fig. 13–5–1 will show you the only real differences: first, the AA coils replace the permanent magnet and, second, the damper vanes DV which move in air pockets minimize, by air friction, the fluctuations of the pointer about its average position when it deflects. Another important difference, which cannot be seen in the figures, is that the moving coil C is wound on a non-conducting coil form and the metal in the instrument is kept to a bare minimum in order to eliminate eddy currents as much as possible. No ferromagnetic material is used in the construction of the meter.

The field coil AA and the moving coil C are connected in series, so the same current flows through both and is in phase. Figure 20–5–1 (b) shows the direction of the current in AA and in C at a particular moment, and the torque on C is in a direction to turn the pointer out of the page. (For the position shown for coil C in the figure, the pointer is at zero on the scale.) When the current reverses, it reverses in both sets of coils together, and the torque on coil C still tends to turn the pointer out of the page. Thus, on alternating current, the torque on the coil C is fluctuating but is always in the same direction.

Let τ represent the instantaneous torque on the C coil and B represent the instantaneous magnetic flux density at the C coil due to current flowing in the AA coils. Then τ is proportional to the product IB (see for example Sec. 13–3), but the geometry of the instrument does not permit simple calculation of the factor of proportionality. Further, since there is no ferromagnetic material in the meter, B is directly proportional to the current i flowing in the AA coils. Hence τ is proportional to i^2. Let k represent the factor of proportionality. In general k is a function of the angular position of the C coil because the field is not radial, but k is independent of time when the C coil has arrived at a certain deflection. From the above discussion, τ is related to i by the equation

$$\tau = ki^2 \qquad\qquad (20\text{–}5\text{–}1)$$

If a sinusoidal alternating current is flowing through the meter, $i = I_m \sin \omega t$, so

$$\tau = kI_m^2 \sin^2 \omega t \qquad\qquad (20\text{–}5\text{–}2)$$

Let T represent the time average torque on the coil C during a full cycle of the alternating current. However, in this particular case all half cycles are alike, so a time average for a single half cycle will serve. (If the negative half cycle were not symmetrical with the positive half cycle, the time average of τ for a full cycle would have to be taken.) Thus

$$T = \int_0^{\pi/\omega} \tau \, dt / (\pi/\omega) \qquad\qquad (20\text{–}5\text{–}3)$$

Regardless of the way in which τ varies with time, as long as it is cyclical, coil C will deflect to a position where T is equal to the restoring torque of the hairsprings, and it will shiver about this position. The damp vanes will minimize the shiver and the pointer will remain essentially stationary on the scale. Let D represent the deflection of the pointer on the scale. Moreover, D is directly proportional to T because, by Hooke's law, the restoring torque of the hairsprings is directly proportional to the deflection of the pointer. Thus, if we let k' represent this constant of proportionality, we may write

$$D = k'T = k'(\omega/\pi) \int_0^{\pi/\omega} \tau \, dt \qquad\qquad (20\text{–}5\text{–}4)$$

In this particular case, where i is a sinusoidal function of time, we may substitute the value of τ from (20–5–2) into (20–5–4) and obtain

$$D = k'k[(I_m^2 \omega/\pi) \int_0^{\pi/\omega} \sin^2 \omega t \, dt] \qquad\qquad (20\text{–}5\text{–}5)$$

where k has been taken out in front of the integral because it is independent of time once the coil has reached its deflection D. But, from Sec. 4–11, we recognize the term in the square bracket of (20–5–5) as $I_m^2/2$, or as the square of the root mean square (or effective) current. That is, the term in the square bracket is I_{eff}^2. (In the past we have represented I_{eff} by I without a subscript, but let us use the subscript here in order to distinguish it from a steady direct current.) Equation (20–5–5) becomes $D = k'kI_{eff}^2$ or

$$I_{eff} = \sqrt{D}/\sqrt{k'k} \qquad (20\text{–}5\text{–}6)$$

When the electrodynamometer is used on steady direct current, the same argument as above applies except that the time average torque is the same as the instantaneous torque, since the torque is constant. Also the time average of I_{d-c}^2 is simply I_{d-c}^2, since I_{d-c} is constant. Thus for steady direct current, (20–5–6) becomes $D = k'kI_{d-c}^2$ or

$$I_{d-c} = \sqrt{D}/\sqrt{k'k} \qquad (20\text{–}5\text{–}7)$$

Thus the same relationship holds between I_{d-c} and deflection as holds between I_{eff} and deflection for alternating current, with k and k' the same in the two equations.

In Sec. 4–11 we defined I_{eff} for sinusoidal alternating current as *the current that will produce heat, in a given resistance, at the same rate as will the same number of amperes of steady direct current.* Thus I_{eff} is defined in terms of its numerical equivalent in steady direct current. Hence *the electrodynamometer instrument may be calibrated on steady direct current and then used to measure root mean square current on alternating current.* Thus we may calibrate the electrodynamometer by the use of a potentiometer and standard cell as outlined in Sec. 20–1 and have a proper calibration for its use on alternating current.

The electrodynamometer may be made into an ammeter by use of a properly selected shunt or into a voltmeter by use of a proper series resistance as a multiplier. For direct current and for power frequencies on alternating current the calculation and connection of shunts and multipliers offers but little more difficulty (see Problem 20–17) than the same problem for D'Arsonval meters on direct current. However, for higher frequencies the problem is more complicated, with regard to both the performance of the meter and its conversion to an ammeter or a voltmeter. Thus you should consult a book* on electrical measurements when the problem of higher frequencies arises.

For instruments which read properly only on alternating current, it is impossible to make direct calibrations against the primary electrical standards. Thus an instrument that reads properly on both alternating and direct current must be used to transfer the calibration from the primary standards to the a-c instruments. When properly designed and constructed, the electrodynamometer ammeter and voltmeter are very satisfactory as transfer instruments. In fact this function is their primary use,* since they are too expensive and

---

* For example, F. K. Harris, *Electrical Measurements* (New York: John Wiley & Sons, Inc., 1952), pp. 412–18.

consume too much power to be generally useful as measuring instruments in many commercial circuits.

Since no iron is used in the electrodynamometer construction, the magnetic fields produced by the coils are of low magnitude (of the order of 5×10^{-3} wb/m²). Hence the instrument must be shielded magnetically in order that stray magnetic fields will not influence the readings seriously.

From (20–5–6) we see that the scale of an electrodynamometer is not linear, because I is proportional to the square root of D. Such an instrument is said to have a *square law response*. Nonlinearity also results because, as pointed out above, k is a function of D. The division marks on the scale are crowded together at the low end of the scale and are spread out at the upper end.

Although the self-inductance of the coils of an electrodynamometer meter is usually small enough so that the meter does not offer appreciable inductive reactance at power frequencies, this is not the case for high frequencies. Thus the electrodynamometer is useful only in the lower frequency range.

20–6 THE THERMOCOUPLE AMMETER AND VOLTMETER

When two dissimilar metals are joined at two junctions and there is a temperature difference between the junctions, a thermoelectric emf is developed. If a complete circuit is available, this emf will cause a current to flow. Figure 20–6–1 shows the two dissimilar metals joined at the two junctions marked *HJ* (hot junction) and *CJ* (cold junction). An ordinary D'Arsonval type of d-c millivoltmeter is shown in the figure as *MV* and is used to measure the potential difference across the terminals S_1 and S_2 of the thermocouple. This terminal potential

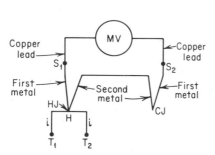

Figure 20–6–1. Thermocouple ammeter.

difference is less, of course, than the emf of the thermocouple because a current is flowing in the circuit through the coil of *MV* and thus through the resistance of the thermocouple.

The emf e of a thermocouple, made up of a given pair of metals, is found experimentally to depend on the temperature difference between the junctions. Over a limited temperature range this functional relationship may be expressed as

$$e = a(t_1 - t_2) + b(t_1 - t_2)^2 \qquad (20\text{–}6\text{–}1)$$

if the cold junction is kept at a constant (or very nearly constant) temperature. In (20–6–1), $(t_1 - t_2)$ is the temperature difference between the junctions, and a and b are constants whose values depend on the pair of metals used and the temperature of the cold junction. Here b is much smaller numerically than a so, if $(t_1 - t_2)$ is not large, e varies approximately linearly with the temperature difference between the junctions. The properties of a thermocouple make it primarily an instrument for measurement of temperature differences, and a thermocouple is often used as a thermometer.

If a current i is sent through the heater H in Fig. 20–6–1, HJ will be at a higher temperature than CJ, and the temperature difference depends on the magnitude of the current flowing through H. Thus the reading of MV depends on the magnitude of the current flowing through H, and the reading of MV can be used as a measure of i. T_1 and T_2 are the terminals for connection of H in series in the circuit whose current is to be measured. Note that i does not flow through the thermocouple circuit.

The rate at which heat is developed in H is given by i^2R, where R is the resistance of the heater and where the current may be either alternating or direct current. Since i enters as the square, this instrument also has a square law response and, on alternating current, measures the root mean square or effective current.

The relationship between the rate at which heat is developed in H and the temperature difference between HJ and CJ is complicated; also, the relationship is different for different kinds of construction of the meter. It depends primarily on the heat insulation around HJ and the location of CJ in the instrument. Cold junction CJ should be located so that there is no temperature difference between the junctions when no current is flowing in the heater. Because of these complications, the functional relationship between i and the deflection of MV is not computed; the instrument is, rather, calibrated against a meter of known calibration, such as an electrodynamometer, and the scale of MV is marked to read the current through H directly.

In many thermocouple meters, HJ is welded directly to the mid-point of H in order to secure good thermal contact and thus quick response of the meter. Since the contact of HJ with H is a finite volume, rather than a point, there will be a potential drop through this volume due to the current i. If i is flowing in one direction, this potential drop will be in the same direction as the thermoelectric emf in the thermocouple circuit, whereas a reversal of i will make this potential drop opposite to the thermoelectric emf. Thus the potential difference across MV depends on the direction of the current through H. This potential drop is small, but the thermoelectric emf is not very large (usually in the range of 5 to 15 mv), so, in some instruments, this potential drop is enough to prevent accurate calibration of the instrument on direct current. Some thermocouple meters show only a very small d-c reversal effect of this sort and are used as transfer instruments to carry the calibration from a potentiometer and standard cell to other thermocouple meters where the d-c reversal effect is appreciable.

Because the heater and its leads have very low self-inductance and because the heater requires only a small amount of power from the circuit, the thermocouple ammeter is useful at high frequencies. In fact its chief use is in the high-frequency range and, when properly designed, it gives satisfactory measurements up to 100 megacycles.

The thermocouple meter can be made into a satisfactory voltmeter, by use of a series multiplier, for frequencies up to about 15 kilocycles. Above this frequency there is great difficulty in constructing multiplier resistors that are sufficiently accurate and frequency independent.

We have discussed only the basic principle of operation of the thermo-couple meter. For the many important practical features, concerning design and use, a book* on electrical measurements should be consulted.

20–7 A MOVING IRON A-C AMMETER OR VOLTMETER

The moving iron types of ammeters and voltmeters are the most used for current and voltage measurements at power frequencies. The essential prin-ciple of operation is simple. The current to be measured flows through a fixed coil, which is usually a short solenoid. A piece of soft iron (usually a special alloy) is attached to a staff that can turn, but turns against the restor-ing torque of a hairspring. The soft iron is in the region of the field of the solenoid and becomes magnetized with a pole strength that depends on the flux density of the field in which it is located. Hence the pole strength of the soft iron at any moment depends on the current that is flowing in the wires of the solenoid. The design is such that the field of the solenoid acting on the soft iron produces a torque on the staff. When the current in the solenoid reverses, the magnetism in the soft iron also reverses and the torque on the staff remains in the same direction as before. Thus an unidirectional torque on the staff results.

The instantaneous magnetic flux density B, at the place where the soft iron is located, depends on the instantaneous current i flowing in the wires of the solenoid. As we pointed out above, the instantaneous pole strength of the soft iron depends on the current i. The instantaneous torque τ on the staff depends on the product of B and the instantaneous pole strength of the soft iron; hence τ depends on the square of i. The staff deflects to a position where the time average torque on the staff is equal to the restoring torque of the hairspring, and shivers about this position. A pointer, attached to the staff, moves over a scale, and the position of the pointer on the scale depends on the time average torque T, and T depends on the time average of i^2. The time average of i^2 is the mean square current; hence the scale can be marked so that the pointer reads root mean square or effective current, I_{eff}. The functional relationships, stated very qualitatively above, for the most part are too com-plicated for calculation, and no attempt is made to calculate the exact relation-ship between I_{eff} and position of the pointer on the scale. Rather, the instru-ment is calibrated against a transfer meter, such as the electrodynamometer, that was calibrated previously against a potentiometer and standard cell.

There is a wide variety of designs of moving iron instruments, but we shall consider only one as an illustration. For a more complete coverage, and greater detail, you should consult a book† on electrical measurements.

Figure 20–7–1 shows schematically a repulsion type instrument of the concentric-vane form. Figure 20–7–1 (a) is a vertical cross section through the meter. The solenoid, staff, pivots, hairspring, pointer, and scale are labeled, and you can recognize them readily. This instrument uses two soft

---

* For example, M. B. Stout, *Basic Electrical Measurements* (Englewood Cliffs, N.J.: Prentice-Hall, Inc., 1950), pp. 432–37; or, for more detail, F. K. Harris, *Electrical Measurements* (New York: John Wiley & Sons, Inc., 1952), pp. 431–43.

† See Stout, pp. 423–29; Harris, pp. 400–12.

iron vanes, one of which, fastened on the inside surface of the solenoid, is called the fixed vane, and is shown as *FV* in Fig. 20–7–1, both in (a) and (b). The other vane, fastened to the staff, is called the moving vane and is shown as *MV* in the figure. At the moment represented in Fig. 20–7–1 (a), the current is flowing in the direction indicated by the dots and crosses in the circles that represent the solenoid wires, so the magnetic field in the solenoid is directed upward in Fig. 20–7–1 (a) at this moment. Thus the soft iron vanes are magnetized with north poles at the top and south poles at the bottom as shown by the letters *N* and *S* above and below the vanes. Since like poles repel, there will be a force on the moving vane *MV* that results in a torque on the staff in the sense shown by the arrow marked τ in the figure. When the current in

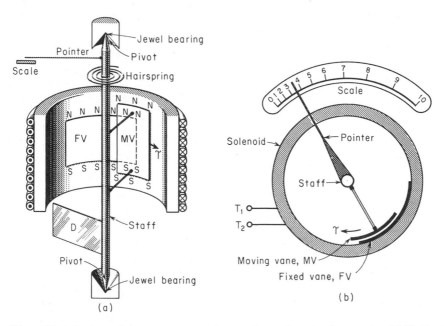

Figure 20–7–1. A repulsion type concentric-vane form of moving iron meter. (a) Vertical cross section. (b) Top view.

the solenoid reverses, the magnetic polarities of both vanes reverse together and the torque is in the same direction as before. To minimize the shiver of the pointer about its deflected position, there is a damper, shown as *D* in Fig. 20–7–1 (a), that moves with the staff and is enclosed in an air pocket.

The top view of the instrument in Fig. 20–7–1 (b) also shows the iron vanes *FV* and *MV*, the pointer and scale, and in addition shows the terminals T_1 and T_2 by which the instrument is connected into the circuit. The nonlinearity of the scale is indicated by the markings. The fixed iron vane *FV* has been indicated in Fig. 20–7–1 (a) as having the same vertical length at the right and left sides. Actually this length may be varied as the designer sees fit, and the distribution of the markings on the scale is changed accordingly. By empirical cut-and-try, a shape for *FV* can be found that will expand the scale in any part desired except at the low end. Usually the designer shapes FV to produce as nearly a linear scale as possible, but the scale is never very close to linear at best.

There are several advantages of the moving iron instruments. The construction is relatively simple and makes for a fairly rugged meter at a lower cost than other types. Since the moving parts carry no current, the hairspring can be designed for restoring torque requirements without thought for its current carrying capacity and resistance. Also, if the instrument is burned out, the solenoid only need be replaced, because usually the moving parts are not damaged and thus repair costs are less. The chief disadvantage arises from its lower sensitivity and lower accuracy.

The magnetic flux density produced by the solenoid is small, so the instrument must have a magnetic shield in order to reduce errors due to stray magnetic fields.

AMMETER. The moving iron instrument is primarily an ammeter and its range can be adjusted by a proper choice of solenoid. For an ammeter of low current range, many turns of fine wire are used on the solenoid so that the small current will produce the necessary flux density to actuate the moving parts. The low current limit for the instrument is set by the impedance of the solenoid, because the greater the number of turns the greater the resistance and inductance of the solenoid. A 100 ma instrument may have an impedance of as much as 100 ohms and such a high impedance may appreciably alter the circuit in which the milliammeter is installed for measurement.

For higher range ammeters, a few turns of heavy wire are used on the solenoid. The high current limit is set by the difficulty of winding a few turns of very heavy wire and by the heat that the instrument can dissipate. In the larger portable instruments, a range up to 200 amp is practical, and in large switchboard instruments a range up to 600 amp is common. For higher ranges, a current transformer is used with a low range ammeter.

Shunting of the moving iron instrument is not entirely practical. This is due to the low sensitivity of the instrument and thus the relatively high resistance required in the shunt. A high resistance in the shunt means more heat liberated in the instrument and thus a larger instrument so that the heat can be dissipated.

For multirange ammeters, the solenoid has two or more independent windings. A range selector switch selects the winding to be used on a particular range. The selector switch may put two windings in series for a low range and the same two windings in parallel for a high range.

Because of the relatively large self-inductance of the solenoid (compared with a thermocouple instrument) and the eddy currents induced in the vanes and magnetic shielding, the moving iron instruments are suitable for low frequencies only. Usually an ordinary moving iron ammeter may be used up to 500 cycles/sec with sufficient accuracy.

VOLTMETERS. A series resistor may be used as a multiplier in the ordinary fashion to convert a moving iron instrument into a voltmeter. The instrument may contain its multiplier inside the case for ranges up to about 750 v, but above this a low range voltmeter is usually used in connection with a transformer. Multirange voltmeters, if properly designed, are practical for the lower ranges of voltage.

If the multiplier of a certain voltmeter has the correct resistance at a certain frequency it will not be correct for any other frequency, because the inductive reactance of the solenoid changes with frequency. Also, the higher the frequency the greater the effect of eddy currents both in the vanes and in the magnetic shielding around the instrument. In general, a moving iron voltmeter designed and calibrated for power frequencies may be used in the range from 25 to 125 cycles/sec with the accuracy specified by the manufacturer for the meter.

USE ON DIRECT CURRENTS. Moving iron ammeters and voltmeters may be used on direct current, but the readings may be less accurate than on alternating current. The loss in accuracy arises from the hysteresis (see Chapter XVII) of the iron. Even the softest iron lags, in magnetization, behind the changes in the magnetic field about it. If the magnetic field is increasing the iron has less magnetization, at a given coil current, than it would have for a decreasing field. On alternating current this hysteresis causes no appreciable difficulty because the magnetization is changing both up and down many times per second. However, on direct current, the reading of the instrument will depend on the nature of the magnetization changes prior to the particular reading being taken. If the magnetization has decreased prior to the reading, the magnetization will be too high and the meter will read too high. If, on the other hand, the magnetization has increased prior to the reading, the magnetization will be too low and the meter will read low. The electrodynamometer avoids this difficulty because it is constructed without iron.

Usually the ferromagnetic material, selected for the vanes of a moving iron instrument, has only a small hysteresis effect, and the meters read fairly accurately on direct current. There is usually not more than 3% error, and with some instruments the error is less than 0.5%. However, a D'Arsonval type is much more accurate and sensitive for d-c work and should be used when possible.

20–8 VOLTMETER-AMMETER METHOD OF MEASURING D-C POWER; ERROR OF CONNECTION

The purpose of this section is to summarize some rather obvious notions in preparation for a discussion of the wattmeter.

On steady direct current, as we pointed out in Chapter I, the power used by a load is simply the product of the current flowing through the load and the potential difference across the load. We can measure the current flowing through the load by means of an ammeter and the potential difference across the load by means of a voltmeter. We should like to take the product of the ammeter reading and the voltmeter reading as the power used by the load, but unfortunately this method of calculation involves an error of connection for which we must make a correction.

Figure 20–8–1 shows two possible ways of connecting the voltmeter and ammeter in the circuit. Let P_L represent the power used by the load, and it is P_L that we wish to determine. Let P represent the product of the ammeter reading and voltmeter reading, P_A be the power used by the ammeter, and P_V be the power used by the voltmeter. Let us consider the situation presented by each circuit in Fig. 20–8–1. The symbols for current and potential difference on the circuit diagrams are self-explanatory.

CIRCUIT 1. In this circuit, the voltmeter reads directly the potential difference V_L across the load, but the ammeter reads the sum of the load current I_L and the voltmeter current I_V. Hence you can show that

$$P_L = P - P_V \qquad (20\text{–}8\text{–}1)$$

If the resistance R_V of the voltmeter is known, P_V may be computed at once and correction may be made for it. However, if I_L is very large compared with I_V, P is a good approximation of P_L and it may be unnecessary to correct for P_V.

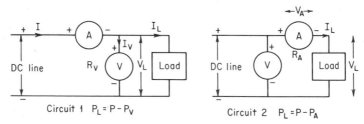

Figure 20–8–1. Measurement of d-c power with an ammeter A and voltmeter V.

CIRCUIT 2. In this circuit the ammeter reads directly the load current I_L, but the voltmeter reads the potential drop V_A across the ammeter plus the potential drop V_L across the load. Hence you can show that

$$P_L = P - P_A \qquad (20\text{–}8\text{–}2)$$

If the resistance of the ammeter is known, P_A may be computed at once and correction may be made for it. However, if V_L is very large compared with V_A, then P is a good approximation of P_L and it may be unnecessary to correct for P_A. Note that V_L is more likely to be large compared with V_A if I_L is small, so, in contrast with circuit 1, P is a good approximation of P_L for small load current in circuit 2.

20–9 THE ELECTRODYNAMOMETER WATTMETER ON DIRECT CURRENT; ERROR OF CONNECTION

The same electrodynamometer construction, that we described in Sec. 20–5 by the use of Fig. 20–5–1 may be adapted for measurement of power and, when so adapted, is called a *wattmeter*. The change is in the circuit connection, not in the structure of the instrument, so we shall think of the same construction as that shown in Fig. 20–5–1 (b). We may represent the changes in a schematic circuit diagram without redrawing the details of the structure.

Figure 20–9–1 shows the circuit diagram of the wattmeter and shows it connected to measure the power that a d-c line is supplying to a load. Here AA is the fixed coil of the electrodynamometer, as before, and note that it is connected in series in the line, so it becomes the ammeter coil of the watt-meter. The moving coil (previously designated C) is shown as V in Fig. 20–9–1; it has a carefully selected high resistance R in series. Note that the V coil (with its resistance R) is connected in parallel with the load and thus becomes the voltmeter of the wattmeter. The points marked V_1 and V_2 are the voltmeter terminals of the instrument and are available as binding posts on the outside of the meter. The ammeter terminals A_1 and A_2 are also available as binding posts on the outside of the meter. Note carefully that the fixed and moving coils are *not* connected in series as they were in the electro-dynamometer ammeter and voltmeter. As in the use of the electrodynamo-meter for an ammeter or voltmeter, the magnetic flux density is small and the instrument must be shielded against stray magnetic fields.

Compare Figs. 20–9–1 and 20–8–1, and note that if V_1 is connected to A_2 as shown by the solid line in Fig. 20–9–1, we have the same circuit as circuit 1

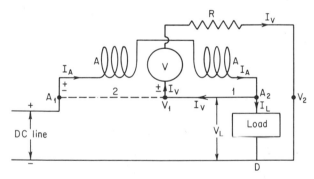

Figure 20–9–1. Electrodynamometer wattmeter hooked in a DC line to measure the power used by the load.

of Fig. 20–8–1 and thus the same error of connection. Hence, for this con-nection, (20–8–1) gives the power used by the load if we let P represent the power read by the wattmeter. For this reason, the wire from V_1 to A_2 in Fig. 20–9–1 is marked with a "1." On the other hand, if we remove the wire from V_1 to A_2 in Fig. 20–9–1 and make the connection shown by the dotted line from V_1 to A_1, we have the connection of Circuit 2 in Fig. 20–8–1. Hence the dotted connection from V_1 to A_1 in Fig. 20–9–1 is labeled "2" and when the 2 connection is used, (20–8–2) gives the power used by the load if P is the power read by the wattmeter. Note that the number 1 and number 2 connec-tions are *never* used at the same time.

So far we have assumed that the deflection of the V coil in Fig. 20–9–1, and thus the deflection of the pointer on the scale, is a measure of power. Let us show that this is indeed the case for steady direct current. By the same argument as that used in Sec. 20–5, the torque on the V coil is proportional to the product of the current I_A in the AA coil and the current I_V in the V coil. This time, however, the two currents are not the same. Since we are considering steady direct current, the torque on the V coil is constant. Let us represent it by T and obtain

$$T = kI_A I_V \qquad (20\text{-}9\text{-}1)$$

where k is a factor of proportionality. In general k is a function of the angle through which the V coil has deflected, because the magnetic field of the AA coil is not radial. This situation with regard to k is the same one encountered in the electrodynamometer ammeter and voltmeter.

The V coil will deflect to the point where the restoring torque of the hairspring is equal to T. Let D represent the deflection of the pointer on the scale, and the restoring torque of the hairspring will be directly proportional to D, because the spring obeys Hooke's law. Hence D is directly proportional to T and we may write

$$D = k'T \qquad (20\text{-}9\text{-}2)$$

where k' is the constant of proportionality that depends on the spring. Put (20-9-1) into (20-9-2) and we have

$$D = kk'I_A I_V \qquad (20\text{-}9\text{-}3)$$

Now let V_V represent the potential difference across the V coil circuit from V_1 to V_2 and let R_V be the total resistance of R plus the resistance of the V coil. Then $I_V = V_V/R_V$, and (20-9-3) becomes

$$D = kk'I_A V_V/R_V \qquad (20\text{-}9\text{-}4)$$

Let P replace the product $I_A V_V$, and P represents the same quantity that it did in equations (20-8-1) and (20-8-2), because it is the product of the current through the ammeter and the potential difference across the voltmeter. Then we may write (20-9-4) as

$$D = kk'P/R_V \qquad (20\text{-}9\text{-}5)$$

Thus the wattmeter may be calibrated in a d-c circuit by using an ammeter and a voltmeter (or better still by using a potentiometer and standard cell in the manner indicated at the end of Sec. 20-1); and subsequently it will measure power. If connection 1 of Fig. 20-9-1 is used, we must employ (20-8-1) to compute the power used by the load after reading the wattmeter. Similarly if connection 2 is used, we must employ (20-8-2) to compute P_L. Some wattmeters have compensating coils to correct for the error of connection. Usually such a wattmeter has only the three binding posts A_1, A_2, and V_2 because circuit 1 is used and V_1 is connected permanently to A_2 through the compensating coil. (Solve Problem 20-24.)

CONNECTION OF A WATTMETER INTO A CIRCUIT. When connecting a wattmeter into a circuit, note that one ammeter binding post and one voltmeter binding post are marked "$\pm$" (see A_1 and V_1 in Fig. 20-9-1) or, on some meters, marked "O." In making the connection, be sure that the voltmeter binding post with this special marking is on the same side of the line as the ammeter coil AA as shown in Fig. 20-9-1. Connected in this fashion, the AA coil and the V coil are essentially at the same potential. If the V_1 binding post were connected to D and the V_2 binding post connected to A_2 (or A_1), there would be a large potential difference between the AA coil and the V coil, and the electrostatic force between the coils would cause an error in the wattmeter reading. Also there might be an insulation breakdown between the coils if the line potential difference were high.

The direction of deflection of the V coil will be unchanged if both I_A and I_V are reversed, as we have seen in the discussion of the electrodynamometer type ammeter and voltmeter. However, if either I_A or I_V is reversed but not the other, the direction of deflection of the V coil will reverse. With binding posts A_1, A_2, V_1, and V_2 available for connection, it is possible to send I_A and I_V either way through their respective coils. Thus it is possible to make the V coil deflect in either direction. However, a wattmeter almost always has its zero at the left end of the scale, and its pointer must deflect to the right. Hence there is only one correct method of connection. For most wattmeters, if the connection is made as shown in Fig. 20–9–1 (with the $\pm$ ammeter terminal connected on the line side and the other connected on the load side), the wattmeter will deflect in the correct direction. If it does not you need only reverse the ammeter connections. Do not reverse the voltmeter connections, because you have already connected the $\pm$ voltmeter terminal on the same side of the line as the AA coil and it must stay there.

Never, through carelessness or lack of information, make the mistake of connecting the ammeter terminals, instead of the voltmeter terminals, across the load, because the ammeter will burn out very promptly when the circuit is connected to the line.

RATING OF A WATTMETER. A wattmeter has three ratings that must not be exceeded. The first is the maximum current that the ammeter coil AA can safely carry. If this rating is exceeded, you may smell insulation burning and may be able to shut off the current in time to save the meter, but it is better to have an ammeter in series and be sure that the current does not exceed the rating.

The second is the maximum voltage that may be applied across the voltmeter terminals V_1 and V_2. If this rating is exceeded, too large a current will flow through the V coil and its series resistor R. Again you may be able to save the meter after you smell insulation burning, but it is much better to use a voltmeter across the line and be sure that this rating is not exceeded.

These two ratings are either marked on the face of the meter or indicated by numbers near the binding posts.

The third rating is the power and, as long as the pointer of the instrument does not go beyond full scale, the power rating has not been exceeded.

On direct current, the power is the product VI, and it is entirely possible to exceed either the V or the I rating of the meter when the pointer is far below full scale deflection. We shall see that this same wattmeter measures power correctly, with the same calibration, when used in an a-c circuit. In an a-c circuit it is particularly easy to exceed the current or voltage rating of the wattmeter when the meter is being used well below its power rating, because the power factor of the load may be low.

20–10 THE ELECTRODYNAMOMETER WATTMETER ON SINGLE PHASE ALTERNATING CURRENT

We wish to show the same electrodynamometer wattmeter that we discussed and calibrated in the last section will measure power correctly in a sinusoidal a-c circuit. This means, of course, that it takes proper account of the phase angle between the current and the voltage.

Figure 20–10–1 shows the same circuit as does Fig. 20–9–1 except that the wattmeter and load are connected to a sinusoidal a-c line. Let i_A and i_V represent the instantaneous currents in the AA coil and V coil, respectively, and τ be the instantaneous torque on the V coil. As before, τ is proportional to the instantaneous currents in the AA and V coils, so we may write

$$\tau = k i_A i_V \qquad (20\text{–}10\text{–}1)$$

where k is the factor of proportionality. As before, k is a function of the angular position of the V coil, since the magnetic field of the AA coil is not

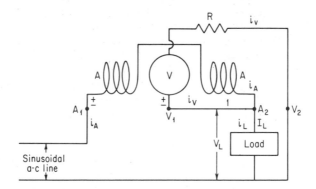

Figure 20–10–1. Electrodynamometer wattmeter on sinusoidal a-c line.

radial, but k is not a function of time once the V coil has taken its deflected position.

The V coil will deflect to a position where the time average torque T is equal to the restoring torque of the hairsprings; then the V coil will shiver around this position. The damper vanes will *minimize* the shiver so the pointer on the scale will indicate an essentially constant reading. The time average torque T should be taken for a complete cycle of change of the alternating current, but since all half cycles of the sinusoidal alternating current are alike in their effect on the V coil, we can take the time average for half a cycle and write

$$T = (\omega/\pi) \int_0^{\pi/\omega} \tau \, dt = (k\omega/\pi) \int_0^{\pi/\omega} i_A i_V \, dt \qquad (20\text{–}10\text{–}2)$$

Let D represent the deflection of the pointer on the scale and, as we have argued before, $D = k'T$. Hence we may write

$$D = (k'k\omega/\pi) \int_0^{\pi/\omega} i_A i_V \, dt. \qquad (20\text{–}10\text{–}3)$$

Now we must know i_A and i_V as functions of time before we can evaluate (20–10–3). Since this is a sinusoidal a-c circuit, i_A and i_V will be sinusoidal, but they will not necessarily be in phase. Hence let us write $i_A = I_{Am} \sin \omega t$ and $i_V = I_{Vm} \sin (\omega t + \alpha)$, where I_{Am} and I_{Vm} are the maximum values of i_A and i_V, respectively, and α is the phase angle between the two currents. Then (20–10–3) becomes

$$D = (k'kI_{Am}I_{Vm}\,\omega/\pi) \int_0^{\pi/\omega} \sin \omega t \sin (\omega t + \alpha)\, dt \qquad (20\text{–}10\text{–}4)$$

By the same argument as that used in Sec. 4–9 to reduce (4–9–1) to (4–9–4), (20–10–4) becomes (see Problem 20–25)

$$D = k'k(I_{Am}/\sqrt{2})(I_{Vm}/\sqrt{2}) \cos \alpha \qquad (20\text{–}10\text{–}5)$$

Then, if we let I_A and I_V represent the root mean square (or effective) values of the current in the AA coil and V coil, respectively, we have

$$D = k'kI_AI_V \cos \alpha \qquad (20\text{–}10\text{–}6)$$

Remember that α is the phase angle between the currents I_A and I_V, not the phase angle between I_A and the load voltages as we should like to have it for power measurement. The V coil must have self-inductance because, if it were non-inductively wound, the magnetic flux from the AA coil would exert no net torque on it. Hence I_V is not in phase with V_L. However, in a well-designed and constructed wattmeter, the total resistance R_V of the V coil branch is very large compared with the inductive reactance of the V coil, and I_V lags V_L by a very small phase angle (usually of the order of 1' to 2'). Hence, for any except very precise measurements, we may consider that $\alpha = \phi$ where ϕ is the phase angle between I_A and V_L. Also, since the phase angle of the V coil branch is so small, we may consider that the impedance of the V coil branch is R_V and write (20–10–6) as

$$D = k'kI_AV_L (\cos \phi)/R_V \qquad (20\text{–}10\text{–}7)$$

But

$$P = I_AV_L \cos \phi \qquad (20\text{–}10\text{–}8)$$

so

$$D = k'kP/R_V \qquad (20\text{–}10\text{–}9)$$

and the wattmeter reads power directly, taking due account of the phase angle between the current and voltage. Symbol P is the power reading of the wattmeter as it was in use on direct current. Since it is I_A, not I_L, that appears in (20–10–8), we have the same situation that we had in circuit 1 of Fig. 20–8–1 and must use (20–8–1) to compute the load power P_L from the watt-meter reading P. If the wattmeter is compensated, as discussed in the previous section, I_L will appear in place of I_A in the above derivation, and the wattmeter will read the load power directly without correction. Equation (20–10–9) is the same for a given wattmeter on alternating current as (20–9–5) is for the same wattmeter on direct current, with the same numerical values for k', k, and R_V. Thus the wattmeter may be calibrated on direct current and used for power measurements on alternating current. The scale of the wattmeter is not linear, because k' is a function of the angular position of the V coil. However, the scale turns out to be much more nearly linear than that of the electro-dynamometer ammeter or voltmeter.

Because of its inductance, the electrodynamometer wattmeter is limited to use at low frequencies, where its inductive reactance is small. For example, the Weston Model 432 has a standard frequency coverage of 25 to 125 cycles per second, but can be compensated for use up to 2500 cycles per second with an accuracy of 1% at full scale.

We have discussed only the fundamental principles of one type of wattmeter and further have limited the consideration to a wattmeter for a two-wire single phase line. For the many important additional considerations you should consult a book* on electrical measurements.

When using a wattmeter on alternating current, the same precautions must be taken with regard to ratings and connection into a circuit as those discussed in Sec. 20–9 for use on direct current. In fact, as pointed out there, it is much easier to exceed the current and voltage ratings on alternating current for a low power reading than it is on direct current.

20–11 THE ELECTRODYNAMOMETER WATTHOUR METER FOR DIRECT CURRENT OR SINGLE PHASE ALTERNATING CURRENT

The purpose of a watthour meter is measurement of the total energy delivered to a load during a time interval $t_2 - t_1$. If v is the instantaneous potential difference across the load and i is the instantaneous load current, the total energy W delivered to the load during the time interval is

$$W = \int_{t_1}^{t_2} iv \, dt = \int_{t_1}^{t_2} p \, dt \qquad (20\text{--}11\text{--}1)$$

where p is the instantaneous power. When energy delivered to a load is being measured, the time interval is long compared with the time for an a-c oscillation. For example, in a laboratory measurement the time interval may be a few minutes, but in a commercial measurement of the energy sold by a power company to a customer, the time interval is usually a month.

The time average power P, as measured by a wattmeter, on alternating current is the time average over several a-c cycles, but P will change with time as the load changes. Thus for energy measurements, P is a function of time, and we may compute the total energy delivered to a load during a time interval by

$$W = \int_{t_1}^{t_2} P \, dt \qquad (20\text{--}11\text{--}2)$$

In other words, we could read a wattmeter each time before the power changes (due to a change in the load), multiply the wattmeter reading by the length of time that the meter had that reading, and add all such products for the time interval $t_2 - t_1$. The watthour meter is an instrument that carries out this process automatically. The reading of the watthour meter is taken at the beginning of the time interval and again at the end of the interval. The difference of the two readings is the energy delivered to the load during the time between readings. It should be clear that the instrument that the power company installs in a home or factory is a watthour meter, not a wattmeter.

---

* See Stout, pp. 442–49 and 459–61; and Harris, pp. 474–510.

When we pay our electric bill for the home we are paying for the total electrical energy used in the home during the past month.

In (20–11–2), if P is in watts and t is in seconds, W is in watt-seconds or joules, the usual energy unit for the mks system. The joule is too small an energy unit for commercial purposes. If P is in watts and t is in hours, W is in watthours. This unit is still too small, although an electrical energy measuring meter is usually called a watthour meter. For commercial purposes, P is in kilowatts and t in hours, so that W is in kilowatthours. The monthly electrical bill expresses the energy in this unit of kilowatthours (kw hr).

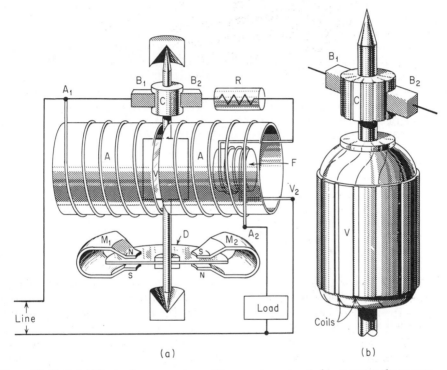

(a)   (b)

Figure 20–11–1. (a) Electrodynamometer watthour meter connected to measure the energy which the line has supplied to the load. (b) Cylinder with V coils wound on it, to an enlarged scale.

Now we wish to see how one type of watthour meter operates and thus how it arrives at the answer for the integral in (20–11–2). Figure 20–11–1 (a) shows an electrodynamometer type of watthour meter and its connection in a line to measure the energy that the line has supplied to the load. It is most easily explained if we consider that it is a modified electrodynamometer wattmeter. In Fig. 20–11–1 (a), AA shows the ammeter coil of the wattmeter, just as before; V is the voltmeter coil, and the chief change is made here. Instead of being a single coil, V is 8 or 10 separate coils wound on a non-metallic cylinder, insulated from each other, and each coil has its own pair of commutator segments on the commutator C. Figure 20–11–1 (b) shows schematically the cylinder that is used as a form for the V coils and shows 6 of the 8 or 10 separate coils. The wires that make up the coils are parallel with the lines that represent the coils. Figure 20–11–1 (a) shows a single one of these coils, and it is the particular one whose commutator segments are in contact with the brushes B_1 and B_2 at the moment of the picture. This particular coil is the one that is in a position to experience a maximum torque due to the magnetic field of the AA coil.

There are no hairsprings on the staff, so the V coil rotates continuously like the armature of a motor, and the V coil is often referred to as the armature. Notice that the V coil has its high non-inductive resistance R in series just as in the wattmeter, and that the V coil circuit is connected across the line just as it is for the wattmeter.

Let T_f represent the time average torque on the particular V coil that is connected in the circuit at the moment, where the time average is for several cycles of the alternating current. Then T_f is the forward or driving torque on the armature of the motor. The torque on the V coil is the same as for the wattmeter, so in (20–10–2) T_f replaces T for this argument. If we substitute the sinusoidal functional relationships of i_A and i_V and carry out the same procedure as that used to secure (20–10–6) from (20–10–4), we have

$$T_f = kI_A I_V \cos \alpha \qquad (20–11–3)$$

If the inductive reactance of the V coil circuit is very small compared with its resistance, we may carry out the same argument as that used to secure (20–10–9) from (20–10–6) and have

$$T_f = kP \qquad (20–11–4)$$

Thus the time average torque at a particular time is proportional to the time average power being supplied to the load at that time. (This statement neglects the error of connection. In Fig. 20–11–1 (a) we have the connection of circuit 2 of Fig. 20–8–1. We shall continue to neglect this error of connection.)

If T_f were an unbalanced torque, the armature would rotate faster and faster until finally it would fly apart when it reached a speed where the strength of the materials could no longer supply the required centripetal force. Also it would measure nothing in particular in the process. Hence we must have a reverse torque on the armature shaft. For reasons which will develop shortly, let us arrange it so that the reverse torque is proportional to the speed of rotation of the armature. To supply this reverse torque, an aluminum disk, shown as D in Fig. 20–11–1 (a), is fastened to the shaft of the armature and rotates between the poles of two permanent magnets M_1 and M_2. The motional emf induced in D causes eddy currents to flow in the disk. Since the induced emf is proportional to the speed of rotation, the magnitude of the eddy currents is also proportional to the speed of rotation. By Lenz's law, the eddy currents flow in a direction such that their interaction with the magnetic fields of the magnets opposes the motion of the disk. Hence the eddy currents produce a reverse torque on the armature shaft that is proportional to the speed of rotation of the armature. Let T_R represent this reverse torque, and we may write

$$T_R = k_1 S \qquad (20\text{–}11\text{–}5)$$

where S is the speed of rotation in revolutions per second and k_1 is the constant of proportionality.

Under the action of the forward torque of (20–11–4), the armature will speed up until the reverse torque is equal to the forward torque and then the armature will turn with constant speed. Thus we may equate (20–11–4) and (20–11–5) and have

$$kP = k_1 S \qquad (20\text{–}11\text{–}6)$$

When P changes, T_f will change, and the speed of rotation will change to a new value where (20–11–6) is again satisfied. Thus, with this arrangement, the speed of rotation of the armature is always proportional to the power being used by the load. This relationship is essential to the operation of the watthour meter and results only if T_R is proportional to the speed of rotation.

Put the value of P from (20–11–6) into (20–11–2) and we have the total energy supplied to the load, in the time interval $t_2 - t_1$, given by

$$W = (k_1/k) \int_{t_1}^{t_2} S\, dt \qquad (20\text{–}11\text{–}7)$$

Since $S\, dt$ is the number of revolutions that the armature makes in a time dt, $\int_{t_1}^{t_2} S\, dt$ is the total number of revolutions that the armature makes in the time interval, whatever the functional relationship may be between S and t. Thus

$$W = (k_1/k) \quad \text{(total number of revolutions)} \qquad (20\text{–}11\text{–}8)$$

Attached to the shaft of the meter, but not shown in Fig. 20–11–1, is a gear train with dials that measure the total number of revolutions made by the armature. The watthour meter is calibrated against a wattmeter and clock, so that the dials are calibrated in watthours (or, more often, kilowatthours).

Before or during calibration, the speed of rotation, at a given value of P, may be adjusted by adjusting the distance between the shaft and the pole pieces of the magnets M_1 and M_2. As M_1 and M_2 are moved away from the shaft, the effective radius at which the force due to the eddy currents acts is increased and the armature has a lower speed at a given power.

In the above discussion we have neglected entirely the reverse torque due to friction, since we have considered that T_R is due to the eddy currents only. The air friction (called *windage*) on the armature is proportional to the speed of rotation for the low speeds at which the armature turns and thus enters with the effect of the eddy currents in the calibration. However the friction of solid on solid is essentially independent of speed. This type of friction is present in the bearings, in the gear train, and where the brushes rub on the commutator. If the armature is at rest, it cannot start turning, even though the load is using power, unless the power is great enough so that T_f is greater than the frictional torque. When the armature is turning, the frictional torque is independent of speed and thus cannot enter into the theory properly, thereby causing an error. Hence friction is minimized in the construction. The commutator is made small and the brushes press against it with a small pressure. In order to secure good electrical contact even with a light pressure, the commutator is made of silver and the brushes have gold or silver tips. The bearings are hardened steel points in jewel cups, which also minimize friction.

Even after friction is reduced to a minimum in the construction, it is still too large, so the compensating coil F, in Fig. 20–11–1 (a), is used to reduce the error further. Note that F is in series with the armature but is inserted in the AA coil so that its magnetic field increases that of the AA coil and thus increases the torque on the armature. If the line voltage is constant, the current through the armature circuit is constant, and thus F furnishes a constant additional torque on the armature. Such a constant additional torque can overcome the constant frictional torque. Coil F is adjusted in position to a point where the armature will start turning as soon as the load starts to draw a small power. In this position the additional torque due to F very nearly compensates the frictional torque. If F is placed too close to V, the armature will creep, even though the load is taking no power. Thus F is placed as close to V as possible with no creep of the meter at zero load.

The electrodynamometer type of watthour meter operates properly on either direct or alternating current, as does its counterpart in wattmeter construction. However it is rarely used commercially on alternating current, because the induction type wattmeter is less expensive and more satisfactory for a-c measurement of energy. For the theory and construction of the induction type of watthour meter, you are referred to a book* on electrical measurements.

PROBLEMS

20–1 In the slide-wire potentiometer of Fig. 20–1–1 the slide wire is 160 cm long and has a resistance of one ohm per cm. Battery B is a 4 v lead storage battery with an emf of 4.21 v and with negligible internal resistance. The standard cell has an emf of 1.019 v and an internal resistance of 150 ohms. The galvanometer has a resistance of 200 ohms, a current sensitivity of 5.00×10^{-7} amp/cm deflection on its scale, and a scale length of 50 cm. The potentiometer is standardized with C set at 101.9 cm on the slide wire. (a) What is the magnitude of the driving current I_s and what is the value of the resistance Rh? [Ans: Rh = 261 ohms.] (b) After the potentiometer is standardized as above, the operator sets out to measure the emf of the unknown cell. He moves C to 160 cm on the scale but forgets to throw switch S from the standard cell position and forgets to change the protective resistance, so PR is zero. What current flows in the galvanometer and standard cell branch when K is closed and which way does it flow? May the standard cell be used immediately following this treatment? Is it probable that the galvanometer was damaged? [Ans: 1290 μa from left to right.] (c) What is the minimum value that PR should have had in part (b) in order that the galvanometer would not deflect beyond the end of the

* For example, F. K. Harris, *Electrical Measurements* (New York: John Wiley & Sons, Inc., 1952), pp. 517–31.

scale? Would this value of PR protect the standard cell adequately? [*Ans: PR* = 23,000 ohms.]

20-2 Note that, on the circuit diagrams in both Figs. 20–1–1 and 20–1–2, the galvanometer G is a part of a low resistance circuit when the protective resistance is reduced to zero. If a certain galvanometer requires 2000 ohms $CDRX$ (critical damping resistance external), what will be its behavior as balance is approached and PR is reduced to zero? In Fig. 20–1–2, what is the minimum protective resistance that must be left in series with this galvanometer for critical damping if a standard cell is being used whose emf is 1.01840 v and internal resistance is 200 ohms?

20-3 If, in Fig. 20–1–2, the total resistance in the part of the driving circuit $UVabde W'MNW$ is 82.3000 ohms, what must be the magnitudes of resistors F and h? The requirement is that the current in the B battery part of the circuit will remain constant at I_s when the plug is moved from the 1 hole to the 0.1 hole and that the current in the part of the driving circuit specified above by the letters from U to W will be 0.1 I_s to six significant figures. [*Ans: F* = 9.14444 ohms, *h* = 74.0700 ohms.]

20-4 (a) A Kelvin double bridge (see Fig. 20–2–1) is balanced with a copper rod for lk and the following data are obtained: $R = 0.005546$ ohm, $A/B = a/b = 300/10,000$. What is the resistance of the copper rod between p' and p? (b) If $r_1 = 0.010$ ohm, $r_2 = 0.001$ ohm, $r_3 = 0.100$ ohm, $r_4 = 0.100$ ohm, and $Y = 0.001$ ohm, what is the value of

$$bY(A/B - a/b)/(a + b + Y)$$

[which is the second term in (20–2–3)]? What is the resistance of the copper rod between p' and p? Assume that the ratios A/B and a/b are known to be as given in part (a) within 0.01% and that R is correct to ± 2 microhm. Carry out your calculations to the same accuracy as the ratios and R are known. [*Ans: X* = 16.644 × 10⁻⁵ ohm.]

20-5 If the copper rod in Problem 20–4 part (a) has a length of 30.23 cm and a diameter of 0.6315 cm, what is the resistivity of the copper of which the rod is composed?

20-6 The coils of a pair of Helmholtz coils, which have a mean diameter of 1.00 m, are labeled as having 180 turns of wire on the two coils. The coils are wound with standard annealed copper wire. When used in an experiment there is reason to believe that the magnetic flux density B at the center of the coils does not have the magnitude computed from the Helmholtz coil formula, and finally the experimenter becomes suspicious of the label that says that the coils have 180 turns. It is impossible to see all the turns to count them, but it is possible to see that there is an integral number of turns. The experimenter measures the diameter of the wire and finds 1.63 mm. With a Wheatstone bridge he finds that the total resistance of the copper wire in the coils is 5.21 ohms. How many turns of wire are there on the coils? [*Ans:* 200 turns.]

20-7 (a) Derive equation (20–2–10) from (20–2–7) and (20–2–9). (b) What is the value of α for standard annealed copper? [*Ans:* 0.00427/°C.]

20-8 (a) It is often convenient to change a temperature coefficient α_{t1} that is based on R_{t1}, the resistance at t_1, to the coefficient α_{t2} based on R the resistance at t_2, without computing the coefficient based on the resistance R_0 at 0°C, as an intermediate step. Show that $\alpha_{t2} = \alpha_{t1}/[1 + \alpha_{t1}(t_2 - t_1)]$. (b) What is the temperature coefficient of resistance of commercial aluminum based on resistance of the aluminum at 30°C? [*Ans:* 0.0037/°C.]

20–9 When a certain d-c motor is at room temperature, its field coils, which are wound with standard annealed copper wire, have a resistance of 200 ohms as measured with a Wheatstone bridge. After the motor has run for some time the temperature of the field coils becomes 85°C. If the motor is operating on a 110 v d-c line, how much will the field current be decreased due to this temperature rise? [*Ans:* 0.112 amp.]

20–10 The same ballistic galvanometer that was calibrated in Problem 13–13 is used in the circuit of Fig. 17–1–1 for measurement of change in the magnetic flux through the toroid when the switch *RS* is opened. The search coil has 50 turns of wire and the total resistance of the *BG* circuit is 10,000 ohms. When the switch *RS* is opened the following values are recorded for the successive maxima of the galvanometer deflections, in cm, on the same side of zero: $d_1 = 50.0$, $d_3 = 37.0$, $d_5 = 27.4$, $d_7 = 20.6$, $d_9 = 15.3$, and $d_{11} = 11.3$. (a) What is the average value of the logarithmic decrement for the galvanometer with this search coil circuit? [*Ans:* 0.298.] (b) What is the change in the magnetic flux linking the search coil as the switch is opened? [*Ans:* 4.0×10^{-4} wb.]

20–11 (a) A search coil, with 2.00 cm² area of face and 10 turns of wire, is situated at a point *P* in a magnetic field with its face perpendicular to the magnetic flux lines. The search coil is connected to a ballistic galvanometer, and the total resistance of the circuit, including the ballistic galvanometer and search coil, is 1000 ohms. When the search coil is snatched from its position in the magnetic field to a place where there is no magnetic field, the ballistic galvanometer deflection shows that 2.55×10^{-6} coulomb flows through the circuit. What is the magnetic flux density at the place where the search coil was initially located? [*Ans.* 1.28 wb/m².] (b) The search coil is replaced at the point *P*, again with its face perpendicular to the magnetic flux lines. Now the search coil is moved quickly to a point *P′*, and a charge of 3.05×10^{-8} coulomb flows through the ballistic galvanometer circuit. At *P′* the face of the search coil is also perpendicular to the magnetic flux lines. What is the difference in the magnitude of *B* at *P* and *P′*? Is there any way to tell whether *B* is larger or smaller at *P′* than it is at *P* and, if there is, explain the method? [*Ans:* 1.52×10^{-2} wb/m².]

20–12 You are to determine the magnitude of the magnetic flux density of the earth's magnetic field at a certain place by the use of a search coil and a ballistic galvanometer. You know the direction of the earth's field at the location by the use of a compass needle and a dip needle. For the measurement, the search coil is to be rotated quickly through a quarter turn starting with its plane perpendicular to the earth's field and ending with its plane parallel to the earth's field. The ballistic galvanometer at your disposal has a sensitivity of 3.30×10^{-8} coulomb/mm deflection, and you desire a deflection of at least 10 cm for the measurement. Also the galvanometer has a period of 40 sec and requires at least 2000 ohms in its circuit in order that it shall have a sufficiently small logarithmic decrement. A rough measurement shows that the magnetic flux density of the earth's field is of the order of magnitude of 10^{-4} wb/m². Calculate the product

NA for the search coil and then, with the aid of sketches, show how you would build the search coil. Remember that the coil must start from rest, rotate through 90° in a time that is short compared with the period of the galvanometer, and come to rest at its final position. If the coil wobbles about at either its initial or final position, it will, of course, produce erratic galvanometer behavior. Decide on the dimensions of the coil that you will use and the number of turns of wire that you will put on the coil.

20–13 In the Model FM multirange fluxmeter discussed in Sec. 20–4, what is the resistance of the shunt for each of the multiplier positions 1, 3, 10, 30, and 100?

20–14 An electrodynamometer ammeter and a D'Arsonval ammeter are connected in series in a circuit that has a half-wave rectified sinusoidal alternating current flowing in it. Figure 20–P–1 shows the current as a function

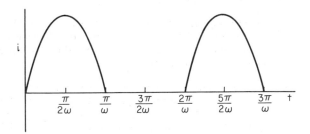

Figure 20–P–1. Half-wave rectified sinusoidal alternating current.

of time. The maximum value of the current is 10 amp. What does each meter read? [*Ans:* D'Arsonval, 3.19 amp; electrodynamometer, 5.00 amp.]

20–15 An electrodynamometer ammeter and a D'Arsonval ammeter are connected in series in a circuit that has a full-wave rectified alternating current flowing in it. The maximum value of the current is 10 amp. What does each meter read? [*Ans:* Direct current, 6.38 amp; alternating current, 7.07 amp.]

20–16 An electrodynamometer ammeter and a D'Arsonval ammeter are connected in series in a circuit where the current is given by the equation $i = 2.5$ amp $+ 10$ amp sin ωt, where $\omega = 377/$sec. What does each ammeter read? [*Ans:* Direct current, 2.5 amp; alternating current, 7.5 amp.]

20–17 An electrodynamometer, without shunt or multiplier, has 113 ohms resistance in its AA coils (see Fig. 20–5–1) and 75 ohms resistance in its C coil and hairsprings, as measured with a Wheatstone bridge. A test shows that 45.00 ma direct current will deflect its pointer to the end of the scale. (a) Calculate the non-inductive resistance that must be put in series as a multiplier when the AA and C coils are connected as shown in Fig. 20–5–1 (a) in order that the meter shall be a 150 v d-c meter. [*Ans:* 3144 ohms.] (b) The self-inductance of the AA and C coils in series is a function of the orientation of the C coil, because the mutual inductance of the two coils changes as the C coil rotates (see Sec. 8–6), and the total self-inductance is greatest when the C coil is in a position where the pointer is at the upper end of the scale. In this position the above electrodynamometer has a total self-inductance of 0.098 henry. The meter reading at the upper end of the scale can be estimated within ± 0.2 v. If 150 v, 60 cycles/sec alternating current is applied across the terminals of the electrodynamometer [with the multiplier calculated in (a) in series], will the meter read 150 v within the accuracy of reading the scale? Discuss the situation in this respect for higher frequency alternating current.

20–18 A certain moving iron 150 v voltmeter has a resistance of 850 ohms and a self-inductance of 0.100 henry in its solenoid. It requires 0.0500 amp for full-scale deflection of the pointer. (a) What is the non-inductive resistance of the multiplier for this voltmeter if the voltmeter reads correctly on a 25 cycle/sec line? [*Ans:* 2150 ohms.] (b) If the voltmeter is used on a 150 v (as measured by a thermocouple meter) 2500 cycle/sec line, what is the current flowing through the meter? If the scale of this voltmeter is essentially linear from the 130 v mark to the 150 v mark, what voltage does the pointer indicate? (This calculation neglects eddy current error due to the higher frequency.) [*Ans:* 0.0443 amp, 133 v.]

20–19 At how high a frequency may the voltmeter of Problem 20–18 be used with no more than 1% error in the voltage indicated at full-scale deflection of the pointer? (Again this calculation neglects the eddy current error at the higher frequency.) [*Ans:* 675 cycles/sec.]

20–20 A load is connected to a d-c line with an ammeter and voltmeter as shown in circuit 1, Fig. 20–8–1. The ammeter reads 5.00 amp and the voltmeter reads 109.2 v. The 150 v scale on the voltmeter is being used and the data on the face of the meter says that the meter has a *sensitivity* of 100 ohms/v. This sensitivity applies to all scales, of course. (a) What is the resistance of the voltmeter on the 150 v scale? [*Ans:* 15,000 ohms.] (b) What is the power used by the load? [*Ans:* 545 w.] (c) What are the load current and load resistance? (d) What is the percentage difference between P and P_L? [*Ans:* 0.15%.]

20–21 The load resistance in Problem 20–20 is changed and the rheostat (not shown in circuit 1, Fig. 20–8–1) in the line is changed. The voltage is lower and the connection to V is changed to the 15 v scale of the same voltmeter. After these changes, and with another ammeter that is 1 amp full scale, the new ammeter reads 0.100 amp, and the voltmeter reads 12.56 v. (a) What is the power used by the load? (b) What is the percentage difference between P and P_L? [*Ans:* 9.1%.]

20–22 A load, ammeter, and voltmeter are connected as shown in circuit 2 of Fig. 20–8–1. The data on the face of the ammeter show that 50 mv drop in potential across the terminals is required for full-scale deflection of the meter. This information applies to all ranges of the meter, of course. The ammeter is on the 1 amp range and reads 0.100 amp. The voltmeter reads 12.56 v. (a) What is the potential drop V_A across the ammeter? [*Ans:* 5 mv.] (b) What is the power used by the load? [*Ans:* 1.26 watts.] (c) What is the percentage difference between P and P_L? Compare your answer with that for part (b) of Problem 20–21.

20–23 The ammeter in Problem 20–22 is changed to the 50 amp range on the same instrument and the load is changed so the ammeter reads 45.5 amps. The voltmeter still reads 12.56 v. (a) What is the power used by the load? [*Ans:* 569 watts.] (b) What is the percentage difference between P and P_L?

20–24 Redraw Fig. 20–5–1 (b), but use the electrical connection and labeling of the wattmeter in Fig. 20–9–1 and on it draw a winding, in series with the V coil, which can make the compensation (due to the error of connection number 1) referred to at the end of the paragraph following (20–9–5). Explain how your compensating coil accomplishes the objective.

20–25 Starting with (20–10–4), derive (20–10–5).

20–26 For the compensated wattmeter of Problem 20–24, used in a sinusoidal a-c circuit, explain why I_L would appear in place of I_A in (20–10–7). Here I_L is the root mean square (or effective) load current.

20–27 The case of an electrodynamometer, like the one in Fig. 20–5–1, is opened and the connection between the AA coil and the C coil is removed. In an experimental test it is found that the pointer will deflect to the end of the scale when a direct current of 1.00 amp is sent through the AA coil at the same time that a direct current of 0.0100 amp is sent through the C coil. Measurement with a Wheatstone bridge shows that the C coil has a resistance of 300 ohms. What resistance must be put in series with the C coil in order to make this instrument into a wattmeter that reads 200 watts for full-scale deflection? [*Ans:* 19,700 ohms.]

20–28 An experiment is to be performed, using a circuit that contains an inductor with a resistance of 10 ohms and a self-inductance of 0.10 henry, in series with a bank of capacitors whose capacitance can be varied from 50 to 100 μf. The circuit is to be connected to a 100 v 60 cycle/sec line. During the experiment the capacitance is to be changed by 5 μf steps over the available range. (a) A wattmeter, that has a maximum rating of 7 amp, 150 v, and reads 1000 watts full scale, is available. Is it safe to use this wattmeter to measure the power input from the line to the circuit? Why? (b) If a 5 ohm resistor is added in series with the inductor and the capacitor bank, is it safe to connect the AA coils of this wattmeter in series with the inductor and the V coil across the inductor in order to measure the power input to the inductor? Why?

20–29 Figure 20–P–2 shows an a-c circuit with an ammeter A, voltmeter V, and wattmeter W used to make measurements on the inductive load shown. The meter readings are ammeter 2.50 amp, voltmeter 120.0 v, wattmeter 105.0 watts. The marking on the face of the wattmeter shows that the

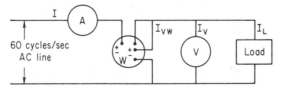

Figure 20–P–2. Wattmeter W, ammeter A, and voltmeter V hooked in an a-c circuit to make measurements on a load.

total resistance of its voltage circuit is 2000 ohms. The voltmeter has a sensitivity of 100 ohms/v on the 150 v scale that is being used. (a) What is the power used by the load? [*Ans:* 96.8 watts.] (b) What is the load current? [*Ans:* 2.47 amps.] (c) What is the power factor of the load? [*Ans:* 0.326.] (d) What are the equivalent resistance and reactance of the load? [*Ans:* $R_{load} = 15.8$ ohms, $X_{load} = 45.8$ ohms.]

APPENDIX

A–I ELECTRICAL QUANTITIES IN THE ELECTROSTATIC SYSTEM OF UNITS (ESU)

The esu system is not a rationalized system of units.

1. QUANTITY OF ELECTRICITY OR CHARGE, Q. See Sec. 9–4, where the stat-coulomb is defined by the use of Coulomb's law. The statcoulomb is the basic definition on which this system is built. There are 2.082×10^9 electrons/statcoulomb.

2. ELECTRIC CURRENT, I. (Sec. 1–4, 2.)* From (1–4–1), the statampere is defined as follows. *A statampere of current is flowing if electric charge is passing a cross section in a circuit at the rate of one statcoulomb per second.* From this definition, and that of the statcoulomb, it follows that a stat-ampere of current is flowing if electrons are passing a point at the rate of 2.082×10^9 electrons/sec.

3. ELECTRIC FIELD INTENSITY, E. (Sec. 9–5.) *An electric field has unit intensity at a point if one statcoulomb of charge placed at the point would experience a force of one dyne.* This definition, of course, assumes that the presence of the statcoulomb of charge at the point does not alter the field in which it is placed. In this system, the unit of E is dynes/statcoulomb or statvolt/centimeter.

4. ELECTRIC POTENTIAL DIFFERENCE, V. (Sec. 1–4, 5; Sec. 10–2.) *Two points are at a potential difference of one statvolt if one erg of work is involved in the transfer of one statcoulomb of charge from one point to the other.* Thus 1 stat-volt = 1 erg/statcoulomb.

5. RESISTANCE, R. (Sec. 1–4, 6.) *A conductor has a resistance of one statohm if one statampere of current flows through the conductor when the potential difference across it is one statvolt.* Thus, 1 statohm = 1 statvolt/statampere.

6. WORK, W. (Sec. 1–4, 7.) From (1–4–7) and (1–4–8), $W = QV = IVt$. If Q is in statcoulombs, V in statvolts, and t in seconds, W is in ergs.

7. POWER, P. (Sec. 1–4, 8.) Since work is in ergs and time is in seconds in this system, power is expressed in ergs/sec.

---

* References given in this fashion indicate the place in the text where the physical concept is discussed. The physical concepts are, of course, independent of the system of units employed.

8. CAPACITANCE, C. (Sec. 4–1 and Chap. XII.) The defining equation is

$$C = Q/V \qquad (4\text{-}1\text{-}2)$$

the same as in the mks system. Hence, *a capacitor has a capacitance of one statfarad if there is a potential difference of one statvolt between its plates when the charge on each plate is one statcoulomb.* 1 statfarad = 1 statcoulomb/statvolt. In this system of units, the capacitance of an isolated sphere in empty space turns out to be equal to the radius of the sphere when the radius is expressed in centimeters. Hence you will often encounter capacitance in this system expressed in "centimeters of capacitance" or just "centimeters." 1 statfarad = 1 cm of capacitance.

9. ELECTRIC DIPOLE MOMENT, p. (Sec. 10–10.) The definition of electric dipole moment is the same ($p = ql$) as it is in the mks system. Hence in esu, the unit of p is statcoulomb centimeter.

10. POLARIZATION, P. (Sec. 11–3.) The defining equation for P is

$$\boldsymbol{P} = \sum \boldsymbol{p}/\Delta V \qquad (11\text{-}3\text{-}3)$$

just as it is in the mks system. The unit of P in esu is, from (11–3–3), statcoulomb/cm².

11. ELECTRIC SUSCEPTIBILITY, η. (Sec. 11–4.) For a class A dielectric, $P = \eta E$ in this system, so $\eta = P/E$. We can see that this definition is the same as the one in (11–4–1), since $\varepsilon_0 = 1$ and has no unit in the esu system. Using the unit for the statcoulomb given in Sec. 9–4, you can show that P and E have the same units in the esu system, so η is dimensionless.

12. PERMITTIVITY OR DIELECTRIC CONSTANT, ε. (Sec. 11–5.) As in (11–5–14), $\varepsilon = \varepsilon_r \varepsilon_0$. But in the esu system, ε_0 equals unity and has no unit, so $\varepsilon = \varepsilon_r$. Thus the permittivity (or dielectric constant) of a medium in the esu system is the same as the relative dielectric constant of that medium in the mks system as stated previously in Sec. 11–5. In the esu system, ε is related to η by the equation $\varepsilon = 1 + 4\pi\eta$ and ε is dimensionless as is η.

13. ELECTRIC DISPLACEMENT, D. (Sec. 11–6.) The defining equation for D in the esu system is

$$D = E + 4\pi P$$

as compared with (11–6–1) for the rationalized mks system. From the above definition of D and the fact that E and P have the same units in the esu system, the unit of D is dyne/statcoulomb. From $P = \eta E$, and $\varepsilon = 1 + 4\pi\eta$, and the above defining equation for D, you can show that $D = \varepsilon E$ in the esu system as it does in the mks system [see (11–6–3)].

14. MAGNETIC UNITS. Since one rarely encounters magnetic calculations carried out in the esu system, we shall not define any magnetic units in this system.

A-2 THE ABSOLUTE ELECTROMAGNETIC SYSTEM OF UNITS (EMU)

The emu system is not a rationalized system of units.

1. UNIT POLE, UP. (Sec. 17-6 and Sec. 14-5.) This system of units is based on the definition of the unit pole, UP, and the definition in turn is based on Coulomb's experimental law of force between point poles in empty space as given in Sec. 17-7, equation (17-7-8). However, this is not a rationalized system of units, so the factor 4π does not appear in Coulomb's law when the law is expressed for this system. Further, the arbitrary choice is made that the permeability μ_0 of empty space shall be unity and shall have no units. Thus, Coulomb's law for empty space becomes, in this system,

$$F = m_1 m_2 / r^2 \qquad \qquad (A-2-1)$$

Then, as stated in Sec. 14-5 where this system was introduced, *the unit pole is defined as a pole of such strength that it will repel a like pole* (like as to magnitude and kind) *at a distance of one cm in empty space with a force of one dyne.*

From the above definition, we may substitute units into (A-2-1) as follows: 1 dyne = 1 (UP)^2/cm^2

or $\qquad\qquad$ 1 UP = 1 dyne$^{1/2}$ cm = g$^{1/2}$ cm$^{3/2}$ sec^{-1} $\qquad\qquad$ (A-2-2)

and thus obtain the unit equivalents of the UP for this system.

2. MAGNETIC FIELD INTENSITY, H. (Sec. 14-5.) A magnetic field exists in a region if a magnet pole in the region experiences a force. By definition, *the magnetic field intensity at a point is the force that would be exerted on a unit north pole placed at the point*. The definition, of course, assumes that the presence of the unit pole at the point does not alter the field whose magnetic field intensity is being determined. From this definition, the unit of H is dynes/UP, and this combination of units is called the oersted; i.e., 1 dyne/UP = 1 oersted.

3. ELECTRIC CURRENT, I. (Sec. 14-5 and Sec. 1-4, 2.) From (14-5-7), Sec. 14-5, *the abampere is defined as a constant current of such magnitude that, flowing in a single turn circular loop of wire of one cm radius, it produces a magnetic field intensity of 2π oersteds at the center of the circle.*

4. QUANTITY OF ELECTRICITY OR CHARGE, Q. (Sec. 1-4, 2.) From (1-4-3), *the abcoulomb is defined as the charge that, in one second, passes through a cross section of a conductor in which there is a constant current of one abampere.* Thus 1 abcoulomb = 1 abampere sec.

5. ELECTRIC POTENTIAL DIFFERENCE, V. (Sec. 1-4, 5 and Sec. 10-2). *Two points are at a potential difference of one abvolt if one erg of work is involved in the transfer of one abcoulomb of charge from one point to the other.* Thus 1 abvolt = 1 erg/abcoulomb.

6. RESISTANCE, R. (Sec. 1-4, 6.) *A conductor has a resistance of one abohm if one abampere of current flows through the conductor when the potential difference across the conductor is one abvolt.* Thus 1 abohm = 1 abvolt/abampere.

7. WORK, W. (Sec. 1–4, 7.) From (1–4–7) and (1–4–8), $W = QV = IVt$. If Q is in abcoulombs, V in abvolts, and t in seconds, W is in ergs.

8. POWER, P. (Sec. 1–4, 8.) Since work is in ergs and time is in seconds in this system, power is expressed in ergs/sec.

9. CAPACITANCE, C. (Sec. 4–1 and Chap. XII.) The defining equation is (4–1–2) or

$$C = Q/V \qquad (A–2–3)$$

the same as in the esu and mks systems. Hence, *a capacitor has a capacitance of one abfarad if there is a potential difference of one abvolt between its plates when the charge on each plate is one abcoulomb.* Thus 1 abfarad = 1 abcoulomb/abvolt.

10. ELECTRIC FIELD INTENSITY, E. (Sec. 9–5.) *An electric field has unit intensity at a point if one abcoulomb of charge, placed at the point, would experience a force of one dyne.* This definition, of course, assumes that the presence of the abcoulomb of charge at the point does not alter the field in which it is placed. In this system, the unit of E is dynes/abcoulomb or abvolts/cm.

11. INTENSITY OF MAGNETIZATION, $\mathscr{I}$. (Sec. 16–3.) *Intensity of magnetization of a material is defined as the vector sum per unit volume of the magnetic moments of the Amperian current loops.* In this system, magnetic moment has the unit of UP centimeter (see Sec. 17–6 for relationship between pole strength and magnetic moment) so $\mathscr{I}$ has the unit of UP/cm². Using the unit equivalents of equation (A–2–2), this unit is equivalent to dynes/UP, i.e., 1 UP/cm² = 1 dyne/UP.

12. MAGNETIC FLUX DENSITY, B. (Secs. 3–1, 3–2 and Chap. XIV.) In this system B is defined by

$$B = H + 4\pi\mathscr{I} \qquad (A–2–4)$$

(Compare this equation with (16–4–1) in the mks system and remember that the 4π appears here because the emu system is not rationalized, and μ_0 does not appear here because μ_0 equals unity and has no units in the emu system.) Since both H and $\mathscr{I}$ have the unit of dyne/UP (or oersted), B also has this unit. However, it is important to know whether one is considering B or H in a particular problem, because B (not H) enters into all formulas for forces on moving charges and formulas for induced emfs. Thus B is given the *gauss* as its unit in the emu system even though the gauss and the oersted are the same in terms of fundamental units.

13. MAGNETIC FLUX, Φ. (Sec. 3–3.) From (3–3–1), $\Phi = BA$, and Φ is the total number of magnetic flux lines through an area A just as it is in the mks system. In the emu system, Φ is assigned the *maxwell* as its unit and 1 maxwell = 1 gauss cm², or, 1 gauss = 1 maxwell/cm².

14. MAGNETIC SUSCEPTIBILITY, χ. (Sec. 16–5.) As in (16–5–1) for the mks system, in the emu system magnetic susceptibility of a medium is defined by the equation

$$\chi = \mathscr{I}/H \qquad (A–2–5)$$

Since $\mathscr{I}$ and H have the same units, χ is dimensionless as it is in the mks system.

15. MAGNETIC PERMEABILITY, μ, AND RELATIVE PERMEABILITY. (Sec. 16–5.) In emu, permeability of a medium is defined by

$$\mu = 1 + 4\pi\chi \qquad \text{(A–2–6)}$$

Since χ is dimensionless, μ is also dimensionless, as is μ_0. Also, since μ_0 is unity in this system, μ is equal to relative permeability μ_r, since $\mu_r = \mu/\mu_0$. In the emu system, μ is the same numerically, for a given medium, as μ_r in the mks system.

Put (A–2–5) into (A–2–4) and use (A–2–6), with the result that

$$B = \mu H \qquad \text{(A–2–7)}$$

the same relationship between B and H as in the mks system [see (16–5–4)].

16. SELF-INDUCTANCE, L. (Sec. 3–7.) The defining equation is (3–7–5) or

$$L = -e_L/(di/dt) \qquad \text{(A–2–8)}$$

Hence, the abhenry is defined as a unit of self-inductance as follows. *An inductor has a self-inductance of one abhenry if one abvolt of self-induced emf is set up in the inductor when the current flowing in the inductor is changing at the rate of one abampere per second.* Thus, 1 abhenry = 1 abvolt sec/abampere.

17. MUTUAL INDUCTANCE, M. (Secs. 8–4 and 8–5.) The defining equation is (8–4–4), or

$$M = -e_2/(di_1/dt) \qquad \text{(A–2–9)}$$

Hence the abhenry is defined as a unit of mutual inductance as follows: *Two coils (or circuits) have a mutual inductance of one abhenry if one abvolt emf is induced in the secondary when the current in the primary is changing at the rate of one abampere per second.* Again, 1 abhenry = 1 abvolt sec/abampere.

18. ADDITIONAL ELECTRICAL UNITS. Since one rarely encounters calculations in the emu system involving electric dipole moment p, polarization P, electric susceptibility η, and electric displacement D, we shall not define units for these quantities in the emu system.

A–3 TABLE OF CONVERSION FACTORS

The mks electrical units belong to the rationalized mksa system. In this system, permittivity of empty space has the value

$$\varepsilon_0 = \frac{1}{4\pi \times 8.98776 \times 10^9} \frac{\text{coulomb}^2}{\text{newton m}^2} \left(\text{or } \frac{\text{farad}}{\text{meter}}\right)$$
$$\cong 8.85 \times 10^{-12} \text{ coulomb}^2/\text{newton m}^2,$$

and permeability of empty space has the value

$$\mu_0 = 4\pi \times 10^{-7} \frac{\text{weber}}{\text{amp meter}} \left(\text{or } \frac{\text{henry}}{\text{meter}}\right)$$

Both esu and emu are unrationalized systems.* See last page of the table for instructions for its use.

* For conversion of a formula in one system of units to the same formula in another system of units, see W. R. Smythe, *Static and Dynamic Electricity*, 2d ed. (New York: McGraw-Hill Book Co., Inc., 1950), pp. 585–89.

Quantity	Conversion Factor		
	Conversion Number	Unit of	
		Numerator	Denominator
Angle, plane	1.745×10^{-2}	radian	degree
	57.30	degree	radian
	2.778×10^{-3}	revolution	degree
	2π	radian	revolution
	360	degree	revolution
Area, A	1×10^{-4}	meter²	cm²
	9.290×10^{-2}	meter²	foot²
	6.452×10^{-4}	meter²	inch²
Capacitance, C	1.113×10^{-12}	farad	statfarad (esu)
	1×10^{9}	farad	abfarad (emu)
	1×10^{-6}	farad	microfarad, μf
	1×10^{-12}	farad	micromicrofarad, $\mu\mu f$
Charge, electric (or quantity of electricity) Q, q	3.336×10^{-10}	coulomb	statcoulomb (esu)
	10	coulomb	abcoulomb (emu)
Current, i, I	3.336×10^{-10}	amp	statamp (esu)
	10	amp	abamp (emu)
Density	1×10^{3}	kg/meter³	g/cm³
	16.02	kg/meter³	pound/foot³
	515.4	kg/meter³	slug/foot³
Distance (or length) l, L	1×10^{-2}	meter	cm
	2.540×10^{-2}	meter	inch
	0.3048	meter	foot
	1×10^{3}	meter	kilometer
	1609	meter	mile
Electric displacement (or induction), D	$1/(12\pi \times 10^{5})$	coulomb/meter²	esu of displacement (no name assigned)
	$10^{5}/4\pi$	coulomb/meter²	emu of displacement (no name assigned)
Electric field intensity, E	1×10^{2}	volt/meter or newton/coulomb	volt/cm
	2.998×10^{4}	volt/meter	dyne/statcoulomb (esu)
	2.998×10^{10}	volt/meter	dyne/abcoulomb (emu)

Quantity	Conversion Factor		
	Conversion Number	Unit of	
		Numerator	Denominator
Energy (or work), W	1×10^{-7}	joule	erg
	3.6×10^6	joule	kwhr
	4.186	joule	calorie
	1.356	joule	ft lb
	1055	joule	Btu
	1.60×10^{-13}	joule	Mev
Force (or weight), F	10^{-5}	newton	dyne
	0.1383	newton	poundal
	4.448	newton	pound (force)
	9.807×10^{-3}	newton	gram (force)
Inductance, L or M	1×10^{-9}	henry	abhenry (emu)
	8.987×10^{11}	henry	stathenry (esu)
	1×10^{-6}	henry	microhenry
	1×10^{-3}	henry	millihenry
Magnetic field intensity, H	$10^3/4\pi$	amp turn/meter	oersted (emu)
	1×10^3	amp turn/meter	abamp turn/cm (emu)
	39.37	amp turn/meter	amp turn/inch
Magnetic flux, Φ	1×10^{-8}	weber	maxwell, or line (emu)
	1×10^{-5}	weber	kiloline (emu)
	2.998×10^2	weber	esu of Φ (no name assigned)
Magnetic flux density, B	1×10^{-4}	weber/meter^2	gauss, or line/cm^2 (emu)
	1.550×10^{-2}	weber/meter^2	kilolines/inch^2
	2.998×10^6	weber/meter^2	esu of B (no name assigned)
Magnetomotive force, mmf	10	amp turn	abamp turn (emu)
	$10/4\pi$	amp turn	gilbert (emu)
Mass	1×10^{-3}	kilogram	g
	14.59	kilogram	slug
	0.4536	kilogram	pound (mass)
	2.205	pound (mass)	kilogram
Pole strength, m	$4\pi \times 10^{-8}$	weber (mks Kennelly)†	unit pole (emu)
	0.1	amp meter (mks Sommerfeld)‡	unit pole (emu)
	$4\pi \times 10^{-7}$	weber (mks Kennelly)	amp meter (mks Sommerfeld)

Quantity	Conversion Factor		
	Conversion number	Unit of	
		Numerator	Denominator
Potential difference and emf, V, $\mathscr{E}$	299.8	volt	statvolt (esu)
	1×10^{-8}	volt	abvolt (emu)
Power, p, P	1×10^{-7}	watt	erg/sec
	745.7	watt	horsepower
	1.356	watt	footpound/sec
	4.186	watt	calorie/sec
Resistance	8.987×10^{11}	ohm	statohm (esu)
	1×10^{-9}	ohm	abohm (emu)
Resistivity	1×10^{-2}	ohm meter	ohm cm
	1×10^{-11}	ohm meter	abohm cm (emu)
	8.987×10^{9}	ohm meter	statohm cm (esu)
Speed	0.3048	meter/sec	foot/sec
	0.4470	meter/sec	mile/hr
	0.2778	meter/sec	kilometer/hr
Volume	1×10^{-6}	meter³	cm³
	2.832×10^{-2}	meter³	foot³
	1.639×10^{-5}	meter³	inch³
	1×10^{-3}	meter³	liter

† Not used in this text, see footnote in Sec. 17–6.
‡ Used in this text.

INSTRUCTIONS FOR USE OF TABLE OF CONVERSION FACTORS. In making a conversion of a quantity from one system to another, be sure that the proper units are on the number to be converted (e.g., 1.52 radian, 6.15 statcoulomb, 5×10^{7} maxwell). Next secure the appropriate conversion factor from the table. The second column gives the conversion number and the third and fourth columns give the units which belong to the conversion number; the third column is the unit of the numerator of the conversion number and the fourth column that of the denominator (e.g., the conversion factors 57.30 degree/radian, 3.336×10^{-10} coulomb/statcoulomb, 1×10^{-8} weber/maxwell). Then perform the operation (multiplication or division) with the conversion factor which will cancel the units which you wish to eliminate and retain the units which you wish to retain. For example, suppose you know that the magnetic flux density of a certain magnetic field is $B = 5.5 \times 10^{3}$ gausses and you wish to know the magnetic flux density of this same field expressed in weber/m². From the table, the conversion factor is

$$1 \times 10^{-4} \frac{\text{weber/m}^2}{\text{gauss}}$$

The unit to be canceled is the gauss and the unit to be retained is weber/m². Hence we multiply the value of B by the conversion factor

$$B = 5.5 \times 10^3 \text{ gauss} \times 1 \times 10^{-4} \frac{\text{weber/m}^2}{\text{gauss}} = 0.55 \frac{\text{weber}}{\text{m}^2}$$

and the result has the desired unit. Hence, 5.5×10^3 gausses is the same magnetic flux density as 0.55 weber/m².

From the conversion factors given here you may obtain certain other desired conversion factors. For example, suppose that you wish the number of inches per foot. Under the heading "Distance" in the table you obtain the conversion factors for meter/foot and meter/inch and perform the operation which will let "meter" cancel and leave "inch/foot" as follows:

$$\frac{0.3048 \text{ m/ft}}{2.54 \times 10^{-2} \text{ m/in.}} = 12 \frac{\text{in.}}{\text{ft}}$$

As a second example, suppose that you wish the conversion factor from statvolts to abvolts. From the heading "Potential Difference" in the table you obtain the information so that you can perform the following operation.

$$\frac{300 \text{ v/statvolt}}{10^{-8} \text{ v/abvolt}} = 3 \times 10^{10} \frac{\text{abvolt}}{\text{statvolt}}$$

and, thus, have the desired conversion factor.

It is sometimes convenient to recognize that each conversion factor (with its numerator and denominator units) given in the table is equal to unity. For example, from the "Area" heading in the table we have $1 = 1 \times 10^{-4}$ m²/cm², or 1 cm² $= 1 \times 10^{-4}$ m², or 1×10^4 cm² $= 1$ m².

Similarly, from the heading "Magnetic Field Intensity," we have $1 = (10^3 \text{ amp turn/m})/4\pi$ oersted, or 4π oersted $= 10^3$ amp turn/m, or $4\pi \times 10^{-3}$ oersted $= 1$ amp turn/m.

A–4 LIST OF PRINCIPAL SYMBOLS

Quantity	Symbol	mks unit	Definition and Physical concept, Sec. No.
Admittance			
complex	Y	mho	7–8
magnitude	y	mho	7–8
Angle	$\alpha, \beta, \theta, \phi$	radian	
Area	A, a	meter²	
Capacitance	C	farad	4–1
Charge	q, Q	coulomb	1–4
per unit length	b, λ	coulomb/meter	9–10, 10–8
surface density of	σ	coulomb/meter²	9–9
volume density of	ρ	coulomb/meter³	10–11
Coercive force	H_c	ampere/meter	17–2
Conductance	G	mho	7–8
Coupling, coefficient of	K	—	8–7

Quantity	Symbol	mks unit	Definition and Physical concept, Sec. No.
Current	i, I	ampere	1–4
amperian	I_a, I_a', I_a''	ampere	16–2
density, displacement	j_D	ampere/meter^2	14–10
density, linear Amperian	j_a	ampere/meter	16–3
effective, alternating	I	ampere	4–11
maximum, alternating	I_m	ampere	4–6
Dielectric constant,			
relative	ε_r		11–5
Dipole moment, electric	p	coulomb meter	10–10
Displacement, electric	D	coulomb/meter^2	11–6
Distance	r, d, L, l	meter	
Electric field intensity		newton/coulomb,	
	E	or volt/meter	9–5
Electric permittivity	ε	$\begin{cases}\text{coulomb}^2/\text{newton meter}^2 \\ \text{or farad/meter}\end{cases}$	11–5
of free space	ε_0		9–4
Electric polarization	P	coulomb/meter^2	11–3
Electric susceptibility	η	—	11–4
Electromotive force	emf, $\mathscr{E}, e$	volt	1–4, 3–4, 3–5, 15–1, 15–2
Energy	W	joule	
density, electric		joule/meter^3	12–5
density, magnetic		joule/meter^3	16–8
kinetic	KE	joule	
potential	PE	joule	
Field intensity, electric	E	newton/coulomb or volt/meter	9–5
magnetic	H	ampere/meter	14–2, 16–4
Flux, magnetic	Φ	weber	3–3
Flux density, magnetic	B	weber/meter^2	3–2
Force	F, f	newton	
Frequency, electrical	f	cycles/sec	
angular, electrical	ω	radians/sec	
Impedance,			
complex	Z	ohm	7–7
magnitude	z	ohm	4–8, 5–4, 7–7
Induction, electric			
(or displacement)	D	coulomb/meter^2	11–6
Intensity of magnetization	$\mathscr{I}$	ampere/meter	16–3
Length	L, l, s, r	meter	
Logarithmic decrement	λ		13–6
Magnetic field intensity	H	ampere/meter	14–2, 16–4
Magnetic flux	Φ	weber	3–3
Magnetic flux density	B	weber/meter^2	3–2
Magnetic moment	M	ampere meter^2	13–7, 17–5
Magnetic permeability	μ	$\begin{cases}\text{weber/ampere meter} \\ \text{or henry/meter}\end{cases}$	16–5
of free space	μ_0		14–1
Magnetic pole strength	m	ampere meter	17–6
Magnetic susceptibility	χ		16–5

Quantity	Symbol	mks unit	Definition and Physical concept, Sec. No.
Magnetization, intensity of	$\mathscr{I}$	ampere/meter	16–3
Magnetomotive force	mmf	ampere turn	16–9, 17–9
Moment of inertia	J	kilogram meter^2	
Mutual inductance	M	henry	8–4, 8–5
Natural logarithm, base	e		
Permeability, magnetic	μ	$\{$ weber/ampere meter	16–3
of free space	μ_0	$\{$ or henry/meter	14–1
relative	μ_r	—	16–5
Permittivity, electric	ε	$\{$ coulomb^2/newton meter^2	11–5
of free space	ε_0	$\{$ or farad/meter	9–4
relative	ε_r	—	11–5
Polarization, electric	P	coulomb/meter^2	11–3
Pole strength, magnetic	m	ampere meter	17–6
Potential difference, electric	v, V	volt	1–4, 10–2
effective, a-c	V	volt	4–11
maximum, a-c	V_m	volt	4–6
Potential energy	PE	joule	
Power	p, P	watt	
Quantity of electricity			
or charge	q, Q	coulomb	1–4, 9–3, 9–4
Reactance	$X = X_L - X_C$	ohm	7–7
capacitive	X_C	ohm	4–6
inductive	X_L	ohm	5–4
Relative dielectric constant	ε_r	—	11–5
Relative permeability	μ_r	—	16–5
Reluctance	$\mathscr{R}$	ampere turn/weber	17–9
Resistance	R, r	ohm	1–4
temperature coefficient of	α	degree^{-1}	
Resistivity	ρ	ohm meter	20–2
Retentivity	B_r	weber/meter^2	17–2
Self-inductance	L	henry	3–7
emf of	e_L	volt	3–7
Surface density of charge	σ	coulomb/meter^2	9–9
Susceptance	B	mho	7–8
Susceptibility			
electric	η	—	11–4
magnetic	χ	—	16–5
Time	t, T	second	
Torque	τ	meter newton	
Velocity, linear	v	meter/sec	
angular	ω	radian/sec.	
of light	c	meter/sec.	
Volume	v, V	meter^3	
Work or energy	W	joule	

A–5 FUNDAMENTAL PHYSICAL CONSTANTS

The following values are based on R. T. Birge, *Rev. Mod. Phys.*, **13**, 233 (1941); J. W. M. DuMond and E. R. Cohen, *ibid.*, **20**, 82 (1948), **21**, 651

(1949), **25**, 691 (1953); E. R. Cohen, J. W. M. DuMond, T. W. Layton, and J. S. Rollett, *ibid.*, **27**, 363 (1955).* All data in this table are on the physical scale of atomic masses.

Gravitation constant (G)	$(6.670 \pm 0.005) \times 10^{-11}$ newton m²/kg²
Volume of mole of ideal gas at NTP	$(22,420.7 \pm 0.6)$ cm³
Standard atmosphere	$(101,324.6 \pm 0.4)$ newton/m²
Mechanical equivalent of heat	(4185.5 ± 0.4) joules/kcal
Avogadro's number (number of particles in one mole)	$(6.02486 \pm 0.00016) \times 10^{23}$
Atomic mass unit (amu)	$(1.6597 \pm 0.0001) \times 10^{-27}$ kg
Density of mercury at NTP	$(13,595.04 \pm 0.06)$ kg/m³
Gas constant per mole (R_0)	(8.31696 ± 0.00034) joules/mole (K deg)
Boltzmann's constant (k)	$(1.38044 \pm 0.00007) \times 10^{-23}$ joule/(K deg)
Speed of light (c)	$(2.997929 \pm 0.000008) \times 10^{8}$ m/sec
Faraday (charge carried by one mole of monovalent ions)	$96,521.9 \pm 0.11$ coulombs
Electronic charge (e)	$(1.60206 \pm 0.00003) \times 10^{-19}$ coulomb
Planck's constant (h)	$(6.62517 \pm 0.00023) \times 10^{-34}$ joule sec $= 4.135 \times 10^{-15}$ ev sec
Constant in Stefan-Boltzmann law (σ)	$(5.6687 \pm 0.00010) \times 10^{-8}$ joule/(K deg)⁴m² sec
Constant in Wein's displacement law	$(2.89782 \pm 0.000013) \times 10^{-3}$ m (K deg)

Mass-energy conversion factors:

$$1 \text{ kg} = (5.61000 \pm 0.00011) \times 10^{29} \text{ Mev}$$
$$1 \text{ electron mass} = 0.510976 \pm 0.000007 \text{ Mev}$$
$$1 \text{ atomic mass unit} = 931.141 \pm 0.010 \text{ Mev}$$
$$1 \text{ proton mass} = 938.211 \pm 0.010 \text{ Mev}$$
$$1 \text{ neutron mass} = 939.505 \pm 0.010 \text{ Mev}$$

Particles:

	Atomic mass (amu)	*Mass* (kg)	*Charge*
electron	$(5.48763 \pm 0.00006) \times 10^{-4}$	$(9.1083 \pm 0.0003) \times 10^{-31}$	$-e$
proton	1.007593 ± 0.000003	$(1.67239 \pm 0.00004) \times 10^{-27}$	$+e$
neutron	1.008982 ± 0.000003	$(1.67470 \pm 0.00004) \times 10^{-27}$	0

A–6 GREEK ALPHABET

A	α	Alpha	N	ν	Nu
B	β	Beta	Ξ	ξ	Xi
Γ	γ	Gamma	O	o	Omicron
Δ	δ	Delta	Π	π	Pi
E	ε	Epsilon	P	ρ	Rho
Z	ζ	Zeta	Σ	σ	Sigma
H	η	Eta	T	τ	Tau
Θ	θ	Theta	Y	υ	Upsilon
I	ι	Iota	Φ	ϕ	Phi
K	κ	Kappa	X	χ	Chi
Λ	λ	Lambda	Ψ	ψ	Psi
M	μ	Mu	Ω	ω	Omega

* See also minor corrections *Phys. Rev. Letters*, **1**, 291 (1958).

INDEX